THE TRADITIONAL CRAFTS OF PERSIA

THE TRADITIONAL CRAFTS OF PERSIA

Their Development, Technology, and Influence on Eastern and Western Civilizations

Hans E. Wulff

THE M.I.T. PRESS
Massachusetts Institute of Technology
Cambridge, Massachusetts, and London, England

Library of Congress Catalog Card Number: 66–22642
Printed in the United States of America

PREFACE

When in 1937 the late Reza Shah Pahlavi addressed the staff and students of the Technical College at Shiraz, he seemed pleased that the work at the college was aiming at the training of Western-type technicians and engineers. These were the men he needed for his program of industrialization and for the development of his country. I was then principal of the College. Standing in front of a table with tools and machine parts made by the students, holding a precision instrument in his hand, and facing the staff, he said: "You must be proud that your students can produce an instrument like this which, until recently, had to be imported from abroad." But later in his speech he added: "This is all very well, but doing this work, don't forget that this country has a great tradition of craftsmanship of a different kind." Turning toward the government officials he asked them to make sure that the technical colleges established classes for training in traditional crafts like silversmithing, engraving, wood carving, brocade weaving, and the like.

These classes were opened not long afterwards. To integrate them into my college I had to study the crafts closely, and this was the beginning of my interest in them, an interest which led me to the recording of most of the crafts which were still alive at that time. I was greatly encouraged in this work by Professors Dr. Wilhelm Eilers of Würzburg University and Dr. Walther Hinz of Göttingen University, both urging me to include the craftsmen's own language into my records. It was a pleasant surprise to find that the Persian craftsmen, with few exceptions, were not suspicious of a foreigner investigating their craft secrets. It took a while to gain their confidence, but once that was established most of them were proud to show their skill; they permitted photographing and patiently answered questions.

The work came to a sudden end in 1941 through the events of World War II; notes, diagrams, and photographs were lost and not recovered until fifteen years later. Many photographic prints were not suitable for book publication, but wherever possible new photos were taken during a recent visit to Persia. In other cases drawings were made from poor photographs and my original sketches. I would like to express my gratitude to Mr. Otto Ernegg, Mrs. Ida Schünemann, and my daughter-in-law, Mrs. Kay Wulff.

The technical terms given in the text are those recorded when with the craftsmen in the bazaars, the peasants in the villages, and the tribesmen in their tents, who often gave the terms in their local dialects. Not all of these people were able to assist me with the spelling of the words, but wherever possible I tried to verify my own spelling. Here my gratitude goes to Mr. J. Y. Cadry of Sydney, Australia, who patiently and willingly helped with many linguistic queries. Despite all this there is still a considerable number of technical terms which seem not to be part of literary Persian. They have been spelled phonetically as well as an engineer could do it, but I leave it to the linguists to make the final decision.

I am deeply grateful to Dr. Joseph Needham of Cambridge University for much factual information on technical exchanges between China and Persia, but more important still was the encouragement he gave me through correspondence and in conversation to go ahead with the work and prepare it for publication.

I am also greatly indebted to the late Dr. Erwin Gauba, formerly professor of Botany at the University of Tehran, for his invaluable assistance in the identification of the useful timbers of Persia. To Dr. Leo Koch of Sydney, formerly Professor of Geology at Tehran University, go my thanks for his help in analyzing metals, alloys, and minerals used by the craftsmen.

An almost inexhaustible source of information was my friend the late Max Otto Schünemann, the pioneer of Persia's modern textile industry, who had lived in the country, on and off, since 1901. English not being my native language, I needed and received valuable help from Mrs. Marjorie Carne and Mr. John Gordon of Sydney, and most of all from Dr. Sheila Rowley of Sydney, who read the whole manuscript carefully and patiently and made numerous suggestions for better English expression.

The transliteration adopted for the Persian and Arabic terms uses the Latin alphabet in such a way that each Arabic letter is represented by a single Latin sign. Since there are more Arabic letters than Latin ones, diacritical signs will be used to determine the different S-sounds, Z-sounds and the like.

ا at the beginning of a word written a, e, i, o, or u. In the middle or at the end of a word ā

آ ā	ج j	ذ z̲	ش š	ع ᶜ	گ g	ه h
ب b	چ č	ر r	ص ṣ	غ ġ	ل l	ى ī or y
پ p	ح ḥ	ز z	ض ż	ف f	م m	
ت t	خ ḫ	ژ ž	ط ṭ	ق q	ن n	
ث s̲	د d	س s	ظ ẓ	ک k	و ū or v	

ء at the beginning of a word omitted, in middle, or end position ᵓ

Long vowels have accents: "ā," "ē," "ī," "ō," and "ū," but the two diphthongs occurring in Persian, viz., "ai" and "ou," will be written without accents. Since the Arabic script does not distinguish between short "i" and "e" on the one hand and "o" and "u" on the other, I relied on my hearing and found that, in general, "e" was preferred to "i" and "o" to "u." Umlaut "o" and "u" in Turkish words will be written "ö" and "ü." In the combination of خ and و in some Persian words, the و is mute and will be written "w̤" as in *ḫw̤ordan*. The vowel preceding the final and mute ه is "e" as in *mošteh*; ن before "b" and "p" is pronounced "m" and will be written "ṃ." Since the *ezāfeh* is often omitted in some parts of the country, particularly in dialects, it will only be written where it has been used. To avoid misinterpretation, no English plural s has been used where a Persian word appears in an

English sentence in the plural form, thus "many *qanāt*" rather than "many *qanāts*."

Where words are composites, a hyphen has often been used to facilitate recognition of the word's parts, e.g., *noqreh-sāz* instead of *noqrehsāz*.

Hans E. Wulff

Sydney, Australia
August 1966

TABLE OF CONTENTS

I

METALWORKING CRAFTS

2

WOODWORKING CRAFTS

3

BUILDING CRAFTS AND CERAMIC CRAFTS

4

TEXTILE CRAFTS AND LEATHER CRAFTS

5

AGRICULTURE AND FOOD-TREATING CRAFTS

OUTLOOK

303

BIBLIOGRAPHY

305

REVIEW OF RELEVANT LITERATURE

315

GLOSSARY OF TECHNICAL TERMS

331

INDEX

LIST OF ILLUSTRATIONS

I

METALWORKING CRAFTS

Metallurgy in Ancient Persia

Archaeological evidence seems to confirm that North and Central Persia are the regions of the world's oldest metallurgy. Man could only discover the usefulness of metal in a land where metals and their ores existed. Persia is by nature rich in metal ores.[1] The peoples of the early river valley civilizations of Egypt, Babylonia, the Indus, and the Oxus could not, despite all their achievements, become the first metallurgists. Recent excavations have shown that metallurgical activity was relatively late in these civilizations.

The mountain range reaching from the Taurus to the southern shores of the Caspian was rich in all kinds of ores and fuel, and the knowledge of metallurgy spread from there to other centers in Asia, Africa, and Europe.[2] Excavations by Brown[3] in Northwest Persia, Ghirshman[4] at Tepe Giyān in West Persia and at Siyalk in Central Persia, Schmidt[5] at Tepe Ḥiṣār in Northeast Persia, and Herzfeld[6] at Tall-e Bakūn in South Persia led to the conclusion that, toward the end of the Neolithic age, "after an early period of lush vegetation a gradual drying up of the valleys set in and the people began to settle in the plains."[7] Ghirshman dates this period as being in the fifth millennium B.C.

The oldest human settlement identified in the plain is at Siyalk, near Kāšān, south of Tehrān. Traces of man's first occupation have been found there just above

[1] E. E. Herzfeld and A. Keith in A. U. Pope and P. Ackerman, eds., *A Survey of Persian Art*, p. 50.

Publication details of sources cited in footnotes may be found in the Bibliography.

[2] R. J. Forbes in C. Singer, *A History of Technology*, p. 576.

[3] T. B. Brown, *Excavations in Azarbaijan.*

[4] R. Ghirshman, *Iran.*

[5] E. F. Schmidt, *Excavations at Tepe Hissar.*

[6] E. E. Herzfeld, *Archaeological History of Iran.*

[7] R. Ghirshman, *op. cit.*, p. 29.

virgin soil at the bottom of an artificial mound[8] (Fig. 1). Objects of this material culture were black smoked pottery, hand-

Figure 1 The Prehistoric Site of Siyalk near Kāšān

formed without a wheel. Baked clay and stone spinning whorls indicate the beginning of a textile industry. Tools are of stone, along with flint knife blades, sickle blades, axes, and scrapers. Metal tools begin to appear toward the end of the fifth millennium. "These were always hammered copper. Man was beginning to understand the properties of metal; he had found that copper was malleable, but was still ignorant of the art of casting. The civilization of this phase belongs to the very end of the Neolithic age."[9]

Herzfeld,[10] Schmidt,[11] Contenau and Ghirshman,[12] and Brown[13] found similar material cultures on a large semicircle around the Central Persian desert, the oldest levels of all of them belonging to the transition stage from Stone Age to Metal Age.

The absence of any traces of prehistoric smelting furnaces indicates that man must have forged native copper into shape for his first metal tools. In fact, native copper is found to this day in and near Anārak, only 140 miles from Siyalk. M. Maczek,[14] who between 1936 and 1940 modernized the traditional mining and smelting methods there, reports that at this time a considerable part of the production of Anārak came from native copper. The Urgeschichtliches Institut of Vienna University is at present carrying out research into the connections between ore deposits in the area and excavated copper tools, using spectrographic analysis.[15]

During the early parts of the fourth millennium copper continued to come into general use, still hammered for arrowheads, awls, garment pins, and jewelry (Fig. 2). But a marked change in metal technology occurred during the second half of that millennium, together with changes in other parts of the material culture: copper was now smelted from ore and cast.

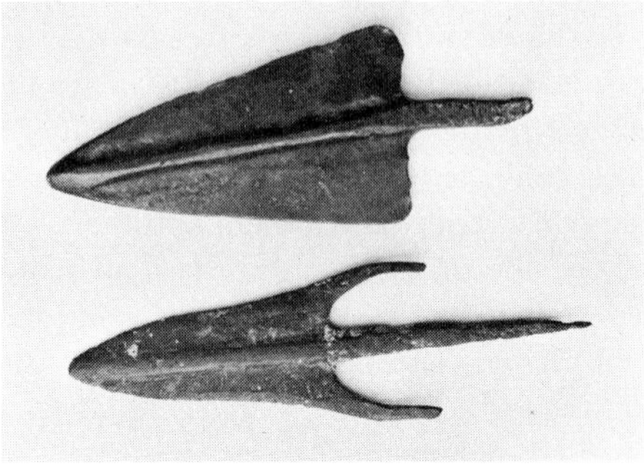

Figure 2 Forged Copper Arrowheads

Copper ore deposits were frequently noted throughout antiquity. Strabo[16] mentions Kermān as particularly rich in

[8] *Ibid.*
[9] *Ibid.*, p. 30.
[10] E. E. Herzfeld, *op. cit.*
[11] E. F. Schmidt, *op. cit.*
[12] G. Contenau and R. Ghirshman, *Fouilles de Tépé Giyan.*
[13] T. B. Brown, *op. cit.*
[14] M. Maczek, "Der Erzbergbau im Iran," p. 197.
[15] M. Maczek, E. Preuschen, and R. Pittioni, "Beiträge zum Problem des Ursprungs der Kupfererzverwertung in der Alten Welt," pp. 61–70.
[16] Strabo XV, 2, 14 c. 726.

copper. Sir Aurel Stein[17] discovered a Sumero-Indus civilization smelting copper in Balūčistān. Piggott[18] clearly shows that during the second millennium the Kulli and Amri-Nal copper finds in Balūčistān are closely linked with Persia on the one hand and with Harappa in the Indus valley on the other. Gabriel[19] found remnants of smelting furnaces and huge slag heaps near Šāh Balland and Robaṭ in Balūčistān. Copper ores are still found in Rās Kūh and the Ḫwājeh Amrān ranges in Balūčistān. The medieval Chinese historian Hiuen Tsang mentions that rich copper mines existed in that part of the Persian Empire which we know today as Afghanistan (i.e., Šāh Maqṣūd, Safēd Kūh, Tazīn, Šādkānī, and Silvātū.)[20] In northern Persia a string of copper mines extends from Transcaucasia to the Pamir. The Arabian geographer Ibn Ḥauqal writes of copper mines at Kal-Sab-Zaveh, Sabzvār, and Fahr Dāwud near Mašhad, as well as Boḫārā in Transoxania. The copper mines of Kāšān, Anārak, Iṣfahān, and Boḫārā were the most important for the Arabian caliphs of the ninth century A.D., as these paid no less than 10,000 dinar annually in taxes.[21] Only a hundred years ago a geographer[22] reported that nearly every district in Persia had its own copper mines. In the north are the easily reducible carbonate ores of Mt. Sahand and the Qarādāġ ranges. Most of the other copper ores in Persia are sulphides. The smelting of these ores requires a roasting process before the actual reduction takes place. Assyrian records[23] mention that the Persians roasted their (sulphide) ores in furnaces of 7-foot height, whereas the actual reduction took place in small blast furnaces about 9 inches in diameter and 18 inches deep. In 1935 several prehistoric smelting furnaces were unearthed near Anārak by Mr. M. O. Schünemann,[24] some of them still containing remnants of copper and slag (Fig. 3). A smelting

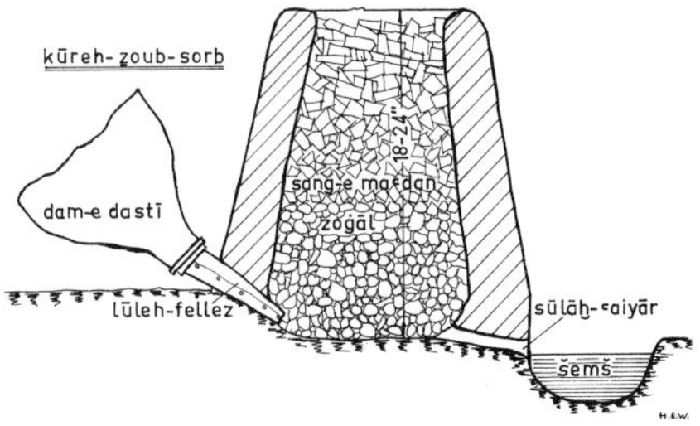

Figure 3 A Lead Smelting Furnace from the Anārak District

furnace that the writer measured on the excavation site of Harappa in 1963 had a height of 7 feet, an inside diameter of 2 feet, 9 inches, and had clearly visible inlets for air and outlets for combustion gases. The walls of this furnace were thickly lined with copper slag. This should be of interest in the light of the previously mentioned links between Persia and prehistoric India.

Copper tools of the fourth millennium B.C. contain varying quantities of gold, silver, lead, arsenic, antimony, iron, nickel, and tin. We may assume that the early smelters tried all kinds of ores in their endeavor to obtain metal, thus accidentally producing copper alloys. Tin ore is found in northern Persia at Mt. Sahand

[17] M. A. Stein, *Archaeological Reconnaissance of N.W. India and S.E. Iran.*

[18] S. Piggott, *Prehistoric India to 1000 B.C.*, pp. 112 ff.

[19] A. Gabriel, *Aus den Einsamkeiten Irans*, pp. 131–132.

[20] R. J. Forbes, *Studies in Ancient Technology*, p. 301.

[21] *Ibid.*, p. 302.

[22] J. E. Polak, *Persien, das Land und seine Bewohner*, p. 174.

[23] R. C. Thompson, *A Dictionary of Assyrian Geology and Chemistry.*

[24] M. O. Schünemann (verbal information).

near Tabrīz, in the Qarādāġ ranges, both close to the copper mines, and on the southern slopes of the Alburz near Astarābād and Šārūd. Stream tin and gold are found near Kūh-e Zar (Damġān district), at Kūh-e Banān, between the copper mines of Anārak and Iṣfahān, and twenty-two miles west of Mašhad at Robaṭ-e Alokband, again near copper mines. It is therefore not difficult to see how the metallurgists eventually discovered alloys, and the superior strength, hardness, and casting qualities of copper-tin bronzes. Analyses of objects excavated by Brown[25] reveal that the copper tools, belonging to the oldest level in Tepe Geoy (about 3000 B.C.), are made of copper of an unusually high purity. From 2500 B.C. on, samples show about 5 per cent tin, this content increasing to 10 per cent over a period of 1,000 years. Presumably the metallurgist had by then changed from simultaneous smelting of copper and tin ores to separate smelting of both metals and subsequent controlled alloying. The consistent tin content of the metal objects is difficult to explain otherwise.

Stone tools still remained in use during the Copper Age, but were gradually replaced by metal axes, celts, and hoes.[26] The beginning of the third millennium shows the growth of a new culture at the foothills of the Iranian Plateau—the first state of Elam, with Susa as its center. Signs of a rupture in the material culture of the settlements on the highlands can be observed. These changes seem to have been wrought by people from Central Asia.[27] Persia must have absorbed these influences. Excavations show a modification of the older culture, but essentially it continues its own style. Here we see a role that Persia played through six millennia, namely that of being a highway for people and for the passage of ideas between East and West, one to receive, to recreate, and to retransmit.[28]

From the beginning of the third millennium, the written records of the Mesopotamian kingdoms of Sumer, Babylon, and Elam often mention people and events on the Persian highlands, and the historical development is well established from then on. With the growth of the kingdoms of Mesopotamia the need for raw materials increased.

> Owing to its [Persia's] proximity and its unusual mineral wealth, it was the centre of attraction for all who were strong enough to attempt the annexation of its western districts. While Persia was a transit country for lead coming from Armenia and for lapis lazuli from Badakhshan, its own mineral wealth included gold extracted in Media, copper and tin.[29]

During the second half of the third millennium B.C., the use of metals increased. Graves in Susa, Tepe Ḥiṣār, Tepe Giyān, and Tepe Geoy contained many bronze tools as well as bronze and silver jewelry. The change from stone to copper was a gradual one, but in Persia the Bronze Age was well established by 2000 B.C. Most of the bronze objects of that period seem to have been cast in soft stone molds where half of the object was carved into one stone and the other half into another. The molds were complete with risers and air vents (Fig. 4).

The first iron appears at this time,[30] although only for jewelry. The high nickel content (about 5 per cent) indicates that it must have been meteoric iron. Terrestrial iron, which was used in Mesopotamia as early as 2700 B.C., did not come into regular use in Persia until after 1000 B.C. With the arrival of the Indo-Europeans at the beginning of the first millennium B.C., we observe a marked increase in the use of

[25] T. B. Brown, *op. cit.*, pp. 179, 186.
[26] R. Ghirshman, *op. cit.*, p. 40.
[27] *Ibid.*, p. 46.
[28] *Ibid.*, p. 50.
[29] *Ibid.*, p. 71.
[30] T. B. Brown, *op. cit.*, p. 204.

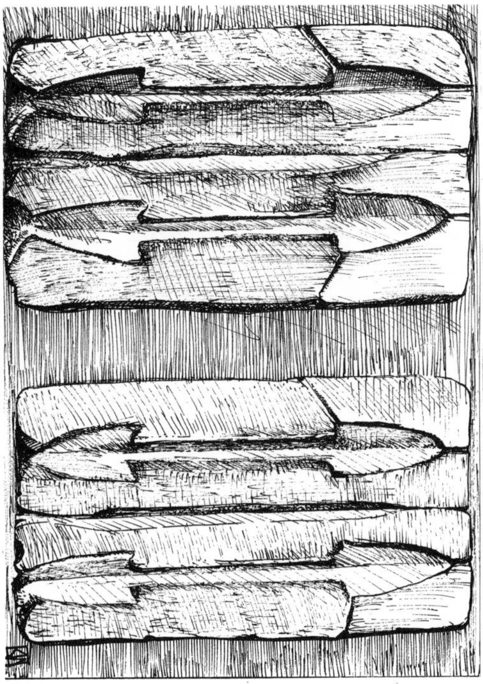

Figure 4 Stone Mold for Arrowheads from Susa, c. 2000 B.C.

iron, although there does not seem to be a connection between the two events. At the prehistoric site of Siyalk these migrants from the northern steppes built a new fortified town on the remnants of the old settlement, which had been abandoned for almost 2,000 years. They must have been horse and cattle breeders with a growing inclination toward agriculture. The two cemeteries near the new town were systematically investigated[31] between 1933 and 1937. The first graveyard (Siyalk A), which can be dated with certainty as having been used between 1200 and 1000 B.C., contained numerous bronze objects, such as weapons, tools, ornaments, and horse bits, as well as a little silver jewelry.[32] One object in particular should be of interest: a sword with a bronze handle, hilt, and a bronze back supporting a thin steel blade, riveted onto the bronze back.[33] The second graveyard (Siyalk B), which was begun about 1000 B.C., shows increasing use of iron besides bronze,[34] particularly noticeable in the graves of the richer people. Apart from the commonly used weapons and tools, the archaeologists found a large number of skillfully forged steel forks, presumably toasting forks, ranging in length from 8 to 30 inches with a hollow socket for an extension stick.[35] A unique find in one of the graves was a slightly curved drinking tube of the kind described by Xenophon[36] as used by the Persians and often shown on Assyrian cylinders.[37]

During the first millennium B.C., Persia continued to be a supplier of metals, as shown by Assyrian annals:[38]

> The increased use of iron during the first millennium had a far reaching effect on the economic structure of society. Although known to the Hittites and the rulers of Mittanni in the fifteenth century B.C. and in Egypt in the fourteenth century B.C., this metal did not become widespread until the ninth to seventh centuries B.C. The use of new tools led to increased production, and this inevitably caused a considerable drop in the price of goods. Improved methods of agriculture opened up new tracts of hitherto uncultivated land. Rich sources of iron ore enriched countries that had previously played only an unimportant part in international trade, and this particularly affected northern Iran and the neighbouring countries. From Spain to China, the great changes taking place in the world led to an outburst of commercial activity in which Iran must have participated.

R. J. Forbes[39] recalls the Greek tradition that the Chalybes, subject people to the Hittite kings in Asia Minor between 1400

[31] R. Ghirshman, *Fouilles de Sialk*, Vols. 1 and 2.
[32] R. Ghirshman, *Iran*, pp. 78–81.

[33] R. Ghirshman, *Fouilles de Sialk*, Vol. 2, p. 44.
[34] *Ibid.*
[35] *Ibid.*, p. 52.
[36] Xenophon, *Anabasis*, iv.5.24.
[37] R. Ghirshman, *Fouilles de Sialk*, Vol. 2, p. 54.
[38] *Ibid.*, p. 86.
[39] R. J. Forbes in C. Singer, *op. cit.*, p. 594.

and 1200 B.C., introduced the cementation of iron, thus inventing hardenable steel. Egyptian letters mention Armenia as the main supplier of iron during that time. The downfall of the Hittite kingdom occurred about 1100 B.C., and Forbes believes that Armenian and Chalybian ironworkers migrated into neighboring countries, thus spreading their crafts. The appearance of iron and steel in northern Persia about this time seems to be proof of this theory. Forbes dates the permanent establishment of an iron culture as distinctly different from an occasional occurrence of some iron articles as follows:

1900–1400 B.C.	Armenia
1400–1200 B.C.	Hittite Kingdom
1200–1000 B.C.	Persia
1200– 700 B.C.	Egypt
900 B.C.	Assyria
600 B.C.	Hallstatt (Celtic Europe)

This might be the place to discuss the "Indian, Seric, Chinese, and Parthian" steels mentioned by the Roman historians. Pliny[40] (23–79 A.D.) believes the so-called "Seric" steel to be Chinese. Forbes,[41] however, is of the opinion that it is in reality Indian steel coming from the famous smelting center of Hyderabad. Cast steel ingots, so-called wootz,[42] were produced there for centuries, 5 inches in diameter and ½-inch thick, and were exported into many countries. The Achaemenian kings had received such steel from India, and we are told that Alexander the Great obtained three tons of it from Indian kings and had it forged into equipment and weapons.[43] Pliny tells us that the Romans bought steel from the Axymites in Abyssinia, who kept the Indian origin of it a secret, allowing the Romans to attribute it to China (Sericum) from its name, "Seric" steel. Forbes[44] links "Seric" with an Indian tribe, the Cheres. Indian steel found its way as an important export item through Persia, Arabia, and Syria, where Damascus was not only a trading place for it but became also a center for the working of steel into arms and tools. Diocletian (245–313 A.D.) established armament factories in Damascus that were removed to Samarkand and Ḫorāsān by Tamerlan in 1399 A.D.

Our knowledge of the antiquity of the iron and steel industry in China has to be revised in the light of recent research by Joseph Needham. Previously it was held[45] that the Iron Age began in China under the Chou (1030–221 B.C.), had a transition stage under the Ts'in (255–209 B.C.) and the early Han (209 B.C.–25 A.D.),[46] during both these periods bronze and iron still being used together, and that only in the later Han period (25–220 A.D.) did China come into the full Iron Age.

Needham[47] bases his new chronology for the development of iron and steel in China on Chinese sources and comes to the following conclusions:

(*a*) Wrought iron has been smelted in China from the sixth century in furnaces of which no traces have been found so far nor are any textual references to the smelting process known.

(*b*) Cast iron appears from the fourth century B.C. on in the form of agricultural implements, tools and weapons, and the molds for all these. Cast iron has already been recognized as a Chinese invention by earlier research workers,[48] but Needham

40 Pliny, *Historia Naturalis*, xxxiv.145.
41 R. J. Forbes, *op. cit.*, p. 409.
42 From Skr. *vagra*, meaning "thunderbolt."
43 C. Singer, *op. cit.*, Vol. 2, p. 57.

44 R. J. Forbes, *op. cit.*, p. 439.
45 *Ibid.*, p. 383.
46 T. S. Dono, "The Chemical Investigation of the Ancient Metallic Cultures in the Orient," pp. 287–325.
47 J. Needham, *The Development of Iron and Steel Technology in China*, pp. 2–44.
48 T. T. Read, "Chinese Iron a Puzzle," pp. 398–457.

gives as the reasons for the early discovery the use of minerals rich in phosphorus for the iron smelting, the availability of high temperature refractory clay, and the use of the double-acting cylinder bellows for metallurgical purposes.

(*c*) Whereas the steelmakers of the Old World carburized low-carbon wrought iron to obtain steel, it seems that the principal process in China was the decarburization of high-carbon cast iron by "fining" in a blast of air.

(*d*) From the fifth century A.D. onward a great deal of steel was made in China by a method which Needham calls co-fusion, a process in which layers of wrought iron and cast iron were fused together at the appropriate heat so that the end product had the right carbon content to be classified as steel.

(*e*) In the third century A.D. Chinese smiths produced laminated damascene by welding hard and soft steels into weapons. We know from the Chinese chronicle *Ko-Ku-Yao*[49] that Sasanian (212–656 A.D.) steel was imported from Persia. The book particularly mentions the winding lines on the surface of the steel, so this imported Persian steel must have been damascened steel. This seems to confirm Needham's suspicion that the damascening technique must have come from Persia if it was not Indian wootz. The Parthian or Persian steel so often mentioned by the Romans was regarded as being only second in quality to Indian steel, and it is believed today[50] that it was produced from flat wrought iron disks by carburization (cementation) with charcoal in crucibles, a technique that spread over Arabia, Mesopotamia, and Damascus, eventually reaching Toledo, a center of Arabic science and technology in Spain.

[49] B. Laufer, *Sino-Iranica*, p. 515.

[50] R. J. Forbes, *op. cit.*, pp. 409 ff.

Ancient smelting sites have been found in Persia in the Qarādāġ ranges near Tabrīz where magnetic iron and hematite are found. Robertson[51] describes ancient iron furnaces which he found there: "The furnace has two hearths, the smaller one 14 inches square and 9 inches deep, the larger one being sunk 3 feet deep into the ground and with walls 2–3 feet high, covered with a fire resistant stone cupola." Other old iron mining and smelting centers have been located in the Alburz mountains, near Rašt and Massula, where the inhabitants are blacksmiths to this day, west of Tehrān and near Qazvīn, where hematite ore is still mined, and to the east near Firūzkūh, on the foothills of Mt. Damavand. Apart from minor iron ore deposits near Damġān, Semnān, Šāhrūd, Kāšān, Kohrūd, and the Kūh-e Banān mountains near Iṣfahān, there are vast red ocher deposits on the island of Hormuz in the Persian Gulf and, above all, the magnetic iron mountain southeast of Bafq in Central Persia, which is estimated to contain thirteen million tons of iron.[52] It stands as a lonely cone in the open plain, visible for more than forty miles. The iron ore mines and smelting works of Kermān have been famous during the time of the ᶜAbbasid caliphs, but have not been worked in later times.[53]

In their language the Persians distinguish between wrought iron and hardenable steel. The former is called *āhan* (Skr. *ayas*, Ger. *Eisen*, Eng. iron, Sp. *hierro*, L. *ferrum*); steel is *pūlād* in middle Persian, *fūlād* in modern Persian. It may be worth while for a linguist to trace the etymology of the names for steel similar to *pūlād* in the Armenian, Ossetic, Grusian, Turkish, and

[51] J. Robertson, "An Account of the Iron Mines of Caradagh," pp. 84–86.

[52] M. Maczek, "Der Erzbergbau im Iran," p. 198.

[53] R. J. Forbes, *op. cit.*, p. 387.

Russian languages. The Mongol name for steel is *bolot*.[54]

In his book *On the Qualities of Swords* the Arabian alchemist Alkindi (about 873 A.D.) called the two forms of iron "female" and "male." *Marmahānī* (female), modern Persian *marmāhan*, was wrought iron, whereas *sābūrqānī* (male) was the iron that could be hardened. He ascribed the superb qualities of the damascene steel, which he called *fīrind*, to the right mixture of the two sexes. In the *Šāhnāmeh* of Firdousī (c. 1000 A.D.) the heroes' weapons were made of *fūlād*, and the popular leader Kāveh was a blacksmith; the banner of the freedom fighters was his leather apron.[55]

Since damascene steel is so closely connected with Persia, a description of its nature and manufacture will throw some light on the high standard of the country's ancient metallurgy. First it is necessary to point out that there are two distinctly different types of damascene steel: laminated damascene steel and damascene crucible steel. Laminated damascene steel is produced by piling together bars of carbon steel and mild steel, as we call them today, and what Alkindi called "male" and "female" iron,[56] welding them, drawing the welded packet under the hammer, folding it up, rewelding it, and repeating this procedure for a number of times. The end product consists of a great number of alternating laminations of mild and carbon steel. When the finished product after polishing is subjected to an etching process with vinegar or sulphuric acid (*jouhar*), a macroscopic structure of variegated, watery lines (*fīrind*, *jouhar-dār*) becomes apparent because the essentially ferritic laminations of the mild steel appear as white lines, whereas the pearlitic carbon steel with its possible enclosures of temper carbon will produce darker lines. This technique was already known in prehistoric times;[57] the Romans used it for centuries in the manufacture of swords and cutlery,[58] and it has been applied by the Japanese swordsmiths for their famous Samurai swords since about 1000 A.D. It has been calculated that a section of such a sword blade consists of about four million laminations.[59] The process was introduced to Europe by the crusaders; the swordsmiths of Solingen have been making damascene steel since the twelfth century. The same technique is still used by the Pandai-Vesi of Bali and other smithing tribes of Indonesia.[60]

The other type, the crucible damascene, known in India as wootz, had long defied a critical analysis, until the French Inspector of Assays at the Paris mint, Bréant, in a series of more than 300 brilliant experiments in less than six weeks, discovered the true nature of this steel. He had used for this purpose 100 kg of wootz, given to him by the East India Company of London. Independent of Bréant, the Russian metallurgist, Anossoff, reproduced this steel in his ironworks at Zlatoust in the Ural in an ingenious combination of his own scientific analysis with oral tradition.[61] It appears that Anossoff was a colonel in the Russian army during the occupation of the Emirate of Boḫārā in the 1820's, and that he contacted Persian ironworkers in that region. He described his method in a paper, "On the Bulat." What he wrote

[54] *Ibid.*, p. 443.

[55] J. Hammer-Purgstall, "Sur les lames des orientaux," p. 66.

[56] *Ibid.*

[57] H. H. Coghlan, *Notes on Prehistoric and Early Iron in the Old World*, p. 134.

[58] B. Neumann, "Römischer Damaststahl," pp. 241–244.

[59] O. Johannsen, *Geschichte des Eisens*, p. 8, and G. Hannak, "Japanischer Damast-Stahl," pp. 87–90.

[60] M. Covarrubias, *Island of Bali*, and R. Goris, "The Position of the Blacksmiths."

[61] C. S. Smith, "Four Outstanding Researches in Metallurgical History," pp. 17–26, and P. A. Anossoff, "On the Bulat," pp. 157–315.

about there was clearly crucible steel, mild steel carburized with charcoal and other organic matter. But later he asked a certain Captain Massalski, whose regiment was stationed in the Boḫārā region, to investigate further on steelmaking there, on which Massalski reported.[62] Contrary to the description in Anossoff's paper, he found that the crucible was filled with two parts of chipped mild steel and one part of finely broken-up cast iron covered with charcoal. The use of cast iron in crucible steelmaking resembles the Chinese process mentioned by Needham as co-fusion.[63] Massalski reported that the crucible content was completely melted, and he noted that at the melting point a "boiling" of the charge could be observed. This indicated a partial oxidization of the carbon in the cast iron. Massalski mentioned a further alloying component, the adding of 130 to 170 grams of silver to the molten crucible charge of about 2.5 kilos. Massalski continued that, when the silver was added, the charge was covered again with charcoal and left to a slow cooling of about three hours. Then the ingot was taken out of the crucible and cleaned, and he reported that the damascene lines could already then be observed on the surface. If the steelmakers found them to be too coarse they knew the steel would be too brittle, and they heated it again to bright red heat for seven minutes. After that a hammer test was made, and if the steel did not crumble then they knew it was all right, and it was forged out into blades and eventually quenched in boiling oil.

Massalski's observations in Boḫārā vary from Anossoff's description. The reason could be that the Boḫārā smiths employed by Anossoff in his steelworks did not know the method as reported by Massalski, or that they did not want to give all their trade secrets away. But Anossoff was so successful that his steel mill produced great quantities of this *bulat* (the Russian name for damascene steel), and only the simultaneous development of alloyed steels prevented a significant revival of the *bulat.*

Belaiew, another Russian metallurgist, studied Anossoff's paper, and in 1906 analyzed a number of original old Persian swords with modern microphotographic methods. He concluded:[64]

1. Steel that appeared in Europe during the Middle Ages as damascene steel was known in Russia under its Persian name, *bulat* or *pūlād.*

2. Characteristic of this type of damascene steel is a peculiar kind of patterned watery surface, different from the more linear laminated damascene.

3. It is Russian tradition that *bulat* originated in India and later spread to Persia. Anossoff's research and reproduction of *bulat* proved and Belaiew's microscopic analyses confirmed that *bulat* was made in a crucible from pure mild steel and was cemented with charcoal to a carbon content of 1.0 to 1.7 per cent in the finished product.

The process is likely to be similar to the production of wootz as described by Johannsen[65] for the nineteenth-century ironworkers of Hyderabad, India:

> Mild steel is put into small crucibles of only 0.33 litre, together with charred rice husks, the charcoal of *Cassia auriculata* and the leaves of Asclapias, a plant which issues a milky juice when cut. The charge is 0.4 kg iron per crucible; 15 to 20 sealed crucibles are placed into a furnace and melted for 6 hours and slowly cooled. The ingots are smeared over with a mixture of clay and limonite and forged into discs of 6 to 8 kg weight. Forging of tools and weapons is done at a dark red temperature with final cold

[62] Massalski, "Préparation de l'acier damassé en Perse," pp. 297–308.

[63] J. Needham, *op. cit.*

[64] N. Belaiew, "Damascene Steel," pp. 417 ff., and "On the Bulat."

[65] O. Johannsen, *op. cit.*, p. 19.

working. Etching with vitriol brings out the lines.

An important part, both with regard to duration and intensity of the process, was the melting in the crucible and the slow cooling afterwards. The oriental writers and Western investigators point out that the molten state in the crucible should be maintained for hours and the cooling should be extremely slow and should take place with that of the furnace. If this was done, a hypereutectic alloy (with more than 0.83 per cent carbon) separated its excess cementite (iron carbide) along very extended dendritic axes. After forging the steel cake, these straight axes gradually changed into a wavy or mottled macrostructure so characteristic for damascene steel.

The high degree of elasticity and the marked absence of brittleness find their explanation in the microstructure. Belaiew's microphotographs[66] of original Persian damascene steels as well as Anossoff's reproductions show the cementite bands broken up into extremely fine globulites or spheroids of cementite. This kind of structure has not the brittleness of ordinary hypereutectoid steel with its pike and needle-like cementite structure. Modern techniques in steel production likewise aim at globular (spheroid) structures in certain steels. This shows that the Indian and Persian damascene steels well deserve the special position in metallurgy they had for more than two millennia.[67]

This description of bronze and iron in Persia would not be complete without mentioning the bronzes of Lūristān, the mountainous province of Western Persia. From about 1930 onwards[68] an increasing number of beautiful metal objects appeared on the antique market, coming from clandestine excavators who had found that carefully paved stone tomb pits contained gifts and tokens for the dead of an ancient culture hitherto unknown. Design and craftsmanship of the metalwork are of such high standard that the experts are all the more puzzled about the people who created this civilization. A number of objects have Assyrian writings on them, so that the dating at least is well established. A few of them belong to the period from the twelfth to the tenth century B.C.; the majority, however, to the eighth and seventh centuries B.C.[69] Few material cultures of the old world are as complex in style as the Lūristān bronzes. Strong influence from Assyrian, Hittite, Hurrian, and even Scythian elements can be traced, but also many of the Persian forms of the Siyalk A and B styles are obvious. The Lūristān craftsmen must have mastered the art of bronze casting, but also the beginning of an iron technology. Most of the bronzes seem to have been cast in the *cire perdue* technique. They are elaborate in their detail, form, and ornamentation (Fig. 5), which could only have been achieved by this casting method. The horse almost shows the wax coils used in the modeling process; the same can be said about the ibex mounted pin. But the stone mold already used during the third millennium (cf. p. 4) must also have been in use for the making of some of the Lūristān bronzes. A two-part carved stone mold in the Tehrān Mūzeh Bāstān shows every detail of a richly ornamented battle axe of 1000–800 B.C. (Fig. 6). The observer should note that the mold halves have carved-out rests for a core in order to produce the hollow handle socket. Every one

66 N. Belaiew, *op. cit.*, Plates XLI–XLIII.

67 For further detail on the production of wootz and damascene see G. Pearson, "Experiments and Observations on a Kind of Steel called Wootz," pp. 322–346; J. Stodart, "A Brief Account of Wootz or Indian Steel," p. 570; and K. Harnecker, "Beitrag zur Frage des Damaststahls," p. 1409.

68 A. U. Pope and P. Ackerman, *op. cit.*, p. 14.

69 E. Diez, *Iranische Kunst*, pp. 23 ff.

Figure 5 Bronzes from Lūristān, c. 1000 B.C.

in that area. Gold and silver vessels were beaten thinly into beautiful shapes, ornamented with *repoussé* work. Diez[71] points out that similar styles in beaten metalwork belonging to this time can be found in Persia, South Russia, Siberia, and China. He agrees with other modern authors that the creators of this peculiar animal style must have been the Scythians, kinsmen of the Iranians.

The Medes, who ascended to power in Northern Persia during the seventh century, have left us little metalwork, although some of the metal objects excavated recently in Āẕarbaijān seem to indicate a gradual development from Scythian influence toward a true Median style during that time. When, between 559 and 530 B.C., Cyrus the Great had unified the Median and Persian kingdoms, the first supranational empire came into existence, which reached its greatest extension under Darius I, the Achaemenian. By then a new phase in industrial arts had set in, raw materials came from all parts of the empire, and craftsmen from other countries worked at the palaces in Susa and Persepolis. This new development is best illustrated from

of the thousands of objects which have found their way into the great museums and collections of the world is most artistically treated, be it sword, dagger, chariot pole end, rein ring, horse bit, mirror, talisman, vase, chalice, or goblet. The Lūristān metallurgist was equally good as a coppersmith. A number of copper or low tin bronzes, beaten into ceremonial drinking vessels and sword sheaths, have survived. All these are decorated with intricate *repoussé* work.

The recently discovered Treasure of Sakiz in Āẕarbaijān, south of Lake Urūmīyeh, forms an important link between prehistoric metallurgy and that of historically established periods. It is a rich collection of gold, silver, and brass objects. Four different styles can be clearly distinguished: Assyrian, Scythian, Assyro-Scythian, and Medo-Iranian,[70] an assortment typical for the political struggle for domination during the seventh century

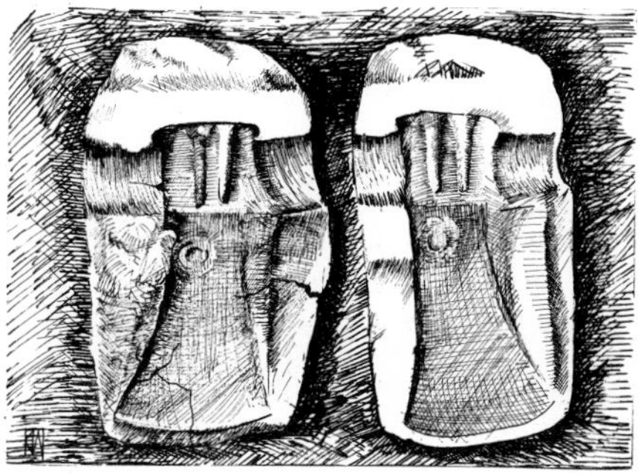

Figure 6 Stone Mold for a Battle Axe from Ḥaṣanlū/Āẕarbaijān, c. 1000 B.C. (*Mūzeh Bāstān, Tehrān*)

70 R. Ghirshman, *Iran*, p. 107.

71 E. Diez, *op. cit.*, pp. 23 ff.

the text of the Susa foundation charter,[72] which refers for example to metals: "... Gold has been brought from Sardis and Bactria and has been treated here ... the silver and copper were brought from Egypt, ... the goldsmiths who worked the gold were Medes and Egyptians ..."

The excavations of Achaemenian, Parthian, and Sasanian sites by French, German, and American archaeologists have brought to light an enormous wealth of objects of a rich material culture which now fill the museums of Europe, America, and, above all, the Mūzeh Bāstān of Tehrān. They include bronze and iron arms, bronze horse bits, chariot fittings, tools, jewelry, sculptures, gold and silver dishes, vessels, and "builder's hardware" for the palaces.[73] A new metal appears for the first time during this period, namely zinc, not yet in its metallic form but alloyed with copper as brass. Southern Persia is particularly rich in zinc ores; the main deposits are between Iṣfahān and Anārak in the Kūh-e Banān mountains north of Yazd. Here Marco Polo saw the important "tuttia"[74] factories at Cobinan (his spelling for Kūh-e Banān). *Tūtiyā* is obtained from finely ground calamine, which is mixed with charcoal and granulated copper, placed in crucibles, and then heated. Metallic zinc thus reduced with the charcoal vaporizes but apparently then alloys with the copper in the sealed crucibles to form brass. Brass is first mentioned during the time of King Sargon II (eighth century B.C.). Forbes[75] believes that the Mossynoeci or Muški, Hebrew Meshech, a people of Asia Minor, discovered brass alloying and introduced it into Persia during the reign of the Achaemenians.[76] The Greek writer Zosimos, born 400 B.C., is familiar with its manufacture from Kadmeia or Calamine, a silicate of zinc on the one hand and copper on the other. He calls it the yellow or Persian alloy and names a mythical Persian, Papapnidos son of Sitos, as its inventor.[77] The Greek writer of the second century A.D. known as Pseudo-Aristotle mentions it in his *Paradoxographia*:[78] "... they say that the bronze of the Mossynoeci is very bright and light, not because of its tin content but on account of it being alloyed with an ore found in their country." The Chinese chronicle *Sui-šu* (617 A.D.) refers to brass as *t'ou-ši*, coming from Sasanian Persia.[79] According to the *Kin-č'u-swi-ši-ki* (sixth century A.D.), needles and girdle buckles were made of brass, the metal coming from Persia. A book on early technology, the *Ko-ku-yao-lun*,[80] tells us of Chinese counterfeit brass, but that the genuine *t'ou-ši* came from Persia and was made from natural copper and zinc bloom. The same source states that the Persians were the first to mine zinc and to alloy brass.

The Persian alchemist Al-Jāḥiẓ (d. 869 A.D.) knew that gold could not be made from brass, and Ibn Al-Faqīh mentions that brass production was a government monopoly in Persia. He left a description of the zinc mines of Mt. Dunbāvand in the province of Kermān. Avicenna (980–1037 A.D.) knew the method of smelting brass from copper and calamine and stated that

[72] R. Ghirshman, *Iran*, pp. 181, 187.

[73] E. F. Schmidt, *The Treasury of Persepolis*, *Persepolis*, and *Flights over Ancient Cities of Iran*.

[74] "Tuttia," Pers. *tūtiyā*, is derived from *dūd* (meaning "smoke"), which refers to the white vapors of the sublimated zinc emanating from the crucibles during the smelting process.

[75] R. J. Forbes, *op. cit.*, p. 280.

[76] Cf. Ezekiel 27:13.

[77] R. J. Forbes, *op. cit.*, p. 284.

[78] J. Beckmann, *Paradoxographoi* or *Scriptores Rerum Mirabilium*.

[79] Theophilus Presbyter, *Diversarum Artium Schedula*, pp. 64–65, and Theophilus, *On Divers Arts*, pp. 143–144, and Theophilus, *The Various Arts*, Book III, chapters 65–66.

[80] B. Laufer, *op. cit.*, pp. 511–512.

the process spread from Persia to India and China. The same process is fully described by the monk Theophilus.[81] A further description of the smelting process is given by the Persian writer Jawbarī (fl. 1225 A.D.).[82] The geographer Al-Dimašqī (fl. 1300 A.D.) is the first to mention metallic zinc as coming from China, where the smelting was kept a secret.[83] The German physician Bontius (1535–1599 A.D.) knew about *tūtiyā* deposits near Kermān.[84] In modern Persian, bronze (*safīdray*) is clearly distinguished from brass (*berenj*) made from copper and from *tūtiyā*, the latter now meaning calamine only.[85]

Trade within the Achaemenian empire reached extensions which make it understandable that, for the first time in history, their beasts of burden had their hooves protected against the rough roads by copper horseshoes.[86] Trade, the unification of administration of the empire, and a systematic collection of taxes favored the general introduction of a monetary system. Croesus of Lydia had previously introduced the world's first bimetallic (gold-silver) coinage system, which was adopted by Darius[87] for his empire. Some of the 22,000 clay tablets unearthed at Persepolis between 1931 and 1934, which formed part of the royal accountancy, are wages lists for the building workers. These documents prove that payment in money gradually replaced payment in kind.[88] The bimetallic monetary system has survived 2,500 years, considering that the U.S.A. had a currency based on gold and silver until recently.

These two metals have not been the most important ones in the past, nor have they been responsible for the material culture of the Metal Age. But with the development of monetary systems based on precious metals, these gain an importance far beyond that of their previous use for jewelry and personal ornaments. The river Hyktanis in Carmania (Kermān) is mentioned by Strabo[89] to be rich in alluvial gold. Assyrian texts[90] refer to gold deposits in Kavand (Zenjān). Other important deposits are mentioned by medieval historians near Damġān, Mašhad, in the Tīrān mountains near Iṣfahān, and near Taḫt-e Sulaimān in the western oil fields. In recent years Schranz[91] discovered reef gold in the copper mines of Anārak. Subsequent working of the reef proved to be disappointing and has since been abandoned.

Since the greater part of the gold worked in the past has been alluvial gold, there is only the refining process to be mentioned, as the mere melting of gold did not offer any difficulties to the Persian metallurgist used to the melting of bronze for so many centuries. The cupellation process that separates the precious from the base metals with the aid of lead added to the melt and subsequent oxidization of both lead and base metals must have been known for a long time, since most gold and silver objects of antiquity show a high degree of purity. The modification of the cupellation, the chlorination of the silver from the gold-silver alloy obtained by lead cupellation, was already known in the

[81] Theophilus Presbyter, *Diversarum Artium Schedula*, pp. 64–65.

[82] P. Schwarz, *Iran im Mittelalter nach den arabischen Geographen*, p. 252.

[83] R. J. Forbes, *op. cit.*, p. 284.

[84] *Ibid.*, p. 271.

[85] *Tūtiyā* migrated with the metal to China as *t'ou-ši*, to Spain as *atutia*, still with the Arabic article, to Portugal as *tutia*, to France as *tutie*, to Italy as *tuzia*, and to England as tutty. Persian *berenj* is found in Kurdish (*pirinjok*) and Armenian (*plinj*).

[86] R. Ghirshman, *Iran*, p. 187.

[87] *Ibid.*, p. 181.

[88] *Ibid.*

[89] Strabo XV, 2.14 cap. 726.

[90] R. J. Forbes, *op. cit.*, p. 150.

[91] Dr. Ing H. Schranz, Report to the Department of Mines, Tehrān, 1937.

second century B.C.[92] and is still practised to this day by the bazaar goldsmith.

Silver and lead are both obtained from the same mineral, viz., galena, of which Persia had rich deposits in historical times. Ancient writers mention silver mines of Bactria and Badakšan.[93] Herodotus[94] says that Darius obtained his silver from Cappadocia and Carmania. Marco Polo,[95] Abulfeda, and Ibn Ḥauqal mention silver and lead mines of Badakšan. The Chinese historian Hiuen Tsang (seventh century A.D.) praises the quality of the Bactrian silver.[96] The ʿAbbasid caliphs had silver and lead mines in Fārs, Ḫorāsān, and Kermān.[97] Kermān bronzes, containing approximately 10 per cent silver, have a special reputation for hardness and wear resistance. They are still used for making certain forming tools, such as minting dies, used for the striking of coins. When searching for antique coins in 1937 the writer was offered, by a Šīrāz coppersmith, some coins that obviously had been minted a few days before. When hard pressed, the coppersmith produced an original, much used, set of minting dies for coins from one of the Persis principalities of the twelfth century. An analysis of both parts of the die set revealed that it contained copper, tin, and silver in the proportion of 74:16:10.

After the downfall of the Achaemenian empire after Alexander the Great's conquest, the Macedonian's successors, the Seleucids, capitalized on the unity within the civilized world under Hellenism. They controlled the great crossroads between India and China on the one hand and the Mediterranean on the other. Persia exported iron, copper, tin, and lead from state-owned mines[98] and profited from the Indian steel transit trade. During the reign of the Parthians (250 B.C.–224 A.D.), Rome became an increasingly important economic factor in metal trade that covered Persia's own production and the continued transit from India. Parthian silver coins must have been minted in immense quantities. When the writer lived in Persia before World War II the tetradrachms of the Parthian time were still accepted as currency in remote districts, solely on their silver content.

The succeeding dynasty of the Sasanians (224–656 A.D.) brought about a revival of the Achaemenian culture and their crafts. Metal products of the Sasanian time found their way into Europe during the Dark Ages, mainly via Byzantium, and have influenced our own working techniques, as will be shown in later chapters of this survey. What we know as Islamic art is essentially based upon Sasanian tradition and craftsmanship. The caliphs in Baghdad, the Mongol and Turkish conquerors, and the Safavid emperors all based an important part of their economy on the working of metal mines and supplied the craftsmen of the country with material to be converted into valuable goods for export and home consumption. It is safe to assume that the working techniques in the mines have been the same through the centuries until the arrival of Western experts during our own time.

Ore Mining and Metal Smelting

Although the sinking of vertical shafts and horizontal tunneling are ancient Persian techniques, used for the country's underground water supply probably for millennia, these methods were not, as one would expect, applied to mining. The

[92] E. J. Holmyard, *Alchemy*, p. 41.
[93] E. Mackay, *The Indus Civilization.*
[94] Herodotus, *The Histories*, v. 49.
[95] Marco Polo, *The Travels of Marco Polo*, I.xxiv.
[96] Si-Yu-Ki, *Buddhist Records of the Western World*, Vol. 2, p. 278.
[97] R. J. Forbes, *op. cit.*, p. 189.
[98] R. Ghirshman, *Iran*, p. 420.

common practice was to "follow the lode" (*dombāl-e rageh raftan*). ᶜAlī Zāhedī, a mining foreman of Anārak, in his seventies, told the writer that he had been in the mine since he was ten and that not until 1935 was a vertical shaft first sunk, when Dr. Schranz and his team introduced it together with mechanized vertical haulage at the copper mine of Talmesī.

It is demonstrated by the many abandoned mine entrances (*dahān-e maᶜdan*) on the copper mountain of Anārak that ever since prehistoric times miners (*maᶜdančī*) have first located a worthwhile outcrop of the ore (*sang-e maᶜdan, maᶜdaniyāt*), and then followed the lode (*rageh*), cutting it out of the surrounding rock with a miner's hammer (*čakoš*) and chisel (*fūlād*), with picks (*kolang*), or breaking the ore out with heavy crowbars (*gāz-e kūh-kan*). Samples of all these tools have been found in disused parts of the mine, some going back to pre-Islamic times. The crowbars are 1¼ inch in diameter and 6 feet long. Figure 7 shows the entrance to such a "follow the lode" mine.

The minerals were packed into leather bags (*dūl-e čarmī, kīseh*) tied up with leather straps (*darband*) or into leather buckets (*tōbreh*) with an iron handle (*band*). Miners' assistants carried these containers, weighing about 85 pounds each, to the mine top, either following steps hewn into the sloping rock or handling them in teams from one gallery to the next if the ascent were too steep. A good deal of the gangue (*dāš*) had to be carried to the top in the same way unless there was space available in nearby disused sections of the mine.

As the miners worked themselves further into the mountain the need for artificial light and ventilation arose. The Persian miners to this day prefer an oil lamp (*čerāġ*); the reason for their preference is that it is a good indicator of danger, flickering or going out when the air is foul (*havā kasīf*). There are several ways to assure a good air supply. One already known from the pre-Islamic sections of the mine and still in use is a relatively small ventilation shaft (*bādū*). It is built into the corner of the shaft and is made up of

Figure 7 Entrance to a Mine that "Follows the Lode"

earthenware pipes (*gong, sefālīn*), each about 18 inches long, or of stone slabs built across the corner of a shaft, and forming a triangular duct. The miners' lamps are placed at the bottom of these chimneys; the hot air causes an updraft inside the chimney, and the outgoing air is replaced by fresh air coming down the shaft. Another method of ventilation was the connection of a previously worked shaft with a new one, thus causing a cross draft, often reinforced by lighting a fire in the inclined old shaft. Still another way of getting fresh air into the mine was the building of so-called wind catchers (*bādgīr*, Fig. 157) on the top of an old shaft outlet, thus forcing the air from the continuously blowing desert wind into the mine. The copper mountain of Anārak is studded with these wind catchers; some of them are over 60 feet high.

Where the roof of the mine is not sufficiently safe, mine props (*čūb-bastī*) have to be built in. The presence of underground water has rarely been a problem on the fringe of the Central Persian desert. When modern mining machinery began to work deeper ore strata, any underground water could be harnessed with motor pumps, and it has proved to be a boon to isolated mining communities.

There is a great variety of ores such as copper, silver, lead, zinc, antimony, and arsenic in the Anārak district. This area still yields considerable quantities of native copper (*mes-e čakošī*). Most of it contains nickel, some up to 50 per cent. Copper ores also found are carbonates, oxides, sulphides, and copper-lead pyrites.

The second important metal mined in the district is lead. There are a number of smaller mining communities not far from Anārak at ᶜAlam, Kūh-e Kahiyār (Osbaḫ-Kūh), and Naḫlak. The geographer Gabriel[99] gives a description of life in such a mining village in 1934:

> Here [at Naḫlak] lead is mined and smelted from the ore in a primitive way and transported on camel back to Anārak in ingots of 30 kg weight. About 100 people work in the nearby mines. They are all without their families, come from Anārak, Čūpānan, Jandaq and other places and usually stay until they become victims of lead poisoning and are thus forced to give up their work. Young and old find work in Naḫlak, the wages are four to seven qirān a day [$.70 to $1.12]. They start work at daybreak. In the afternoon you can see the tired people coming out of the mine with their heavy picks and an oil lamp.

Many improvements have been introduced since this was written thirty years ago. The miners' homes, where they now live with their wives and children, have running water, and every family has a vegetable garden. Humans and plants are no longer poisoned by the lead fumes because roasting the lead ores has been abandoned. The community enjoys the services of a permanent medical officer. There is no more children's work; all children are going to school. Before modernization there was no mechanical separation of the ore from the gangue. Children and young people used to help to concentrate the metal to anything from 10 to 40 per cent by handpicking. Today, with water available, lead ores are treated in a washing section (*sang-šūʾī*). All other sulphide ores have to be roasted (*falaqeh kardan*) in a roasting furnace (*kūreh-falaqeh*) before they can be reduced to metal.

Previously a good deal of the smelting (*ẕōb kardan*), especially of lead ores, was done on a small-scale basis. The furnaces were similar to the one shown in Fig. 3, a

Figure 8 A Lead Smelting Furnace at Anārak (*photographed by M. Maczek*)

hole dug into the ground with low cylindrical walls around it and charged with charcoal and lead ore. A metal tuyère (*lūleh-ye felezz*) connected the furnace with simple skin bellows (*dam-e dastī*). The charcoal fire reduced the ores to lead, which ran through a hole in the bottom of the furnace into a pit (*čāl*) in front of it, where it was left to set into ingots (*šemš*) of about 10 kg weight. When private enterprise recently undertook mining on a larger

[99] A. Gabriel, *Durch Persiens Wüsten*, p. 61.

Figure 9 A Smelting Furnace at Anārak (*photographed by M. Maczek*)

scale, shaft furnaces were introduced with a capacity of 200 to 600 kg per day. These furnaces (Figs. 8 and 9) work on the same principle as the ancient ones but are operated with large double-acting concertina bellows (*dam-e fānūsī*, Fig. 10) similar to those used by the blacksmiths. Lead ore dust (*ḫāk-e sorb*) is mixed with charcoal dust (*ḫāk-e zoġāl*), together with small quantities of clay (*gel-e ros*), then formed by hand into balls (*gondeleh*) and sintered in a small furnace. The sintered balls are added to the ordinary ore and smelted, thus permitting utilization of the ore dust, which often amounts to 30 per cent of the output. Copper ore dust is similarly treated and smelted together with the ordinary copper ore in the relatively large copper furnaces (*kūreh-ye ẕōb-e mes*, Fig. 11). These are operated with a set of two large round concertina bellows of about 2 feet 9 inches in diameter housed in a separate building and connected to the tuyères with leather hoses (*nāyeh*). These shaft furnaces have a slag-tapping hole (*sūlāḫ-e dāš*) and below it a hole to tap the metal (*ᶜaiyār*). The copper produced is reasonably pure. It was cast into ingots and used to be sold to the copper sheet makers of Kāšān, Iṣfahān, and Kermān.

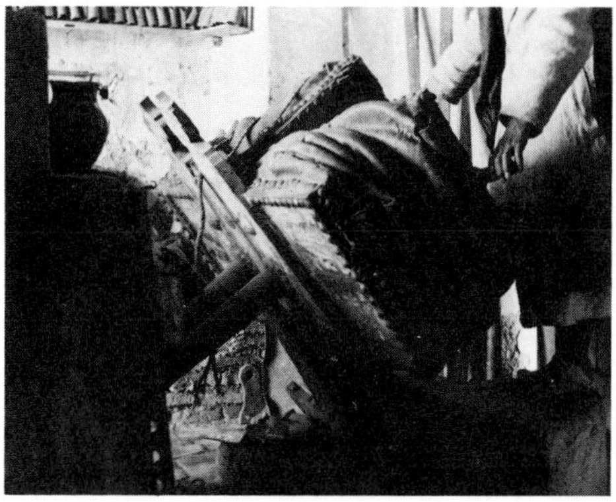

Figure 10 Bellows for the Smelting Furnace

Figure 11 Copper Smelting Furnace at Dohāneh Siyāh (*photographed by M. Maczek*)

Since the opening of the electrolytic refinery near Tehrān, all Anārak copper is sold there and the craftsmen buy it in the size and gauge required. Private mine operators pay the Department of Mines an annual fee (*ᶜušr*) for a mining license.

Bronze and Iron Founder

Within the rigid framework of the system of division of labor, traditional in Persia, the foundryman (*rīḫtehgar*) has his special place. He sells few of his products directly to the consumers, except some mortars (*hāvan*), pestles (*dasteh-ye hāvan*), pedestal lamps (*čerāġ-e pā*), camel bells (*zang-e šotor*), door knockers (*dasteh-ye dar*, *dastgīreh-ye dar*), and some builder's hardware. Most of the castings are for the needs of other trades, such as fittings, handles (*dasteh*), and taps (*šīr*) for the samovar maker, spouts (*dāneh*) and handles for ewers (*dasteh-ye āftābeh*), and recently also replacements for modern machinery. Because of this limitation, foundries are only in large cities where sufficient orders from other tradesmen are available to make the running of a furnace worthwhile.

The principal metals are copper (*mes*), bronze (*safīdray*, *mafrāġ*, *boronz*), brass (*berenj*), nickel-silver (*varšou*), and the famous silver-bronze (*haft-jūš*) of Kermān, an alloy (*eḫtelāt*, *maḫlūṭ*) of seven metals, viz., copper, silver, tin, traces of antimony, lead, gold, and iron. It is particularly suited for the manufacture of stamping dies on account of its hardness and wear resistance. Cast iron (*čodan*) and malleable cast iron (*čodan-e qaičī*) came in the wake of Western industry, and these two are only used to make spare parts for machines, vehicles, etc. Iron casting is usually done by a foundryman who specializes in it, and in a different workshop.

None of the historic molding processes, like carved stone or the lost wax molding, are used any more. Today's molding techniques do not differ much from those used in Europe in smaller foundries. In Šīrāz the foundryman uses a fairly pure sand (*gel*) and mixes it with cottonseed oil (*rouġān-e pambeh*) to obtain the necessary plasticity. In Iṣfahān a loamy sand (*šen*, *rīg*) is used, mixed with about 2 per cent of salt to make it more plastic. The molding sand is kept in a large sand box (*rīgdān*).

The mold (*qāleb*) is made in a set of molding boxes (*darajeh*); one-half (*nar*, *qāleb-e bālā*) has a pair of location pegs and the other half (*mādeh*, *qāleb-e pāʾīn*) has two corresponding holes. The older type of molding box is made of wood, whereas the more modern one is of cast iron or an aluminum alloy. Each half has reinforced edges (*lab*, *zeh*) on the inside; they make the frames more rigid and at the same time prevent the sand from falling out. The molding sand is sieved over the pattern (*šakl*, *šakl-e miṣālī*), first with a fine sieve (*alak*), and when the pattern is covered then the box is filled up through a coarse sieve (*kām*). The sand is solidified with a ramming iron (*bōkū*, *bōkūb*, *kūb*). Before molding the pattern is dusted with finely ground charcoal (*ḫāk-e zoġāl*) shaken through the pores of a dusting bag (*kīseh-ye zoġāl*). The molds are again dusted after removal of the patterns (Fig. 12). The resulting hollow mold (*qāleb*) may still require a core (*langar*), which is made in a core box (*qāleb-e langar*). The core is reinforced with twisted wire (*maftūl*). Cores above a certain length are supported by chaplets (*dōpā*). Patterns are mainly made of brass, since most articles are cast over and over again, but occasionally wooden patterns are used.

The runners for the metal (*nāvdān*, *rāh-gā*, *sar-e darajeh*) and the risers (*darajeh*) are cut with a spatula (*kār-tīġ*). Air vents (*havā-kaš*, *nafas-kaš*) are prepared with a needle (*mīl-e nafas-kaš*), and finally the whole mold is painted inside with a mix-

Figure 12 A Copper Founder Joining Mold Halves at Šīrāz

ture of water, charcoal dust, and gum tragacanth for which a fine brush (*qalam*) is used. The molds ready for pouring are placed into a row (*bast*) and tied together either with a large clamp (*fešārī*) or with a chain and wedge (*gāz*, Fig. 13). Metals are melted in crucibles (*bōteh, būteh*) holding between 50 and 100 pounds. The crucibles are made of refractory clay or a mixture of clay (*ḫāk-e ros*) and graphite (*medād*). They are carried in specially fitted crucible tongs (*ambor-e bōteh, ambor-e tōġ*) that have a cranked handle (*gīreh*) on the one side and a carrying bar (*kamčeh*) on the other. The furnace (*kūreh*) is of the beehive type with a charging hole (*sar-e kūreh*) in the front. Charcoal (*zoġāl*) has been the only fuel in the past, but recently coke (*zoġāl-e kōk*) and oil (*naft*) have come into use as well. Blast air is produced by a set of double bellows (*dam, dam-e dō dam, dam-e ṭorafeh*) through a pair of tuyères (*lūleh*). Combustion gases escape through a flue (*gorāz-gā, dūd-kaš*), and the ashes collect in an ash pit (*pas-e kūreh*). After melting (*godāḫtan, ẕōb kardan, ẕoub kardan, āb*

Figure 13 Pouring the Metal into the Molds

kardan), the metal is stirred with an iron bar (*sīḫ*), and before pouring (*rīḫtan, rīzeš kardan*) the founder never fails to invoke God's blessing for a perfect casting by a short "*Bismillāh*" (in the name of God). After they are cooled down the molds are opened, and two assistants are kept busy with cutting off the risers (*darajeh borīdan*, Fig. 14) and filing away (*souhān-kārī*) joints, air vents, and burrs.

Figure 14 Founder's Assistant Cutting off the Risers

Coppersmith, Brazier, Tinsmith, Oven Maker, and Tinner

Fine Metalwork in the Past

By the beginning of the ninth century the majority of the Persians had become Moslems. Islam became a new inspiring force. Persian influence in arts and crafts, blended in Baghdad with Byzantian elements, spread over the whole of the new Islamic empire[100]—over the Middle East, as far west as Spain, over Central Asia as far east as the frontiers of China, and to India in the south. In turn, Persian art was enriched by styles and methods of the countries it had influenced so much. The sponsors for the arts were in the first place the worldly rulers, but political power was seldom stable for any length of time, and we find the creation of new centers for the arts in the wake of the shifting political power, from Baghdad to Boḫārā, Samarkand, and Ġaznā in the east to Ray and Nīšāpūr in the north, to Marāġa, Tabrīz, and Sulṭāniyeh in the northwest, back to Samarkand, to Ray, again to Tabrīz, from there to Qazvīn, Iṣfahān, and Šīrāz, finally to Tehrān. In all these centers the arts and crafts flourished for centuries afterwards, thus favoring a wide spread of culture.

The range of metal objects comprises trays, salvers and platters, bowls, cauldrons and dishes, ewers, jugs and mortars, lamps and candlesticks, incense burners, mirrors, and many other utensils. There is a wide range, too, in the working techniques. The objects may be cast, beaten, wrought, cut, pierced, or drawn from metal. The decoration may be applied by engraving, chiseling, damascening, by inlay, embossing, or solid relief, open lacework, niello, enamel, incrustation, or gilding.

Although inlaid or incrustated metal had already been worked from the second millennium B.C. on, it became fashionable at the beginning of the thirteenth century, simultaneously with the arrival of the Mongols. The linear design was chased into the metal with a punch or engraved with a rowel, and a strand of precious metal was forced into the groove. Larger

100 G. Wiet, *Histoire de l'Egypte* "... la Perse fut donc la grande éducatrice des musulmans et non seulement dans la domaine de la littérature, mais dans ceux de l'art et de l'administration."

areas were recessed, and the raised edges were hammered down to grip a piece of silver or gold inlay. One of the finest specimens of Persian art in this technique is the Baptistère de Saint Louis, which came to France during the Middle Ages and is now in the Louvre. Incrustation is *al-ajam* in Arabic, from *ajamī*, meaning "Persia," indicating from where the Arabs learned the technique, which they later spread as far as Morocco.

The scientists and the engineers had most of their instruments made in brass. The most famous of them are the astrolabes of the astronomers, navigators, and surveyors. The spherical astrolabes (*aṣṭurlāb-e kūrī*) had the stars represented by inlaid silver pieces of varying sizes according to the brightness of the stars, and had the constellations engraved on the base metal. The linear astrolabes (*aṣṭurlāb-e ḫaṭṭī*) show amazing accuracy and precise gradation, even by modern standards (Fig. 15).

Figure 15 A Persian Astrolabe

Figure 16 A Coppersmith's Stall at Iṣfahān

Figure 17 A Furnace for Melting Copper at Šīrāz

Present Day

Most visitors to a Persian bazaar are impressed by what they see at the stalls of the coppersmith. Here is traditional craftsmanship at its best. Figure 16 shows the master coppersmith and his assistant in the midst of their products, doing their work in dignity while the noises of the great bazaar of Iṣfahān pass in front of their workshop.

Copper Sheet Maker

Before the arrival of factory-rolled copper sheet, the large centers of coppersmithing such as Kāšān, Iṣfahān, Šīrāz, Kermān, and others had a specialized group, the sheet makers (*godāzandeh-ye mesgarī*). In smaller communities sheet making was done by the coppersmith himself. The sheet maker either bought the ready cast ingots (*šemš*, *šumš*) from the metallurgical center of Anārak or melted scrap metal into ingots himself (*godāzandeh* actually means "melter"). For this purpose he used a furnace and crucibles similar to those used by the foundry man (q.v.). He lifted the crucibles out of the furnace with special tongs (*aṃbor-e kaj*) and poured the metal into ingot molds (*rījeh*). His main work was to beat the ingot into sheets. This beating out (*čakoš zadan*, *čakoš-kārī*) was done with the aid of one or two strikers in two distinctly different operations, viz., first to stretch the metal (*vāčīdan*) with the peen of the stretch hammer (*čakoš-e kaf*), and then to smooth it out (*ṣāf kardan*) with a flat hammer (*čakoš-e čārsū*). By this time the metal was no longer malleable (*čakoš-ḫwor*) and had to be annealed (*dast afšār*). These processes were continued until the right size and the required thickness were reached. The sheet maker aimed at beating the metal as close as possible to the shape needed by the coppersmith.

During a visit to Persia in 1963 the writer observed a revival, or was it survival, of this ancient trade, though in a modified, more modern version as an ingot foundry (*zoub-kārī*) combined with a rolling mill (*kārḫāneh navard*). This shop is situated in the heart of the Šīrāz coppersmith bazaar. The millowner buys all the copper scrap from his clients at a rate of 22 rials (about 30 cents) per kg and adds raw copper ingots as he needs them. He melts the metal in large crucibles in an oil-fired under-floor furnace (*kūreh-zoub*, Fig. 17). While the metal is melting, several cast iron flat ingot molds are assembled on the floor of the mill (foreground, Fig. 17) and the metal is cast (*rīḫtan be qāleb*). After they are cool, the ingots are handed over to the rolling section (*navard-kārī*, Fig. 18). The ingots are rolled out (*navard šodan*) into strips (*mes-e navard*) to a width of 18 to 20 inches with one or two annealings (*tābīdan*) in the flue of the furnace. The clients order their sheets according to gauge and size. Rectangles are cut off the strips for side walls of vessels, round pieces (*gerdeh*) for the bottoms. In this way the client has only a minimum of reject material but is paying 70 rials ($1.00) per kg for the rerolled and ready-cut copper.

The writer could not establish how many of these rolling mills are working. Where they do not exist, the coppersmiths buy copper sheets from the Tehrān refinery or imported ones.

Figure 18 Copper Rolling Mill in the Šīrāz Bazaar

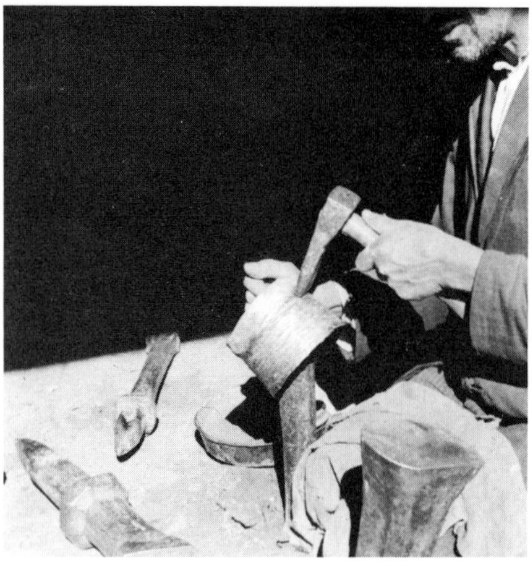

Figure 19 Stretching the Copper

Coppersmith

The main products of a coppersmith (*mesgar*) are vessels of various sizes and shapes. Smaller ones are beaten (*čakoš-kārī*) out of one piece, often to great depth, by stretching (*bāz kardan*) with annealing after each pass (Fig. 19). Larger objects are often beaten in the same way out of one round sheet (Fig. 20), an operation requiring great skill; alternately, the vessels are made up of two parts: first a flat sheet (*ṣafḥeh*) is bent (*ṣafḥeh gerd kardan*) into a cylindrical mantle, then a round sheet (*gerdeh*) has its rim (*bon*) turned up by hammering (*čakoš ḫwordan*) and is beaten mildly hollow (*goud šodan*) with a flat, square-faced hammer (*čakoš-e čahār-sūk*, Fig. 21). The joint is a toothed seam (*darz-e dandāneh*), a kind of dovetailed joint. To make it the coppersmith cuts teeth (*dandāneh čīdan*) all the way around the joints approximately $\frac{3}{8}$-inch square. The two edges are then joined (*ham kardan*) in such a way that one tooth fits into a gap on the opposite side. Hard solder (*laḥīm-e noqreh*) and borax (*taneh-kūr, tangār*) are applied and the whole is heated to soldering temperature in the open forge (*kūreh*). In the subsequent beating out of the metal the joint becomes perfectly flat. All one can see is a silvery zig-zag line from the different color of the solder, but it is a reliable joint. A folded or overlapping joint was not known until recently, hence its name "foreign joint" (*pīč-e farangī*). Some coppersmiths can make a copper weld (*mesjūš*) in the open forge without using any solder. With the arrival of the oxyacetylene torch this art of welding (*jūš kardan*) has almost died out.

Figure 20 Beating a Large Vessel from a Round Sheet

Figure 21 Beating a Dish Hollow

For the shaping of his work the coppersmith has a series of anvils (*sendān*) of different shapes driven into the ground or placed onto wooden stocks (*kondeh-čūb*). To name some of them: *taḫt, sendān-e taḫt* is a large anvil with a flat top, about 6 inches square; *nīmrāh, sendān-e motavasseṭ* is likewise flat but only 3 inches square (background, Fig. 22); *sendān-e kāseh-mīḫ* is a flat, round anvil; *niqolvar, mīḫqolvar* are anvils with curved tops (foreground, Fig. 22); *sendān-e lab-gardān* is an anvil used for the turning over (*lab gardānīdan*) of doubled edges (*lab-gardān*). A peculiar type of snarling iron for hollow objects, the *nā, nā-tāreh, mīḫ,* combines a secure position for the anvil with a comfortable seat on a wooden fork (*čūġ*) for the smith (Figs. 23 and 24). The many operations in the completion of a copper vessel require a set

Figure 22 Shaping a Copper Vessel

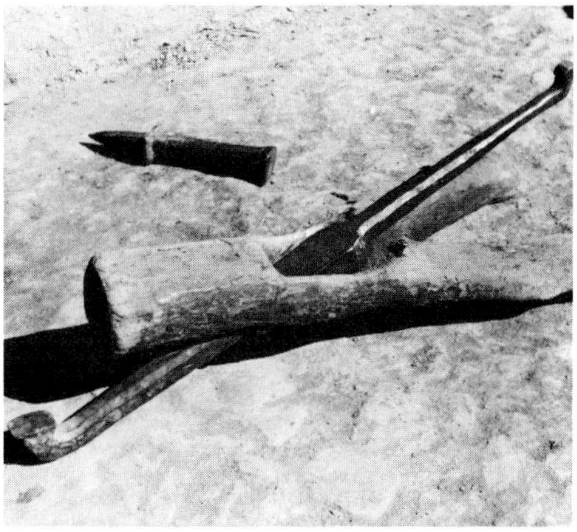

Figure 23 A Snarling Iron

Figure 24 A Coppersmith Sitting on a Snarling Iron (*right*)

of different hammers; here we have a flat hammer (*čakoš-e čārsū*), a round-faced flat hammer (*čakoš-e damgerd*), a ball-pointed hammer (*čakoš-e sīnehdār*), a peened stretch hammer (*čakoš-e kaf*, *čakoš-e dambārīk*), a double-ended edging hammer (*čakoš-e dōbahrī*), a riveting hammer (*čakoš-e miṭraqeh*, *parčkon*), a wooden mallet (*čakoš-e čubī*) and, finally, a handleless hammer, a kind of flat, hardened iron (*qāleb-e taneh*) that is much used for the planishing (*ṣāf kardan*) of surfaces in the final pass (Fig. 25). For cutting metal there are tin snips

Figure 25 Hammers and Planishing Iron

(*gāz*, *qaičī*). Figure 26 shows one which has one handle (*dasteh*) flat to place it firmly on the ground for cutting; the other handle has a hook (*mīḫ*) for easy lifting after a full cut. The snips have hollow ground cutting edges (*tīġeh*). This shape is only now coming into use in Western countries.

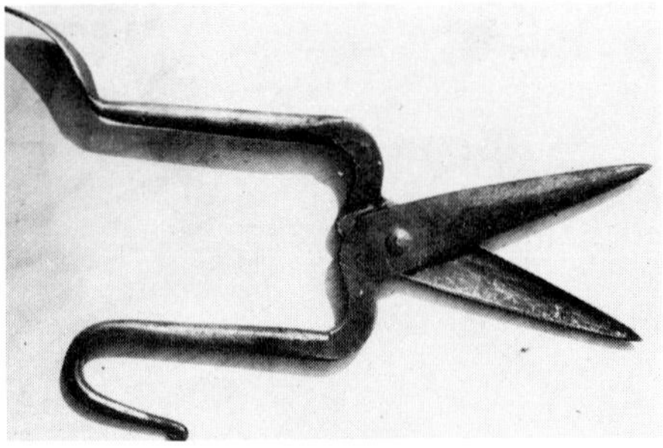

Figure 26 Tin Snips

Whether the coppersmith uses imported factory-made copper or the blank made by the sheet maker, he starts off with a material of greater thickness than that of the final product. In controlled stretching, planishing, and flanging (*labeh gereftan*) he turns it into a vessel (*tašt šodan*). Not only are the edges of larger vessels turned but also a steel wire (*maftūl*) is often beaten into the doubling (Fig. 27). Tongs (*ambor-dast*) allow the handling of the hot copper; tongs with a round mouth (*ambor-ḥalqeh*) are used when the rim or flange has already been formed. Handles, spouts, and feet of vessels are often riveted on. The rivet head is formed by a header (*qāleb-e mīḫparč*); holes are made with a punch (*sombeh*). Metal wire for rivets or decorative purposes is drawn from a round ingot bar in a series of passes through a drawing die (*ḥadīdeh*) with intermittent annealing. Such wires and sometimes handles and other fittings are forged into special swageing dies (*qāleb-e ḫūšeh*) in order to give them a pearled surface. All round articles are beaten into shape to such a degree of accuracy that they can afterwards be put onto a scraping and polishing lathe (*żarbgāh-e čarḫ*, *čarḫ-e dūvāl*) to give them the final smooth and polished surface.

The wooden frame of the polishing lathe (Fig. 28) carries a bearing (*dōpā*) on one side of a movable crossbar (*kūleh*) in which the iron axle (*mīl-e ṭavaq*) of a wooden mandril (*čūb-e ṭavaq*) is running. The crossbar is adjustable by pegs (*mīl-e darajeh*) in a row of holes (*sūrāḫ-e darajeh*). A dead center (*morġak*) is on the other side of the frame. The wooden mandril has a double purpose; first it supports the article to be turned, which is pressed against it by the dead center; second it takes the bowstring (*zeh*) of the fiddle bow (*kamāneh*) that is moved back and forth by the operator, thus turning the mandril. For heavier work the bow is replaced by a leather belt (*dūvāl*), which is pulled by two men in

Figure 27 Coppersmiths Planishing (*left*) and Flanging (*right*)

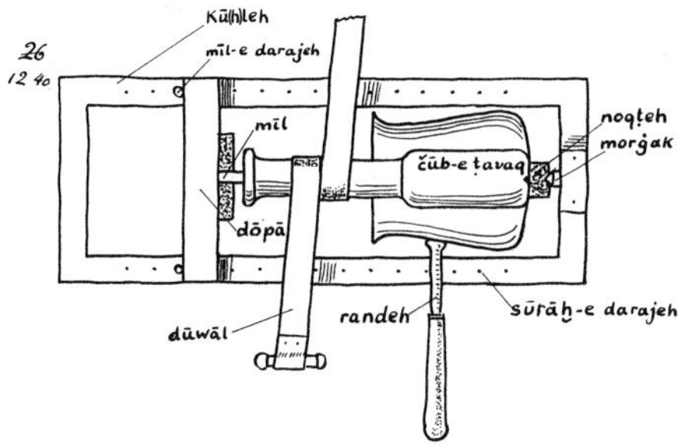

Figure 28 A Polishing Lathe

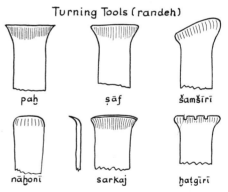

Figure 29 Turning Tools

such a way that the belt is tight in the one direction in which the lathe works and slack on the return movement. A polishing lathe reconstructed after the description of Theophilus (about 1125 A.D.)[101] has many features similar to the one still used in Persia.

[101] W. Theobald, *Technik des Kunsthandwerks im zehnten Jahrhundert*, p. 444.

The turner holds the scraping tools (*randeh*) on a supporting bar. A number of differently shaped tools (Fig. 29) enables him to follow the varying forms of the objects to be scraped. The scrapers are kept sharp on a honing stone (*sang-e rūmī*). The final polish (*pardāḫt*) is obtained by applying an abrasive, a kind of natural emery (*ḫāk-e āġor*) that is mixed with poppy seed oil (*rouġan-e ḫašḫāš*) and applied with a felt pad (*namad*).

All copper oxides that become available during the heating and beating operations and the copper shavings (*randeš*) from the scraping are carefully collected and sold to the potter, who uses them for the coloring of his glazes.

The more common products of the coppersmith are cooking pots and kettles (*dīg*) with their lids (*sar-e dīg*), large rice strainers (*palāyeš, ābkeš*), water decanters (*tong*), and many different trays (*sīnī*). A speciality of some coppersmiths is the manufacture of large copper boilers (*tūn-e ḥammām*) for the public bath (*ḥammām*). They are made of large heavy-gauge copper sheets, riveted together and afterwards soft-soldered (*laḥīm-e qalᶜ*) to make them watertight. In smaller communities the coppersmith does all the sheet metal work available, apart from the standard products outlined above. He works in brass, tin plate, and even in iron sheet metal. In larger centers, however, certain products and certain metals are handled by specialists. These are the brazier, the tinsmith, and the oven maker.

Brazier

The brazier or brassworker (*davāt-sāz, davātgar, rūʾī-gar*) works mainly in brass, but often in nickel-silver, when he is called *varšou-sāz*. The names *davāt-sāz* and *davātgar* are derived from the old writing set (*davāt*), a combination of an inkpot and a container for pens and penknife. These sets, often elaborately decorated, have now given way to the Western fountain pen. The main product of the brassworker is now the samovar, a kind of tea urn that came from Russia during the nineteenth century together with the habit of tea drinking. The popular beverage before its arrival was coffee; a tea house is still called *qahveh-ḫāneh*, i.e., coffee house. The brazier still makes a smaller type of coffee urn (*qahveh-rīzī*) and an even smaller coffee pot (*qahveh-jūš*), sometimes called *ketrī*. Another standard product of the brassworker is the charcoal brazier (*manqal*), so popular for room heating in winter and for cooking small meals. Its frame consists of a number of plain or embossed brass strips forming a polygon, lined with fire clay bricks and with cast brass feet under the corners. A special type of *manqal* is sometimes made with a grill above an ash tray. It is called *manqal-e boḫārī*, i.e., stove-brazier, or *manqal-e farangī*, foreign brazier. It is actually a transition between a brazier and a Western type stove. It needs less fanning and is often used by the bazaar cooks. Little cooking stoves heated with charcoal (*tābeh, tāveh*) are likewise made by the brazier.

The products mentioned so far are of a rather utilitarian nature, but the skill of this craftsman is shown in the making of large and small trays and salvers (*sīnī, naᶜlakī*) used in the household for many purposes. The better ones of these trays are embossed or engraved, showing ornaments or writings. This kind of work is usually done by another craftsman, the engraver (*qalamzan*). The most valuable ones are silver and copper encrusted.

Since the rules of the Qorʾān require the Moslem to clean himself with water after an answer to a call of nature, there is always a special water can (*āftābeh*) near the toilet. The common ones of these spouted cans (Foreground, Fig. 16) are made by the coppersmith, the better ones by the brazier. He makes a larger variation of this can as well, actually a set consisting of a ewer and a hand-washing pan (*āftābeh-ō-lagan*), the latter having a depression in the center covered by a brass sieve (*kafgīr*). This set is used at mealtimes. A servant holding the pan (*lagan*) in one hand pours water from the ewer over the diner's hands between courses. Metal flower vases (*goldān*), ash trays (*zīr-e sīgār*), milk jars (*šīrdān*), decanters (*tong*), spoons (*qāšuq*), and forks (*čangāl*) are other products of the *davāt-sāz*.

So far as the brazier's tools are concerned, they are essentially the same as those of the coppersmith. He has a few special anvils, e.g., an angled round snarling iron (*mūš-borīdeh*), a craned snarling iron (*šotor-gelū*, background Fig. 30),

Figure 30 A Samovar Maker Beating Nickel-Silver at Borūjerd

a heavy anvil rammed into the ground (*qolvār-būzā*), a similar one but smaller with a flat face (*mīḫ-nīmeh*), and a medium one in a stock (*qolvār-vasaṭ*). For this kind of work all hammers are well polished and have slightly curved surfaces; one is *sīneh-dār-čārsū*, with a square face; another is *sīneh-dār*, having a round face; and *sīneh-dār-dokmeh* is a hammer with a small, pointed, button-shaped face.

The busy braziers of Iṣfahān and the famous samovar makers of Borūjerd in Lūristān even have two other independent craftsmen working for them, the brass finisher (*souhān-kār*) and the brass polisher (*pardāḫt-kār*, *ferčeh-kār*). The finisher buys the raw castings for the brazier's hardware from the foundry, e.g., handles for the samovar (*dasteh-samōvar*), the tap (*šīr*), the samovar base (*korsī*), the feet for the base (*zīr-e korsī*), steam valves (*boḫār-kaš*), ewer handles (*dasteh-āftābeh*) and many other parts. The finisher works in the brazier's bazaar, sits behind a filing block, and has to file (*souhān kardan*) the castings smooth, drill the riveting holes with a bow drill (*mateh-kamāneh*), prepare the rivets (*mīl*, *pīč-āmoreh*), and cut the threads (*pīč kardan*, *pīč tarāšīdan*) with a cutting die (*ḥadīdeh*). The work is then handed over to the brazier. He is more skilled in hard soldering (*jūš dādan*, *laḥīm-e noqreh dādan*) than the coppersmith. He has several sizes of brazing furnaces (*kūreh*) in his workshop, the smaller ones in pot form that obtain their blast air from skin bellows (*dam-e dūlī*) of the same type as described by Theophilus.[102] To obtain the leather for the bellows a goat is skinned starting from the tail, the skin pulled over the head without slitting it along the belly. After it is tanned in tallow to make it soft and pliable, the four leg ends are tied up, and the neck is fitted over the blow pipe of the furnace. The slit rear end is fitted with two wooden slats (*čūb-e dam*, *čūġ-e dam*, *panjeh*) about 12 to 15 inches in length, having two leather loops for thumb and fingers of the operator's hand. When using them, the brazier's assistant opens the slats widely, lifting the skin at the same time, thus letting as much air in as possible. Upon reaching the end of the intake stroke he closes the slats tightly and moves the whole skin close to the blowpipe (*sar-e dam*), pressing the air into the furnace. It is amazing to see how skillfully small amounts of air can be blown into the furnace when difficult brazing work has just reached a critical stage (Fig. 31).

The larger furnaces are fitted with the concertina type of bellows (*dam-e fānūsī*), always working in pairs for a constant air stream. The brazier pays much attention to the finish of his work by scraping it

[102] *Ibid.*, pp. 64, 265.

Figure 31 A Tinner Operating His Skin Bellows

carefully on the fiddle- or belt-operated polishing lathe. His toolbox includes a few more special scrapers, a round-edged scraper (*randeh-nīmbor*), a square-faced broad scraper (*randeh-taḫt*), and an oblique-edged scraper (*randeh-kaj*). Wherever applicable he also brings his work to a bright shine (*pardāḫt*) with Tripoli sand and iron oxide powder (*ḫāk-e ros*, *gel-e māšī*). This work is today often handed over to the independent polisher with his buffing machine.

Tinsmith and Oven Maker

The tinsmith (*ḥalabī-sāz*) has taken over a good deal of the work that used to be done by the coppersmith, the reason being that cheap tinplate from empty petrol containers is available, and also that imports of rolled tinplate from overseas have increased. Apart from a lot of work in tinplate (*ḥalabī*), the tinsmith also uses galvanized iron (*āhan-e safīd*), and his range of work is similar to that of a Western sheet metal worker. Here are a few examples of his production: gutters (*nāvdān*), down pipes (*lūleh-nāvdān*), iron-clad roofs (*šīrvāneh*), ridge sheets (*ṭōreh*) of these roofs, hardware for the household like spraying cans (*ābpāš*), buckets (*saṭl*), storage containers for drinking water (*saqqā-ḫāneh*), kerosene cans (*āftābeh-naftdān*), funnels (*qīf*), and many others, often simplified copies of Western industrial products.

In most communities the tinsmith also makes stoves and ovens (*boḫārī*). With the increasing availability of cheap hard coal they are replacing the charcoal-operated braziers. These ovens are made in black sheet metal, and the lower parts are lined with bricks. The tinsmith makes the stove pipes (*lūleh-ye boḫārī*), the elbows (*zānū-ye lūleh*), and the oven bases (*zīr-e boḫārī*). In large cities the oven maker is a specialist and is then known as *boḫārī-sāz*. Lately, since the government banned the ruthless cutting of trees for firewood and charcoal making, kerosene and fuel oil have come into widespread use, and a variety of efficient room and water heaters operated with these fuels are now produced by the oven maker.

Most of the tools of the tinsmith are similar to those of the coppersmith and the brazier. Typical for the tinsmith, however, are large-horned anvils (*sendān*) and a set of sheet metal rollers (*ḥalabī-ḫamkon*) for rolling the plate into cylindrical or conical shapes. This device has exchangeable rollers (*tūpī*, *qāleb*) for beading, flanging (*labeh gereftan*), and round cutting. The tinsmith does his soldering with soft solder (*laḥīm-e qalᶜ*). He uses a soldering iron (*āhan-e laḥīm, houviyeh*) which, unlike its Western namesake, is made of wrought iron and not of copper. The iron is heated in a small pot forge with skin bellows; the solder, a mixture of tin and lead, is kept in a dish (*ṭabaq*) on top of the forge. To clean the surfaces of the joining parts and the edge of the soldering iron the tinsmith uses sal-ammoniac (*nešādor*) applied to the preheated surfaces.

Tinner

Copper and brass vessels used for food preparation are tinned with pure tin (*qalᶜ*) from the inside. This is done by a special craftsman who does this work for the coppersmith and the brazier in contract or takes worn copper or brass vessels from the public for retinning. In larger towns the tinners (*safīd-gar, ṣaffār, qalᶜ-gar*) have their stalls not far from the coppersmiths' but in the villages the tinning is either done as a side line by the coppersmith himself, or a traveling tinner may visit the open market from time to time, setting up his working place under a tree. Such a tinner's equipment is most simple. A small hole about 15 inches in diameter and 12 inches deep, dug into the ground, forms the furnace. A long iron nozzle (*lūleh*) reaches the bottom of the hole; skin bellows (*dam-e dastī*) are attached to the other end of the nozzle. Not far from the furnace, near a wall in the bazaar or under a low branch of the tree the tinner has a second hole (*čāleh*) in the ground. It is shallow and filled with sharp river sand (*šen*) and gravel (*rīg*). The vessel to be tinned is cleaned (*tamīz kardan*) in the following way: The tinner or his assistant (*šāgerd*) fills it partly with the sand and gravel mixture, then he places it in the gravel-filled hole, stands with his bare feet inside the vessel, and holding himself on a beam or a branch of the tree he rotates the vessel swiftly with his feet so that the gravel will clean it efficiently from inside and outside (Fig. 32).

After the sand and dirt are washed off, the vessel is mildly heated over the furnace. When a cotton pad (*pambeh, dast-pambeh*) just begins to scorch, a mixture of pure tin and sal-ammoniac is applied with the pad. The vaporizing sal-ammoniac produces a metallically clean surface, the tin melts, and under constant rubbing of the pad an even distribution of the tin over the whole vessel is achieved. Larger vessels are moved over the forge until tinning is completed. During this operation the tinner holds the vessel with a pair of tongs (*ambor-e safīdgarī*). If the vessel has a wide rim, special open-mouthed tongs (*ḥalq-ambor*) are used (Fig. 33). The tin is bought in the bazaar in the form of large sheets (*varaq, varaqeh-ye qalᶜ*) or in sticks (*šemš, šemšeh*).

Figure 32 A Tinner Cleaning a Copper Vessel

Figure 33 A Tinner Heating a Vessel over the Forge and Applying Tin

Jeweler, Goldsmith, Silversmith

As in many crafts the demarcation line between related branches is not well defined, so it is in this group of craftsmen handling precious metals. In larger cities, the jeweler (*javāhir-sāz*) makes jewelry and personal ornaments only, whereas the goldsmith (*zargar*) and the silversmith (*noqreh-sāz*, *noqreh-kār*) produce other objects in gold and silver respectively, such as snuffboxes (*qōṭī-tūtūn*), cigarette cases (*qōṭī-sīgār*), sugar bowls (*qandān*), tea glass holders (*jā-estekān*), drinking glass holders (*jā-līvān*), flower vases (*goldān*), dishes (*kāseh*), trays (*sīnī*), and many other things. In smaller communities one man, the goldsmith, is the only craftsman in precious metals. The jeweler's work comprises the usual ornaments, bracelets (*dastband*), necklaces (*gelūband*), amulet containers (*bāzūband*), rings (*angoštar*), garment pins (*sanjāq*), and chains (*zanjīr*), to name only a few. The magnificent rhions, goblets, dishes, and jewelry from Achaemenian, Parthian, and Sasanian times, brought to light by the archaeologists, show that the goldsmiths of Persia were already masters in their craft thousands of years ago. But it is felt that their work should not be described here as it is adequately treated in a number of art histories. A rather original survival from the past seems to be jewelry worn by the women of the various nomadic tribes, the bracelets and pendant plates of the Turkomans, and the wrought silver ankle rings of the Baḫtiyārī, Qašqā'ī, and other tribal people. Either they are made of thin silver plate and richly embossed or, as in the case of the Turkoman jewelry, the silver base is plated with soldered-on gold sheet. Peculiar effects are obtained by partly cutting away the gold so that the silver base comes through (Fig. 34), or the gold sheet is embossed from the rear before it is soldered on. Many of these pieces of jewelry are encrusted with semiprecious stones, especially carnelians and turquoises (Fig. 35). Another feature of this type of jewelry is the use of coins or imitation coins suspended from pendants and brooches. In other cases the suspended objects are flowers, hearts, fishes, or little balls with granulation soldered on. Most

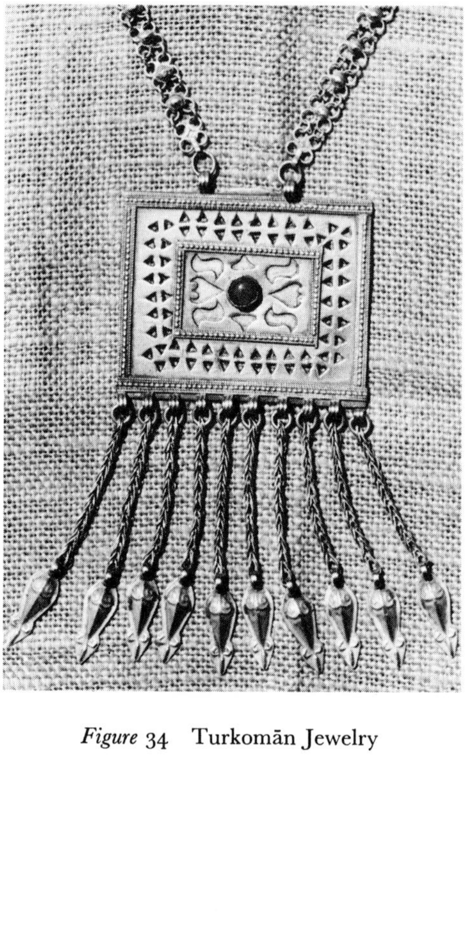

Figure 34 Turkomān Jewelry

of these ornaments are made of sheet silver, beaten into dies, and then the two halves are soldered together. An unusual technique is applied in the making of some ankle rings and bracelets. They are forged of pure silver approximately 0.3 mm thick, hollow inside, then filled with a mixture of hot pitch and resin, and finally after they are cooled down the surface is embellished by embossing from the outside. Another

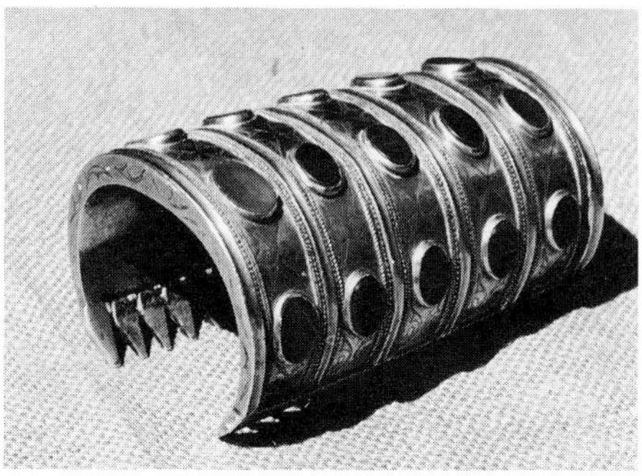

Figure 35 A Turkomān Bracelet

technique for which the Persian jeweler is known is filigree work (*melīlehkārī*); the term *melīleh* applies also to fine gold and silver thread for textile work. In Northern Persia, particularly in Tehrān and Tabrīz, niello work (*savād-e sorb*) has become quite popular, probably under Russian (*Tula*) influence during the last century. Colored glaze enamel (*mīnā*) has been made in the south, especially in Iṣfahān, since the time of Šāh ᶜAbbās.

Objects in precious metals are often bought as investments. Their possession is a mark of prestige for the owner, and they offer him security in times of war. The jeweler's customer is therefore much concerned with the purity of the metal. If the craftsman does not do his own refining (*qāl kardan*) he buys his metals from a reliable refiner (*qālgar, qālčī*) who in turn obtains scraps, filings, and melting ashes from the goldsmith. The age-old cupellation process is still in use. Since the quantities of gold and silver to be refined are usually not excessive, crucibles (*būteh*) are used that are lined with a mixture of wood ash (*ḫākestar*), sand (*šen*), and ground potsherds. Lead is melted into the precious metal, and the dross that forms on the surface and contains all the base metal impurities is continually removed by scraping it over the edge of the crucible until the molten precious metal shows a brightly shining surface (*ṣūrat*). If gold is to be refined, salt is added to the alloy after the completion of the cupellation. The salt is stirred into the metal, and dross forming on the surface is scraped over the edge of the crucible as before, until all traces of silver are removed. Fine gold (*zar-e aṣl*) and fine silver (*noqreh-ye hezār, noqreh-ye qorṣ*) are then tested on the touchstone (*miḥakk*) with acid (*tīzāb*).[103] The metals are weighed, and in order to obtain an alloy of a specified quality the required quantities of base metal (*bār*) are added. The whole is remelted, cast into ingots, and beaten out to the required shape and thickness. Smaller pieces of gold and silver are rolled on a small locally-made, hand-operated rolling mill. The mill (*čarḫ*) has two smooth rollers (*mīl*) that fit into a housing (*darvāzeh*). Two bronze bearings (*bālištak*) are fitted into this housing and adjusted with two screws (*pīč*). A handle (*dasteh*) is directly connected to one of the rollers. The craftsman of today prefers rolling the metal (*čarḫ gardāndan*) to the rough beating on the anvil.

The gold- and silversmith prepares his own hard solders (*laḥīm-e noqreh*) by adding copper and zinc to the precious metals to reduce the melting point. They are fully aware of the effects of these alloying elements and keep a series of solders with graded melting points that they use at the

[103] *Ibid.*, pp. 73, 84.

Figure 36 A Silversmith Working at a Beaked Anvil

Figure 38 A Silversmith at His Polishing Lathe

Figure 37 A Silversmith at Work (*note the wooden filing block in right foreground*)

Figure 39 A Silversmith Working over His Filing Dish

various stages of the work. Tools typical for the gold- and silversmith are: a beaked anvil (*sīḫ-e neṣfehʾī*, Fig. 36), flat pliers (*dam-pahn*), narrow pliers (*dam-bārīk*), round-nosed pliers (*dam-maftūl*), and a wooden filing block (*damāġeh*, Fig. 37). To prevent scratching of the soft material, a wooden vice (*gīr-e čūbī*) is used. Piercing of metal is done by a chisel (*qalam*) or a jeweler's fretsaw (*arreh zargarī*). The goldsmith's polishing lathe is similar in function, though smaller, to the one of the coppersmith. It is usually bow-operated (*čarḫ-e kamāneh*). Figure 38 shows a silversmith just taking a polished vessel off the lathe. All the craftsmen of this group, when handling precious metal, work over a leather mat (*naḫ*) or a large dish (*tāvaq*, Fig. 39) to collect all filings (*sūāleh*) for later refining. Prior to the application of any decorative work the goods are white-pickled (*jūšīdeh*) in hot diluted sulphuric acid (*jouhar-e gūgerd*) or in hot alum solution (*zāq*). This involves repeated heating, pickling, and brushing with pumice powder (*sang-e penz*), Tripoli sand (*ḫāk-e makeh*), or red oxide (*ḫāk-e ros*) with a coarse brush (*ferčeh*, Fig. 40). Finally large

Figure 40 Apprentices Cleaning and Pickling

surfaces are polished by rubbing them with a burnishing steel (*ṣaiqal, miṣqal*), using soap (*ṣābūn*) as a lubricant. The man who specializes in this rather difficult operation is called *ṣaqlgar* or *ṣaiqalgar*. In communities with division of labor the semifinished goods are sent to the embosser or the engraver. The smaller gold- and silversmith does all the decorative work himself.

It has been mentioned that certain crafts, especially metal crafts, are traditionally exercised by members of ethnical groups. Significant in the jewelers' craft are the Sobbī gold- and silversmiths of Ḫūzistān, particularly of Ahvāz. They belong to a people who come from the marshes along the border between Iraq and Persia. They are all members of the gnostic religious group of the Mandaeans, being neither Moslem nor Jewish nor Christian, and they have a language of their own. In their villages they do no agricultural work apart from growing some fruit and vegetables for home consumption. They are the ironsmiths for the surrounding Moslem villages, and curiously enough are the musicians for festive occasions and makers of musical instruments, especially a kind of violin (*zabbebeh*). They are also famous as boat builders.

Metal Embosser, Engraver, Gem Cutter, and Signet Maker

Decorative work on metal objects, mainly of gold, silver, and brass, but sometimes of copper and white nickel alloys, is executed in several techniques for which the general public uses the term *qalamzanī*, i.e., chisel work. In the south, e.g., Šīrāz, this means an embossing or chasing technique, referred to in Western books on art as repoussé. The specific term the Persian craftsman uses for this kind of work is *monabbat, monabbat-kārī*, or *barjesteh-kār*; the embosser is called *monabbat-kār*. It is a plastic deformation of the metal with non-cutting, round-edged punches, hammered-in from the front of the workpiece or from the rear.

In preparation for his work the embosser, also called *qalamzan-e monabbat*, fills the object to be embossed with a hot mixture of pitch (*qīr*) and fine sand or ashes (*ḫākestar*) that after cooling is sufficiently hard and heavy to act as a base, yet plastic enough to give way when the embossing chisel drives the metal back (Fig. 41). For flat objects such as trays,

Figure 41 A Metal Embosser Working on a Vessel Filled with Pitch

salvers, and so forth, a wooden board of suitable size is covered with one or two inches of this pitch mixture, and the heated metal object is cemented onto the pitch (Fig. 42). The work thus prepared is placed on a wooden stock (*kondeh*) that in Iṣfahān is low and rammed into the ground. The embosser holds the work (*gīr dādan*) firm in place by a leather belt (*tasmeh*) slung around the workpiece and his knees. He works in a kneeling position behind the stock, pressing the workpiece tightly onto the stock. When necessary to move the work he just lifts one knee, thus

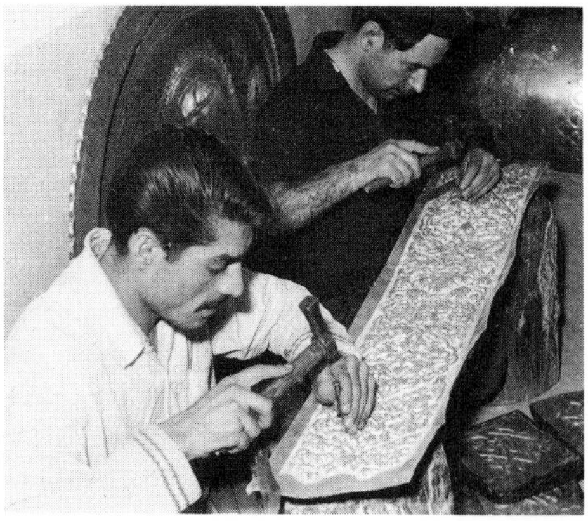

Figure 42 Embossers Working on a Silver Panel at Iṣfahān

loosening the belt. In Šīrāz the stock is higher, and a sitting board is attached to it. The embosser holds the work down by placing his foot in a leather sling.

The parts to be decorated are first painted with a watery mixture of chalk (*gač*) and a vegetable glue (*serešk*) that dries quickly. The design (*naqšeh*) is then drawn by pencil onto this grounding. Equal divisions of the surface, proper distances from the edge, and circles are marked with a pair of compasses (*pargār*). In Iṣfahān, where much work is done in large series, the design is usually drawn on paper and the outlines marked by lines of fine holes pierced (*sombeh kardan*) into the paper with a needle. This pattern is placed on the chalk grounding and dusted with a bag (*kīseh*) containing finely ground charcoal dust (*ḫāk-e zoġāl*). The embosser is now ready to begin the chasing of the metal with a special embossing hammer (*čakoš-e qalamzanī*) that has one flat and one pointed end. There is a variety of chisels (*qalam-e monabbat*) for the different operations (Fig. 43). They are made of hardened steel (*fūlād-e ḫošk*).

The first operation in embossing is the chasing of the outlines (*kār-e qalam-gīrī, nīmbor*) of the design with a chisel having either a short, linear edge (*qalam-e pardāz*) or, for longer lines, a long, linear edge (*qalam-e qorsūm*). For round lines a number of crescent-shaped chisels (*qalam-e nāḫonī*) of varying curvature is used. After all outlines have been embossed the background (*zamīn*) is recessed (*kaf-taḫt, forū raftan*) with a large flat square chisel (*qalam-e būm, qalam-e kaf-taḫt*) or, for round work, with a flat oval chisel (*qalam-e ḫūšeh*); *nīm-vār* is a square chisel with rounded corners. After these two operations the metal has become work hardened (*ḫošk-šodeh*) and has to be annealed (*tāfteh* or *narm šodan*) after it has been loosened from the pitch board by being warmed over the forge, or by having the pitch melted out in the case of hollow vessels. If the work is to have a pronounced relief (*barjesteh*), these parts are now beaten out from the rear (*barjesteh kardan*) with a round-edged chisel (*ḫošeh*). For the finishing stage (*rūsāzī*), pitch is applied again. Outlines are corrected, shadowing lines are obtained on the surfaces (*rūš*) with a serrated chisel (*qalam-e sāyeh*), and the background is beaten to a uniform grain with a chisel having a small circle as a face (*qalam-e yak tū*) or for finer work with a pointed chisel (*sombeh*). Other special chisels (*qalam-e qorsūm*) for surface finishing (*kār-e qorsūm*) are: *dō-tū*, showing two concentric circles; *deraḫtī*, with an oval face; *bādāmī*, which is almond shaped; *mūhī*, which is a chisel marking rows of parallel hair lines; and *gorsavād*, which is one marking crossed lines. If any parts are to be pierced out (*mošabbak*), it is done at this stage with sharp-edged cold chisels (*qalam-e nīmbor*) of various sizes, straight or curved. The pitch is removed once more, and the burr (*pīlis*) of the rough edges is then smoothed by filing (*souhān-kārī*). The work is annealed again and pickled, and, in the case of silver, often blackened with lamp soot and oil or with sulphur (*gūgerd*). A final polish of the silver surface brightens the relief parts and leaves the background dark for contrast.

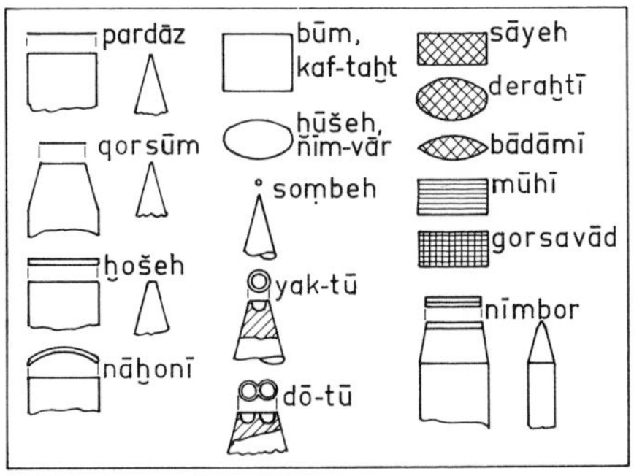

Figure 43 Working Ends of Embossing Chisels

In the north of the country, a different technique is employed, that of engraving, also called *qalamzanī* in general, but *qalam-kandan*, which means digging-in with a chisel, if one wants to be specific. Here the metal is actually cut away in fine chips. In Iṣfahān this work is referred to as *qalam-e ᶜaksī*, pictorial chiseling. In Tehrān, Qom, Kāšān, and Iṣfahān most engravers employ both techniques, and often an interesting combination of the two where embossed surfaces are engraved upon for fine linear detail and shadowing. Where engraving is employed, two different techniques are used for the removal of the chips. In the north, e.g., Tabrīz, Zenjān, and Tehrān, engraving tools with wooden knobs are used. The engraver pushes the tool into the metal by pressing the knob with his hand. In the center of the country, in Iṣfahān and Kāšān, the engraving tools are similar to the embossing chisels except that they have a sharp edge, cut away under an angle of about 60°, and are kept sharp on a honing stone. Under constant beating with a light hammer, the engraver keeps the tool moving, following the lines of the design (Fig. 44).

Another variety of decorative work is pierced or fretwork (*mošabbak* or *šabakeh*, cf. Arab. *šbk*, meaning "making a net"). It is often done by the engraver, but, if sufficient work is available, by a specialist, the *mošabbak-kār*. In Iṣfahān and Tehrān much work of this kind is applied to articles such as incense burners (*mošabbak qalᶜeh*), lamp shades, and vases (Fig. 45).

A further craft should be mentioned here, the gem cutter (*ḥakkāk*). There is quite a demand for cut semiprecious stones. People use these turquoises, agates, amethysts, and many others, either as ornaments or as amulets against the evil eye. An invocation of the deity is often engraved on these stones. The engraving of symbols and writings on gem stones and their use as personal signets for signing documents can be traced back to early historic times in Persia and is still popular (Fig. 46). The gem cutter's main tool is a special lathe (*čarḫ-e ḥakkāk*) whose spindle is operated with a fiddle bow (*kamāneh*). He can attach a grinding wheel (*sang-e sāʾī*) for the roughing of the gem stones to the end of the spindle, or a wooden block (*čarḫ-e pardāḫt*) to which water and Tripoli sand are applied for polishing. Where

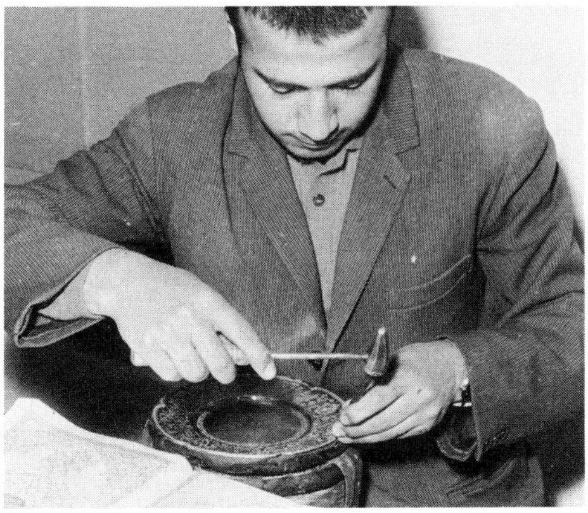

Figure 44 An Engraver Cutting Lines with a Sharp Chisel at Iṣfahān

Figure 45 A Lampshade in Fretwork Technique

Figure 46 A Talisman Gem (*above*) and Sasanian Seals (*below*)

natural grinding stones are not available the gem cutter uses special disks cast from a mixture of emery powder (*soṃbādeh*) and molten shellac (*lāk*). Finally the *ḥakkāk* can replace the grinding spindle by a much smaller one having a genuine diamond set at its end. An apprentice (*šāgerd*) keeps this spindle rotating with the fiddle bow at great speed. The gem stone is then held in a hand vice (*gīreh-ye dast*) or set in wax (*mūm-e ᶜasal*), and the master (*ustād*) presses it against the rotating diamond. By moving the gem carefully the *ḥakkāk* follows the design, thus cutting it into the stone. He is often asked to cut names into metal signets for the poorer people who cannot afford a cut gem.

A craftsman exclusively occupied with cutting metal signets is called a signet maker (*mohr-tarāš*, *ḥakkāk-e mohr-naqš*). He usually has his stall near the gate of a mosque where illiterate people have their letters written by professional scribes. A seal with such a signet (*mohr-e esm*) is accepted in Persia in lieu of a personal signature. The signet maker has a small forge and casts blanks for the signets in bronze which he smoothes (*ṣāf kardan*, *savī kardan*) with a file. For the engraving he holds them in a wooden vice (*gīr-pā*, *gīr-e čūbī*, *gīr-e dast*) tightened with a wedge (*čūb-e gōveh*) and cuts the names of his clients with an engraving tool. Very small signets are engraved (*naqš kardan*, *ḥakkākī kardan*) with a hand-pushed chisel (*qalam-bā-zūr*), larger ones with chisel and hammer (*qalam-ō-čakoš*, Fig. 47).

Both the gem cutter and the signet maker also do the deep cutting of silver objects in preparation for niello work or glazed enamel (*mīnā*).

A different kind of gem cutting is still a major industry in Ḫorāsān. The raw material is the turquoise (*fīrūzeh*) which comes mainly from the mines at Nīšāpūr, west of Mašhad, or from Qūčān and Kašmar, northeast of Mašhad. The raw

Figure 47 A Signet Maker

gems are graded according to quality, and the sections (*qesmeh*) in the mines are named according to the terms for these qualities. A very light-colored stone is called *čoġāleh*, one with a little more color *ᶜajamī*. The quality *ṭufūl* has the full turquoise color; it is mainly found in bands (*loᶜāb*) between layers of the matrix stone (*sang*). *Šajarī* is a grade where the turquoise is mixed with matrix spots (*lakkeh*).

The turquoise cutter (*ḥakkāk*, *fīrūzeh-tarāš*) buys the raw material from the mines, and it is usually the master who trims the raw stones from the surrounding matrix with a sharp-edged hammer working on a trimming stone. His assistants do the grinding and polishing. Although some of the larger firms in Mašhad already do work on motorized wheels, most of the 500 turquoise cutters in that town are still working on a bow-operated cutting bench (*dastgāh-e ḥakkākī*, Fig. 48). The movable center part of this bench is an iron spindle (*šōqeh*) that has a pushed-over, wide wooden pulley section (*taneh-šōqeh*) about 2 inches in diameter. A grinding wheel (*čarḫ*, *čarḫ-e ḥakkākī*) about 18 inches in diameter is cast from a mixture of resin (*lāk*), tallow (*pī*), wax (*mūm*), whiting (*sang-e safīdāb*), and emery (*somḅādeh*). It is pushed over the spindle against the pulley and tightened over a large washer (*gūiyak*) with a nut (*qorṣak*). The spindle runs in a wooden frame (*čahār-čūb*) between two upright posts (*pāyeh*), one of which can be loosened by the removal of a wedge (*gāz*); this is necessary to exchange various grades of wheels. A gut string (*zeh-rūd*) is slung around the pulley and attached to a bow (*kamāneh*). As the bow is moved backward and forward the wheel is kept in motion although only the forward stroke is a grinding stroke. A wooden hoop (*čaṃbar*) is fixed to the frame around the path of the wheel as a guard to protect the grinder against the flying of sludge.

In the first stage the stones are roughed (*tarīb kardan*) to shape. The trimmed rough

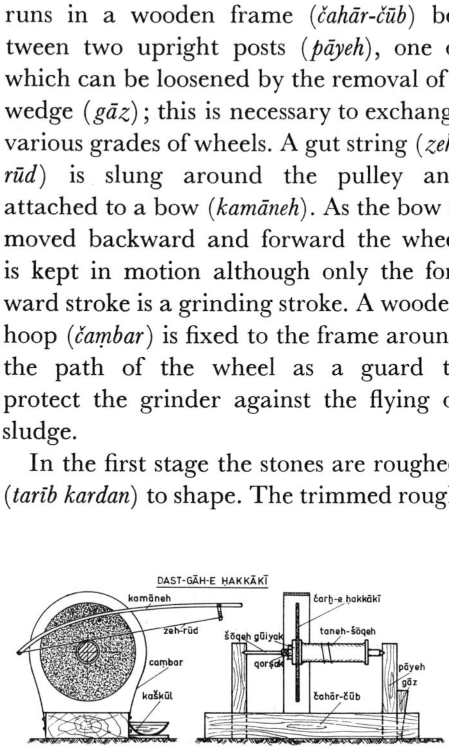

Figure 48 A Gem Cutter's Grinding Wheel

stones are held by hand against the rotating emery wheel and dipped into a water dish (*kaškul*) from time to time for cooling and lubrication. The roughly ground gems (*ḫām-tarāš*) are glued onto the ends of short wooden sticks (*sar-čūbī*) with an adhesive (*časb-e kandeh*) made from shellac, wax, and whiting and kept warm over a charcoal brazier. A young assistant is kept busy doing this work. The next steps are smoothing (*qeltondegī*) of the stones on the sticks (*kandeh*) on a finer wheel, followed by a still finer wheel (*čarḫ-e jelā*) that has no emery in the compound but a polishing powder (*rūbā*) instead. The aim of this second smoothing (*jelā kardan*) is the removal of all scratches and results in a mat luster (*jelā*). A pre-final polish is obtained on a disk made of willow wood (*čarḫ-e bīd*) worked with a paste of red ocher (*gel-e armanī*) and water. The final high gloss is put on with a leather-covered wooden disk (*čarḫ-e čarmī*) saturated with a paste of water and whiting. Most turquoises are shaped as round or oval cabochons with a more or less curved face (*rū*), an almost flat reverse (*kaf*), and a mildly beveled edge (*fārsī*). The grinder protects his hand during the grinding with cloth strips (*latteh*) wound around the finger nearest to the wheel.

Goldbeater, Wire Drawer, Gold-Lace Spinner

In sufficiently large communities each one of these three crafts may be exercised by a specialist, but it is often found that one craftsman is skilled in the three of them; again in other places a goldbeater finds sufficient work to make a living whereas the trades of precious metal wire drawing and gold-lace spinning are combined. In the following each group will be treated separately.

Goldbeater

Goldbeating as an art is of great antiquity. Leaf gold has been found in Egyptian tombs of about 2500 B.C.[104] Pictorial representations of the goldbeater at work have been discovered in tombs of the same period. Homer refers to goldbeating, and Pliny[105] tells us that one ounce of gold was beaten out to 750 leaves, each one four fingers wide and the same length. With a highly developed metallurgy in Persia it is not surprising to find gold-leaf ornamentation in Persepolis[106] of the Achaemenian period and in all subsequent dynasties.

Persian weapons and armor are often decorated with beaten-on gold; miniature painters use the greatest part of the leaf gold produced, and the ceramic industry uses considerable quantities for the gilding of glazed tiles. All this leaf gold is produced by the goldbeater (*zar-kūb*, *ṭelā-kūb*). He refines the gold he needs to a high degree of purity by cupellation and chlorination and pours it into square ingots. Most of the gold used in Persia for beating into leaf is pure; rarely are copper or silver added to obtain red or green gold, respectively. The ingot is beaten out to a strip; a more modern goldbeater may have a mill (*čarḫ*) to roll it out. It is stretched to a thickness at which a mark can be made into the metal by a fingernail. When this gauge is reached, the gold is cut into squares of approximately 2 inches. These squares are placed between sheets of paper measuring about 5 inches square. The paper is made of the fibrous bast of the mulberry tree,[107] has been dressed with a mixture of tragacanth size and yellow ocher, and polished with a burnishing tool (*ṣaiqal*) to a high shine. About 175 to 200 of these paper squares with gold in between are tightly packed into a parchment pouch,[108]

104 *Ibid.*, p. 180.

105 Pliny, *op. cit.*, xxxiii.61.

106 E. F. Schmidt, *The Treasury of Persepolis*, pp. 71–73.

107 The use of the mulberry bast for papermaking is a Chinese invention, whence it came to Persia and reached Europe during the Middle Ages via Arabia and Byzantium (J. Karabacek, "Das arabische Papier," p. 182).

108 Pliny, *op. cit.*: *masurpium*.

the whole packet being called "cutch" by the English goldbeater. The packet is beaten for about half an hour with a flat-faced hammer (*čakoš-e ṭelā-kūbī*) weighing about 7 kg. By then the first traces of gold begin to appear at the edges of the packet. The beating takes place on a polished marble block or an iron anvil. Having reached this stage, the cutch is opened, and the still relatively thick gold leaf is cut into four parts. These are now placed between sheets of second-grade quality of so-called goldbeater's skin about 4.5 inches square. The fine membrane is the outer part of the blind gut of cattle.[109] The gut measures about 32 × 4.5 inches, and the appendices of some 140 oxen are needed to supply the 900 to 1,000 skins necessary to form this packet, called "shoder" by the English craftsman. The shoder is beaten for about two hours with a hammer weighing about 4 kg. Surplus gold coming out at the edges is scraped off, and the beating continues until the gold inside the squares has reached the four corners. The shoder is then opened and each leaf is cut into four pieces again and this time placed between sheets of first-grade quality goldbeater's skin, again 900 to 1,000 to a pouch, forming a "mold." The beating is continued with a 3-kg hammer for about four hours. By then the leaves have reached the stage when they become slightly translucent. They are transferred into books of about 20 sheets of paper, the gold leaf itself having a size of 4 × 4 inches and a thickness of less than 0.00015 inch (Fig. 49).

The process of goldbeating as done in Persia to this day is almost identical with the methods described by Pliny[110] for Roman times, by Theophilus[111] for the

Figure 49 Goldbeaters at Work

twelfth century A.D., and by fifteenth- and sixteenth-century writers,[112, 113] and it was still the same in England at the beginning of this century where London was the center of the goldbeaters' trade. In 1963 the writer observed several goldbeaters in the bazaar quarters of Hyderabad (India). There the gold and silver leaf is also used for ornamentation, but some of it goes into local medicine, special powers being attributed to these precious metals.

A sideline of the goldbeaters' trade is the gilding of woodwork and the incrustation or damascening of steel with gold. The main products of the gold-inlayer (*ṭelā-kūb, mākū-kūb*) today are steel ornaments, especially sculptured animals having religious significance and being carried in the processions of the Moḥarram feast days. The main tool is a sharp short-edged knife (*kārd-e ṭelā-kūbī*). The area where gold incrustations are to be applied is finely serrated (*zabr kardan*) in crosswise directions. Figure 50 shows the incisions made by the beater on a sculptured steel stag. Gold or silver wire, only 0.0028-inch thick, is placed on the roughened surface and hammered into it with the peen of a pointed hammer (*čakoš-e ṭelā-kūbī*, Fig. 51). Burnishing (*maṣqal kardan*) with a polished

[109] *Goldschlägerhaut* is the term used in the gut trade in German abattoirs to this day for the appendix of cattle.

[110] Pliny, *op. cit.*, xxxiii.61.

[111] W. Theobald, *op. cit.*, p. 23.

[112] J. Amman, *Eygentliche Beschreibung aller Stände.*

[113] C. Weigel, *Abbildung der Gemein-Nützlichen Haupt-Stände*, p. 298.

agate (*maṣqūl*, Fig. 52) brings the gold or silver to a bright shine and probably improves the bond with the surface of the steel, and it eliminates any traces of the roughening.

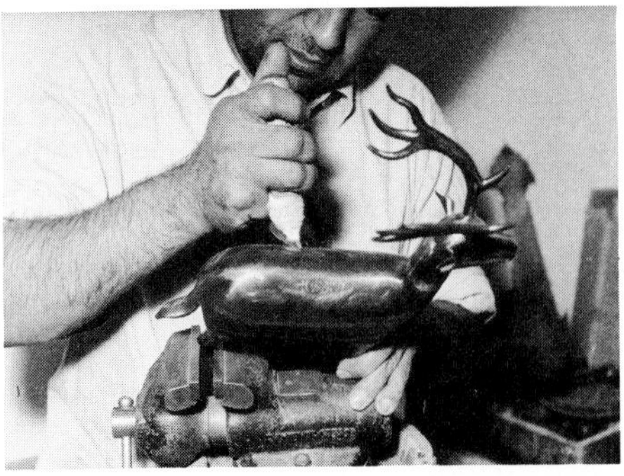

Figure 50 Roughening the Surface of a Steel Ornament, Preparing It for Gold Incrustation

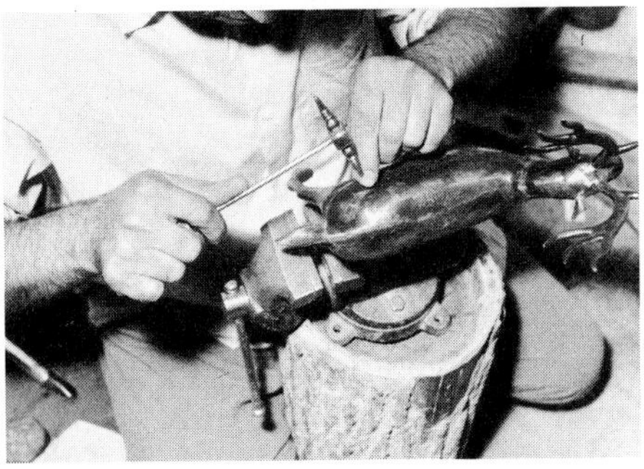

Figure 51 Beating in the Gold Wire

Figure 52 Burnishing the Surface

This incrustation process was known in Europe during the Middle Ages. Theophilus[114] describes it in all detail as applied to weapons, coats of arms, spurs, and so forth. It must have been popular, as he explicitly mentions a mechanized version of the roughening tool in which a sharp-edged steel chisel is attached to a spring-loaded lever, set into vibratory motion by a gear wheel acting as a ratchet. A sword dated 1435 A.D. in the possession of the writer is most elaborately gilded in this way, and despite obvious use of the weapon the gilding is well preserved.

Wire Drawer

The wire drawer (*sīm-kaš, zar-kaš*), is concerned with the manufacture of gold and silver wire, which he supplies almost exclusively to either the goldsmith, the gold inlayer just described, or the gold-lace spinner, whose work will be described later in this section. The production of steel wire, once important for the armorer's work, ceased when chain armor disappeared in Persia more than 150 years ago.

Gold wire has been found in Egypt in tombs of the First Dynasty (about 3500 B.C.). Its uniform cross section presupposes the use of a drawing die,[115] as must also have been the case for gold wires found in Mycenae and Troy.[116] The Greeks called wire *mitos* or *stēmos*, the Romans *filum*, in each case meaning "thread." If the gold wire was to be spun around linen or silken thread the precious metal was flattened. However, references exist describing a different method, namely, the cutting of thin gold sheet into narrow strips that were then wound or spun around a thread. Exodus 39:3 mentions

[114] W. Theobald, *op. cit.*, p. 458.

[115] H. Schäfer, *Ägyptische Goldschmiedearbeiten*, p. 14.

[116] H. Schliemann, *Mykene*, p. 166, and W. Dörpfeld, *Troja und Ilion*, p. 369.

this process: "... and they did beat the gold into thin plates and cut it into strips, to work it in the blue, or in the purple, and in the scarlet, and in the fine linen with cunning work." Claudianus,[117] who wrote during the fourth century A.D., mentions a Roman woman cutting strips of gold for lace spinning; Theophilus[118] also quotes cut strips of gold for brocade lace, and as late as Biringuccio[119] this cutting process must have been in use. He tells us that women's hands are particularly steady in cutting the narrow strips.

Brocade cloths of the Sasanian period (third to sixth centuries A.D.) have come to us, but investigations did not go to the point of finding out how the gold wire had been prepared and how it was spun around the thread.

Today the preparation of the gold and silver wire is done in two, or if used for lace spinning, in three, stages: coarse drawing (*maftūl kašīdan*), fine drawing (*sīm kašīdan*), and wire flattening (*naẖ kūbīdan*).

Coarse drawing: Materials used are pure gold or pure silver and sometimes a silver core covered with a brazed-on gold cover. In the final drawing process, the latter results in a wire with a silver core and a relatively thin gold skin (comparable to modern so-called rolled gold).

The metal is cast into a round ingot of about ¼-inch diameter that is drawn down to a gauge of about 0.02 inch. Figure 53 shows this bench: a self-gripping pair of pliers (*ambor*, Fig. 54) draws the metal through the holes of the die (*ḥadīdeh, fūlād*). The die is supported by two iron bars (*mešqāz*). The gripping pliers are connected with a chain (*zanjīr*) linked with the winding shaft (*manjar*) by a hook (*qolāb*) on the latter. The shaft itself is

Figure 53 A Drawing Bench for Coarse Wire

Figure 54 Self-Gripping Pliers and Die

turned over a gear (*čarẖ*) for the first ten or so passes, and when the wire has become sufficiently thin the turning handle (*dasteh*) is shifted over from the far side to the near side to drive the shaft directly. All parts are placed into a rigid wooden frame (*čahār-pāyeh*) consisting of four legs (*pā*) stiffened by four tie bars (*qaid*).

Fine Drawing: After the wire has become sufficiently fine, it is transferred from the coarse- to the fine-drawing bench (*dastgāh-e zarkašī* or *sīmkašī*). The wire drawer sits behind the drawing reel (*manjeh*) and turns it round with a crank handle (*dasteh*).

[117] C. Claudianus, *Carmina*, p. 10.
[118] W. Theobald, *op. cit.*, p. 140.
[119] V. Biringuccio, *Pirotechnia*, M.I.T. Press edition, p. 382.

The wire to be drawn is wound onto an idling reel (*sabok-čarḫ*) from where it is drawn through the die onto the drawing reel. Both reels have bronze bushes (*lūleh*) for better running and turn on steel axles (*mīl-e manjeh*) fixed to the bench top. Figure 55 shows the Persian fine-drawing bench of 1939 and Fig. 56 a medieval bench from *Mendelsches Stiftungsbuch*; they are almost identical.

The drawing die is made of high carbon steel that is not, however, hardened. When a drawing hole is worn out it is closed up again as it is hammered on a little anvil (*sendān*). A number of sharp tapered reamers is always handy to ream the hole to the correct size after closing up. Figure 55 shows both anvil and reamers. When the full length of the wire has been drawn through the first pass, the now

Figure 55 Fine Wire Drawing (*note the small anvils at the top right and tapered reamers*)

Figure 56 A Medieval Drawing Bench for Fine Wire (*from* Mendelsches Stiftungsbuch)

empty idling reel is placed on the axle in front of the operator, an additional rewinding pulley (*jarr*) is placed on an extra axle (*mīl-e jarr*) on the bench, and the rewinding pulley is connected with a grooved pulley (*kandeh*) on the idling reel through a transmission cord (*band*, Fig. 57). The full drawing reel is now placed opposite the rewinding pulley and the

Figure 57 Rewinding Fine Wire

Figure 58 Three Italian Wire Drawing Benches (*from* The Pirotechnia *by Vannoccio Biringuccio, Basic Books Inc., Publishers, New York, 1959*)

rewinding (*bar-gardānīdan*) is achieved in less than a minute. After resetting the reels the bench is ready for the next pass. Figure 58 shows three Italian wire drawing benches of 1540,[120] again not much different from the Persian benches of 1939.

Wire Flattening: Up to this stage the wire has been of a round cross section. If it has to be flattened this has to be done to a thickness of $\frac{4}{1000}$ of an inch at a width of $\frac{1}{32}$ inch or less. Considering that the mechanical strength of pure gold or silver is very low, it is all the more surprising how accurately the crude-looking flattening bench (*dastgāh-e naẖ-kūbī*) works

Figure 59 A Flattening Bench

Figure 60 A Wheel for Winding Reels

(Fig. 59).

The wire is first transferred from the drawing wheel to a number of much smaller reels (*baqāreh*). The transferring is done on a slightly modified spinning wheel (*čarẖ*, Fig. 60). The reel carrying the round wire is placed on a shaft (*kafgīrak*, right foreground, Fig. 59), and the wire is led through a guiding ear (*qalāġ*) attached to a springy bow (*kūk*) right between the two brightly polished steel rollers (*čarẖ-e naẖ-kūbī*). These rollers run on two shafts (*mīl-e čarẖ*); both have their bearings in a rigid housing (*qōtī-ye čarẖ*). The lower bearings are fixed whereas the upper shaft has its bearings sliding inside the housing. A long iron bar (*langar*) with spoon-shaped ends (*kafgīrak-e langar*) presses over a pair of wooden blocks (*gūšī*) onto the bearings of the upper rollers, thus producing an even yet flexible pressure between the steel rollers so that the soft gold or silver wire is flattened to a constant and accurate thickness. The pressure is maintained on the bar (*langar*) by a solid wooden board (*taẖteh-ye langar*) under the bench connected with the bar through a pair of rope slings (*ṭanāf, ṭanāb*) and loaded with a heavy stone (*sang*). After the flattened wire has left the rollers it is led under a guide roller (*rāh-qās*) running on a thin steel shaft (*mīl-e rāh-qās*) onto the reel that

[120] *Ibid.*, p. 379.

winds up the finished product (*naqd-e pīč*). This reel runs on a steel shaft (*mīl-e pīč*) housed in two bearing pillars (*sotūn*). This shaft is driven over a cord pulley (*kandeh*) and a transmission cord (*band*) from a larger pulley (*qorṣ-e band*) fixed to the main roller shaft. In order to spread the winding flat wire equally over the reel, the guide roller makes oscillating side movements caused by the connection of the guide roller's shaft to an eccentric pin (*harzeh-gard*) on another pulley that is driven from a cord pulley on the far end of the main shaft (*kandeh sar-e mīl-e čarḫ*). The velocity ratio of the pulleys of the winding mechanism is adjusted in such a way that the winding speed is slightly greater than the speed at which the wire leaves the rollers. The flattened wire is therefore under a small tension, a fact which contributes largely to the proper winding of such a delicate wire. The rollers operate at a speed of about 60 to 80 revolutions per minute. After the bench has been properly set the work is usually done by an apprentice.

Figure 61 A Spinning Head

Gold-Lace Spinner

The last and most delicate step in the production of gold lace (*golābetūn, melīleh*) is the spinning of the flat metal wire around a thread (*golābetūn pīčīdan*). The work is done on a gold-lace spinning bench (*čarḫ-e zarī, čarḫ-e sīmpīčī, čarḫ-e naḫtābī*). The most important part of this bench is the actual spinning head or spindle (*dūk*), shown in Fig. 61, that runs in a bearing block (*arūčak*) attached to a housing pillar (*darvāzeh*) with a pair of wedges (*gōveh*). The thread, *rīsmān* if cotton and *abrīšam* if silk, moves through the hollow center of the spindle. The front of the spinning head has the form of a pair of wings (*parvānak*) whose ends open up into a fork (*ᶜaqrabak*) on each side. Attached to the spindle is a freely turning gold-wire reel (*moġāreh*). The gold wire is led from the reel over one fork and twisted onto the thread. The spinning head is then set into motion, and as the flat wire is spun around the thread, the thread moves slowly through the head while its speed is adjusted in such a way that the flat wire just covers the silk or cotton thread, neither doubling up on it nor leaving any blank spaces (Fig. 62). Figure 63 shows the whole bench; the gold-lace spinner (*golābetūn-sāz*) is driving the main pulley (*qorṣ-e avval*) with a crank

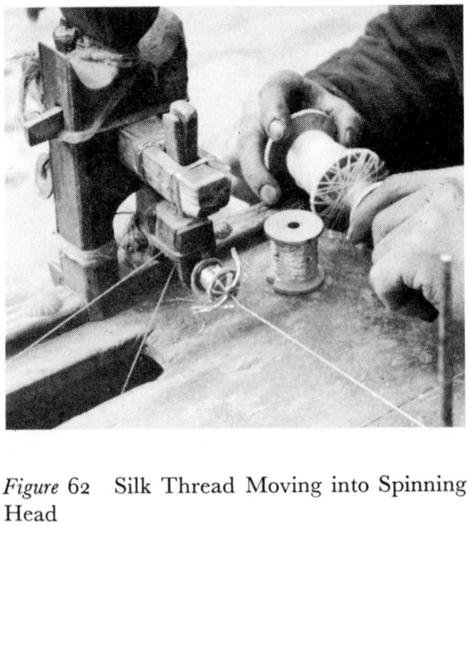

Figure 62 Silk Thread Moving into Spinning Head

Figure 63 A Bench for Spinning Gold Thread

handle (*dasteh*). An intermediate pulley (*qorṣ-e dōvom*) with two different diameters (Fig. 64) is provided to bring the spindle to the required high speed. The smaller end of this pulley is driven over a flat belt (*tasmeh*) from the first, hand-operated, pulley, and a transmission cord (*band*) links the larger grooved end with a small grooved pulley (*kandeh*) on the spindle. From the shaft of the intermediate pulley another shaft branches off, carrying a stepped pulley to which the reel (*kilāf-e farangī*) receiving the finished product is directly attached. This stepped pulley permits the choice of the speed at which the thread is pulled through the spinning head and thus controls the proper coverage of the thread. The latter runs into the head from a bobbin (*kilāf*) at the side of the bench over a guide pin (*mīl*) and a guide reel. The bobbin carries a weight bag (*langar*) to make sure that the thread is always under tension. All moving parts are within a rigid frame (*čahār-pāyeh*) to which the bearing columns (*sotūn*) are attached. When the gold-wire reel is empty, the transmission cord controlling the forward motion of the thread is taken off, the forked wings are put aside, and the reel is refilled from a larger bobbin (Fig. 65).

Figure 64 A Pulley for Driving the Spindle

Figure 65 Refilling the Gold-Wire Reel

Ironworking Crafts

In the foregoing sections on trades working nonferrous metals, it has been pointed out that a clear-cut division between related crafts does not normally exist but that the requirements of the community determine the range of work available to a craftsman. These requirements have also shaped the guild codes specifying the range of work in which the members can engage.

This holds, of course, in the ironworking trades too. The general blacksmith is the most important representative of this group and can be found in many communities, from large cities to medium-sized villages. Wherever specialization is possible a farrier will be found in rural areas, and wherever the use of vehicles has been established a wheelwright is likely to be found. In some communities the work of these three may overlap. The other ironworking crafts, from cutler to locksmith, are usually specialized trades in larger towns, and their work is rarely done by the general blacksmith.

Blacksmith

The history of smithing as a craft is connected with tribal organizations that carried out the ironworking craft almost to the point of exclusion of other people. To what extent the smith in towns has learned his trade from the wandering smith-tribes is difficult to say, but the fact that these tribes have survived to this day is certainly a remarkable phenomenon.

The transitions from a stone culture to bronze and later from bronze to steel tools were steps of such importance that the people who knew how to handle the new materials were respected, even admired, for their knowledge. They in turn were able to obtain privileges from those who needed their products, privileges which often came close to a monopoly for the smithing tribe. As to this day the wandering ironworker plays an important part in the rural districts of Persia, it is perhaps not out of place to study the special position of the itinerant artisan in Western Asia. It has been shown that during the second millennium B.C. the Chalybes were the iron and steel experts of the Hittites. With the decline of the Hittite empire the Chalybes must have migrated into neighboring countries, i.e., into the Greek settlements of Asia Minor. The Greeks named steel after them, viz., *chalybs*. The Greek poet Apollonius of Rhodes (245–186 B.C.) writes this about the Chalybes:[121]

> That folk drive never the ploughing oxen afield. No part have they in planting of fruit, that is honey sweet to the heart. Neither bend they like the pasturing folks over meadows aglitter with dew. But the ribs of the stubborn earth for treasures of iron they knew. And by merchandising of the same they do live, never dawning broke bringing respite of toil unto them, but ever midst the smoke and flame of the forge are they toiling and plying the weary stroke.[122]

Another group of ironworking tribes were the Turanians,[123] a people living east of the Iranians, having an important place in the latter's fight for supremacy in Central Asia. Some historians identified the Turanians with the Scythians[124] who, according to Herodotus, had iron in abundance. The Turanians may have been the ancestors of the so-called smithing Tartars of Southern Russia who worked small iron ore deposits as late as the beginning of this century. They produced iron blooms of 2 to 5 pounds weight, which they forged into iron hardware for the needs of the rural population.

121 R. J. Forbes, *op. cit.*, p. 400.
122 Apollonius of Rhodes, *Opera*, II.v.1001–1007.
123 O. Johannsen, *op. cit.*, p. 9.
124 *Ibid.*

Herzfeld[125] has the following to say about the blacksmiths in Arabia:

> The real Arab nomads who have not changed their manner of life from time immemorial, do not count a blacksmith as a member of their tribes, yet murder of a smith, because he is a specially valuable man, demands a far heavier vengeance than the murder of an ordinary tribesman. Such customs are no recent development but are inherited from remote antiquity when the smiths were foreigners, who came from far lands to practise their art among the tribes to whom metallurgy was unknown.

According to the same source, the Caspians, inhabitants of Northwest Persia, were the earliest metallurgists in history.

Undoubtedly the Persian Koulī, often called the smithing gypsies, belong to the same category (Fig. 66). They roam over the Iranian Plateau in small tribal groups. The men are blacksmiths who buy scrap iron these days that they forge into rural implements such as spades, plowshares, forks, threshing blades, sickles, locks, and the like. The women are experts in sieve making and rope braiding. It may be mentioned here that ironworking gypsies still wander through wide parts of Europe manufacturing and selling iron hardware like traps for rabbits, foxes, or rats, and sieves and many other articles needed by the rural population. It may also be mentioned that the famous iron industry of Central India was under the control of a few tribes, one of whom produced the Kutub column near Delhi, 6 tons of pure wrought iron, 24 feet high and 15 inches in diameter. The ironworkers were probably all members of the Lohar caste who to this day wander through the Indian countryside supplying the cultivator with the necessary iron implements. If we further consider that the gypsy language points to an Indian origin for these people, we have a case where the tradition of a technology that originated at the dawn of history is carried on by tribes whose origin points to Western Asia.

Figure 66 A Koulī Smith with Skin Bellows and Earth Forge

The ironworkers of Sīstān, Zābolistān, and Balūčistān (Fig. 67) as well as the Sobbī of Ḫūzistān are probably descendants of the metallurgists of these regions who were already active during the second millennium B.C. To round off this aspect,

Figure 67 Balōč Smiths (*note improvised blower*)

[125] E. E. Herzfeld and A. Keith in A. U. Pope and P. Ackerman, *op. cit.*, Vol. 3, p. 50.

attention may be drawn to the iron-workers of Indian-cultivated Bali (Indonesia), the Pandai-Vesi,[126] who have a religion of their own with gods connected with their metallurgy, a kind of Bali "Hephaistos."

Places in Persia that have been famous for ironwork during the Middle Ages are Šīrāz,[127] Kermān,[128] both for swords, cutlery, lance tips, and locks, and Jojānīyed[129] for fine steel tools.

At the time when this survey was made the blacksmith (*āhangar*) was still the most important ironworker despite the rapid development of his modern rivals, the fitter and turner and the motor mechanic. In the meantime the blacksmith has in many places changed over from his traditional products to the demands of the growing modern industry. The source of raw material has changed in line with this development. The local production of iron and steel ceased during the second half of the last century; the smiths had to rely on the supply of imported European steel, mainly in the form of scrap from discarded machinery and motor vehicles. The latest development is an effort by the government to revive the plans of Reżā Šāh for a modern steel plant near Tehrān; the well advanced work was interrupted through the 1939–1945 war.

Until recently the Persian blacksmith had used locally produced charcoal for fuel. The development of the coal mines of Šemšak near Tehrān to supply the blast furnace and the steelworks and of a few smaller mines in the country has made it possible for the blacksmith to change over to hard coal.

The outfit of the smithy is as follows:

126 M. Covarrubias, *op. cit.* and R. Goris, *op. cit.*

127 Ḥamdullāh Mustawfī al-Qazvīnī, *The Taʾrīḫ-e Guzīdeh.*

128 Marco Polo, *op. cit.*, p. 32.

129 Qazwini, Zakarīya ibn Muḥammad ibn Maḥmud al-, *Kosmographie,* Vol. 2, p. 140.

Figure 68 A Covered Forge

The forge (*kūreh*) is the center of the workshop. In most cases the forge is of the covered type (*kūreh dīvārī*, Fig. 68). The cover of the forge leads into the flue (*dūdkaš*); the fire is kept in good shape by a poker (*sīḫ-e kūreh*), and slag is removed with a slag hook (*qolāb-e kūreh*). Hand-operated bellows (*dam*) provide the blast for the forge. Smaller smithies have skin bellows (*dam-e pūst-e boz, dam-e dūlī*,[130] Fig.

130 R. J. Forbes (*op. cit.*, pp. 112–120), believes that the skin bellows are the oldest type, which originated at the time of early metallurgy and spread with it. Classical writers mention them (Homer, *The Iliad*, xviii.468; Vergil, *Georg.* iv.171; Livy 38–71; Horace, *Sat.* i.v.19). Theophilus (*op. cit.*, iii. Ch. 4) uses them for the small forge, and they are to this day the bellows of the smithing gypsies.

66) to operate a forge dug into the ground (*kūreh-zamīnī*). Larger workshops have a concertina type of bellows (*dam-e fānūsī*) and are either single- or double-acting (*dam-e dō dam, dam-e dō dastī, dam-e dō lūlehʾī*, Fig. 69). The air flow of these bellows is controlled by simple flat valves

Figure 69 Double-Acting Bellows

Figure 70 An Anvil Set in the Ground

(*pestāneh-ye dam*), and iron tuyères (*lūleh*) lead the air into the forge. Piston-type or pump bellows[131] used in the Far East are unknown in Persia.

The anvil (*sendān*) has a pointed end set in the ground (*sendān-e ḫeštī*, Fig. 70) for lighter work. For heavier work it is supported by a solid wooden block (*kondeh, zīr-e sendān*, Fig. 71). The anvil is not as elaborate as its Western counterpart but has a hardened surface (*ṣafḥeh, ṣafḥeh-ye sendān*) and a beak for round work (*šāḫ*). The smith uses a medium-sized hand hammer (*čakoš*) and the striker a sledge hammer (*potk*), both having strong handles (*dasteh*) of ash wood (*čūb-e zabān-gonješk*) to which the hammer is fixed with iron wedges (*gōveh*). There are also a number of

Figure 71 An Anvil Placed on a Wooden Block

[131] R. J. Forbes (*op. cit.*, p. 115) traces the pump bellows to a Southeast Asian origin and the concertina bellows to Siberia. The latter are mentioned in the West for the first time by Ausonius (*Mosella* v.27). Theophilus describes them (*op. cit.*, iii. Ch. 84) for the large bell-casting furnace.

set hammers (*qarār, qarār-e rū*), a planishing hammer (*ṣāfī*), swages (*qarār-e zīr, roḫ*), punching hammers (*soṃbeh*) and the corresponding hole-blocks (*ṣafḫeh-ye sūrāḫ, sendān-e sūrāḫ*), a hot chisel (*tīzbor*) and its counterpart the anvil chisel (*tīzbor-e zīr*), a forging vice (*gīreh-ye āteškārī*), and a variety of fire tongs (*aṃbor-e kūreh, aṃbor-e āteškārī*), flat ones (*dam-pahn*), round-nosed ones (*dam-gerd*), rivet-heating tongs (*aṃbor-e mīḫparč*), tongs to hold round bars (*aṃbor-e jūl, aṃbor-e lūleh*), others to hold a chisel or a square bar (*aṃbor-e qalamgīr*), and tongs with bent tips (*aṃbor-e kaj*).

The blacksmith distinguishes between wrought iron (*āhan*) and tool steel (*fūlād, pūlād*). When hardened the steel is called *fūlād-e ḫoškeh, fūlād-e ābdār*. A kind of fine Indian steel particularly suitable for cutlery is called *rūhan* or *rūhinā*. The fundamental operations of the blacksmith in Persia are essentially the same as those in Europe. There is the drawing out (*kašīdan*), the upsetting (*jā zadan*), the flattening (*pahn kardan*) the round forging (*gerd kardan*), the cutting off (*qatᶜ kardan*, and the punching of holes (*sūlāḫ kardan, sūrāḫ kardan*).

The Persian blacksmith is a master in forge welding (*jūš-e āteš, jūš dādan, tan-kār*) and in forge brazing (*jūš-e mes, jūš-e berenj*), using copper or brass for a solder and borax (*būrak, būrāq, būreh*) as a flux.[132]

Certain tools, e.g., horn rasps (*som sāb*) are made of mild steel and surface hardened by sprinkled-on horn meal or recently with imported cyanide (*sīānfūr, sīānūr*, meaning Fr. *cyanure*).

To name a few products of the blacksmith, the most important ones in rural areas are plowshares (*gouāhan, gōhan, gāvāhan, lapak*, Fig. 72), spades (*bīl*, Figs. 70, 73) and hoes (*kolang*, Fig. 74), earth-moving scoops (*marz-kaš, kerō*), and the chains (*zanjīr*) to pull them. Other forged tools for the peasant are a small weeding spade (*pāšgūn*), sickles (*dās*), all iron parts of the threshing wain (*čūm*), such as the shaft (*mīl-e čūm*), the threshing pegs (*parreh-ye čūm*) or the threshing disks (*tōveh-ye čūm*),[133] the shafts for flour mills (*mīl-e asīyāb*) and the millstone couplings (*tavar* or *aspareh*). In the fertile province of Gorgān the old wooden plow is gradually being replaced by a modern iron plow (*gāvāhan-e dō dasteh*), apparently designed under Russian influence. In the same region the wooden harrow has given way to an all-iron harrow (*čangeh*). The Caspian districts are rich in game, and the blacksmith there supplies iron traps (*taleh*). For the building trade the smith forges door hinges, in the Iṣfahān area a pivot type on both ends of a door wing (*pāšneh, pāšineh*); (*cf.* Zend *pāršnī*, meaning heel) fitting into holes in the lintel and the threshold respectively. In other parts of the country a forged hinge band (*loulā*) is customary. The catch (*čeft*) for the door latch is forged in iron, and iron door knockers (*kūbeh-e dar, yarāq-e dar*) often show some decorative treatment. A heavy comb (*āhanjeh*) is used by the carpet weaver. Twelve to fifteen steel leaves are forged to shape, packed into a bundle, and riveted together at one end, then they are spread out to a distance suiting the warp of the carpet weaver.

Nail Smith

A special type of heavy nail (*mīḫ*) with a large buckle (Fig. 75) is used to attach hinges to doors, to nail door panels on-

[132] The use of borax as a flux came to us from Persia. In "borax" the "x" came from Spanish spelling, now written *boraj*, having been introduced there in the ninth century A.D. by the Arabs (Mid. P. *furak*, N.P. *burak*, Arm. *porag*, Arab. *buraq*, Russ. *bura*, and so forth). Cf. B. Laufer, *Sino-Iranica*, p. 503, and W. Theobald, *op. cit.*, p. 302.

[133] Cf. P. H. T. Beckett, "Tools and Crafts in South Central Persia," p. 147, describing the work of a rural blacksmith near Kermān.

Figure 72 Forged Plowshares

Figure 73 A Forged Spade

Figure 74 A Hoe Forged in Two Parts To Be Riveted Together

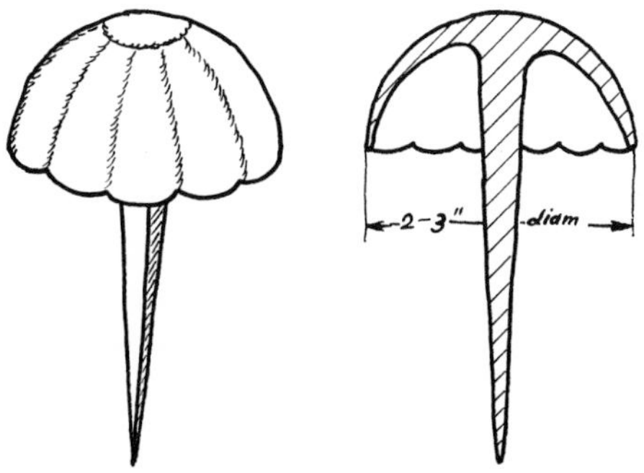

Figure 75 A Decorated Buckled Door Nail

to crossbeams, and so forth. The demand for this kind and other heavy nails was still so great in Iṣfahān in 1939 that two nail smiths (*mīẖ-sāz*) could make a living. While all other tools of the nail smith are the same as those of the blacksmith, a nail-forming anvil (*sendān-e mīẖ-sāzī*) serves his special requirements. It is mushroom-shaped and has a hole in the center. The nail smith forges the tapered end of the nail from a round bar. He cuts it from the bar with a hot chisel, leaving some extra material at the thick end. This is brought to red heat, the thin end placed in the hole of the mushroom anvil, and with heavy strokes the steel is forged over the surface of the anvil, thus quickly forming a nice round head.

Farrier

Copper shoes as a protection for the hooves of beasts of burden have a long history in Persia,[134] and the Parthians, the eastern cousins of the Persians, famous for their horsemanship, are credited with the introduction of the iron horseshoe.[135] Today, the farrier (*na^{c}lband, na^{c}lgar, na^{c}lčī*) forges a horseshoe (*māl, na^{c}l*) that covers most of the hoof's surface (Fig. 76). The edges of the shoe are upset (*čīdan, jā zadan*)

[134] R. Ghirshman, *Iran*, p. 187.
[135] *Ibid.*, p. 285.

with a heavy upsetting hammer (*čakoš-e naʿl-čīn*) in order to provide a strong rim. In reshoeing a horse, old hoof nails (*mīẖ-e naʿl*) are removed with a nail extractor (*parčbor*, Fig. 77), the hoof (*som*) is smoothed with a large hoof knife (*som-tarāš*, *nāẖon-gīr*, Fig. 78), the shoe is nailed on with a light hammer (*čakoš-e naʿlbandī*), so that the points of the nails (*nōk-e mīẖ*) come out at the sides of the hoof; they are bent over (*parč kardan*) with the farrier's pincers (*gāz*), and finally the hoof is smoothed on the outside with a hoof rasp (*som-sāb*).

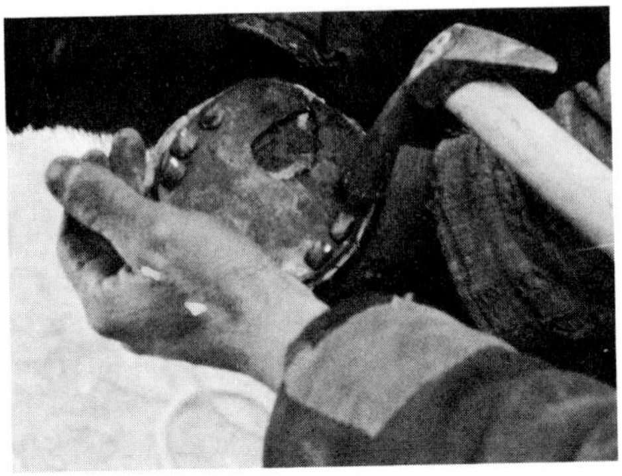

Figure 76 A Persian Horseshoe

Figure 77 A Farrier Extracting Hoof Nails

Figure 78 A Persian Hoof Knife

Cutler, Swordsmith, Scissor Maker, Cutlery Grinder

This group of ironworking crafts also contributed to Persia's fame in crafts. Even at the time of this survey every larger town had at least one smith who specialized as a cutler. But the effects of imported products from Sheffield, Solingen, and Japan could already then be noticed, since several old masters worked with only one assistant and refused to enroll any apprentices, a sure sign for the doom of this noble craft. The structural change in the craft is also illustrated by the changeover in the materials used. Whereas in olden times a carefully cemented carbon steel had to be prepared, today it is much easier and cheaper to buy discarded parts of motor vehicles, in particular half axles and the outer races of heavy ball bearings. It speaks for the skill of the Persian cutler that he forges these materials into useful tools, giving them an appropriate heat treatment, although their complex composition owing to the presence of nickel, chromium, manganese, and so forth, makes this difficult even for a skilled Western craftsman.

This is perhaps the place to mention an attempt to classify swords and the steels used to forge them by the twelfth-century historian Alkindi.[136] In his essay the steels are classified partly according to their properties and partly according to their country of origin. He distinguishes between two main groups of steel:

A. Steel as produced in the ironworks (*maᶜdanī*).

B. Steel not produced in ironworks (*z̲ī lais-e maᶜdanī*), also called *fūlād* or refined steel (*muṣaffā*).

Group A (ironworks steel) is subdivided into two classes:

A-1. Male steel (*saīraqānī*)
A-2. Female steel (*birmāhīnī*)
Out of these two a third one is produced called the composite (*murakkab*) steel.

Group B (refined steel) is divided into three classes:

B-1. Antique steel (*ᶜatīq*) with three subclasses:

a. Yemen steel (*yamānī*)
b. Qalāᶜī steel from an unknown locality
c. Indian steel (*hindī* or *fāqīrūn*)

B-2. Modern steel (*muḥaddas̲*) with two subclasses:

a. Foreign blades (*ġair-e muwallad*) made of steel from Ceylon (*serendīb*) or of steel from Ḫorāsān (*selmanīyeh*), in both cases forged in Yemen. There are seven different kinds of foreign blades:

1. *behānij* with coarse grain (*firind*)
2. *res̲ūs̲* with a fine grain
3. those of Tilmān and Ceylon
4. those forged in Ḫorāsān from Ceylon steel
5. those forged in Mansureh from Ceylon steel
6. the "Persians" forged in Persia from Ceylon steel; also called the "imperials" (*ḫosrouūwānī*), they are decorated with drawings of animals and flowers
7. the swords (*bīż*) forged in Kufa (Iraq)

b. Local blades (*muwallad*) made from steel produced locally, i.e., Persia and Arabia proper. There are five different kinds of local blades:

1. *ḫorāsānī* of Ḫorāsān steel and forged there
2. *baṣrī* of Basra steel and forged there
3. those of Damascus steel and forged there
4. *miṣrī* of Egyptian steel and forged there
5. those named after other localities

B-3. Steel that is neither antique nor modern (*lā ᶜatīq wa lā muḥaddas̲*).

Without going in a more detailed way into Alkindi's account, it shows two things clearly: first, the Arabs and the Persians of the time of the crusades knew the properties of steels of different origin, just as we know the properties of steel from Sweden, Sheffield, or Solingen. Second, Indian, Arabian, and Persian steels played an important part in the metallurgy of that time.

Cutler

Today the cutler (*kārd-sāz, čāqū-sāz, tīġ-sāz*) is concerned with the production of commonly used cutting tools for home and workshop, such as knives (*kārd*), pocket

[136] J. Hammer-Purgstall, *op. cit.*, p. 66.

knives (*čāqū*), pruning knives (*kārd-e deraḫt-čīn*), scissors (*miqrāż, qaičī*), sugar splitters (*qand šekan*), and the like. Figure 79 shows a Zenjān cutler at work. Pot forge and skin bellows can be seen in the foreground. The bellows are operated from the cutler's working place. A stock-anvil is handy at his right. In this workshop the master cutler did all the forging (*āteš-kār*), whereas the filing into shape was left to the assistant sitting behind a filing bench (*kārgāh*) and holding the workpiece in a vice (*gīr-e pā*, Fig. 80). The hardening (*ḫoškeh kardan*) was done again by the master. Most cutlers have a hand-operated grinding wheel (see background of Fig. 79).

The handles for the knives are usually made of goat horn. The assistant puts the horns into the forge and heats them mildly. When the surface begins to scorch, the horns can be straightened and the scorched surface can be scraped clean. Thinner horns are folded over after heating, thus forming the two halves of a handle, whereas thicker horns are slotted with a saw. In each case the knife blade is riveted in. For heavy hunting knives a hole is drilled into the horn to receive the tang of the blade that is riveted over at the end. The horn handles are then filed to shape with a rasp (*čūbsā*) and polished to a nice shine with Tripoli sand.

Figure 79 A Cutler and His Forge

Figure 80 A Cutler's Assistant

Swordsmith

Of this trade, which once was the most noble of all metal crafts, only the names, *šamšīr-sāz, šamšīrgar*, and *sayyāf*, have been left.

Scissor Maker

In many places in Persia some cutlers are fully occupied with the manufacture of a variety of scissors and are then referred to as scissor makers (*qaičī-sāz*). Like the cutler, the *qaičī-sāz* uses imported steel from car scraps for the forging of the scissor blades (*tīġ-e miqrāż*). The blades are carefully filed into shape, having a sharp cutting edge (*dam-e miqrāż*) and nicely rounded backs (*sīneh, pošt-e māhī*). Most scissors have hollow ground blades (*kās*). The finger holes (*jā-ye šast-e dast-ō-angušt*) are forged out and smoothed by filing. In the past a pair of fine paper scissors (*miqrāż-e qalamdān*, Fig. 81) belonged to

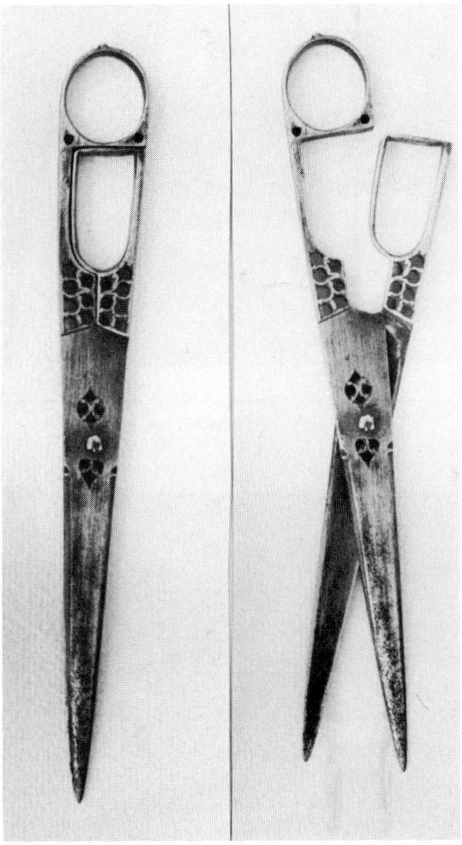

Figure 81 Handmade Scissors

every writing set. The decoration of pierced work (*šabakeh-eslīmī*) is drilled in with a fiddle drill (*mateh kamāneh*) and later shaped with a file. Carpet weavers need a special type of scissors with handles at an angle to the blades (*miqrāż-e šotor*).

Another ironworking craft that has given way to mass-produced imported products is that of the needle maker (*sūzan-sāz*).

Cutlery Grinder

An independent craftsman often working for the cutler, sometimes for the general public in the bazaar or as an itinerant tradesman is the cutlery grinder (*čāqū-tīzkon, qaiči-tīzkon*). Figure 82 shows him squatting behind his grinding bench (*čarẖ-e sangtarāš*). The shaft (*mīl, mīleh*) carries the sandstone grinding wheel (*sang-e sāyī*) or an emery wheel (*sang-e soṃbādeh*). The shaft is supported by a pair of plain bearings (*pā-ye čarẖ*). The grinder's assistant keeps the wheel rotating by pulling and relaxing a belt (*tasmeh, dūvāl*). The grinding (*tīz kardan, tarāšīdan*) is rather rough, but subsequent honing on a whetstone (*sang-e rūmī*) provides a good cutting edge.

Figure 82 A Cutlery Grinder

File Cutter

The file cutters (*souhān-sāz, āj-kon*) of the bazaars of the larger cities are busy craftsmen, because imported files are expensive and the local products are of an amazingly high quality and are made to the requirements of the customers at a reasonable price.

Raw material for smaller files is mild steel that is surface-hardened after cutting. For larger files the good carbon steel of discarded ball bearings is used. The forging up of these bearing races is done in a forge with concertina bellows, but for the subsequent hardening a pot forge with skin bellows is used (Fig. 83). After the blanks have been forged out they are handed over to an assistant who does nothing but file them to shape on a special bench (*ḫarak*, Fig. 84). He places the forged blank to the filing board (*rū-ye ḫarak*) that is fitted with various grooves to receive files of different cross sections. The file is held down by an iron hoop (*āzangū*) attached to the lower board (*taḫteh-ḫarak*). A wedge (*mošteh*) is pushed under the filing board, thus securing the blank for the filing operation (*sābīdan*).

These are the names of the cross sections of the files commonly made:

souhān-e tasmeh'ī, *souhān-e taḫt*, flat file
souhān-e čahārgūš, square file
souhān-e sehgūš, three-square file
souhān-e gerd, round file
souhān-e dom-mūš, small round file (mouse-tail file)
souhān-e nīmgerd, half-round file
souhān-e kārdī, *souhān-e čāqū'ī*, knife-edged file
souhān-e arreh, *souhān-e dō-dam*, cant file
souhān-e gāv-dombal, tapered flat file (cow-tail file)

After they are filed the blanks are handed over to the cutter, a skilled expert. He places the blank on a leaden base (*sorb*), holds it down with his big toe (Fig. 85), and by striking a hammer onto the cutting chisel (*qalam*) he produces a cut (*āj*). During this operation his little finger rests on the blank, and with a rocking movement he shifts the chisel into the next position after each stroke. He uses hammers of varying weight for the different cuts. The cuts are surprisingly uniform in depth and evenly spaced. Four grades of cuts are commonly used:

āj-e zabr, *āj-e dorošt*, *ḫašen*, coarse cut
āj-e narm, *motavasseṭ*, bastard cut
āj-e pardāḫt, *āj-e rīz*, *ẓarīf*, fine cut
āj-e ṣaiqal, extra smooth cut

The cutting chisel is kept sharp on a honing stone (*sang-e sō*). Apart from the cutting chisel, a sharp-edged cutting hammer was used in Europe for file cutting

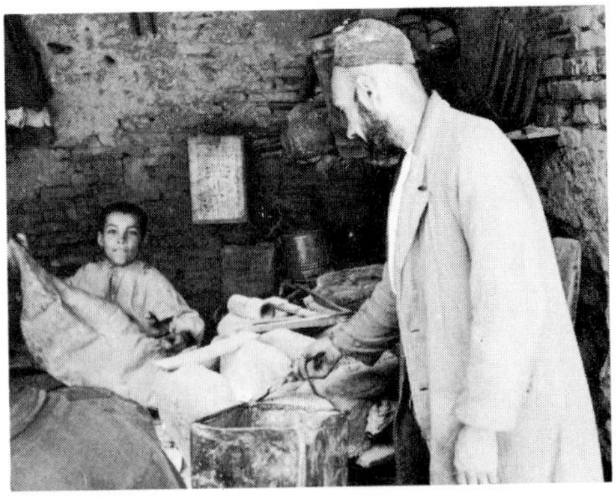

Figure 83 A File Cutter at His Forge

Figure 84 File Blanks Being Smoothed to Size

Figure 85 File Cutting

since medieval times up to the beginning of the machine age (Fig. 86). This type of file-cutting tool was unknown in Persia.

For hardening mild steel, the ready-cut files are covered with a paste of salt and finely-ground horn meal (*ārd-e šāẖ*, *gardeh-šāẖ*), brought to bright red heat, sprinkled over again with the salt–horn-meal mixture—a process which is repeated about six times—and in the end quenched, thus obtaining a good surface hardening. This process was mentioned by Theophilus in his chapter in file making:

Scorch ox-horn in the fire and scrape it off, mix it with one-third of salt and grind it thoroughly. Put the file into the fire and when it is red hot sprinkle the mixture all over it, blow the fire to a bright heat in such a way that the mixture does not fall off. Then take the file quickly out of the fire, quench it in water and dry it over the fire.[137]

Figure 86 A Medieval File Cutter (*from* Mendelsches Stiftungsbuch)

[137] Translated from W. Theobald, *op. cit.*, Book III, Ch. 18.

The hardening of carbon steel is done the same as elsewhere, namely, by heating and quenching (*āb-e tond dādan*) in a water basin (*dasāb*).

Gunsmith

Between 1925 and 1941, when Reżā Šāh Pahlavī, hoping to strengthen the central power, disarmed all nomadic tribes and almost all villagers and townspeople, the craft of the gunsmith (*tofang-sāz*) came to an end. The few remaining members of the craft maintain a small number of licensed shotguns and make ammunition for hunting. The manufacture of new guns is forbidden; in any case, the gunsmith would have found it difficult to compete with imports from Western armament factories.

The following technical terms referring to the gun and its parts have been recorded from an old gunsmith in the Šīrāz bazaar:

tofang, gun
tofang-e sar-por, muzzle-loader gun
tofang-e čaẖmāẖ, *tofang-e čaqmāq*, flintlock gun
sang-e čaẖmāẖ, *sang-e čaqmāq*, flint stone
čaẖmāẖ, *čaqmāq*, firing cock of gun
galangeh-dān, cocking lever on gun
tofang-e sūzanī, needle gun
sūzan, firing needle of gun
tofang-e tah-por, *tofang-e tahī*, breech-loading gun
kamar-šekan, breech of a shotgun
tofang-e gulūleh-zan, rifle
ẖān, rifling
ẖān-dār, rifled
gulūleh, bullet
gūleh, heavy shot for shooting wild pigs
tofang-e sāčmeh-zan, shotgun
sāčmeh, shot
čahār-pāreh, deer shot (up to 12 balls per cartridge)
parandeh-zanī, very fine shot (*parandeh* means "bird")
bārūt, gunpowder
bārūt-e bīdūd, smokeless gunpowder
bārūt-dān, powder horn
bārūt-sanj, powder measure
čašnī, percussion cap
pestānak, anvil on gun to carry percussion cap

fūlmīnāt, priming charge in detonator (Fr. *fulminant*)
lūleh, barrel
tofang-e yak lūleh, single-barreled gun
tofang-e dō lūleh, *tofang-e dō tīr*, double-barreled gun
qofl, gunlock
māšeh, trigger
ḥāfez-e māšeh, trigger guard
darajeh, foresight of a gun
šekāf-e darajeh, backsight of a gun
ḫazīneh, magazine in gun
fešang, cartridge
fešang-e jangī, military cartridge
fešang-e šekārī, shotgun cartridge
fešangkaš, cartridge ejector
pūkeh, cartridge case
sendān-e pūkeh, anvil in bottom of cartridge case
zeh, edge on cartridge case
sūrāḫ-e pūkeh, touch holes in cartridge
sūrāḫ-e sūz, touch holes of gun
namad, felt wad in cartridge
moqavvā, cardboard wad for cartridge
ḫašāb, *šāneh* (=comb), cartridge frame
fešang-e ḫālī, blank cartridge
navār-e fešang, bandelier
dasteh-āčar-e tofang, tool kit for gun maintenance

The gunsmith, the balance maker, and the locksmith all belong to a group of craftsmen coming close to what we call fitter or general ironworker. They have the following tools in common:

gīreh, vice
gīreh-ye movāzī, parallel vice
gīreh-ye lūleh-gīr, pipe vice
gīreh-dast, hand vice
gīreh-kaj, beveling vice
fakk-e gīreh, vice jaw
souhān, file
borādeh, *sūvāleh*, filings, scrapings
qalam, *tīzbor*, chisel
qalam-pahn, *tīzbor-pahn*, broad cold chisel
qalam-dambārīk, cross-cut chisel
qalam-nāḫonī, *tīzbor-e sar-nīzeh*ʾ*ī* (meaning "spear-shaped"), chisel for cutting sheet metal
čakoš, hammer
čakoš-e mīḫparč, riveting hammer
čakoš-e mīḫ-kaš, claw hammer
sombeh, punch
sombeh-nešān, center punch
ḥurūf, letter punches
šomāreh, number punches
sūzan-e ḫaṭṭkaš, scriber
ḫaṭṭkaš-e pāʾīdār, surface gauge
mateh, drill, auger
jān-e mateh, drill point
mateh-gīr, drill chuck
mateh-sangbor, masonry drill
tan-e mateh, brace
zāviyeh-boreš, cutting edge of a tool
šīyār, flute on drill
dom-maḫrūtī, tapered drill shank
dom-gerd, cylindrical drill shank
sāket, *kolāhak*, Morse bush
jeqjeqeh (*jeq-jeq* means "noise"), *qarqareh* (Arab., means "noise"), ratchet drill
derafš, (Tehrān), *derou* (Šīrāz), *derabš* (Iṣfahān), awl
borqū (Iṣfahān), *bolqū* (Šīrāz), reamer
borqū-motaḥarrek, adjustable reamer
borqū-lūleh, tapered pipe reamer
qalāvīz, thread tap
dast-e qalāvīz, tap wrench
ḥadīdeh, thread die
šabr (Ger. *Schaber*), scraper
šabr-pahn (Iṣfahān), *šabr-dampahn* (Šīrāz), flat scraper
šabr-sehgūš, three-cornered scraper
šabr qāšoqī, bearing scraper
arreh āhanbor, *arreh kamāneh*, *arreh kamānī*, hacksaw
arreh mošābak, *lobzeg* (Ger. *Laubsäge*, via Russia), fretsaw
kamān, frame of the hacksaw
mokaʿab-e pāʾīn, fixed end on hacksaw
ḫorūsak, *pīč-ḫorūsak*, saw-tightening screw
ambor-dast, pliers
ambor-dast-e dampahn, *dambārīk*, flat-mouthed pliers
ambor-dast-e damgerd, round-nosed pliers
ambor-dast-e movāzī, pliers with parallel jaws
ambor-dast-e lūlehgīr, pipe wrench
ambor-dast-e ʿāyeq, electrician's pliers
mīḫ-čīn, *qaičī mīḫ-čīn*, wire cutter, side cutter
lūlehbor, pipe cutter
gāz, pincers
qaiči, tin snips
qaičī ahromī, levered shears
tīġ, cutting edge of tin snips
āčār-e zanjīrī, chain vice
lūleh-ḫamkon, pipe-bending device
lūleh-rāstkon, pipe straightener
moqavvā-bor, *pelakbor* (Fr. *plaque* means "washer," "disk"), *manganeh* means wad punch, saddler's punch (also: press, vice, roller)
ambor-e manganeh, *sombeh*, punch pliers for leather

āčār, spanner
āčār-e čakošī, monkey wrench
āčār-e lūlehgīr, pipe wrench
āčār-e faranseh (Fr.), *ačār-e inglīsī* (Eng.), adjustable spanner
āčār-e haftsarī, āčār-e sehtofangeh, multiple-headed spanner
āčār-e boks (Eng. box), box spanner
āčār-e polomb, lead seal pliers
āčār-e pīčgūštī, screwdriver
dasteh-āčār, set of spanners
pīčgūštī-sarkaj, angle screwdriver
*zar*ᶜ (1 *zar*ᶜ = 16 *gereh* = 32 *bahr* = 41 inches), an old standard measure
metr, ruler
metr-e navārī, tape measure
kolīs (Fr. *coulisse*), sliding gauge
kolīs-e sūrāḫ, depth gauge
ḫaṭṭ-kaš, straight-edge
gūniyā, square
gūniyā-lab-e dār, back or try square
gūniyā-vāšō, gūniyā-motaḥarrek, protractor or bevel gauge
gūniyā-fārsī, miter square
ṣafḥeh, ṣāfī, surface plate
pargār, compasses
pargāreh, small compasses
andāzeh, measure, yard, quantity
andāzehgīr-e ḫārejī, outside calipers
andāzehgīr-e dāḫelī, inside calipers
andāzehgīr-e pīč, screw pitch gauges
zāviyeh, zāviyeh-kaš, protractor
fīlervāf (corrupt English), feeler gauge
houviyeh (Tehrān, Iṣfahān), *hōviyeh* (Šīrāz), soldering iron
*qal*ᶜ, tin
*qal*ᶜ*-e laḥīm*, soldering tin
laḥīm kardan, to solder
laḥīm-e berenj, hard solder
jōhar, jouhar, asīd, soldering flux
nešādor, sal-ammoniac
bōrak, būrāq, būreh, tankār, borax

Balance Maker

The use of standard weights is a long-established practice in Persia. Under Darius I (521–485 B.C.) a fully developed system of standardized weights was in existence.[138] In 1937 E. F. Schmidt[139] of the Chicago University Oriental Institute unearthed a beautifully finished grayish green diorite weight (Fig. 87) with a trilingual inscription. The Old Persian version begins: "120 karsha. I am Darius the great King," and so forth. The Babylonian version gives the weight as 20 minae. This standard prototype, as we would call it today, weighs 9,950 grams, and allowing for the chipped-off lower edges a mina would be almost exactly 500 grams.

Figure 87 Standard Weight of Darius I (*from E. F. Schmidt*, The Treasury of Persepolis, *reproduced courtesy of the Oriental Institute, University of Chicago*)

The theory of the balance was known in Persia for many centuries. Abū Jafar al Ḫāzinī,[140] a native of Persia, wrote a long treatise on balances toward the end of the eleventh century A.D. It is based on sound geometrical and mechanical principles and is accompanied by numerous drawings. Al Ḫāzinī also gives a description of the so-called water balance for the determination of the specific gravity. His values for specific gravities of about 50 commonly used substances, which he determined by

[138] F. H. Weissbach, "Zur keilschriftlichen Gewichtskunde," pp. 625–696.

[139] E. F. Schmidt, *Excavations at Tepe Hissar*, pp. 62–63.

[140] N. Khanikoff, *Al Kitāb mīzān al-ḥikma* (*The Book of the Balance of Wisdom*) *by Al Khāzinī*, pp. 1–128.

his own experiments, vary little from accepted modern values. His specific gravity for mercury of 13.56, to quote only one example, is close to the modern value of 13.557, whereas the two values which Robert Boyle found in the seventeenth century by two different methods, viz., 13.76 and 13.36, are considerably less accurate. Against this background it is not surprising to find in Persia to this day a great variety of well-built balances, scales, and steelyards.

In line with the ever changing political development over the centuries a complicated system of weight standards evolved. Accounts of what was in use in the Middle Ages and up to our time are given by A. K. S. Lambton[141] and W. Hinz.[142] One of the first steps in the direction of unification of provincial standards was the equation in terms of metric units by law of 1926. In 1935 the metric system was officially introduced, but the old standards are still widely used. The basic unit of many of these local standards is the *man*.[143] While the actual weight of the *man* varied in different provinces the *man-e Tabrīz* was the most widely used. The following table is based on observations made in Šīrāz in 1938:

Unit	Official Metric Equivalent	Traditional Equivalent
man-e Tabrīz	3.00 kg	2.97 kg
man-e sağat	3.00 kg	2.97 kg
ḫarvār	300 kg	297 kg
man-e šāh	6.00 kg	5.94 kg
čārak	750 grams	740 grams
vaqqeh	375 grams	370 grams
sīr	75 grams	74 grams
mesqāl	10 grams	4.64 grams
noḫōd	0.2 gram	0.193 gram
jou	—	0.048 gram
gandom	—	0.048 gram

The maker of balances and scales (*mīzān-sāz, tarāzū-sāz*) is only found in larger towns. Two main types of balances can be distinguished:

1. Balances and scales with a central pivot: (*a*) those suspended from a fixed point (*mīzān*); (*b*) those held by the hand when in use (*tarāzū*).
2. Balances with an unequal lever and moving weight (steel yard, *kapān, qapān*).

Figure 88 A Balance Suspended from a Fixed Point

141 A. K. S. Lambton, *Landlord and Peasant in Persia*, pp. 405 ff.

142 W. Hinz, *Islamische Masse und Gewichte umgerechnet auf das metrische System*, pp. 1–36.

143 In other places spelled "*mann*," "*maund*," etc. This unit is in fact a direct descendant of the ancient *mina*. For its history throughout Persia and the Islamic world, see W. Hinz, *op. cit.*, p. 16.

Balance Suspended from a Fixed Point

This balance (Fig. 88) is mainly used by the bazaar merchant in his permanent stall and is normally made of steel (*āhanī-dūš*). It moves in a shackle (*darvāzeh*) that provides the bearing (*āvīzān*) for the pivot point (*mīḫ*). Hanging freely from the shackle is a little stirrup (*āvīz*) that holds the shackle legs together. The balance is suspended from a rafter in the ceiling by a hook (*qolāb*). A tongue (*mīl, fāneh, lisān*) to indicate equilibrium is attached to the balance beam and is playing inside the shackle. The balance maker pays great attention to the proper design of the beam (*sāqeh, šāhan, šāhand, šāhang, šāhīn, šāhin*). He is fully aware of what we call the coincidence of the center of gravity for the beam's mass with the pivot point. The end bearing pins (*mīḫ*) of the beam are, like the center pivot, of hardened steel and have a knife edge (*tīz*) in order to reduce friction. Attached to these end bearings are hooked links (*čang*) from which the chains (*zanjīr*) of the weighing scales (*kafeh, kapeh, čapeh, piyāleh*) are suspended, sometimes over an S-shaped hook (*čap-ō-rāst*). Depending on the kind of goods to be weighed the scales are sometimes merely flat boards (*taḫteh*). Balances of the *mīzān* type are used to weigh up to half a *ḫarvār* (about 300 pounds).

Scales Held by the Hand When in Use

Figure 89 shows a pair of scales such as a goldsmith or silversmith would use (*tarāzū-ye mesqālī*). They have all the characteristics of a well-designed balance —good mass distribution on the beam, knife-edged bearings, and indicating tongue. They are usually kept in a wooden case (*qōtī, jaʿbeh*, Fig. 90). The details in design and decoration on the beam, shackle, and weights (*sang-e vazn*, Fig. 91) show that they are made with loving care.

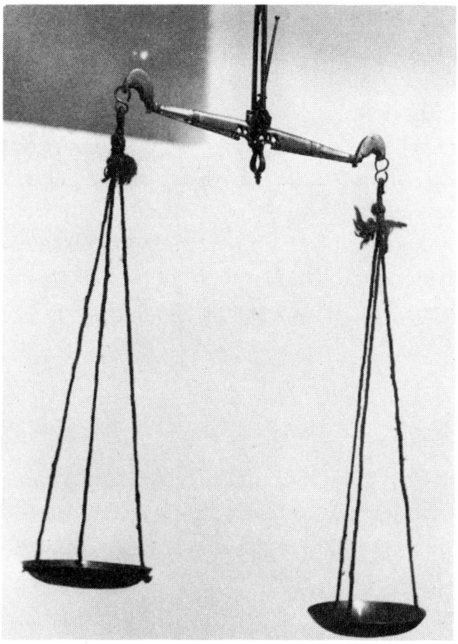

Figure 89 Goldsmith's Scales

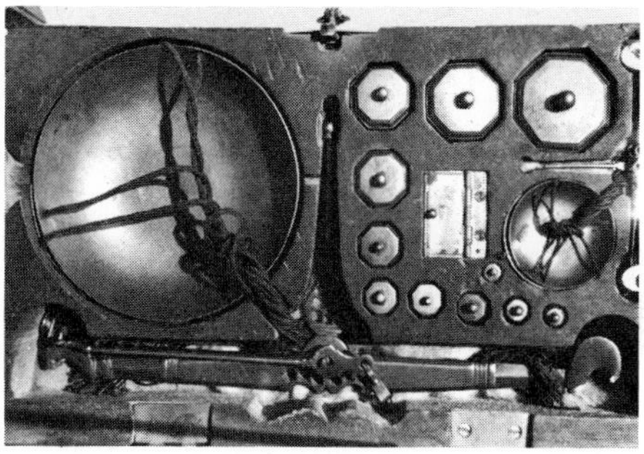

Figure 90 Goldsmith's Scales in a Box

Figure 91 Weights for the Goldsmith's Scales Shown in Fig. 90

The peddler selling his goods from door to door has a much plainer type of scales (Fig. 92). The beam is turned of wood, with holes in the ends for leather straps acting as end bearings. The scales proper are often made in the form of wicker baskets and are suspended from the beam by leather belts. In use the pair of scales is suspended by a piece of rope (*mošteh*, *mangūleh*), which forms the center pivot.

Figure 92 Peddler's Scales

Balance with Unequal Lever and Moving Weight (Steelyard)

The principle underlying this type of balance was already known to Aristotle (384–322 B.C.), who evolved the theory of it in his "Mechanical Problems."[144] Vitruvius mentions it as a useful apparatus in Chapter I of his *De architectura*, which was written about 16 B.C.[145] Many Roman steelyards have been unearthed in most parts of the Imperium[146] that are almost

Figure 93 A Steelyard

identical with the type now used in Persia, and it is safe to assume that they have been the same since Roman times.

Figure 93 shows a steelyard used outside the bazaar of Šīrāz. It is suspended here from a tripod (*seh-pāyeh*), but inside the vaults of the bazaar it would hang on a chain from the ceiling. The load and the suspension shackles are on the right, the beam (*mīl*) with the moving weight (*sang-e qapān*) and its hook (*qolāb*) on the left. There are three shackles provided: one to suspend the load (*darvāzeh-bār, sar-e āvīzān*, Fig. 94, extreme right) and two to suspend the steelyard (*sar-e sabok* and *sar-e sangīn*). They work in the following way: For light loads, i.e., less than one *ḫarvār* (300 kg) the arrangement shown in Fig. 94 is used. The steelyard itself is suspended from the shackle on the top left in Fig. 94 (*sar-e sabok*), while the middle shackle is idle. The short lever arm is about 4 inches long, and the face on the long beam which shows up in this arrangement has divisions (*ḫaṭṭ* or *man*) and quarters thereof (*čārak* in Šīrāz). For loads above one *ḫarvār*, the steelyard is turned over and is then suspended from the middle shackle (*sar-e sangīn*) while the load is still suspended from the end shackle, which has been swung round in the turning process; this time *sar-e sabok* is idle. The long beam now shows another face with divisions for double the weight, and the short lever arm has been reduced from 4 to 2 inches.

Smaller merchants and private people who take delivery of goods do not normally own a steelyard. They can hire one from a man in the bazaar (*qapān-dār*), who charges a small sum (in 1938 one *ᶜabbāsī*, or one farthing) per *ḫarvār* weighed. For this he operates the steelyard and writes the tally down, thus having a record for his fees at the same time.

Figure 94 The Shackles of the Steelyard

Locksmith

One thing that strikes the visitor to Persia is the juxtaposition of the most ancient technical objects with very modern imported European goods. This is the case with locks and keys too.

The locking up of treasures, grain stores, and temples can be traced back to Egypt and Mesopotamia of the second millennium B.C.[147] In the ninth century B.C.

[144] T. Beck, *Beiträge zur Geschichte des Maschinenbaus*, p. 2.
[145] *Ibid.*, p. 41.
[146] A. Neuburger, *Die Technik des Altertums*, p. 209.

[147] V. J. M. Eras, *Locks and Keys Through the Ages*, pp. 20 ff.

Homer described how Penelope took a bronze key with an ivory handle to open her husband's treasury and armory.[148] There are also several references in the Bible to locks and keys,[149] and it appears that the Romans adapted some of these Mediterranean locks to their own use and spread them wherever they colonized.

The Persian locksmith (*qaffāl, qofl-sāz, kelīd-sāz*) as an iron-handling craftsman has a medium-sized furnace with concertina bellows for the forging of the metal parts of the lock. Brazing is done in a small pot forge. Since some locks are partly made of wood the locksmith has to know how to handle this material. His woodworking tools are similar to those of the carpenter.

The locks he makes show a variety of ingenious technical features. Some of them are similar to Egyptian and Greek locks, others to Roman locks; some point to India and China, others have been in use in Europe in the Middle Ages and up to the Industrial Revolution. The construction of the lock will be treated in more detail here, but it is not possible at the present stage of knowledge on this subject to say with certainty where each type of lock originated and how it spread.

From a technical point of view the locks found in Persia can be classified as follows:

A. Fixed Door Locks
   1. Toothed-bolt lock
   2. Tumbler lock
   3. Spreading-spring lock

B. Padlocks
   1. Helical-spring lock (with screw key)
   2. Barbed-spring lock (with push key)
   3. Pipe lock (with screw key)
   4. Letter combination lock (keyless)

[148] Homer, *The Odyssey*, xxi.6, 7; 47–51; 241.

[149] Nehemiah 3:3; Judges 3:23, 25; Isaiah 22:22.

Fixed Door Locks (kelīdūn-e ẖāneh)

1. Toothed-bolt lock (*qofl-e rūmī, kolūndān*)

If the modern reconstruction of the Homerian lock is correct[150, 151, 152] (Fig. 95) the closest to it in function would be the toothed-bolt lock, the lock of Rūm, i.e., Byzantium. This seems to agree with Pliny's claim that a Theodore of Samos invented this lock.[153] It has a strong wooden bolt (*kolūn*, Fig. 96) sliding through the actual lock body, which is attached to the door wings by heavy hand-forged iron nails. The end of the bolt engages in a catch (*mādeh*) on the other wing. To open or close this simple bolt-and-catch arrangement, one side of the bolt carries a number of cut-in teeth (*dandāneh*) into which an iron key (*kelīd, tamlīd*) engages. For each full turn of the key the bolt moves the distance between two teeth, and after several turns the bolt will reach its end position, thus locking or unlocking the door. This lock gives security in a threefold way: (*a*) The bit of the key (*zabān-e kelīd*) must have a certain length, measured from the center of the shank, in order to mesh properly with the teeth and to move the bolt from tooth to tooth. (*b*) The lock body carries a number of fixed pegs and a center plate of steel; both would be called "wards" in Western terms. The key can only be turned if it has notches (*čāḥ-e kelīd*) corresponding to the positions of the ward pegs and the plate. (*c*) To prevent opening of the door by just pushing the bolt away, e.g., from inside, a wooden tumbler (*šaiṭānak*, meaning "little devil") is situated inside the lock. This tumbler normally falls into the notch in the end position of the bolt and locks it

[150] A. Neuburger, *op. cit.*, p. 339.

[151] V. J. M. Eras, *op. cit.*, p. 34.

[152] Lt. Col. Fox-Pitt-Rivers, *On the Development and Distribution of Primitive Locks and Keys*, p. 23.

[153] V. J. M. Eras, *op. cit.*, p. 34.

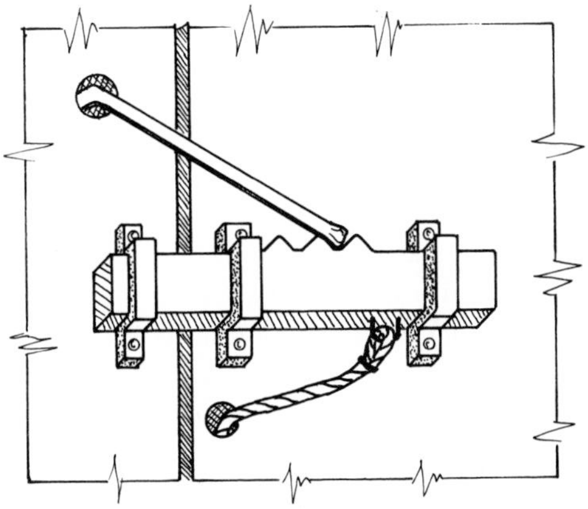

Figure 95 Reconstruction of the Homerian Lock (*after A. Neuburger,* Die Technik des Altertums)

Figure 96 A Toothed-Bolt Lock

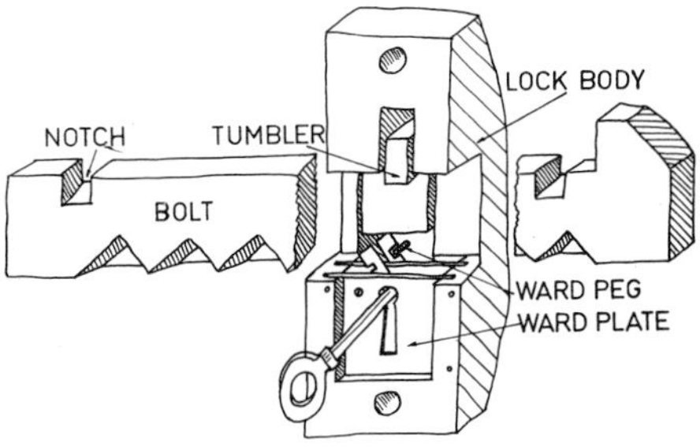

Figure 97 A Toothed-Bolt Lock (*bolt partly removed*)

there (Fig. 97). During the first turn the key lifts this tumbler, and from then on the bolt is free to slide. Lt. Col. Fox-Pitt-Rivers found this kind of lock in India[154] and China[155] about 1880, both having all the features described above. Hommel[156] also describes and illustrates a similar lock for China.

2. Tumbler lock (*kolūn*)

This lock can be found in all parts of Persia and is also of great antiquity in its construction. Keys for this type of lock dating back to about 2000 B.C. have been found in Ḫorsābād, the ruins of ancient Niniveh.[157] Bolts and tumblers, both in stone, have been excavated by Ghirshman at Čogā Zaṃbīl near Susa. He describes this lock, dating from the thirteenth century B.C., and thinks that the stone bolt has been attached to a wooden door by means of bronze clamps.[158] Keys from the time of Rameses II (1291–1225) B.C.[159] are still in existence. Needham[160] shows that these locks were used in Old Loyang and mentions a Chinese tradition that a fifth-century B.C. locksmith, Kungshu-Phan, was the inventor of the tumbler lock. This lock was in general use in classical Greece under the name of Balanos lock, *balanos* meaning "acorn." The Romans made it of metal and improved it by introducing steel springs for the action of the tumblers. Many keys and a considerable number of whole locks have been unearthed in former Roman colonies,[161] from Britain to North

[154] Fox-Pitt-Rivers, *op. cit.*, p. 23, and Plate X, Figs. 113–116.
[155] *Ibid.*, Plate X, Figs. 117–119.
[156] R. P. Hommel, *China at Work*, pp. 296 ff.
[157] V. J. M. Eras, *op. cit.*, p. 20.
[158] R. Ghirshman, "Tchoga Zanbil près de Suse," p. 113.
[159] A. Neuburger, *op. cit.*, p. 338.
[160] J. Needham, *The History of Science and Civilisation in China*, Vol. 4, Part II, p. 238.
[161] Fox-Pitt-Rivers, *op. cit.*, pp. 7–9.

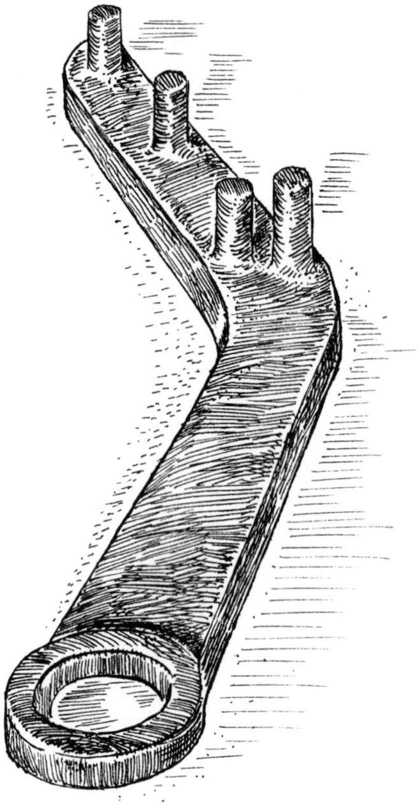

Figure 98 Key of a Tumbler Lock from Palestine

Africa, Palestine[162] (Fig. 98), and Asia Minor.[163] The Arabs took it over, and their merchants spread it as far as Indonesia.[164] Fox-Pitt-Rivers mentions it as being in use in remote parts of Britain, in Norway, Austria, and Germany about 1875,[165] and the doors at Pembroke College, Cambridge, were still locked with genuine tumbler locks in 1963. Figure 99 shows an application to a Persian garden gate (1938). The lock itself is built into the wall, and the wooden key can be passed into the lock through a hole in the wall. A tumbler lock dismantled into its parts is shown in Fig. 100 and with the key in position in Fig. 101. The bolt has a number of notches into which tumblers (*šaiṭānak*, *fāneh*) drop when the lock is being closed, thus securing the bolt. For opening, a key (left foreground, Fig. 100) is inserted into the hollow end of the bolt (*kelīd-ḫwor*) through a slot in the lock body. Pegs or elevations on the key correspond to the notches for the tumblers. The key is then lifted, thus pushing up the tumblers, and when the key is pulled the bolt is withdrawn. There is a wide range of permutations possible through varying numbers and different arrangements of the tumblers. This gives the lock a high degree of security, probably the strongest reason for its survival for more than four millennia. A close inspection shows that the principle on which our modern "Yale" lock is built is exactly the same, another proof of the soundness of the basic principle.

A variation of the tumbler lock is used in the Yazd-Iṣfahān area. The tumblers, in a wooden lock, control a vertical iron bolt (*nar*, meaning "male") that fits into an iron catch (*mādeh*, meaning "female").

3. Spreading-spring lock

Completely different principles apply in the design of this lock, mainly found in Āẕarbaijān. It is an iron box lock (Fig. 102) with two strong springs (*S*) protruding from the box. These springs engage on both sides of the catch hook (*C*). The key has a double bit of such dimensions that when it is turned the springs spread out, disengage from the catch, and the door can be opened. If one or both sides of the bit are too small the spring will not spread enough. If the bits are too large they will not fit into the keyhole. In addition there are ward pegs and a ward plate provided

162 H. B. Hunting, *Hebrew Life and Times*, and drawing by O. E. Ernegg.
163 A. Neuburger, *op. cit.*, pp. 340–341.
164 V. J. M. Eras, *op. cit.*, p. 43.
165 Fox-Pitt-Rivers, *op. cit.*, p. 7.

Figure 99 A Tumbler Lock and Key from Iṣfahān

Figure 101 A Tumbler Lock, Seen from Underneath, Key in Position

Figure 100 A Tumbler Lock Dismantled

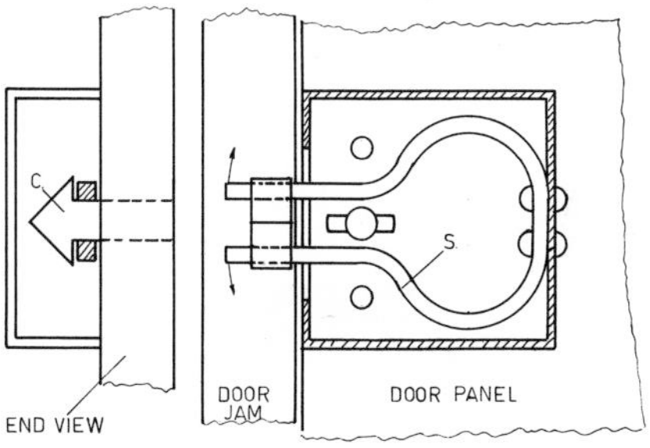

Figure 102 A Spreading-Spring Lock

that have to fit into slots on the key bits, so that altogether the security of the lock is reasonably good.

These three types of fixed door locks are only used for main doors, garden gates, and so forth. Smaller doors, strong boxes, and cupboards are locked by a variety of padlocks.

Padlocks (qofl-e āhan)

1. Helical-spring lock (with screw key, *qofl-e fanar*)

This type of lock seems to be the most popular. Inside a tubular body (*lūleh*, Fig. 103) is a lock guard (*zabāneh*) with a hook engaging in the notch (*kaneh, čak*) of the shackle (*ḥalqeh*). A helical spring (*fanar*) presses the lock guard tightly against the shackle notch, thus keeping it locked. The lock guard carries a small tube that has an interior thread (*pīč-e mādeh*). The thread is produced by brazing a steel wire, wound to a helix, inside the tube. A guide pin (*mīleh, maftūl*) forms the center of the tube. On its round shank the key (*kelīd*) has an exterior thread (*pīč-e nar*), again brazed-on wire, that fits exactly into the tube thread on the guard. The pipe of the key shank must also fit into the guide pin, in length as well as diameter. To open the lock, the key is screwed in up to its shoulder. With another half turn the lock guard is drawn toward the key, thus unlocking the shackle. Considering that change of key diameter, screw pitch, number of thread starts, length, and diameter of guide pin offer a wide scope for permutations, it is understandable that even the modern Persians rely so much on this lock (Fig. 104). The same kind of lock was in use in medieval England, France, and Germany. It has been observed in these countries as late as 1875.[166]

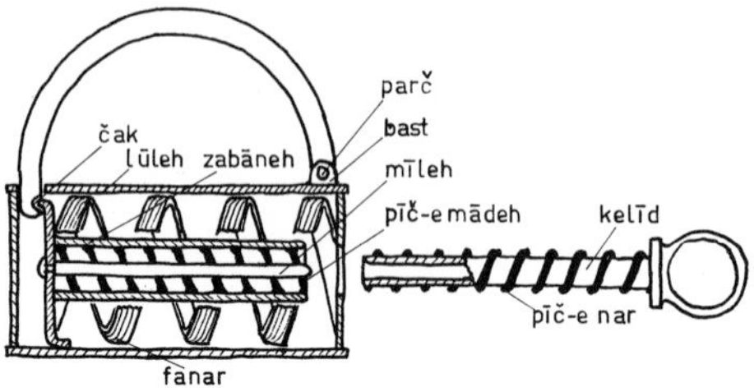

Figure 103 Section of a Helical-Spring Lock

Figure 104 A Helical-Spring Lock with Locking Piece and Key

2. Barbed-spring lock (with push key, *qofl-e fanarī*)

This efficient lock is still widely used. It can be traced back to the Romans, was used all over Europe before the Industrial Revolution,[167] was still in existence in the British Navy at the beginning of this century[168] and is to this day the common lock in China[169] and Southeast Asia.[170] Fox-Pitt-Rivers' theory[171] that it was invented by the Romans and traveled via Persia, Central Asia, to India and China should be difficult to prove with so little historical information on technical things available. The idea of this lock might just as well have traveled the other way or might have spread from the Middle East to Rome and Europe on the one hand and to India and China on the other. In its basic form (Fig. 105) the barbed-spring lock consists of two parts: the lock body (*tan-e qofl*) and the locking piece (*zabāneh*), the latter carrying two sets of barbed springs (*fanar*). For locking, these two parts are pushed together, and the springs spread out upon reaching their end position, thus completing the locking without a key. To open it, a key with two notches is introduced. These notches cover the springs, and when pushed right in, press them together, thus allowing the locking part to be withdrawn by hand. Security is offered by variation of the spring distance. Figure 106 shows a small cupboard lock of the barbed-spring type, with the lock body in the form of a horse giving the lock its name "horse lock" (*qofl-e aspī*). The locking piece with the springs and the shackle is shown above the horse. To open the lock, the push key (bottom of Fig. 106) is inserted from the front.

A variation of this lock is shown in Fig. 107. It combines the features of the barbed-spring lock with those of the screw lock: a locking piece with the barbed springs (bottom in Fig. 107) will lock the shackle when pushed right in. The key, however, is not the simple push type but has a screw (*pīč-e nar*) at its front end that

[166] *Ibid.*, p. 18, and Plate V, Figs. 35–37.

[167] A. Neuburger, *op. cit.*, p. 342, and Fox-Pitt-Rivers, *op. cit.*, p. 16 and Plate V, Figs. 21–26.

[168] V. J. M. Eras, *op. cit.*, p. 44.

[169] *Ibid.*; R. P. Hommel, *op. cit.*, p. 295; J. Needham, *The History of Science and Civilisation in China*, Vol. 4, Part II, p. 241.

[170] Author's own observations in Thailand and Indochina in 1955–1956.

[171] Fox-Pitt-Rivers, *op. cit.*, p. 20.

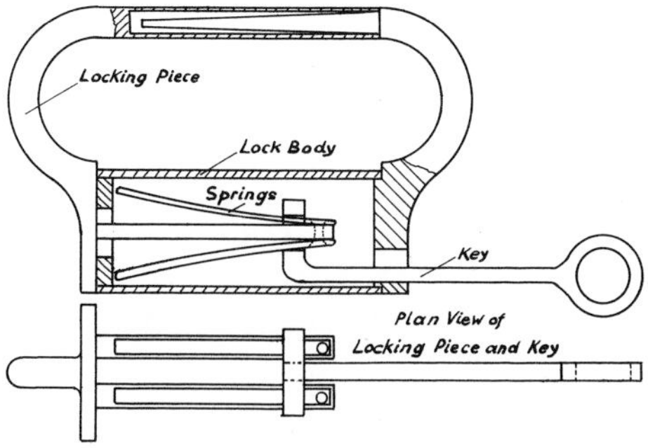

Figure 105 A Barbed-Spring Lock

Figure 106 Parts of the Horse Lock

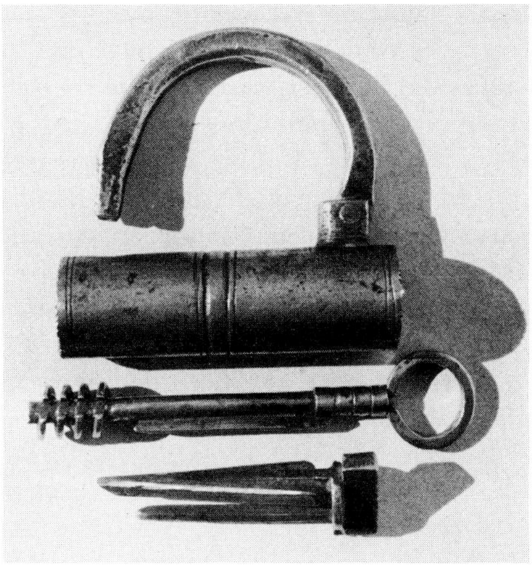

Figure 107 A Barbed-Spring Lock with Screw Key and Locking Piece

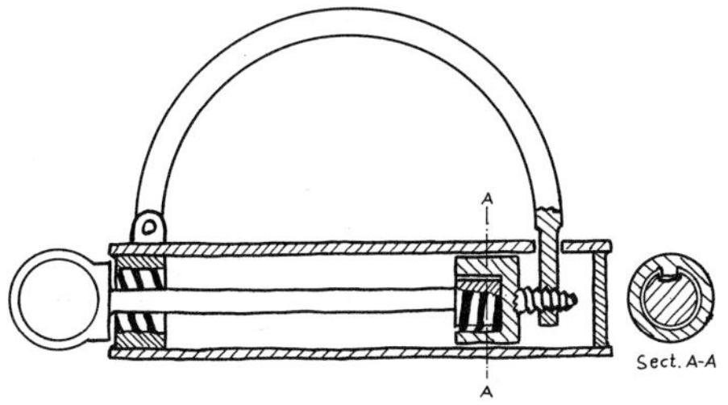

Figure 108 A Pipe Lock

must first be screwed through the threaded front (*pič-e mādeh*) of the body. Only after this can the key be pushed forward, when the two notches in it will compress and release the springs as in the ordinary spring lock. Apart from the variation obtained from the spring arrangement, there is further security through variation in thread size, number of starts, pitch, and sense of thread (left or right hand). Locks of this construction have been observed outside Persia in places as far apart as Burma and Nuremberg in Germany. The Nuremberg lock is now kept in a collection of medieval German locks.[172]

3. Pipe lock (with screw key, *qofl-e lūleh*)

The part characteristic of this lock (Fig. 108) is a small cylindrical locking piece inside a pipe body (*lūleh*). This piece has a threaded front end fitting into the shackle, locking it when properly screwed in. The key has a threaded end that has to fit into the front end of the pipe. After being screwed through this end, the key is pushed forward. A groove on the key fits

172 *Ibid.*

into a spline on the locking piece. When the key is turned the locking piece can be unscrewed in order to release the shackle. A range of permutations is obtained by varying the thread of the key with regard to pitch, diameter, and sense, and also by varying the dimensions of spline and groove on key and locking piece respectively. The locking piece always stays inside the tube.

Pipe locks have also been described for India and medieval Europe.[173]

4. Letter combination lock (keyless, *qofl-e ḥurūfī*)

With so great an importance placed on security by permutation it is not surprising that we find a keyless letter combination lock in Persia. Figure 109 shows a padlock with three lettered rings (*ġaltak-e ḥurūfī, mohr-e ḥurūfī*). The shaft of the locking piece (*mīl-e qofl*) has a long lip with three slots at the middle of each of the lettered rings. The rings have grooves to fit the slots in the lip. When the locking piece is pushed in, it engages the shackle, and as soon as the lettered rings are turned round, the lock can no longer be opened until the rings are brought back into a certain position that is signified by a combination of letters, only known to the owner of the lock, on the front of the lock.

Letter combination locks of similar construction were still in use in France in 1750[174] and have been revived lately for the protection of bicycles and motor cars.

Steel Fretworker

An ironworking craftsman whose products are more on the artistic side is the steel fretworker (*šabakeh-kār*). He makes ornamental steel plates known as *šabakeh-ye eslīmī*. These objects range in height from 3 inches to 3 feet. They have a religious significance and are displayed in the homes of members of craft guilds. Once a year they are carried in the Moḥarram procession on the tops of flagstaffs or suspended from the emblem poles of the various craft guilds. Figure 110 shows such

Figure 109 A Letter Combination Lock

Figure 110 A Pierced Steel Ornament

[173] *Ibid.*, p. 21, and Plate VIII, Figs. 85–89.

[174] D. Didérot, with J. d'Alembert, *Encyclopédie ou Dictionnaire Raisonné des Sciences et des Arts et Métiers*, heading *serrurier*, Figs. 134–140.

an ornament, the inscription reading *ᶜAlī valī-ullāhī*, Ali Lieutenant of God.

The steel fretworker starts from a flat piece of bright steel of about 20 B.W. Gauge. He applies a mixture of chalk and glue water to it to produce a white surface. After drying he transfers the design from a perforated drawing by means of charcoal dust. He drills small holes (*sūlāḫ kardan*) with a bow drill wherever the design requires them. They are widened either by filing (*souhān kardan*) or fret sawing (*borīdan bā arreh*). The burr is taken away with a file (*sābīdan bā souhān*). In most cases a further ornamentation, an incrustation with gold, is applied (*ṭelā kūbīdan šabakeh*). This means roughening the surface (*rūš āj kardan*), beating in gold wire (*sīm-e ṭelā*), and burnishing with an agate (*sang kašīdan*). Many of the ornaments are fitted with brass frames that are gilded and have profiled edges.

2

WOODWORKING CRAFTS

Persian Timber Used by the Craftsman

If we accept the geologists' claim that during the North European Ice Age the Iranian Plateau was passing through a pluvial period,[1] followed by a gradual drying up of an inland lake, we can understand that in the days of the Achaemenian kings there were still large forests in the heart of Persia where today we find rarely more than single trees. Darius says in the foundation charter of Susa,[2] "the *yakā* timber was brought from Gandara and Carmania . . ." I. Gershevitch shows that Old Persian *yakā* is identical with the sissoo tree (*jag* or *jaġ*), which gives a hard, dark brown, and durable timber, and that the tree grows in the sub-Himalayan region of India and Pakistan as well as in Afghanistan and is indigenous in the Balūčistān and Makrān region of Southeast Persia.[3] It has been identified as *Dalbergia sissoo Roxb.* Even a medieval geographer mentions large forests in some parts of the Plateau.[4] Since then, however, the indiscriminate felling of trees for timber and charcoal production has denuded wide parts of the country, and has thus caused extensive soil erosion and subsequent reduction in agricultural production. Only the dense forests of the Caspian provinces north of the Alburz mountain range, with their heavy rainfall, still yield considerable quantities of useful timber. The greater part of the requirements of the craftsmen of today actually comes from there. Apart from this region there are still forests of oak trees in the valleys of the Zagros mountains. Walnut

[1] R. Ghirshman, *Iran*, p. 27.
[2] *Ibid.*, p. 165.

[3] I. Gershevitch, "Sissoo at Susa," pp. 316–320.
[4] Al-Balkhi, *Description of the Province of Fars*, trans. G. Le Strange, p. 24.

and plane trees, cyprus, and pines are grown in the famous Persian gardens wherever there is water to irrigate them. Fast-growing willows and poplars line the irrigation channels; they are the main source for the cheaper building timber today.

The following list of useful timber has been compiled in conversations with woodworking craftsmen and peasants; wherever possible their botanical names are given, in most cases verified by a botanist.[5] The place names given in the list are those where the name of the tree could be found in use. This does not exclude the possibility that the same name is used somewhere else as well, either for the same tree or for another species.

ābnūs, ebony (*Diospyros ebenum*)
āfrā, maple tree (*Acer insigne*) in Šāhī, Sārī, Miyāndareh, Katūl, Ḥajjīlar (Caspian provinces). A big, good-looking tree giving a fine-grained light-colored timber.
āj, maple tree (*Acer laetum*) in Lāhījān (Caspian provinces)
ālāš, beech tree (*Fagus silvatica* or *F. orientalis*) in Manjīl, Kūh-e Darfak, Kelārdašt (Caspian provinces)
ālaš, beech tree (*Fagus silvatica*) in Tališ (Caspian provinces)
aṃbeh, see *deraḫt-e aṃbeh*
ambū, *lambū*, *sepestān*, Sebestens tree (*Cordia myxa*, *C. crenata*) in Bandar ᶜAbbās region
anāb, jujube tree (*Ziziphus vulgaris*); also *senjed*
anjīlī, ironwood tree (*Parrotia persica*) timber used for under-water piles in structural work in Caspian provinces
aqāqī, *aqāqiyā*, acacia tree (*Acacia* spp.)
aqāqī-ye jangalī, a forest variety of acacia
āqčeh-aġāč, elm tree (*Zelkova crenata*) in Gardaneh, Čenārān (Turkoman Steppe)
āqčeh-qaiyīn, maple tree (*Acer monspesassulanum*) in Manjīl (Caspian provinces)
āqṭī, elder tree (*Sambucus niger*)
ār, ash tree (*Fraxinus excelsior*, *F. oxyphylla*) in Šīrāz; see also *zabān-gonješk*
arjan, wild bitter almond tree (*Amygdalus* spp.); *cf.* place name: Dašt-e arjan (Fārs)
arjevān, Judas tree (*Cercis siliquastrum*) wild in Lūristān and Gorgān
ävers̱, cyprus tree (*Cupressus sempervirens*) (Caspian provinces); according to J. E. Polak, *ävers̱* is *Juniperus excelsa*.[6]
āzād, *āzādār*, elm tree (*Zelkova crenata*); the hard wood of this tree is used for the manufacture of the load-carrying shoulder bars of Gīlān and Bandar ᶜAbbās. Cf. E. Gauba, "Botanische Reisen in der persischen Dattelregion," Vol. 2, p. 30
azār, cedar tree (*Cedrus* spp.)
azdār, elm tree (*Zelkova crenata*) in ᶜAlīābād and Ḥajjīlar (Caspian provinces); cf. *āzād*, *āzādār*
azgīl, medlar tree (*Mespilus* spp.) wood for the manufacture of pipe stems
bādām, almond tree (*Amygdalus communis*)
bādām-e talḫ, bitter almond (*A. amara*)
bādām-e šīrīn, sweet almond (*A. dulcis*)
bādām-e kāġẕī, almond var. (*A. fragilis*)
bādām-e aržan, almond var. (*A. orientalis*)
bādām-e boḫūrak, almond var. (*A. orientalis*) (Gīlān)
bādām-e kūhī, (*A. scoparia*) mountain almond
bādrank, lemon tree (*Citrus medica*)
bailak, maple (*Acer insigne*) in Gīlān
bālank, lemon tree (*Citrus medica*)
baᶜlāveh-sir, ash tree (*Fraxinus excelsior*) in ᶜAlīābād, Gorgān (Caspian provinces)
ballūṭ, oak tree (*Quercus castaneifolia*, *Q. iberica*, *Q. atropatena*) in Caspian provinces (*Q. persica*) southwest of Šīrāz in altitudes up to 6,500 feet (E. Gauba, *op. cit.*, p. 46).
bān, see *vān*
ban, *baneh*, Persian turpentine tree (*Pistacia acuminata*, P. Khinjuk)
baqam, *baqem*, logwood (*Haemotoxylon campechianum*)
baqem-e benafš, logwood (*Haemotoxylon campechianum*)
baqem-e qermez, sapan wood (*Caesalpina sapan*)
bīd, willow (*Salix micaus*, *S. fragilis*)
bīd-jūdān(ak), a willow variety (*Salix zygostemon*)
bīd-e majnūn, weeping willow (*Salix babylonica*)
bīd-mašk, musk willow (*Salix aegyptiaca*)
bīd-e muᶜallaq, weeping willow (*Salix babylonica*)
bīd-e siyāh, a willow variety (*Salix* of unknown variety)
bīd-e zard, a willow variety (*Salix acmophylla*)
bīd-ḫeštī, willow (*Salix fragilis*)
bondoq, nicker tree (*Caesalpina bonducella*)

[5] E. Gauba, author of "Botanische Reisen in der persischen Dattelregion"; *Arbres et Arbustes des forêts caspiennes de l'Iran*; "Ein Besuch der kaspischen Wälder Nordpersiens."

[6] J. E. Polak, *Persien, das Land und seine Bewohner.*

buzbarak, maple tree (*Acer laetum*)
buzbarg, *buzvālak*, maple tree (*Acer laetum*) in Šahristān, Gorgān, Miyāndareh, Katūl, ᶜAlīābād, Dāmiyān, Ḥajjīlar (Caspian provinces)
čandal, see *ṣandal*
čapčapī, cornel tree (*Cornus sanguinea*)
čenār, plane tree (*Platanus orientalis*)
čīd, maple wood (*Acer laetum*)
čūb-e alūbalū, cherry wood (*Prunus cerasus*)
čūb-e anār, pomegranate wood (*Punica granatum*)
čūb-e čopoq, wild cherry wood (*Cerasus orientalis*)
čūb-e funduq, hazel wood (*Corylus avelana*)
čūb-e gerdū, walnut wood (*Juglans regia*)
čūb-e golābī, pearwood (*Pyrus communis*)
čūb-e ḫanjak, turpentine wood (*Pistacia acuminata*)
čūb-e jangalī, general name for forest timber, especially beech wood
čūb-e līmū(n), lemon wood (*Citrus limonum*)
čūb-e nāranj, orangewood (*Citrus* spp.), a hard light-colored wood used in Šīrāz for inlaid work.
čūb-e sīb, apple wood (*Pyrus malus*)
čūb-e tūt, mulberry wood (*Morus alba*, *M. nigra*) for the manufacture of musical instruments.
čūb-e zardālū, apricot wood (*Prunus persica*, *P. armeniaca*) for the manufacture of weaver's shuttles.
dāġdārān, nettle tree (*Celtis caucasia*); cf. *dāġdār*, meaning "spotted," "marked."
damīr-aġājī, ironwood tree (*Parrotia persica*) in Āstārā and Ḥajjīlar (Caspian provinces)
dardār, elm tree (*Ulmus campestris*)
dārvan, elm tree (*Ulmus campestris*)
deleh-kūčī, Caucasian wing nut (*Pterocarya caucasia*) in Gīlān. The wood of the wing nut tree is traded in Europe as Caucasian walnut, but is not to be mixed up with genuine walnut (*Juglans regia*), likewise a native of Persia.
deraḫt-e ḫormā, palm tree (*Phoenix dactilifera*)
deraḫt-e aṃbeh, mango tree (*Mangifera indica*) in Balūčistān
esfandān, maple tree (*Acer laetum*)
esfīdār, white poplar (*Populus alba*)
espīdār, white poplar (*Populus alba*)
fūfel, palisander wood, rosewood (*Dalbergia* spp.); *fūfel* is originally the name for the betel nut
fuzaqareh, a tree akin to the wing nut tree (*Pterocarya fraxinifolia*) in Ḥajjīlar (Gorgān)
gandalāš, maple tree (*Acer insigne*) in Āstārā (Gīlan) a big, good-looking tree, giving a fine-grained light-colored timber
ġār, laurel tree (*Laurus nobilis*)
garūn-sangī, tropical almond tree (*Terminalia catappa*)
garḫat-e eṣmet, Caucasian elm tree (*Ulmus pedunculata*) in Gīlān
gaz, tamarisk tree (*Tamarix* spp.)
gaz-e ḫānsār, gall tamarisk, common tamarisk (*Tamarix gallica*)
gaz-e māzej, manna tamarisk (*Tamarix pentandra*)
geliyūn, elder tree (*Sambucus ebulus*) in Tūnehkabūn (Caspian provinces)
gerezm, a variety of elm wood
ġez ᶜelfī, Kurdistān oak (*Quercus valonia*)
gol-abrīšim, silk tree (*Albizzia julibrissin*)
ḥabb-ulġār, turpentine pistachio tree (*Pistacia Khinjuk*)
ḫalanj, probably tree-heath or briar wood (*Erica arborea*); gives a fine-grained timber used for carved beams and the manufacture of bowls. Cf. A. U. Pope and P. Ackerman, eds., *A Survey of Persian Art*, p. 3607, and F. Steingass, *A Comprehensive Persian English Dictionary*, p. 472.
ḫanjeh, Tamarind tree (*Tamarindus indica*)
ḫormā, see *deraḫt-e ḫormā*
ḫormālū, persimmon tree (*Diospyrus* spp.)
ḫūᵓōl, Caucasian wing nut (*Pterocarya caucasia*) in Tūnehkabūn
jad-mou, grapevine (*Vitis vinifera*); the wood of the grapevine (*čūb-e mou*) is used for inlaid woodwork
jag, *jaġ*, Sissoo tree (*Dalbergia sissoo Roxb.*) indigenous in Balūčistān
janūb, fig tree (*Ficus carica*) in Fārs and Ḫorāsān
julār, beech tree (*Fagus silvatica* or *F. orientalis*) in Nūr (Caspian provinces)
kabūdeh, green pool poplar (*Populus dilatata*)
kačf, oriental beech tree (*Carpinus orientalis*) in Gorgān, ᶜAlīābād, Miyāndareh (Caspian provinces)
kačf, common beech tree (*Carpinus betulus*) in Katūl (Caspian provinces)
kahūr, mesquite tree (*Prosopis spicigera*) indigenous in Persian Gulf region. Cf. E. Gauba, *op. cit.*, Vol. 2, p. 15. The hard, dark wood of the tree is used for the stems of opium pipes.
kāj, pine tree (*Pinus eldarica*) indigenous in Armenia near lake Eldara. Cf. E. Gauba, *Arbres et Arbustes des forêts caspiennes de l'Iran.*
kandar, lote-fruit tree (*Ziziphus vulgaris*, *Z. nummularia*) in Bandar ᶜAbbās; see also *kunār*

karb, maple tree (*Acer campestre*) in Nūr, Darr-e Čalūs (Caspian provinces)

karf, maple tree (*Acer campestre*) in Kelārdašt (Caspian provinces)

karkaf, maple tree (*Acer platanoides*) in Ziyārat-e Nazdīk (Gorgān)

karkū, maple tree (*Acer opulifolium*) in Damiyān, Ziyārat, Katūl (Caspian provinces) (*Acer monspesassulanum*) in Katūl, Ḫorāsān, and Sarhadrūs

karzul, common beech tree (*Carpinus betulus*) in Kelārdašt (Caspian provinces)

kaikō(m), a maple wood (*Acer* spp.) variety from Kurdistān

kavījeh, kevīj, kevīž, medlar (*Mespilus* spp.) a wood from Kermān used for the manufacture of mouthpieces of water and opium pipes; cf. *azgīl*

kīkam, maple tree (*Acer laetum*) in Āstārā and Kūh-e Darfak (Caspian provinces)

Kīš, boxtree (*Buxus sempervirens*) in Lāhījān (Caspian provinces)

kīv, lime tree (*Tilia rubra*) in Āstārā (Gīlan)

kūč(ī), Caucasian wing nut tree (*Pterocarya fraxinifolia, P. caucasia*) in Rūdbār and Darfak (Caspian provinces)

kuf, lime tree (*Tilia rubra*) in Darfak (Caspian provinces)

kunār, lote-fruit tree (*Ziziphus vulgaris, Z. nummularia, Z. spina Christi*) in Fārs, Kermān, and Bandar ᶜAbbās. The hard wood of this tree is used in Bandar ᶜAbbās for the manufacture of load-carrying shoulder bars. Cf. E. Gauba, "Botanische Reisen in der persischen Dattelregion," Vol. 2, pp. 14, 30.

lambū, see *ambū*

lārak, Caucasian wing nut tree (*Pterocarya fraxinifolia, P. caucasia*) in Nūr and Gorgān (Caspian provinces)

lark, Caucasian wing nut tree in Katūl (Māzandarān)

larḫ, Caucasian wing nut tree in Māzandarān; cf. *lārak*

lī, beech tree (*Ulmus* spp.) in Lāhījān and Darfak (Caspian provinces)

livar, oriental hornbeam tree (*Carpinus orientalis*) in Nūr (Caspian provinces)

lour, lūr, Indian fig tree (*Ficus altissima*) in Bandar ᶜAbbās

malaj, elm tree (*Ulmus* spp.) in Šīrgāh, Katūl, Kelārdašt, ᶜAlīābād, Dāmiyān, Ziyārat (Caspian provinces)

mamraz, mimraz, European hornbeam tree (*Carpinus betulus*) in Šīrgāh, Sārī, Ašraf, and Miyāndareh (Caspian provinces)

mašk-bīd, musk willow (*Salix aegyptiaca*)

mašk-fīk, musk willow (*Salix aegyptiaca*) in Katūl (Caspian provinces)

mimraz, see *mamraz*

mirs, beech tree (*Fagus silvatica, F. orientalis*) in Gadūk and Fīrūzkūh (Alburz)

mūtāl, Caucasian wing nut tree (*Pterocaryā fraxinifolia*) in Gīlān

namdār, lime tree (*Tilia rubra*) in Nūr, Šīrgāh, Katūl (Caspian provinces), Tehrān; cf. *narmdār*

nāranj, orange tree (*Citrus* spp.)

narmdār, lime tree (*Tilia rubra*) in Ḥajjīlar (Gorgan); cf. *namdār*

nārvan, cultivated elm (*Ulmus campestris, U. densa*); is grafted onto *vesg*

nīl, elm tree (*Zelkova crenata*) in Āstārā (Gīlān); cf. *āzād*

pājūb, poplar (*Populus euphratica*) in Damġān, Qair, Nirīz

pak, maple tree (*Acer laetum*) in Kelārdašt (Caspian provinces)

pālād, lime tree (*Tilia rubra*)

pālās, lime tree (*Tilia rubra*) in Manjīl (Caspian provinces)

palās, maple tree (*Acer insigne*) a big, good-looking tree, giving a fine-grained, light-colored timber. In Kūh-e Darfak (Caspian provinces).

palat, maple tree in Lāhījān (Caspian provinces)

pisteh ḥaqīqī, pistachio tree (*Pistacia vera*) in Caspian provinces; cf. E. Gauba, "Ein Besuch der kaspischen Wälder Nordpersiens." *Pistacia mutica* in Zagros Mountains, A tree of 18 to 25 feet height; cf. E. Gauba, "Botanische Reisen in der persischen Dattelregion," p. 46.

qairā aġāj, Caucasian elm tree (*Ulmus pedunculata*)

qaraqač, cultivated elm tree (*Ulmus densa*) in Āẕarbaijān

qezelgoz, beech tree (*Fagus silvatica* or *F. orientalis*) in Āstārā (Gīlān)

qoreh āqāj, elm tree (*Ulmus* spp.) in Āstārā (Gīlān)

rāj, beech tree (*Fagus silvatica* or *F. orientalis*) in Manjīl (Caspian provinces)

rāš, beech tree; cf. *rāj*

razdār, alder tree (*Alnus subcordata*) in Āstārā (Gīlān)

safīdār, white poplar, aspen (*Populus alba*) in Fārs, Iṣfahān, and Caspian provinces

safīd-palot, white poplar (*Populus alba*) in Lāhījān, Singarderešt (Caspian provinces), and Fārs

šāh-ballūṭ, chestnut tree (*Castanea vesca*)

saḫdār, yew tree (*Taxus baccata*) in Siyārat and Dāmiyān (Caspian provinces); *saḫt* means "hard"

šāh-tūt, black mulberry tree (*Morus nigra*)

sāj, (Skr. *sāga*) teakwood (*Tectona grandis*)

salam, acacia (*Acacia* spp.) in Fārs, Lār; bark of tree is used for tanning leather

šamšād, boxtree (*Buxus sempervirens*) in Āstārā (Gīlān), Šīrāz, Iṣfahān

ṣandal, sandalwood (*Santalum album*). According to Isḥaq ibn Imrān, sandalwood was imported from China via India (Hindi *čandal*, Skr. *candana*); cf. G. Ferrand, *Relations de voyages*, p. 279.

ṣandal-e surḫ, red sandalwood (*Pterocarpus santalinus*)

saqiz safīd, white turpentine pistachio tree (*Pistacia terebinthus*)

sar, ash tree (*Fraxinus excelsior*) in Katūl (Caspian provinces)

šār, boxtree (*Buxus sempervirens*) in Šīrgāh (Caspian provinces)

sarbīn, cypress tree (*Cupressus sempervirens*) in Manjīl, Kūh-e Darfak (Caspian provinces)

sarv, cypress tree (*Cupressus sempervirens*) cf. New Persian dialects: *sarb*, *salb*, *saul*, *sul*; also place names: Sarvestān, Qalᶜ-e sarv, Qalᶜ-e sulī, Tang-e saulak. Already mentioned in Darius' building inscription of Susa as *tarmiš*, meaning "cypress" or "building timber." Cf. W. Hinz, *Iran*, p. 134.

sarv-e āzād, a cypress variety (*var. horizontalis*) up to 3,000-feet altitude in Alburz mountains in large formations; same in Balūčistān (*var. fastigata*), already shown on bas-reliefs in Persepolis. Cf. E. Gauba, "Botanische Reisen in der persischen Dattelregion," pp. 51–52.

sarv-e kūhī, cypress tree (*Cupressus horizontalis*)

šelīl, smooth almond tree (*Persica loevis*)

šemšād, see *šamšād*

senjed, 1. jujube tree (*Ziziphus vulgaris*); 2. sorb wood (*Eleagnus angustifolia*)

sepestān, see *ambū*

šīldār, elm tree (*Ulmus* spp.) in Ḥajjīlar (Turkoman Steppe)

šīrdār, 1. maple tree (*Acer laetum*) in Rūdbār, Čālūs, Nūr, Šīrgāh (Caspian provinces); 2. yew tree (*Taxus baccata*) in Āstārā (Gīlān)

šīrḫešk, a tree issuing manna (*Cotoneaster nummularia*)

šūḫtāl, yew tree (*Taxus baccata*) in Katūl (Caspian provinces)

sūkūt, musk willow (*Salix aegyptiaca*) in Ḥajjīlar (Gorgān)

sumāq, sumac tree (*Rhus coriaria*); leaves of this tree are used for tanning.

šūn, elder tree (*Sambucus ebulus*)

surḫehdār, 1. yew tree (*Taxus baccata*) in Ziyārat and Dāmiyān (Caspian provinces); 2. alder tree (*Alnus glutinosa*) in Tehrān, Iṣfahān used to produce a red dye.

tabarḫūn, see *ṭabarḫūn*

ṭabarḫūn, the red Hyrkanian willow (*Ziziphus jujuba vulgaris*)

tabrīzī, black poplar (*Populus nigra*, *P. pyramidalis*)

taġar, oriental beech tree (*Carpinus orientalis*) in Katūl (Caspian provinces)

taġār, common beech tree (*Carpinus betulus*) in Gorgān, ᶜAlīābād, Ramiyān, Ḥajjīlar (Caspian provinces)

tal, maple tree (*Acer monspesassulanum*) in Pol-e Safīd (Caspian provinces)

tamar-hindī, tamarind (*Tamarindus indica*)

tilak, ash tree (*Fraxinus excelsior*) in Lāhījān (Caspian provinces)

tūġdān, *tūgdān*, nettle tree (*Celtis caucasia*)

tūseh, alder tree (*Alnus subcordata*) in Gīlān, Māzandarān, and Gorgān; *Alnus barbata* in Georgistān; *Planera crenata* in Šīrāz

tūskāh, alder tree (*Alnus subcordata*, *A. glutinosa*) in Gīlān, Māzandarān, and Gorgān

tūt, mulberry tree (*Morus alba*)

ūjā, elm tree (*Ulmus* spp.) in Šāhī, Sārī, and Katūl (Caspian provinces)

ūlās, common beech tree (*Carpinus betulus*) in Āstārā, Manjīl, Darfak (Caspian provinces)

vān or *bān*, known in Kāšān as "spade handle wood;" *čūb-e bīl dastī* seems to be myrobalan tree (*Prunus cerasifera*) grown in Kohrūd mountains

vašm, wood used for making tool handles grown near Iṣfahān and in Kargez mountains, probably dogwood (*Cornus mascula*)

vezg, wild elm tree (*Ulmus campestris*)

vorṣ, cypress tree (*Cupressus horizontalis*) in Lūristān

zaitūn, olive tree (*Olea europea*)

zaitūn-e talḫ, margosa tree (*Melia azadirachta*)

zān, beech tree (*Fagus* spp.); arrows and spears are made from its wood.

zardālū, see *čūb-e zardālū*

zarīn, cypress tree (*Cupressus sempervirens*, *var. horizontalis*) in Manjīl and Kūh-e Darfak (Caspian provinces)

zabān gonješk, ash tree (*Fraxinus excelsior*, *F. oxyphylla*)

Sawyer

Timber getting, i.e., the felling of trees and their preparation, is a worthwhile occupation only in the Caspian provinces, and there it is mainly done by peasants when no work is to be done in the fields. The dense undergrowth of the forest (*jangal*) is cleared with a long-handled brush-cutting knife (*dās*). The trees are partly cut with an axe (*tabar*) and on the other side of the trunk with a coarse cross-cutting saw (*kalleh-bor*). The blades (*tīġ*) of these saws are imported today, but handles (*dasteh-arreh*) are made by the local blacksmith and the teeth (*dandān*) kept sharp by the sawyers according to the requirements of the timber. Since transport of the whole log would be too difficult in those regions, the timber getters cut it into pieces of suitable length, and trim them to an approximate square with an adze (*tīšeh*). This important tool has a well-fitting socket (*lūleh*) and its edge (*dam-e tīšeh*) is kept sharp with a honing stone. The trimmed logs are rolled over a saw pit (*čāleh-čūb-borī*, Fig. 111) for marking and sawing. Thick branches and smaller parts of the trunk are taken home by the sawyers. They are cut and split into thin boards for fruit packing cases (*ja*ᶜ*beh*), welcome homework for the long winter months. Otherwise unsuitable wood is converted into charcoal (*zoġāl-e čūb*), which still sells well despite the increased use of oil for heating purposes.

On the high plateau, timber (*čūb*) is cut into beams (*tīr*), planks (*alvār*), or boards (*taḫteh*) by specialists, the sawyers (*čūbbor*, *arreh-kaš*, *mošar-kaš*), except in the case of the small village carpenter. The sawyers work in teams of two under contract to cut the carpenter's timber near his workshop or on the building site. They carry their equipment with them. It consists of the sawyer's jack (*ḫarak*, *ḫarak-e čūbborī*, *ḫarak-e arreh-kašī*, Fig. 112), a two-handed saw (*arreh-dō-sar*), an adze, and some marking tools. Heavy roof joists (*ḥammāl*, *ardī*) are only trimmed square with an adze (Fig. 113), lighter ceiling joists (*borm*) are often sawn into half logs (*lapeh*, *āleh*), and logs of more valuable timber are usually trimmed before they are cut into boards. The sawyer's jack is made up of two

Figure 111 Marking Timber before Sawing above a Saw Pit

Figure 112 Sawyers at Work

Figure 113 Trimming a Log

beams (*čūb-e ḫarak*) arranged in V-form and held in position by a cross beam (*pīš-e ḫarak*) that, in turn, is fixed to the main beams by two iron clamps (*mīḫ-e ḫarak*). The whole jack is lifted by a tail support (*dombī*).

After the log has been trimmed, the sawyers take a marking string (*rīsmān*) that has been colored either with red marking chalk (*gel-e oḫrā, gel-e māšī*), which is hematite (iron oxide) from the island of Qešm in the Persian Gulf, or with a yellow powder (*gel-e armanī*), which is limonite, coming from Armenia. The string is held tight over the position where the first cut is to go and with a light flick the chalk is transferred to the timber (Fig. 111). With the aid of two marking gauge blocks (*andāzeh, paimāneh*) of the thickness of the boards to be cut, parallel lines are marked all over the log (*ḫaṭṭ kašīdan*).

The log is now transferred to the jack, and the leading sawyer (*čūbbor, arreh-dehandeh*) mounts the higher side of the jack and leads the saw along the marked line while his offsider (*arreh-kaš*) pulls the saw with heavy strokes from beneath the log. For large logs a portal-like structure is erected that holds the log in a horizontal position, the leading sawyer standing on top of the log and his assistant underneath. All cuts are made through two-thirds of the length, the log is then reversed, and the cuts are completed from the other end. In order to prevent jamming of the saw, the cut is spread open by a wooden wedge (*gōveh*). For the cutting of thinner boards a larger bow or gate saw (*arreh-qabāreh, arreh-qavāreh, arreh-māšū*) is used that enables the use of a thinner saw blade (*tīġ-e arreh*), held tight in the bow frame.

At this stage the sawyer considers the needs of the carpenter and the cabinet-maker. Wherever possible, the splint wood (*javān, kenāreh, ḥāšiyeh*) is first cut away. These splint boards (*pošteh*) are set aside for the cores of veneer work or other less important purposes. Then the heart wood (*pīr, maġz*) is cut. The sawyer is often instructed to cut the timber to the best advantage of a nice grain (*mouj*), particularly for panel boards and veneers (*rūkaš*). When the whole log has been cut, all the boards are placed in a heap with small slats separating them from one another, to allow drying and to prevent warping (*tāb, pīč*). Sawdust (*ḫāk-e arreh*) is carefully collected and sold to the public bath (*ḥammām*) for fuel.

As all this work is done by hand, it is understandable that the sawyer's craft is dying out fast, as for a number of years sawmills in the forests of the Caspian provinces have been able to supply the larger towns with cheaper machine-cut timber, supplemented by imported and locally manufactured plywood (*seh-lā'ī*).

Carpenter, Joiner, Cabinetmaker

Although timber is a relatively rare commodity in most parts of Persia today, the wood worker has always had opportunities to apply his skill, and he is still one of the most respected artisans. Darius mentions in the Susa charter[7] that the woodwork for his palace had been done by men from Sardis and Egypt. The great halls in Susa and Persepolis had walls of stone and brickwork, but the roofs were supported by an intricate system of wooden beams. Charred beams measuring 7 by 10 inches have been unearthed in 1936.[8] These roof beams rested on stone or wooden columns,[9] and King Darius is shown on some of the stone bas-reliefs of the court of reception as sitting on a beautifully carved throne, obviously made of wood.[10] When, during the reign of the

[7] R. Ghirshman, *op. cit.*, p. 166.
[8] E. F. Schmidt, *The Treasury of Persepolis*, p. 19.
[9] *Ibid.*, pp. 20, 54.
[10] *Ibid.*, p. 22, and Fig. 14.

Sasanians (212 to 651 A.D.), the vaulted arch and the cupola replaced the flat roof, tie bars of cedar wood were used extensively to take up horizontal thrust from the arched roofs.

At the time of the Arab conquest (about 650 A.D.) the woodworking crafts were fully established. Mosques often had wooden columns and roof structures; richly ornamented pulpits (*mimbar*) were widely used, ceilings and window openings were ornamented with intricate lattice work; wooden lanterns crowned the tops of minarets, and carved doors added to the dignity of the buildings.[11] Woodwork must also have been used extensively in private homes. Muqaddasī, describing the early centuries after the conquest, says[12] that the city of Ray had a large export industry of wooden products, especially wooden combs and bowls, made from the famous *ḫalanj* wood coming from the Ṭabaristān (Caspian) forests. Qazvīnī confirms this[13] for the thirteenth century A.D. and further praises Ray for its good furniture, also mentioning other places in Persia known for their wood industry such as Ṭarq near Iṣfahān, Gorjaniyeh, and Qom.

That the carpenter's work was well respected can be seen from the fact that some of their products carry their names in inscriptions. Here is one example of many: the richly carved doors of Afušteh near Natanz, dated 1428 A.D., are signed by the woodworker: "done by master Ḥusayn ibn ᶜAlī, joiner and cabinetmaker of Ābādeh."[14] This place, south of Iṣfahān, is famous to this day for its fine wood carving. Olearius, a member of the embassy that the Duke of Holstein-Gottorp sent to the Imperial court at Iṣfahān during the sixteenth century, was much impressed by the fine woodwork he saw in Persia. He says[15] above all he admired the plane tree wood (*čenār*) much used for doors and windows and comments that "when rubbed with a certain oil it becomes finer than our walnut."

The modern woodworker handles a wide range of products such as builder's joinery, furniture, frames for the weaver's looms, wooden locks, and the woodwork on coaches and motor vehicles. There is no clear distinction between carpenter, joiner, and cabinetmaker; they are all commonly called *najjār*. If a distinction were required, a building carpenter would be called *najjār-e seftkār*, a roof truss specialist would be called *ḫarpǎkūb*, and a cabinetmaker *farangī-sāz* or *mobl-sāz*. Woodworkers in technical schools are referred to as *dorūdgar* or *dorūdkār*, a revival of an old name for this trade. Specialists in door and window joinery are often called *dar-sāz* or *ālat-sāz*, and *qāb-sāz* or *qāb-kūb* is a man who specializes in paneled ceilings.

Until recently all carpenters worked on the ground, pressing their work against a wooden block (*mīḫ-e kār*) rammed into the earth. Because of European influence a carpenter's bench is coming into general use. It may vary from a simple arrangement as shown in Fig. 114 (*ḫarpošt, dastgāh-e randeh, dastgāh-e najjārī*) to a regular woodworking bench (*mīz-e kār*). Commonly used marking tools are a straight-edge (*barāstī*), a carpenter's square (*gūniyā*), a variable angle gauge (*gūniyā-bāzšō, gūniyā vāšō*), a bevel gauge (*gūniyā fārsī*), an iron scriber (*derafš*), and a parallel marking gauge (*ḫaṭṭ-kaš, ḫaṭṭ-kaš-e tīġ-dār*); the latter consists of gauge bar (*tīrak*), a gauge body (*taneh*), and a marking point (*nōk* or *mīḫ*). Circles and larger distances are marked with a pair of compasses (*pargār*).

[11] A. U. Pope and P. Ackerman, eds., *A Survey of Persian Art*, p. 903.
[12] *Ibid.*, p. 2607.
[13] B. Spuler, *Die Mongolen in Iran*, p. 437.
[14] A. U. Pope and P. Ackerman, *op. cit.*, p. 2621.
[15] *Ibid.*, p. 2625.

Figure 114 A Carpenter's Bench

Figure 115 Planing Against a Bench Stop

The planing work is held in position by a bench stop (*nīš-e dastgāh*, Fig. 115).

Apart from the large two-handed saw of the sawyer, which the carpenter uses too, he has a heavy crosscut saw (*arreh-qaṭᶜkon*) for cutting timber to length (*qaṭᶜ kardan*) and a bow saw (*arreh-qabāreh, arreh-qavāreh, arreh-māšū*) for ripping work, whereas the carpenter handling mainly the soft willow saplings is satisfied with a medium-sized bushman's saw (*arreh-kalāfī, arreh-kamānī*). Ordinary bench work is done with a common hand saw (*arreh-dastī, arreh-dom-rūbāh*) or with still smaller hand saws (*arreh-ẓarīf, arreh-laṭīf*). For dovetailing and finer cabinetmaking a tenon saw (*arreh-boreš̌t, arreh-ṭarḥ-e farang*) with a heavy iron back (*pošt*, Fig. 116) is used. The Persian carpenter prefers a thin saw blade. Figure 117 shows one mounted in the form of a small bow saw (*arreh-čakī*). The frame (*čahār-čūb, dār-arreh*) is held apart by a stay (*čūb-e kamārī*) and a cord (*zeh*) tightens the blade by twisting with a wooden tongue (*gōveh*). A hole saw (*arreh-mārī, arreh-nōkī*) is shown in Fig. 118; a fretsaw is known as *arreh-mūhī*.

All saws in Persia are pulled toward the operator, and teeth are cut correspondingly. The setting (*čap-ō-rāst*) is done with a setting iron (*āhan-e čap-ō-rāst-kon*), setting pliers (*gāz-e čap-ō-rāst-kon*), or a setting punch (*som̱beh*). For sharpening, the carpenter uses a cant file (*souhān-e dō-dam*) or a half-round file (*souhān-e gord-e māhī*).

Since sawing and planing mean hard manual work, prior to planing the timber is often roughed near to its final size in a more efficient way by the use of an adze (*tīšeh*, Fig. 119) or an axe (*tabar*).

The original Persian plane (*randeh, randeh-fārsī*), which is still widely used, is distinctly different from the imported European plane (*randeh-farangī*). Instead of the knob (*šāḥ*) of the latter it has two handles (*dasteh*) and is therefore often called *randeh-dō-dast* (Fig. 120).

The carpenter usually makes his own planes. The body (*kūleh*) is cut out of a piece of seasoned hard wood, great attention being paid to a perfectly straight sole (*kaf-e randeh, kafkaš*); the mouth (*gelōʾī*) of the plane is carefully carved out to allow the shavings (*pūšāl*) to flow out easily. The plane iron (*tīġ*) is manufactured by the local blacksmith, in these days mainly from discarded car springs. The iron is held in position by a wooden wedge (*barōšāl banabšāl, banāfšāl, gōveh*). The ordinary jack plane (*randeh qāšī*) has a single iron, and therefore is often called *randeh-yak-tīġ*, i.e., single-iron plane, whereas the smoothing plane (*randeh pardāẖt*) has a backing iron (*pošt-e tīġ*) as well and is consequently also called *randeh-dō-tīġ*, i.e., double-ironed plane. If the modern adjustable European plane is used, it is called *randeh darajeh-dār* or *randeh-motaḥarrek*. Since, until recently, no machines have been available to the carpenter, a great variety of special planes is at hand, such as the following:

Figure 116 Tenon Saw and Grease Pot

Figure 117 A Bow Saw

Figure 118 A Hole Saw and Marking Gauge

Figure 119 Roughing with an Adze

Figure 120 A Double-Handled Plane

To prepare the joints of boards for gluing there is the large jointing plane (*randeh-dastgāh, randeh-ṭūlānī, randeh-boland, randeh-fouġān*, Mašhad). The edges of windows and doors are planed with a sash plane (*randeh-baġal, baġal-e dōrāheh*). A much used plane is the rabbet plane (*košterā, košreh*, Fig. 121). If a board is to

Figure 121 A Rabbet Plane

be planed to a certain thickness a rabbet groove is planed first all around the board with this plane, and the remaining wood is then roughed to size with the common jack plane. Curved surfaces are worked with a convex compass plane (*randeh-sīneh, randeh-kaf-e sīneh, sīneh-rand*); hollow surfaces with a concave compass plane (*randeh-kās, kās-rand*).

The Persian woodworker likes to ornament his work with a variety of profiled beads, and for this purpose has a molding plane (*randeh-abzār*) with a number of exchangeable irons. The profiles and their names are shown in Fig. 122. For planing the bottom of recessed surfaces a routing plane (*randeh-tahrand, randeh-kafrand*) is used. Surfaces to be glued are roughed for a better grip with a toothing plane (*randeh-ḫāšī* or *ḫāšū, randeh-ḫašḫāš*, Tabrīz). Plane grooves for paneling work are cut with a grooving plane (*randeh-ye koneškāf*). Prior to sanding and polishing, the wood is smoothed with a scraper (*līseh*) which is sharpened with a hard burnishing steel (*maṣqal*).

Another group of widely used tools are the chisels. Ordinary chisels (*šafreh, šifr, moġār*) are in use for general work. A heavy variety for deep mortise (*kām, kūm*) cutting is shown in Fig. 123 (*eškīneh, eskenā, uskineh, esgeneh*). A hollow or gouging chisel (*moġār-e gīlōʾī, galūʾī, moġār-e lūleh*) cuts rounded surfaces, and a very narrow chisel is called *moġār-e kebrītī*. The handles for all these chisels are made of *vašm* wood growing near Iṣfahān and supplied from there to other parts of the country. The mallets (*toqmāq, toḫmāq, tūqmāq, kedēneh*) have the form of a wooden club (Fig. 123) and are made of *vašm* wood too. If they have the form of a hammer they are referred to as *čakoš-e čūbī*. The ordinary carpenter's hammer for nailing is called *čakoš-e maṭbaqeh* or *maṭvakeh*. Certain finishing work is done with a wood rasp (*souhān-e čūb, souhān-e čūbsāb, čūbsāʾī*). Plane irons and chisels are sharpened on a honing stone (*sang-e sou, sang-e rūmī*); the stone is kept saturated with oil (*rouġan-e čerāġ*), a mixture of linseed oil (*rouġan-e bazrak*) and castor oil (*rouġan-e karčak*). The oil is kept in an oil pot (*ṭās-e rouġan*).

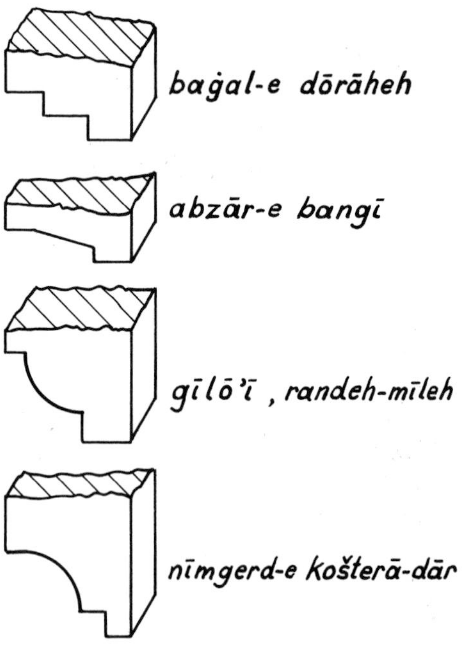

Figure 122 Molding Profiles

Figure 123 A Mortise Chisel and Mallet

Figure 124 A Fiddle or Bow Drill

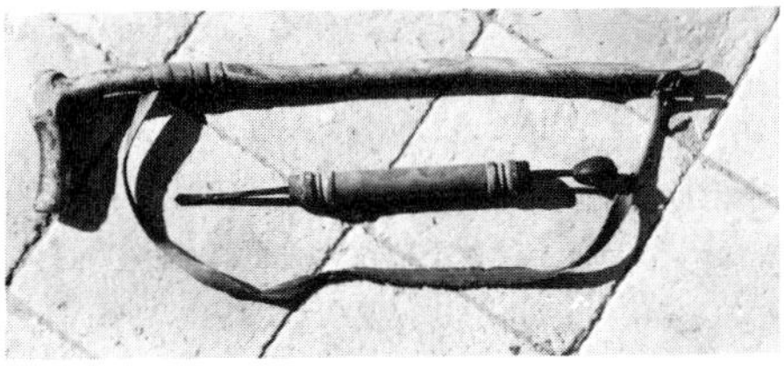

Figure 125 A Fiddle Bow, Spindle, and Nut

A tool with a long tradition is the drill (*mateh*). It is a so-called fiddle or bow drill (*mateh-kamāneh*, Fig. 124). It consists of the spindle (*tan-e mateh*) that carries the drill bit (*tīġ-e mateh*) permanently attached to it. The carpenter has a set of these spindles with different size drill bits at hand. The end of the spindle is of steel and runs inside a hollow knob made from a very hard nut (*mūšk, kolāhak*) specially imported from Arabia for this purpose. The fiddle bow (*kamān*) is made from a piece of wood with a branching end (*seh-šāḫeh*) still attached to it (Fig. 125). One end holds a metal eyelet (*rīzeh*) to which a belt (*tasmeh*) is attached by means of a ring (*ḥalqeh*). Figure 124 shows the drill in operation. The bits used are usually not larger than ⅜-inch in diameter. For bigger holes a ratchet brace (*šotor-galū*) together with drill bits of Western design is nowadays generally used; the drill bits available are screw augers (*mateh-ye pīč, mateh-ye mārpīč*), gouge or shell bits (*mateh-ye qāšuqī, mateh-ye gīlōʾī*), three-pointed center bits (*mateh-ye seh-nīš, mateh-ye bargī*), and small nail bits (*mateh-ye sūzanī*). Occasionally one finds simple gimlets (*mateh-ye dastī*). Countersink bits seem to point to the gunsmith with their names, viz., *mateh-ye ḫazūneh* (magazine drill) and *mateh-ye tūpī* (cannon drill).

Since his timber is expensive, the Persian carpenter is skilled in joining (*etteṣāl kardan*) even small pieces of timber into larger units. There is in the first place the ordinary square joint (*darz*), then the rabbet joint (*dō-rāheh, dō-rāj*), the feather joint (*darz-e qelift*), consisting of two grooved boards joined with a thin feather strip (*qelift*), and the dowel joint (*darz-e mīḫ-čūbī, etteṣāl-e mīḫ-čūbī*), where wooden dowels (*mīḫ-čūbī*) prevent the shift of the boards. For furniture in the stile-and-panel construction, a tongue-and-groove joint (*nar-ō-mādeh*) is widely used. The half-lap joint (*nīm-ō-nīm*) and the mortise-and-tenon joint (*kūm-ō-zabāneh, kām-ō-zabāneh, fāq-ō-zabān*) are the most common ones of the carpenter's joints in building. The corners of frames are usually joined as miters (*fārsī*). To cut the timber to the correct angle for this joint the carpenter has a mitering board (*tang-e fārsī*) on his bench. The corners of drawers (*kašō, jaᶜbeh*) and other parts of furniture are joined at the rear in plain dovetail joint (*dom-e čelčeleh*) and against the front piece in hidden dovetail joint (*dozdī, pūšīdeh*). To conceal the edges of plywood or veneer work, cover strips (*poštband, farang*) are often applied.

Normally the carpenter uses animal glue (*sirīšum*) prepared from bones and leather scraps. For finer work fish glue (*sirīšum-e māhī*) is preferred. It is produced in the Caspian provinces where the air bladders of the sturgeon provide the raw material as a by-product of the caviar industry. For gluing the carpenter has a number of clamps (*qaid, gīr-e dastī, pīč-e dastī, tang*). The names of large sash clamps (*eškanjeh, šekanjeh*) are a reminder of medieval torturing screws. Chests and cupboards are often lined with cloth. The paste used for this work is *seriš-e safīd* and is prepared from the dried and powdered roots of two plants, i.e., desert candle (*Eremurus aucherianus*) and asphodel (*Asphodelus rhamosus*). A few of the carpenter's products are now described in their order of importance: While the bricklayer is erecting the walls, the carpenter sets the frames (*čahārčūb*) for doors (*dar*) and windows (*panjareh*). The frames consist of four parts joined in tenon-and-mortise fashion (Fig. 126): the two vertical posts or jambs (*lengeh-čahārčūb*), the threshold or sill (*āstāneh, āsūneh*), and the door lintel or head (*kolāh-čahārčūb, kolāhak*). In cases where a fanlight or skylight (*katībī, katībeh, ḥafang*) is provided, there is a middle lintel (*kamarkaš*), separating the main window from the skylight. Doors and

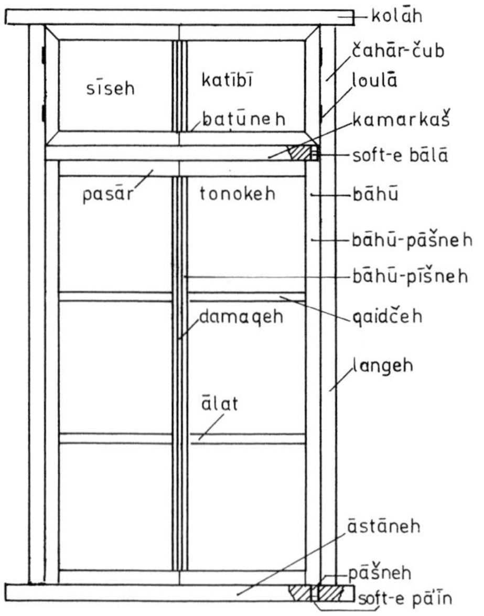

Figure 126 Parts of Door and Window

windows proper are usually made up of two leaves (*lang-e dar* or *lang-e panjareh* respectively). The frames for these (*bāhū, bāʾū*) consist of the outer stiles (*bāhū-pāšneh*), the inner stiles (*bāhū-pīšneh*), and the top and bottom rails (*pasār, pasāv*). The frame is divided into smaller fields by sashbeads (*qaidčeh, ālat*), and the fields are filled in by either wooden panels (*tonokeh*) or glass panes (*šīšeh*), the latter held in position by putty (*baṭūneh*).

To hinge doors and windows, our tubular hinge (*loulā*) has only recently come into use. The old version, already in use during Achaemenian times, provided socket holes (*soft-e pāʾīn*) in the sills and the same in the lintels (*soft-e bālā*). Door and window leaves have their outer stiles extended to form pivots (*pāšneh*) that fit nicely into the sockets. The sockets are usually reinforced by iron plaques (*softeh*).

The work of the ceiling maker (*qāb-sāz*, *qāb-kūb*) should be mentioned next. In past centuries he made those panels and ceilings (*gereh-sāzī*, Fig. 127) in mosques, palaces, and private homes that we still admire for their intricate geometrical design, the selection of suitably colored timber, and the craftsmanship evident from the assembly of the interlocking pieces (Fig. 128). The ceiling maker has the standard equipment of the carpenter; in addition he has a special groove-milling device (*čarḫ-e ālat-sāz*, *ḫarrātī*, Fig. 129). It consists of a drilling spindle (*taneh*) mounted into a frame (*čāranjeleh*). The spindle is driven by a fiddle bow (*kamān*) and its end carries a little milling cutter (*qous*). Figure 129 shows how the prepared ceiling battens (*ālat*) are grooved to receive the panels (*loqāṭ*). Today the majority of houses where a ceiling is provided have it made in plasterwork (see Building Trades). To receive the plaster, small battens (*tōfāl*) are nailed against the ceiling joists. They are made by splitting branch wood, mainly poplar, into halves with an adze. Where in larger communities a man specializes in this work he is called *tōfāl-kūb*.

The cabinetmaker builds the few pieces of furniture needed in a Persian household, such as bedsteads (*taḫt-e ḫwāb*), plain tables (*mīz*), extension tables (*mīz-e kašō'ī*, *mīz-e kašābī*), collapsible tables (*mīz-e tāšō*), and chairs (*ṣandalī*). The table top is called *rū-ye mīz*, the frame *qaid*, *kalāf-e mīz*, and the legs *pāyeh*. After scraping (*līseh kardan*) and sanding (*sombadeh kardan*)

Figure 127 Mosaic Ceiling Work (*partly assembled*)

Figure 128 A Pulpit Panel in Latticework

Figure 129 A Milling Cutter for Ceiling Battens

the surfaces, he fills the pores by rubbing them with pumice stone (*sang-e penz*, *kaf-e dariyā*) and linseed oil, and finally he applies French polish (*lāk alkol*).

The cabinetmakers of Qazvīn were known for a few specialities. One of them was the framed mirror with doors (*jā^cbeh-āyineh*, *āyineh-dardār*) fulfilling a traditional need for the Moslem, not to look into a mirror before the morning ablutions. The mirror doors (*dar-e āyineh*) were therefore made to be closed at night. The carpenter made all the wooden parts, fitted the hinges (*loulā-sīmī*), and applied ornamental metal plaques (*pūlak*), and then handed the whole over to a painter (*naqqāš*) for an elaborate decoration (*šajareh*). Thin black outlines (*siyāh-qalam*) were drawn first, then the ornaments were filled in with bright paint while the natural color of the timber formed the background (Fig. 130). The same type of ornamental

Figure 130 A Mirror Frame with Doors from Qazvīn

treatment was sometimes applied to the large center piece (*ḫānčeh*) of a paneled ceiling, to the center board, likewise called *ḫānčeh*, of a low-footed tray, and finally to the threshold of the living room in well-to-do houses, consisting of a wooden board with painted ornamentation (*takayol*).

Another once flourishing craft was that of the jewelry box maker (*mejrī-sāz*). In 1963 there was only one left in Iṣfahān. The *mejrī-sāz* builds wooden boxes and covers them with leather that is then gilded. Women are the buyers of these boxes (*mejrī*), as they are entitled under Islamic law to keep their personal property locked.

The chest maker (*ṣandūq-sāz*) provides the larger trunks (*ṣandūq*) used to bring the wife's dowry and personal possessions into the bridegroom's house after the wedding. These chests are traditionally nicely ornamented, covered with velvet (*ṣandūq-e maḫmal*), or just painted (*rang kardan*) in bright colors. They have decorative metal strips (*bast*, *nō*, *tark*) nailed to their surfaces, a reminder that these chests were once thief-proof strongboxes. The *ṣandūq-sāz* builds them around four-corner stiles (*pā*) that act as the feet of the chest too. The lid (*dar*) is usually slightly vaulted. Hinges (*loulā*) and hasps (*čeft*) are supplied by the blacksmith. The ornamental strips today are made from discarded tinplate containers (*ḥalabī*) cut into shape and for better appearance beaten into a wooden mold (*čūnō*, *čūb-e nō*). Particular attention is paid to the corner reinforcements (*qāleb-e rūš*). Large chests with compartments of drawers (*ṣandūq-e dardār*) are fitted with front doors.

A side line of the carpenters of Gīlān is the making of wooden sandals (*katal*) fitted with leather thongs.

Wheelwright

Until recently Persia has been a land of camels, donkeys, and pack horses for the transporting of heavy loads. Although there has been some transport on wheels in the province of Āẕarbaijān since early times, especially for harvesting (Fig. 131), it was only during the middle of the nine-

Figure 131 An Oxcart from Āẕarbaijān

teenth century that this mode of transport came into wider use in the center and south. About this time the horse cart (*arābeh, gārī*) was introduced from Russia for the transport of goods and the horse cab (*doroškeh*) from the same country for the transport of people. Today both types are gradually being replaced by motor trucks and cars.

Whereas in England a wheelwright combines in his person the skills of a carpenter and a smith, doing all the work in wood and metal to build a vehicle, his Persian counterpart (Fig. 132) is essentially a carpenter who is responsible for the building of a cart or a cab; the necessary metalwork is done by a farrier or a blacksmith to the order of the wheelwright.

The following is a list of technical terms related to the wheelwright (*gārī-sāz, čarḫ-zan*) and his products:

Figure 132 A Wheelwright Bushing a Wheel

čarḫ, cart wheel
tūp-e gū, hub of wheel
kabīzeh, hub cap
ṭouq (meaning "circle around anything"), tire of cart wheel
jīb, *dolqū*, bush inside hub
parreh, wheel spoke
kūm, *kām* (meaning "throat"), holes in hub to take spokes
šamdūnī, bush to attach spoke to rim
mantaš, wheel rim
zeh-mantaš, edge of rim
rezīn, rubber tire
mīl, cart axle
par, flat plate axle
sar-e mīl, journal on axle
mohreh, nut at end of axle
nalbekī, flange on axle to position wheel
fanar, spring
sag-e dast, support for bogie pivot
sar-qāmeh, eyelet at end of springs
pīč-e sar-qāmeh, bolt in spring shackle
korpī, U-bolts to attach springs
rū-bandeh, iron bar to clamp springs onto axle
čūb-e fanar, wooden block below spring
lā-ye fanar, leaf in laminated spring
šāh-fanar, main leaf
vazīr-e fanar, leaf below main leaf
bačeh-fanar, smallest leaf in spring set
tamām-fanar, full elliptic spring
nīm-fanar, semielliptic spring
dastgīr-e pardar, main beam of coach body
āhan ʿaqab-e otāq, cross beam of coach body
qalbīleh, bolster on bogie pivot
qondaq-e qalbīleh, cross bar on bogie
mīl-e qanbāz, *šorb*, pivot for bogie
qaid, bar connecting carriage pole to bogie
āhrūh, pole support
mālband, carriage pole
rikāb-e mālband, square-shaped iron to receive pole
tah-mālband, eyelet at end of pole
qaiš, pegs to attach drawing harness
čūb-e vezg, elm wood (for making pole)
sar-e qočāk, ferrule at end of pole
šotor-mohreh, iron bar to support footboard
dāyāq-e farš, rear support for footboard
otāq, coach compartment
ṣandalī, driver's seat
otāq-e nešīman, compartment with main seats
ṣandalī-dozd, emergency seats in compartment
rūneh, iron hoop to suspend coach compartment
rikāb-e gelgīr, footboard
gelgīr, mudguard
kalāf-e gelgīr, hoop to support mudguard
korūk, hood of coach
čarm (meaning "skin," "hide," Skr. *čarman*), hood leather
yāʾī, levers to tighten hood
sepāreh, bolt in hood levers
mohreh-yāʾī, nut on lever bolt
sīḫčeh-ye yāʾī (*sīḫčeh* means "spike," "skewer"), hoops on tightening levers
čūb-e korūk, wooden hoops inside hood
penjeh-korūk, iron ends to join all hoops into a fan shape
āhan-e čūb-e korūk, iron joints connecting hoops
dasteh-ye penjeh-korūk, bolt joining hoops
kalāf, iron rail around driver's seat
jāʿbeh, box under driver's seat
pīš-e qalāvor, mudguard in front of driver's feet
zeh-ye varšou, half-round decorative metal beading
ja-čerāġ, lamp holder
čamseh, fabric used for upholstery
dōšak (meaning "cushion"), upholstered seat

Wood Turner

The wood turner is one of the craftsmen in the Persian bazaar who fascinates even the most sophisticated Western observer with his skill. The astonishing part of it is that the lathe used for this work is so simple, almost crude, and yet very fine work is achieved on it.

There must be a long record in the history of this craft. The bas reliefs in Darius' court of reception in Persepolis[16] show the king's throne, footstool, and incense burner stands, all made in beautifully turned woodwork. A more recent witness of the turner's skill was the scientist Alhazen (Ibn al-Haitham), who lived in Basra between 965 and 1039 A.D. Basra at this time was the town with a strong cultural influence from Persia. In his books on optics[17] Alhazen twice mentions the use of a lathe. In one case he used it for the manufacture of parabolic mirrors with which he succeeded in proving his theory of reflection

[16] E. F. Schmidt, *op. cit.*, Fig. 14.

[17] H. J. J. Winter, "The Optical Researches of Ibn al-Haitham," pp. 200, 203, and H. J. J. Winter and W. Arafat, "A Discourse on the Concave Spherical Mirror by Ibn al-Haitham," pp. 10, 16.

in optics; in the other he used the lathe to make an apparatus out of brass to determine the angles of incidence and refraction for rays passing through different media. Considering that this scientist through his experiments found several laws in optics seven centuries before Newton and others found them again, Alhazen's turner must have been a very skilled man.

Chardin, a Western traveler who visited the Imperial court at Iṣfahān in 1665 A.D., mentions the turner's craft in particular:[18]

The turner's trade is also one of the mechanic's arts which the Persians understand well. They have no frame for turning, their method consists only of a treadle to which they fasten whatever they wish to turn. A thong goes twice around the treadle, which a boy holds with both hands, pulling first one hand, then the other, to pull the piece around.

Chardin goes on to describe the drilling of holes on the lathe and the polishing of the turned objects. A recent visitor[19] mentions the use of the lathe by wandering gypsy tribesmen (*Lūtī*), who turn all parts of the spinning wheel on it (Fig. 133).

Figure 133 A Gypsy Wood Turner

[18] Sir J. Chardin in A. U. Pope and P. Ackerman, *op. cit.*, p. 2656.

[19] P. H. T. Beckett, "Tools and Crafts in South Central Persia," p. 148.

The lathe (*dastgāh-e ẖarrāṭī*) that the turner (*ẖarrāṭ*) uses is shown in Fig. 134. A beam 3 to 4 feet in length forms the bed of the lathe (*tīr-e pā, ravānkaš*), which has an end piece (*lengeh, kuluseh*) attached to one side at a right angle. Movable along the beam is a tail stock (*pelleh, taẖteh-dastgāh*) that can be adjusted with pegs (*mīẖčeh, band-e mīl, band-e kār*) fitting into holes in the bed beam. The end piece and tail stock carry wrought iron centers (*sar-mīẖ, morġak, damāġeh*). The wooden piece to be turned, having drilled-in center points

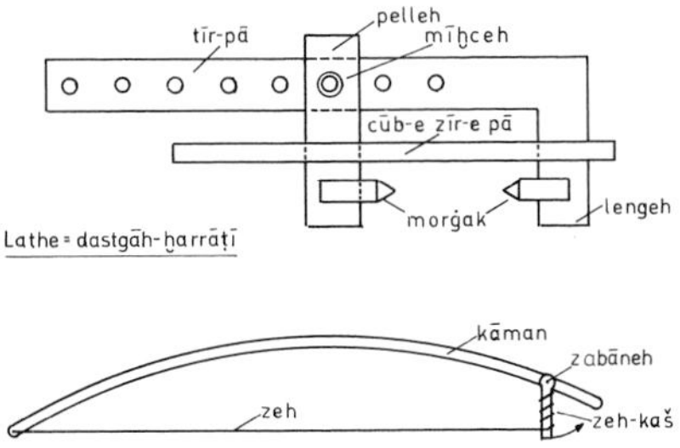

Figure 134 Parts of the Turner's Lathe

(*jamīr*) at the ends, is fitted between the iron centers so that it can rotate freely. Before it is set between the centers the string (*zeh, qoudeh*) of a bow (*kamān, kamāneh*) has been slung around the piece to be turned. The bow has a tightening lever (*zehkaš, qabżeh, qoudkaš*) attached to the handle end. After slinging the string around the workpiece, the turner winds the remaining loose string around the tightening lever, which is finally tilted in line with the handle end of the bow. The turner holds both, tightener and handle end, in his right hand. A tool support bar (*čūb-e zīr-e pā, čūb-e zīr-e pūlād, pīš-pā*) is placed in front of the workpiece, the turner takes one of his turning chisels (*pūlād, qalam, abzār*), places it on the tool support bar, guides it with the big toe of his right foot, and the turning can begin. He moves the bow forward and back, cutting only during the back stroke. One of the most used tools for straight work is a skew-edged chisel (*pūlād-e kaj, moġār-e kaj*). A broad squared chisel is called *eskenak, eskeneh*; a very narrow flat chisel is *nāḫongīr*. For profiled work the turner has either a mildly hollow gouge (*nāḫonī*) or a number of semiround gouges (*longāz, nongāz, galōʾī, gīlōʾī*) of different sizes.

The first operation is the roughing (*andām kardan*) of the outside, followed by a fine cut (*pardāḫt kardan*). Figure 135 shows a peculiar method employed for the drilling of holes, here into pipe stems

Figure 135 A Turner Drilling Pipe Stems (*note drilling guide*)

(*lūleh-ye qaliyān, miyān-e qaliyān, lūleh-ye čubuk*). After turning the stem from the outside, the turner removes it from the fixed centers and places it in the hollow part of a drilling guide (*pīš-mateh, nailāl*), which he holds down with his big toe, at the same time pressing the stem tightly against the other center, likewise with the aid of his big toe. The drill (*mateh*) is inserted with the left hand through a hole in the drilling guide while the foot rests on a board (*šāh-gardeh*) to guide the drilling tool (*kudū-māfak*). When the drill is half through the stem is turned around and the process is repeated from the other end until the two holes meet in the middle, a task not as easy as it sounds. Chisels and drills are kept sharp on a honing stone (*sang-e sou*).

Some of the products of the turner are legs for furniture such as bedsteads, tables, chairs, and stools, pulleys for the weaver's loom, spinning wheels, pipe stems, the latter from medlar wood (*kevīj, azgīl*) or teakwood (*sāj*). Chessmen and the stones for the game of draughts are some of the more refined products. In many villages a turner is mainly occupied with the making of hand spindles (*dūk*, see p. 185) for the home spinning of wool. The turner is then called a spindle maker (*dūk-sāz*). It is important that a spindle is straight. After roughing spindles out, the turner therefore keeps them in a dry place for a while, and before doing the final turning he heats those that have become crooked during the drying period over a charcoal brazier and straightens them with a bending iron (*ḫamgīr*). Simply watching shepherds and villagers spinning all day long, one cannot realize how much trouble was needed to produce a true running spindle.

A specialized turner, almost extinct now, is the ivory turner (*ʿāj-tarāš*), who used to make chessmen and decorations for furniture from ivory (*ʿāj-e fīl*). The only one still working at Šīrāz in 1963 also supplied the inlay workers with ivory beads.

Inlay Worker

When the late Reżā Šāh Pahlavī wanted 400 square yards of wall paneling in his new palace in Tehrān done in inlaid work in 1937, he had a technique in mind known in Persia for centuries as *ḫātam-bandī* or *ḫātam-kārī*. Pope refers to this type of work when he describes ". . . a pair of doors, dated 1591 A.D., of walnut foundation with bone and various other wood inlay, called *khātam-bandī*."[20] The fact that Reżā Šāh was able to employ seventy

[20] A. U. Pope and P. Ackerman, *op. cit.*, p. 2624.

masters and their assistants for three years to complete the task may be an indication as to what extent this craft was still alive. It is still widely used for the decoration of chests, boxes, lecterns, picture frames, parts of musical instruments, and other objects.

Since there are over six hundred individual pieces contained in one square inch of average quality inlaid work of this kind, it will be worth while to see how the Persian craftsmen achieve this degree of precision. These are the steps applied:

Cutting and Preparing the Raw Materials. The inlay worker (*ḫātam-kār, ḫātam-sāz, ḫātam-band*) has to prepare his raw materials, consisting of wood, bone, and metal, long before the actual assembly can begin. In the first place, he needs several varieties of wood of different color such as the dense redwood of the jujube tree (*ʿanāb*), the light-colored orangewood (*čūb-e nāranj*), the dark rosewood (*fūfel*), and for more valuable work genuine ebony (*ābnūs*) and the medium brown teakwood (*sāj*), which is often replaced by the cheaper logwood (*baqam, baqem*). Sitting on the floor behind the work post (*mīḫ-e kār*), which is just a piece of timber rammed into the ground (Fig. 136), the inlay worker cuts the wood with a small bow saw (*arreh baġal-šīšbor*) into thin boards (*lā*) of about $\frac{3}{32}$-inch thickness and 2 × 28 inch size. Depending on the way they will be cut later, these boards are called *lā-ye mos̲allas̲, lā-ye baġal-šīš*, or *lā-ye yaklāʾī*. They are put aside for further drying. Similarly, bones of the camel (*ostoḫẉān-e šotor*) are cut into small strips and placed in large earthenware vats (*hasīn*, Fig. 137) containing a bleaching solution (*āb-e āhak*) of watered quicklime. The bone strips are left in this vat for about three months until they are sufficiently white. The next step in the preparation of the materials is the cutting of the thin wooden boards and the bleached bone boards into very thin beads (*šīš*) about $\frac{3}{32}$-inch wide. This is again done on the work post (Fig. 138). They are sawn close to their final shape. Some of the bone beads are bundled loosely and placed into a second vat containing a green pickling solution (*sabz*). It consists of vinegar

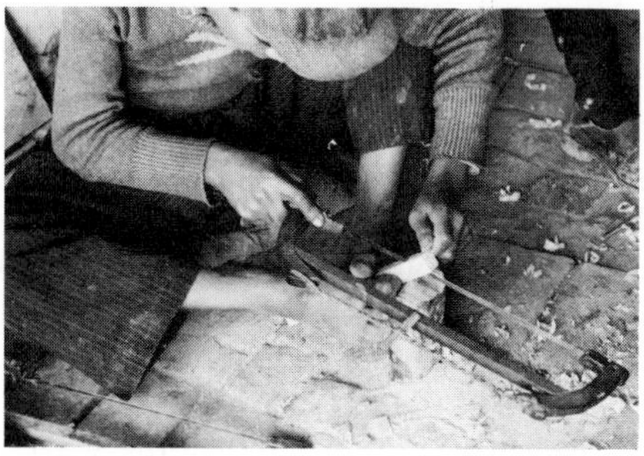

Figure 136 Cutting Boards or Bones for Inlay Work

Figure 137 Vats for the Treatment of Bones for Inlay Work

Figure 138 Cutting Boards into Beads

(*serkeh*) and sal-ammoniac (*nišādor*), to which copper filing dust (*sū'āleh-ye mes*) and copper lathe shavings (*dam-e čarḫ*) are added, both obtained from the coppersmith. The beads remain in the green pickling vat for between four and six months (background, Fig. 137) until deposits of nitric and acetic copper have penetrated throughout and produced a green color. For particularly valuable inlay work, ivory is used instead of bone. It is supplied by the ivory turner.

After having prepared beads of wood and bone, the inlay worker comes to the metal beads. They are normally made of brass (*berenj*) and in exceptional cases of silver (*sīm*). Hand-drawn round wire (*maftūl-e berenj*) is cut into lengths of about 28 inches and beaten with a flat hammer into a sharp triangular groove of a hardened swage block (*qāleb*) and thus formed into a fairly regular triangular shape (*sehpaḫ*).

All this done, the final shaping of the beads can begin. Beads of a small equilateral triangle are called *mos̱allas̱*, larger ones with the shape of a broad-based triangle *baġal-šīš*, *seh-gūš*, and diamond-shaped ones *jou* (meaning "barley grain"). In order to obtain the shapes the inlay worker places a long board with one end on the work post and sits on the other end. This board carries a number of filing blocks (*taḫteh-ye rand*, Fig. 139). If used for

Figure 139 Filing Beads to Shape

a triangular bead, a block called *mos̱allas̱-sāvī* or *baġal-šīš-sāvī* is fixed onto the board, having the groove required for the particular shape. The block for shaping the wire is called *sīm-sāvī*. The bead is placed in the groove, and by filing across the top surface with a flat file the inlay worker obtains its correct size and profile. In this manner wood, bone, and wire beads are completed and put aside in large bundles.

Assembly of Beads into Composite Beads and Rods. At this stage the inlay worker decides on his design, viz., a pleasant looking combination of triangular shapes into hexagons and larger triangles. Having at least three different colors of wood available and bone and metal as well, he has a wide range of possible combinations. The general pattern is the following:

(i) The bundling of the six beads (*šīš pīčīdan*). Three light and three dark *mos̱allas̱* beads are glued together in the form of a hexagon (*A* in Fig. 140). The glue is kept hot in a brass gluepot (*sirīšum-ṭās*) on a charcoal brazier. The beads are pressed together by winding a string (*naḫ*) around them (Fig. 141). After the required number for the work planned has been completed and has become dry, the string is wound off. These small hexagonal compound beads are placed in a filing block of suitable shape, in this case *šīš-sāvī*, and are carefully filed into hexagons.

(ii) These compound beads are spread over with glue, and six brass triangles (*mos̱allas̱-e berenj*) and six wooden diamond beads (*jou*) are glued around the inner hexagon, thus forming a larger one, still called *šīš* (*B* in Fig. 140).

(iii) While they are drying, a different type of composite bead is glued together in a similar way, the so-called corner bead (*parreh*) consisting of one *mos̱allas̱* of a certain color, surrounded by three more *mos̱allas̱* of another color, thus forming a larger triangle (*C* in Fig. 140). For finer

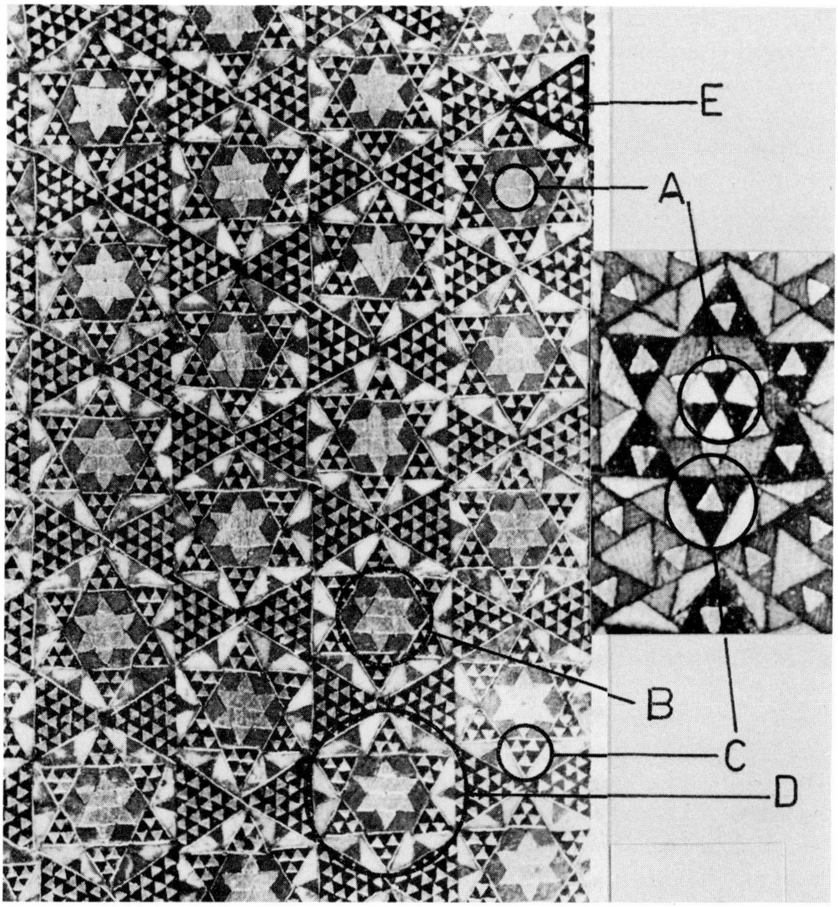

Figure 140 Pattern of Inlay Work (*left: natural size, right: enlarged*)

work these *parreh* beads consist of nine still smaller triangles.

(iv) After the larger *šīš* and the *parreh* have dried and both have been filed to shape in their respective filing blocks (*šīš-sāvī* or *parreh-sāvī*), six of the *parreh* beads are glued to the six sides of the larger hexagon, thus forming a star (*setāreh*). The spaces between the star points are filled in with broad-based triangles (*baġal-šīš*), forming a still larger hexagonal rod (*gol*, *D* in Fig. 140). For the making of such a rod of $\frac{3}{8}$ inch across the flats of the hexagon, 60 to 80 individual beads are required (Fig. 141). For quality work the *gol* rods, and sometimes also the *šīš* and *parreh* beads, are wrapped in thin brass foil (*lā-ye berenj*) that results in fine metal partition lines between the patterns.

Figure 141 Gluing Beads To Form Rods

(v) Applying the same technique as for hexagonal rods, a second type of rod of triangular shape (*tugulū*) is produced (*E* in Fig. 140). The size of these *tugulū* rods is so dimensioned that they fit exactly between two hexagonal *gol* rods. After they are dried, both types of rods are filed to shape in filing blocks referred to as *taḫteh-ye rand-e qofl*.

Joining of Rods into Blocks. When all the rods are prepared, their original length of about 28 inches is cut into eight short pieces 3½ inches in length. On their cut edges they already show the design pattern. Having decided on the size of the inlaid panels required, the inlay worker has prepared light-colored boards (*lā*) or slices of bone to the length of the different panels, 3½ inches wide, and has provided half of them with two glued-on end pieces having the height of the panels. The short hexagonal *gol* rods and the triangular *tugulū* rods are now glued across these boards or bones in such a way that all the space between the end pieces is taken up; another board is placed on top of the assembly, and the whole is put between two strong pressing boards (*taḫteh*) and is inserted into a gap cut into a strong log (*tang*). A pair of wooden wedges (*gōveh*) fills the space of the gap and is driven tight with a hammer. The press thus formed is called *tang-e zangīreh* (Fig. 142). The block of assembled rods is called *qāmeh.*

Slicing of Blocks and Backing Slices. Using a very thin saw, the worker cuts the *qāmeh* blocks into slices of ⅛-inch thickness. The cut runs at right angles to the axis of the beads and shows the full pattern of the assembled rods. Backing boards ¼ inch thick (*āṣer*) and inlaid slices (*lā-ye dōsāyeh*) are alternately glued together into a pack (*toureh*) usually incorporating twelve inlaid slices, and this pack is again pressed together in the wedge press.

Longitudinal Splitting of Packs and Mounting Sheets. The *toureh* is cut up or split (*yak-boroš*) into thin sheets (*yak-lengeh*) with the same fine saw used in the previous process. The cuts are made in such a way that the first one splits the first inlaid slice (*lā-ye dōsāyeh*) in half; the next cut splits the first backing board (*āṣer*), and so on, yielding twenty-four sheets having a layer of about 1/16 inch of inlaid work on the one side and about ⅛ inch of backing board on the other. These sheets, smoothed and sanded on a special filing board (*taḫteh-ye rand-e kašō'ī*), are glued to the objects to be decorated. This gluing is not done in a press, but the thin sheets of inlaid work are rubbed onto the glued surface with the hot peen of a hammer (Fig. 143). Special margin strips (*ḥāšiyeh*) needed in many cases are produced in a similar way. If these margins are of a checkered design they are called *modaḫer*. Finally the inlaid surfaces are sanded (*sāvīdan*), and a special

Figure 142 Joining Rods in the Wedge Press To Form Blocks

Figure 143 Gluing the Inlay Sheets to an Object

lacquer (*rouġan-e sandālūs*) provides both a bright polish and a water-resistant protection for the delicately glued inlaid work. Coarse *ḫātam*, made up from relatively thick beads, is called *matnī*; finer work is called *parreh-varūᶜ*.

Figure 144 A Carved Beggar's Bowl

Wood Carver

It is in the nature of the raw material that not many examples of the wood carver's art have come to us. Historians, however, mention it as one of the important industrial arts of Persia of the past, particularly since the Arab conquest.[21] Some carved wooden objects can be reconstructed from the stone reliefs of Susa and Persepolis; others, created in medieval times, have survived and can be dated, or they even carry the names of their masters.[22] The carved banister rails of Oljaitu's mausoleum at Sulṭāniyeh (built about 1320 A.D.) have been made of a particularly good timber, so that most of them are still in their original positions.

To this day carved objects are made in most parts of the country, but especially at Ābādeh on the High Plateau between Iṣfahān and Šīrāz. Its wood-carving industry has often been mentioned by medieval writers.[23] A modern botanist still mentions it as a consumer of timber for its wood-carving industry.[24] A wide range of articles includes richly carved beggars' bowls (*kaškūl*, Fig. 144), sherbet spoons (*qāšuq-e šarbat, qāšuq-e šāhī*), caskets and chests (*ṣandūq*), frames for chessboards (*taḫteh-ye šaṭranj*), or draught boards (*taḫteh-ye nard*). The School of Fine Arts at Tehrān and the Technical Colleges at Šīrāz and Iṣfahān run courses in wood carving to maintain a high standard of the craft in the traditional techniques, as their products are very much in demand for the tourist and souvenir trade.

The wood carver (*monabbat-kār, monabbat-sāz*) uses a variety of suitable, evenly-grained timbers, such as walnut (*čūb-e gerdu*), rosewood (*fūfel*), red pomegranate (*čūb-e anār-e surḫ*), yellow pomegranate (*čūb-e anār-e zard*), maple (*afrā*); pear (*čūb-e golābī*), however, is regarded as the best for very fine carving.

Relief carving is the normal technique and is referred to as *monabbat* (Fig. 144), a term also used for metal embossing. Another technique frequently applied, sometimes in combination with relief work, is pierced work (*mošabbak*, Fig. 145). Fully sculptured work (*mojassameh*) is rarely done, but if at all, it is done for miniature work such as chessmen (*mohreh šaṭranj*).

Apart from the ordinary tools of the cabinetmaker that the wood carver needs to prepare the wooden objects to be carved, he has a number of special tools, the most important being the chisels (*tīġ-e monabbat-kārī, qalam-e monabbat-kārī*). Special chisels, viz., profiled carving chisels, are referred to as *moġār*. They are: a mildly curved one (*moġār-e nīmrāz, moġār-e nīmbāz, gīlōʾī*), a small half-round

21 Muqaddasī in B. Spuler, *op. cit.*, p. 437.

22 Carved doors of a mosque near Natanz dated 1428 A.D. are signed by the master Ḥusayn ibn ᶜAlī of Ābādeh; cf. A. U. Pope, *op. cit.*, p. 2621. A richly carved sarcophagus (*turba*) dated 1473 A.D. names Ḥasan b Ḥusayn as the carver (*ibid.*, p. 2623).

23 Cf. B. Spuler, *op. cit.*, p. 437, and A. U. Pope and P. Ackerman, *op. cit.*, p. 2626.

24 E. Gauba, "Botanische Reisen in der persischen Dattelregion," p. 44.

gouge (*moġār-e lūleh kūčak*), and a very narrow, high-shouldered straight chisel (*moġār-e kebrītī*). Chisels with a straight cutting edge are called *čāqū*. For fine work the chisels are pushed by hand (*zūrī*); for coarser work they are beaten with a mallet (*taḫmāḫ*). The carver sometimes presses his work against a wooden block (*kondeh*) with an iron center anvil (*mīḫ-kār*). The most unusual one among the carving tools is that for pierced or lattice work that is actually a combination of a file and a saw (*mārpā*, Fig. 145). The

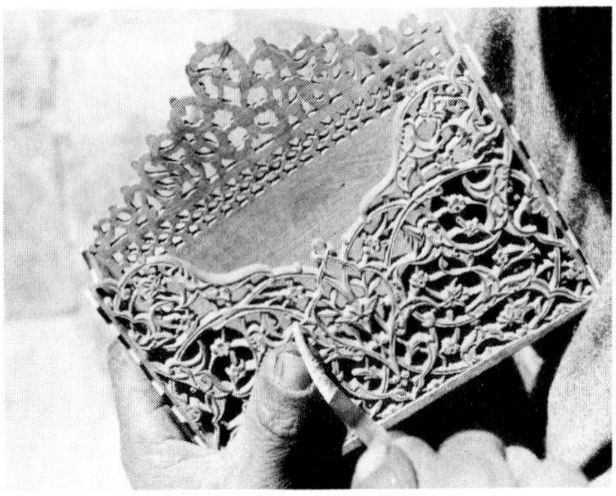

Figure 145 Finishing Pierced Woodwork with Saw File

wooden object is drilled first in the usual way with the fiddle drill, and then the remaining wood is removed with a coarser *mārpā* according to the design, and the pierced work is finally profiled with a finer *mārpā*. The fretsaw (*arreh-mūhī*) was introduced from Europe not so long ago. As it is more efficient in removing larger pieces of wood in pierced work, it is common practice today to use a fretsaw first and to do the finishing and profiling with the *mārpā*.

One of the activities of the wood carver in the past was the manufacture of lattice panels (*gereh*) on doors and windows. Sometimes the spaces were filled with stained glass. Such panels were called *qāmeh*.

Many objects, especially those for the souvenir trade, are decorated with an ornamental margin (*zavār-bandī*). If it is of multicolored wood or in a combination of wood and bone it is called *qātelī* (Fig. 145). Wood carvers specializing in the manufacture of sherbet spoons are called *qāšuqtarāš*. Since the manufacture of a guitar-like musical instrument (*tār*) requires the resonance body to be carved out of a piece of mulberry wood (*čūb-e tūt*), the maker of this musical instrument (*tār-sāz*) is usually a wood carver, and he often decorates his instruments with ornamental carvings.

Another craft closely related to wood carving is that of the printing-block cutter (*qāleb-tarāš*). He is an associate of the textile printer (*čīt-sāz*) and has his working place usually in a corner of one of the larger printing shops, but he is independent and supplies the needs of his host as well as those of other printers. The wood for the printing blocks (*qāleb*) is selected and well-dried pearwood (*čūb-e golābī*). The block is cut across the grain (*rāh-pūd*) and is $2\frac{1}{4}$ inches thick. It is carefully planed with a smoothing plane (*randeh-ṣāf-kon*). After a handle-forming groove has been cut (*dasteh borīdan*) into the sides of the block, the front is whitened with a mixture of glue and chalk powder to receive the design. This is transferred with charcoal dust (*ḫāk-e zoġāl*) through perforations in the design paper. The design is supplied by the printer but often made by a specialist, the textile print designer (*naqqāš*). Both designer's and cutter's work is quite involved, as for each ornament four blocks are required, one for the black lines (Fig. 146) and three for the colors blue, red, and yellow, and all must perfectly match. Most of the carving is done with a cranked chisel (*šotor-galū*), a flat but narrow chisel (*oškaneh*), and a side-cutting chisel (*naqš-bor*), while the background is cut away with a special deep cutting chisel (*ṭāseh-*

Figure 146 A Textile Printing Block

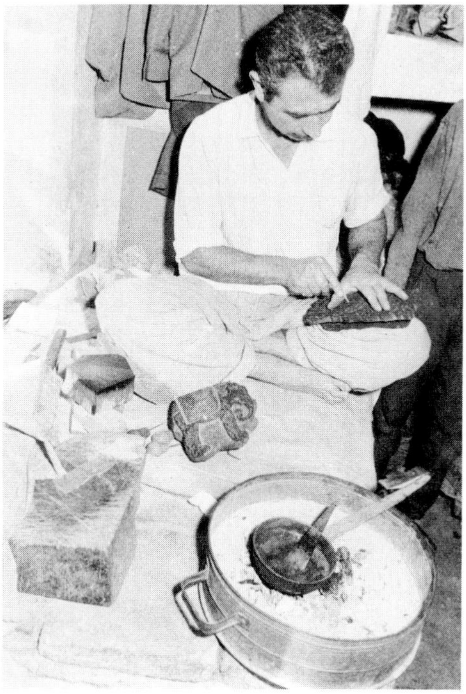

Figure 147 Cutting a Printing Block

kan). New blocks are cut (Fig. 147) to a depth of $\frac{1}{4}$ inch. A good deal of the block cutter's work consists of repairing blocks with broken-off parts. This is done by providing the affected area with a glued-in piece of pearwood and recutting it to the required design. Another of his jobs is the touching-up of used blocks on a sheet of sandpaper to give them back their original sharpness. This has to be followed up by cutting away some of the background if the depth of the design has become less than $\frac{1}{8}$ inch.

Combmaker

The combmaker (*šāneh-sāz*) is one of the more humble craftsmen of the bazaar, and it seems that he is doomed, as he cannot compete with the cheap plastic combs now flooding the market. Wood for the better combs (*šāneh*) is boxwood (*čūb-e šamšād*); pearwood (*čūb-e golābī*) is used for the less valuable ones. The wood is first cut into blanks (*taḫteh, paseh*) $2\frac{1}{2} \times 4$ inches in size. This is followed by the sharpening of the long edges (*dam nāzok kardan*) and the rounding of the short edges (*baġal borīdan*), done by planing (*randeh kardan*) on a planing board (*taḫteh randeh*, Fig. 148). The next operation is the cutting of the teeth, which is done in three stages, the coarse teeth (*dandeh-dorošt*) with a coarse saw (*arreh-dandeh-dorošt*), the fine teeth (*dandeh-rīzeh*) with a finer saw (*arreh-dandeh-rīzeh*), and finally the cutting to the tooth ground with a saw called *arreh-zīr-zan*. All three of these saws are modified tenon saws having a depth-setting device (*poštband*, Fig. 149). During these cutting operations the cutter's index finger is protected by a thimble (*anguštāneh*). This is the way combs are cut in Iṣfahān. In Šīrāz the comb cutter uses a bow-operated circular-saw cutting device similar to the one used for the milling of the ceiling battens (Fig. 129). Scraping (*līseh kardan*) to remove the saw burrs is the

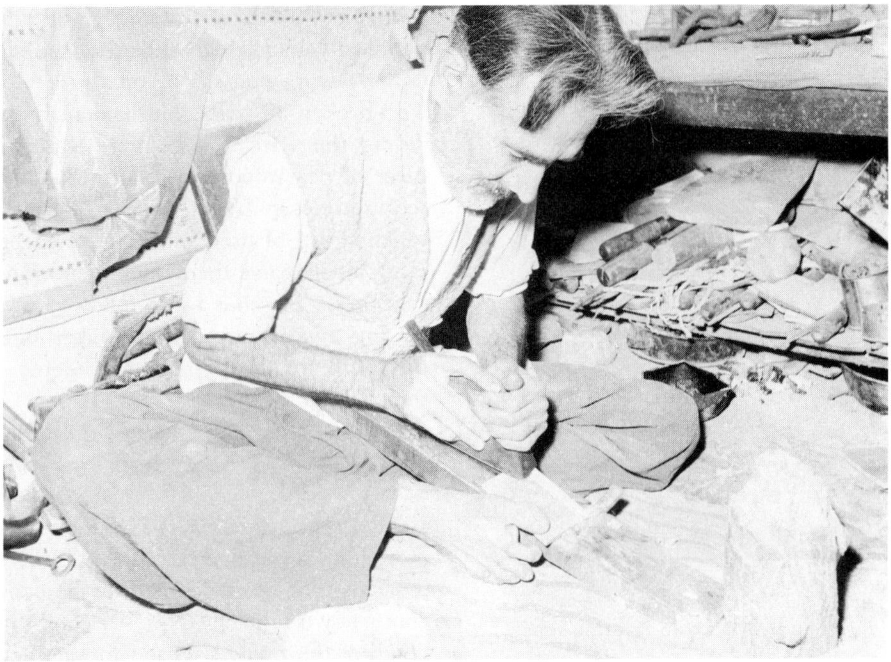

Figure 148 A Combmaker Planing Blanks

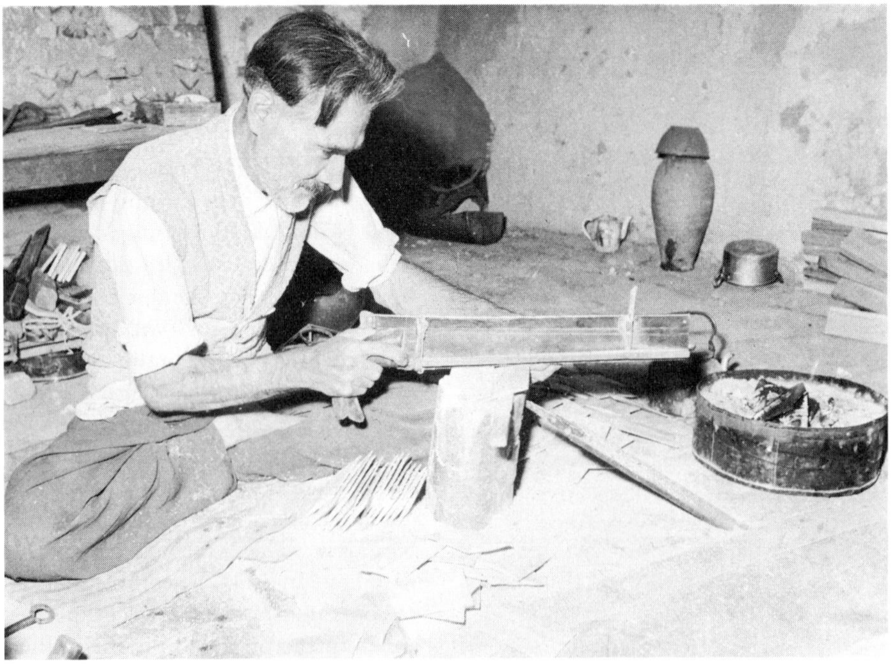

Figure 149 A Combmaker Cutting Teeth

next step, followed by smoothing of the teeth edges (*qolāb kardan*, *gerd kardan*) with a hooked scraper (*qolāb*), and finally the teeth are sharpened (*nōk tīz kardan*) with a file (*souhān*).

Maker of Bellows

The metalworking crafts operating forges and furnaces use many kinds of bellows to supply the combustion air. The maker of bellows (*dam-sāz*) supplies them in all sizes and in a variety of constructions (Fig. 150). He must be able to handle timber, leather, metal, and even raw skins.

Small hand bellows (*dam-e būrī*), simple concertina bellows (*dam-e fānūsī*), and double-acting bellows (*dam-e dō-dam*) consist of wooden boards connected with plied leather (*čarm*). The leather has to be of good quality, and the *dam-sāz* buys the properly tanned and fattened skins from the tanner. A skin, after having been cut to the right size and carefully pleated, is glued and tacked between the properly shaped wooden boards, and the joints are reinforced by nailing leather strips (*tasmeh*, *qaiš*) over the edges. Smaller bellows have the movable board hinged to the nozzle block with a strong piece of leather. Larger bellows have iron hinges (*loulā*) supplied by the blacksmith, and pieces of leather nailed over the hinges to make the joint airtight. All these wooden bellows have valves (*dar-vārjeh*) consisting of wooden flaps (*pestānak*) with leather hinges. The air inlet valves are nailed behind the inlet holes in the boards, and the air outlet valves inside the nozzle block.

The smallest hand-operated bellows (*dam-e dastī*, also called "skin bellows") are made in the following way: The *dam-sāz* buys unopened raw goatskins (*pūst-e boz*) or sheepskins (*pūst-e gūsfand*), soaks them in a lime solution to soften the hair and the remaining flesh, removes both with a sharp scraper, and after thoroughly washing and drying the skins rubs them with tallow (*pīh*) to make them pliable. The leg holes are tied up with leather thongs (*tasmeh*, *qaiš*), the neck hole is attached to an iron nozzle (*lūleh*), and two wooden slats (*čūb-e dam*), to be used by the operator to control the air intake, are nailed to the wide open rear end of the skin.

Figure 150 A Maker of Bellows

This craft is also disappearing as many blacksmiths and metallurgists are changing over to modern hand-operated or even electric centrifugal blowers.

3

BUILDING CRAFTS AND CERAMIC CRAFTS

Building Styles and Techniques through the Ages

Climate, available building materials, and a cultural heritage handed down from the many peoples who have occupied the Iranian Plateau since prehistoric times have all shaped building styles and techniques. Persian master builders have contributed such techniques as vaulting[1] and the dome[2] to the art of building and have introduced styles such as the *apadāna*,[3] the *aivān*, and the pointed arch.[4]

One of the oldest methods of providing shelter for men and domestic animals has been the digging (*kandan*) of caves and tunnels into the hillside, a technique still reflected in the name of the basement (*būm-kand*) or place names such as Samarkand, Mūrkand, Sarāskand, and others. From these caves houses were developed which were partly dug in and partly built by the rammed-earth or *pisé* technique. Ibn al-Balḫī described houses of this type in 1105 A.D.[5] De Morgan[6] surveyed similar buildings which were still in use in West Persia about 1900. De Morgan's drawings show clearly that the dwellings developed from man-made caves. In 1933 Gabriel[7] observed caves dug into the slate and sandstone formations near Birjand in East Persia. They were still in use as human dwellings in summer. From his description they must have been similar to those photographed by the author in 1963 (Fig. 151).

[1] K. A. C. Creswell, *A Short Account of Early Muslim Architecture*, p. 245, Fig. 48.

[2] *Ibid.*, p. 321.

[3] A. U. Pope and P. Ackerman, eds., *A Survey of Persian Art*, p. 318.

[4] K. A. C. Creswell, *op. cit.*, p. 321.

[5] Al Balkhi, *Description of the Province of Fars*, trans. G. Le Strange, p. 25.

[6] J. J. M. de Morgan, *Mission scientifique en Perse*, Figs. 31, 33.

[7] A. Gabriel, *Durch Persiens Wüsten*, p. 175.

Excavations at Siyalk in Central Persia have revealed that the *pisé* technique already existed in the fifth millennium B.C.[8] The fourth millennium brought its gradual replacement by sun-dried bricks, originally oval-shaped mud lumps.[9] Toward the end of the fourth millennium, the flat rectangular mud brick, formed in a wooden mold, came into general use.[10] Already during this period houses had distinct architectural features such as buttresses, recesses, door and window openings, and walls rendered and decorated with white and red mineral paints.[11] Foundations were stones tightly packed in trenches without mortar. Excavations have also revealed that when the town of Siyalk was rebuilt after the arrival of the Iranians (Indo-Europeans, about 1200 B.C.), a new method was used for the rebuilding of the citadel. Stone masonry 40 yards square served as a foundation, and alternating courses of mud bricks and dry stone formed the walls.[12] This building method is still in use in Persia, e.g., for the permanent winter dwellings of the Qašqāʾī nomads of Fārs. Enormous stone walls, laid without mortar, similar to the Cyclopean walls[13] of the Greeks, were built at Masjed-e Sulaimān at the beginning of the first millennium B.C. This kind of wall was never used by the Babylonians, Assyrians, or Elamites, but has been found extensively through excavations in Urartu, an ancient state bordering North Persia. This technique was still applied for the building of the palace terraces at Pasargadae and Persepolis.

When the Achaemenians became the rulers of a vast empire they took advantage of the skills of the conquered nations for the building of their palaces. The foundation charter of Susa describes the building of the palace thus:[14] [Darius says:]

Figure 151 A Summer Shelter in Sīstān

This is the palace which I built at Susa. . . . Downward the earth was dug, until I reached rock in the earth. When the excavation had been made, then rubble was packed down, one part 40 cubits in depth, another 20 cubits in depth. On that rubble the palace was constructed. And that the earth was dug downward, and that the rubble was packed down, and that the sun dried brick was moulded, the Babylonians did all this. The cedar timber was brought from a mountain called Lebanon; the Assyrian people brought it to Babylon; from Babylon the Carians and the Ionians brought it to Susa. The *yakā* timber was brought from Gandara and from Carmania. . . . The ornamentation with which the wall was adorned, that from Ionia was brought. . . . The stone columns which were here wrought—a village by name Abiradus, in Elam—from there were brought. The stone cutters who wrought the stone, these were Ionians and Sardians. . . . The men who wrought the wood, those were Sardians and Egyptians. The men who wrought the baked brick, those were Babylonians. The men who adorned the wall, those were Medes

[8] R. Ghirshman, *Iran*, p. 29.
[9] *Ibid.*, Fig. 6.
[10] *Ibid.*, p. 35.
[11] *Ibid.*, p. 36.
[12] The writer saw this type of wall excavated at Boğazköy in Turkey, the site of the ancient capital of the Hittite empire.
[13] R. Ghirshman, *op. cit.*, p. 123, and Fig. 14*a*.
[14] *Ibid.*, p. 165.

and Egyptians. Saith Darius the King: At Susa a very excellent [work] was ordered: a very excellent [work] was [brought to completion] . . .

Despite these foreign influences, Persian architecture has maintained a distinct character to this day. The so-called *apadāna* had been developed already in pre-Achaemenian times. It is a large room in the center of the building leading to a wide hall, open on one side and having a small room at each end. Columns support the roof beams. Assyrian bas reliefs depicting buildings in Media already show slender columned porticoes.[15] There is not much difference in principle between the Apadāna in Persepolis (Fig. 152) and the present-day peasant house in Āẕarbaijān (Fig. 153). Even the capitals on the wooden columns are only a stylized version of the bull heads of Persepolis (Fig. 154). Persian builders were directly responsible for introducing the *apadāna* style to the Moslem world outside Persia. The historian Ṭabarī (839–922 A.D.) writes that when the Arab governor of Basra, Ziyād, wanted to rebuild the great mosque at Kūfa in 670 A.D., he summoned non-Moslem masons to erect a building without equal:[16] "A man who had served as a builder under the Persian king Ḫosrou replied that this could only be accomplished by using columns from Jabal Ahwas. . . ." This source particularly mentions that the roof was directly supported by the columns without the intermediary of arches. Persian masons were also employed when the Caaba at Mecca was rebuilt in 684 A.D. under Ibn az-Zubair.[17] Further, when the Caliph al Manṣūr set out to build Baghdad (762 A.D.) he gathered engineers, architects, and surveyors from Syria and Persia.[18]

[15] A. U. Pope and P. Ackerman, *op. cit.*, p. 904.
[16] K. A. C. Creswell, *op. cit.*, pp. 13, 156.
[17] *Ibid.*, p. 156.
[18] K. A. C. Creswell, *op. cit.*, p. 163.

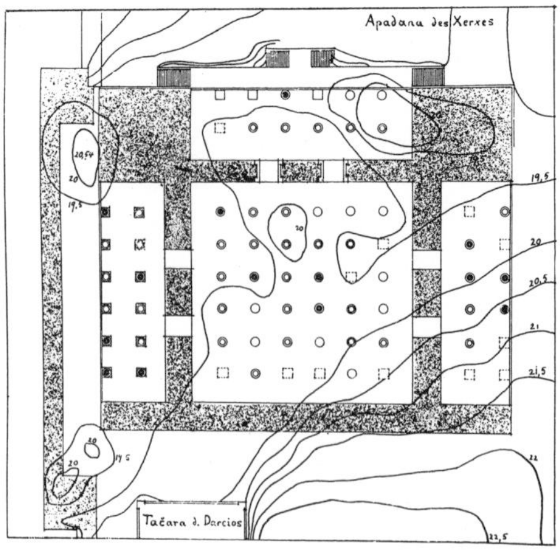

Figure 152 Plan of the Apadāna of Persepolis (*from F. Sarre and E. E. Herzfeld,* Iranische Felsreliefs, *reproduced by permission of the publishers, Wasmuth Verlag, Tübingen*)

Figure 153 A Farm House in Āẕarbaijān

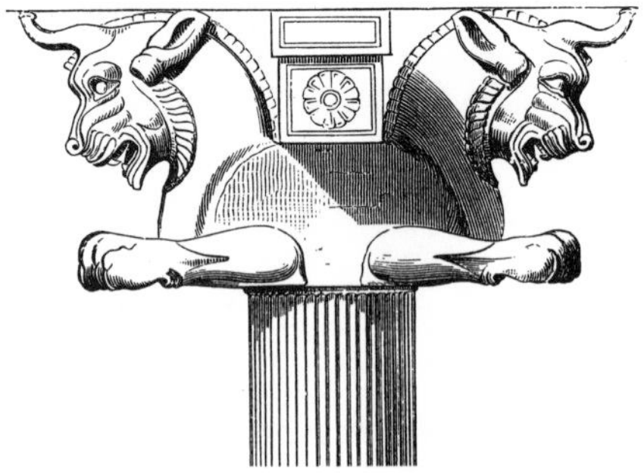

Figure 154 Bull Head Capital (*from A. Springer,* Handbuch der Kunstgeschichte, *reproduced by permission of the publishers, E. A. Seemann, Leipzig*)

With the growing scarcity of timber for building purposes another technique was developed in Asia,[19] most probably in Persia, namely vaulting that permits the roofing of buildings without wooden beams. During the Parthian and Sasanian periods vaulting achieved high technical and architectural standards in public and private buildings. There were two basic forms, the barrel vault to cover rectangular rooms and the dome over a square room. For the transition from the square base to the circular dome the Persian builder invented the so-called squinches (Fig. 155). He maintained these high standards in vaulting right through Islamic times, as witnessed by the many mosques and other public buildings. Even today it can be said that there is hardly a room that a Persian builder could not cover with a vault, from the most humble peasant house on the fringe of the central desert (Fig. 156) to the covering of a cinema in Yazd where a single barrel vault of sun-dried mud bricks spans a hall seating six hundred people.

[19] A. U. Pope and P. Ackerman, *op. cit.*, p. 918.

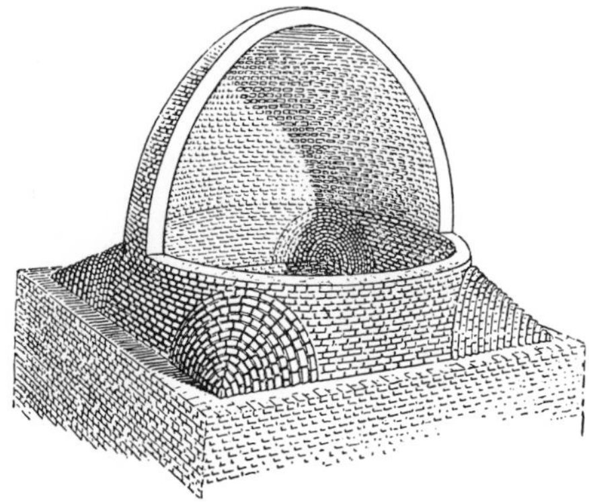

Figure 155 Persian Dome (*from E. Diez,* Iranische Kunst)

Figure 156 Peasant Houses in Ḫorāsān

Figure 157 Wind Catchers in Central Persia (*from A. Costa and L. Lockhart,* Persia, *reproduced by permission of the publishers, Thames and Hudson, Ltd., London*)

Another contribution to architecture by the Persian builder is the *aivān*, which can be regarded as the equivalent of the hall of the *apadāna*, open towards the courtyard, no longer flat-roofed but vaulted since Parthian times.[20] The *aivān* was an important feature already in Sasanian building and has been a characteristic of the Persian mosque since early Islamic times. Ventilation towers or wind catchers (*bād-gīr*, Fig. 157) are a feature peculiar to the houses in Central Persia. They lead the cool, refreshing night winds into the living room in the basement (*zīr-e zamīn*).

It is not surprising to find different building techniques north of the Alburz mountains in the Caspian provinces, with their heavy rainfall and rich forests. Sir Thomas Herbert, who traveled through Persia between 1627 and 1629, noticed the different style:[21] "... the houses (in *Lāhījān*) differ from the common form in Persia. For they are not flat above, but like ours in England in the roof, also tiled and glazed according to English fashion." The English consular agent Rabino writes[22] that "... the houses in Mazanderan are built like a log cabin, the interstices being filled with mud." The present-day house from Gīlān shown in Fig. 158 is of this log cabin construction. Built in the moist lowlands near the Caspian Sea, its foundation is an artificial mound (*čīneh*) rising to about 2 feet above ground level. Eight heavy wooden pillars (*fīq*) are composed of the following parts: Next to the ground is a row of short sleeper beams (*zai*). Short wooden blocks rest on these at right angles.

20 *Ibid.*, p. 422.

21 W. Foster, *Thomas Herbert's Travels*, p. 173.

22 H. L. Rabino, "A Journey in Mazanderan," p. 473.

Above these blocks is a row of strong boards (*katal*) that in turn carry extremely heavy pointed blocks (*kondulū*). Each row of four of these pillars supports two solid floor bearers (*bāj-dār*); twelve floor joists (*gal-e ḫus*) run across these at right angles. They carry the actual floor boards (*ṣāf*). Strong beams on the outer edge around the house form the bottom frame (*nāl*). Thirty vertical verandah columns (*sotūn*) support horizontal purlins (*kašīn*). From these rise the steeply inclined rafters (*saljū*) that carry the thatching (*gālī, lāleh*) that rests on roof battens made from bamboo (*kārfūn*). Bamboo and rushes for the thatching are growing along the many water courses of this region and are cut by the peasants with a long-handled brush-cutting knife (*dās*), the iron part being about 12 inches long and the cutting edge ending in a blunt reaping hook 3 inches long. In the hilly land between the coastal plain and the Alburz mountains there is no need for the pillar basement. There the main frame (*nāl*) is laid directly on the ground (Fig. 159). All the vertical stiles rise from the frame; those forming the actual rooms are nailed across with thin branch wood or bamboo stems and filled with a mixture of wet loam and straw (*kāh-gel*).

Rabino also mentions the "summer houses" of the Caspian provinces,[23] found nowhere else in Persia. "Houses have a sleeping place, *talar*, with a planked platform and a thatched roof. Rice stores, *tilimbar*, are similarly built, but only one-storied" (Fig. 160). Similar structures are also used for barns and silkworm nurseries, also called *tilimbār* or *telembār*. A relic of the ancient past are the houses of the inhabitants of the Kūh-e Hazār mountains. They have circular, rubble-built bases covered with steep, pointed cones made of mud bricks.[24]

[23] *Ibid.*, p. 445.
[24] A. Gabriel, *op. cit.*, p. 77.

Figure 158 A Peasant House in Gīlān

Figure 159 A Peasant House near Rūdbār (*Gīlān*)

Figure 160 Talar in Māzandarān (*from J. J. M. de Morgan*, Délégation en Perse)

Builder

There is no clear distinction in traditional Persian crafts between builder, mason, and bricklayer (*meᶜ-mār, bannā*). They all start as apprentices of a master builder (*meᶜmār-baši*).[25] Those who were more talented than the average bricklayer made Persian architecture famous throughout the Islamic world.

To this day no drawings are prepared for the building (*binā᾽ kardan*) of an ordinary house. The common practice is that owner and builder "draw" the plan (*naqšeh-piyādeh*) on the actual site by marking the walls with powdered lime (*āhak*) or gypsum (*gač*). Common laborers (*ḥammāl*) dig (*kandan*) the trenches (*šāldeh, šālūdeh*) for the foundation (*pai*), about 18 inches deep and slightly wider than the planned thickness of the wall. Whatever earth (*ḫāk*) is dug out is carefully gathered at a spot where it is mixed (*maḫlūṭ*) with burnt lime (*āhak*) and water into a soft paste (*sefteh, šefteh, botō, bātāl*). A layer of about 6 inches of this paste is placed (*riḫtan*) in the trench and coarse stone ballast is thrown (*zadan*) into it. These stones (*sang*) have been brought by donkeys from the nearest quarry (*maᶜdan-e sang, kān-e sang*). They are about 6 to 8 inches in size. With one layer (*čīneh*) of stones in the trench a second layer of mud paste is worked over the stones, ballast follows, and this is repeated until the trench is filled. Within three to four weeks these foundations have sufficiently set to begin building the walls. In due course the lime-mud-stone mixture becomes as hard as rock, as the writer had an opportunity to experience when building a technical college at Šīrāz over the foundations of a caravanserai erected by Karīm Ḫān-e Zand in 1760 A.D.

The following methods are available for the building of walls:

1. *Pisé* or rammed earth walls (*čīneh*), a method commonly used for the walls surrounding yards, gardens, and orchards. The tallest walls in *pisé*, the shading walls of the ice ponds (*yaḫ-čāl*) are usually well over 20 feet high. For this method earth is moderately wetted (*āb dādan*) and mixed with chaff (*kāh*). Laborers tread it barefooted (Fig. 161), thus kneading it (*gel mālīdan*) into a plastic mass (*kāh-gel*). When a sufficient quantity has been prepared a laborer carries it to the building site in a mortar basket (*kappeh*) or throws it in lumps (*mošt*) to the builder (*čīneh-kaš*) who catches it and places it in position. The builder has marked the building line with a string (*rīsmān*) and places the clay lumps on the properly set foundation. When building low garden walls, it is sufficient foundation to place a layer of cut rock (*čefteh*) on the solid ground (Fig. 161). The clay lumps are shaped freehand into a course (*mohreh*) of about half an Iṣfahān cubit (*nīm-zarᶜ, nīmgaz*).[26] From time to time the builder draws a straight-edge (*šemšeh*) along the growing wall for proper alignment and checks it vertically with a plumbline (*šāqul, šāqūl*). The spirit level (*tarāzū*) is gradually coming into use. When a course is finished, the builder smooths the surface by rubbing it (*mālīdan*) with a trowel (*māleh*). When the first course has properly set and hardened, usually after two or three days, the next one is laid and so on until the desired height has been reached. The thickness of the wall diminishes with increasing height; an

25 This refers to the traditional craftsman only. A great number of Persians of the present generation have been trained as professional architects according to Western standards.

26 Seven thousand, five hundred Iṣfahān cubits make a *farsaḫ* (the *parasang* of Herodotus). The latter, being very close to 6 km, makes the cubit 80 cm or 31.5 inches. Cf. W. Hinz, *Islamische Masse und Gewichte umgerechnet auf das metrische System*, p. 64.

Figure 161 The Building of a *Pisé* Wall

8-foot-high wall is 30 inches wide at the bottom and 10 at the top. Yard walls are usually capped with a course of burnt brick (*ājur*) that corbel out for 3 to 4 inches to keep the rain from the wall, which would otherwise too readily soften and gradually be washed away. Garden and orchard walls are mostly capped off with a row of wooden sticks (*eškezeh*), each about 30 inches long and 2 inches thick, placed across the wall. These sticks carry a layer of thorny brushwood (*gavang*, *qūl*) or rushes (*nai*), weighed down with a course of a mixture of loam and lime that sets and becomes water resistant.

2. Mud bricks (*ḫešt*) have been the most common building material in the country since time immemorial. The brickmakers (*ḫeštmāl*) take earth from excavations for the house and obtain additional earth from a pit (*čāl*) they dig nearby. A simple pick (*kolang*) and a spade (*bīl*) are the tools used for the digging. The earth is soaked in ample water, and straw and chaff (*kāh*) are added to the wet mud (*gel-čāl*) and thoroughly mixed by treading it with bare feet, similar to the treading of the *pisé* material except that this mixture is much softer and can be more thoroughly mixed with a hoe in a second operation (Fig. 162). The wet mix is carried in baskets to the site where the brickmaker works, forming a mud heap (*šemšeh-gel*) near him. If the loam is cut from a pit (*čāl*) it is usually hauled to the surface with a windlass (*čarḫ*, *čarḫ-e čāh*, Fig. 163). The windlass is of the same kind as is commonly used in Persia for many other purposes, e.g., well-building and lifting water from wells. Its wooden shaft (*mīl*) is placed into the forked ends of two upright posts (*pā*). Two wooden crosses (*parak-čarḫ*) are mounted on this shaft, their ends joined by traverse pieces which act as handles (*dastak*). A rope (*band-e čarḫ*, *zāzū*) is wound around these traverses. Often the pit is some distance away and it is more convenient to carry the loam to the mixing

Figure 162 Preparing the Loam for Mud Bricks

Figure 163 A Windlass above a Loam Pit

spot on donkey back (Fig. 164). Figure 165 shows the brick molders at work. Each one has a wooden mold (*qāleb*), just an open frame. The molder first covers the ground with a thin layer of chaff, puts the molding frame flat on the ground, and throws a quantity of the mud-straw mix (*kāh-gel*) into the mold, beats it into the corners with his bare hands, and scrapes any surplus off with a small straight-edge (*čūb*). He lifts the frame with a swift movement, leaving the fresh brick on the ground, and places the frame next to the brick just made. Molding (*mālīdan*) row after row in this way, he makes about 250 bricks an hour.

The size of the brick is widely standardized today at $8 \times 8 \times 1\frac{1}{2}$ inches (*andāzeh maidān*). Bricks have been much larger in earlier periods. In Babylon, where the technique was taken over from the Sumerians, they measured $16 \times 16 \times 4$ inches,[27] and at Persepolis they were $13 \times 13 \times 5$ inches.[28] In Sasanian times they were 15 to 20 inches long and 3.5 to 5 inches thick, and they were $9 \times 9 \times 2$ inches in earlier Islamic buildings.[29]

After the bricks have been left in the sun for three to five hours, depending on the weather, they are set on edge (*zanjīrī kardan*) for further drying (Fig. 166). Needless to say, this work is only done during the hot summer months, say between early May and late October, a time when normally not a single cloud appears in the Persian sky.

When the bricks have dried for a day or two they are used straightaway for the building of common houses, for outside and inside walls (*dīvār, tifāl*), even for vaults (*tāq*) and domes (*goṃbad*, Fig. 167).

[27] E. Diez in A. U. Pope and P. Ackerman, *op. cit.*, p. 916.

[28] E. F. Schmidt, *The Treasury of Persepolis*, p. 19.

[29] *Ibid.* and Sir J. Chardin, *Travels in Persia*, p. 258.

Figure 164 Carrying Loam to a Mixing Place

Figure 165 Brick Molding

The courses (*rag*) are laid along a string (*rīsmān*), and bonded with a mud-straw mortar (*kāh-gel*, *melāṭ*, *gel-e melāṭ*), identical to the mix used for brickmaking. The bond is about ¾-inch thick. The bricklayer spreads the mortar with a steel trowel (*māleh*, *māšūn*, *kamčeh*) and checks his level with a plumbline or a straight-edge containing a small pendulum (*šāqūl*). When the wall has reached a height beyond the reach of the builder a wooden scaffold (*čūbbast*, *čūbbandī*, *manzenīq*, *manjenīq*) is erected on the outside of the building and is reached by a ladder (*nardebān*, *sed*). The hot climate of the country requires very thick outside walls, usually 2 to 3 feet deep. Inside walls are mainly single-brick (*yak-ājurī*), sometimes bricks on edge (*tīğeh*, *tīğī*) or hollow-built (*ṣandūqī*) square bricks forming box-like holes. The transition between a vaulted room (*tāq-band*) and the flat roof is also built hollow in order to have less weight on the vault and

Figure 166 Bricks Placed on Edge for Drying

Figure 167 Building a Vault with Mud Bricks in Sīstān

save bricks (Fig. 168). Bricks are laid in bond (*ābčak, roḫbān*) in order to have sufficient strength.

After the bricklaying (*seft kārī kardan, ājur čīdan*) of all the walls, they are usually rendered (*gel rūš kašīdan*) with a coat of mud-straw mix (*kāh-gel*), often enriched with some lime (*āhak*) to make it insoluble after setting. The rendering (*nazok-kār kardan, kāh-gel mālī*) is done with a steel trowel and smoothed with a wooden float (*māleh-čahārsū*). The worker uses a movable trestle (*ḫarak, čahārčūb*) to reach the higher parts of the walls.

3. Burnt bricks (*ājur*) are mainly used for buildings of greater importance. In the past they were used for palaces, mosques, caravanserais, bazaars, and the houses of the rich. The burnt bricks are slightly smaller than the sun-dried bricks owing to the shrinkage in firing them. Apart from the standard size (*fešārī*) of 8.2 × 4 × 2.4 inches, the builder also uses ready-made half bricks (*nīmeh*) and quarter bricks (*čārak, čahār-yak*). If smaller still they are called *kaluk*, if cut off from a larger brick *seh-qaddī*. Many of the medieval tomb-towers, e.g., the Gombad-e Qābūs in Gorgān (twelfth century), even have special bricks with one side round and two sides tapered following the shape of the conic roof top. Angled bricks are used for

Figure 168 A Hollow-Built Transition between Vault and Flat Roof

the inclined window sills (*tūreh*, *gīlōʾī*, *qab-lāmeh*, *kārdī*, *paḫ*). Outside wall corners are sometimes decorated with profile bricks having one round edge (*moujī*), or one toothed edge (*dandān-mūšī*). Door and window openings are often arched over with tapered form bricks unless a wooden lintel beam (*naʿl-e dargā*) is provided.

When laying burnt bricks the builder uses a mixture of hydrated lime (*āhak*) and sand (*rīg*, *šen*, *lamr*) for mortar (*šen-āhak*, *māseh*, *malāṭ*). Sand-lime-cement mortar (*seh-gorgeh*, *bātāl*) is often used for modern urban buildings. For the construction of the huge water reservoir in practically every Persian house, a specially waterproofed mortar (*sārūj*, *čārū*, *āhak-e siyāh*) is prepared by mixing sand, lime, and wood ashes (*ḫākestar-e ḥammām*). Before applying this mortar a certain quantity of the hairy seeds (*lūʾī*) of rushes is added for internal bonding and prevention of cracking. The same mortar is also used for the internal rendering of these water reservoirs. If these seeds are not available, goat hair is used for the same purpose.[30] Outside walls of buildings made in burnt bricks are seldom rendered, but neat joints (*band-kāšī*) in the face brickwork give the surface an attractive finish. A rather modern innovation is a kind of veneer brickwork, i.e., a combination of a mud brick structure with a bonded-in veneer of burnt brick on the outside. In employing this kind of work, the builder often goes to the trouble of calling in the ornamental brickcutter, a specialist whose work is described on page 122.

4. Stone (*sang*) has been used in Persia's architecture for many public and private buildings, although a shift from stone to finer brickwork can be observed during Islamic times, particularly since the thirteenth century.[31] Even today many private buildings are built on a stone base, at least up to a height of about 3 feet above ground level. Such a solid stone base keeps the brick parts of the walls sufficiently far away from the ground to prevent their being exposed to the splashing of the heavy winter rains. Ashlar masonry, laid without mortar, is mentioned by Muqaddasī (tenth century) for Fārs[32] and is still widely used in this province besides rubble laid in mortar (*hazāreh*).[33] When ashlar is set in mortar a special mixture of lime and clay (*dūġāb*) is used for the joints (*darz*, *darz-e sang*). It is applied rather soft and permits an easy setting of the stones with a very thin joint. After a few months it sets to a great hardness.

Better-class houses have stone slabs or burnt bricks, sometimes glazed tiles for flooring, whereas the average home has a floor (*kaf*) made from a hard-setting mixture of lime and plaster, often mixed with stone grit and red iron oxide for coloring. This kind of flooring was already used in Achaemenian times. The treasury and other palaces in Persepolis, unearthed between 1935 and 1939, had this flooring in a well preserved state[34] in most of the rooms.

For the construction of roof and ceiling we find essentially the following three construction methods:

1. In the Caspian provinces with their heavy rainfall (225 inches p.a.) we find rising and hipped roofs, covered with straw (Figs. 158 and 159), shingles (*taḫteh*, *lāt*), or burnt tiles (*sofāl*, *sefāl*, *tūfāl*). The latter are made by the local potter (*sefāl-gar*) from a fat clay. They are flat and have a nose (*dokmeh*) at the back to attach them to the roof battens. Others are thrown on the potter's wheel as slightly tapered cones

[30] Sir J. Chardin, *op. cit.*, p. 262.
[31] A. U. Pope and P. Ackerman, *op. cit.*, p. 899.
[32] *Ibid.*, p. 900.
[33] *Ibid.*, p. 965.
[34] E. F. Schmidt, *op. cit.*, p. 19.

and are halved with a wire when leather hard. These are more like the so-called Roman or Spanish roof tiles and are much used in Māzandarān and Gorgān. Today galvanized iron is frequently used instead of these coverings. Such a roof is called *šīrvāneh*.

2. The roof type mainly in use on the Iranian Plateau, particularly on the slopes of the Zagros mountains, is the flat roof (*bām*, *pošt-e bām*, *rūbūn*). Figure 153 shows its construction: Ceiling joists (*tīr*, *sardar*) are placed on top of the walls and for the open porch over heavy beams (*sarnāl*) supported by columns (*sotūn*). Ceiling boards (*soqāf-pūš*) are placed over the joists, or instead, light ceiling battens (*pardū*, *dastak*) are nailed across them and are covered with braided reed mats (*ḥaṣīr*). A mixture of mud, straw, and some lime, well worked and rather soft, is spread over the ceiling boards or reed mats respectively in many thin layers. Each layer is given some time to dry after which it is compacted with a rolling stone (*qaltabān*). The spreading of these layers is continued until the roof reaches a thickness of about 10 inches in Fārs and Iṣfahān, and about 20 to 25 inches in Āẕarbaijān, where the mud-lime mixture, however, contains a much larger proportion of straw. Great care is taken during the spreading process that the roof is divided into sections 10 to 12 feet wide by molding the mud mixture into channels, slightly depressed in the middle of the roof and deepening toward the edges, where they end in wooden spouts (*nāvdān*). After each rain the roof has to be compacted with the stone roller; otherwise, it would develop cracks while drying. The stone roller remains on the roof. Snow has to be removed immediately, since melting snow penetrates faster than rain. Apart from these maintenance precautions, the mud roofs serve a good purpose in keeping the rooms cool in summer and warm in winter. During the construction of the roof ample salt is strewn on the mats and mixed with the mud to keep insects, in particular white ants and borers, away.[35]

Figure 169 A Peasant House in the Alburz Mountains

It is surprising to see how many building materials and techniques are often applied even to a humble peasant house as shown in Fig. 169. The foundations built in stone rubble are well above the ground, the outer walls (*dīvār*) and the partition walls (*dīvār-e vasaṭ*) are built in sun-dried bricks with the exception of the front (right-hand corner in Fig. 169), which is built in burnt brick. Joists and roof battens are clearly visible. A thick layer of brushwood, an important insulator in the colder north, is already in position on the roof, waiting for the mud-straw mixture to be put on and to be rolled tight. Note should also be taken of wooden ties built into the walls to give them added shear strength, important in a region with frequent earthquakes.

No ceilings are provided in common peasant houses. City homes often have plaster ceilings. In these cases ceiling battens (*tofāl*) are nailed across the joists so that they form a narrowly spaced grill to receive the plaster. Another type of ceiling found in urban houses consists of

[35] Sir J. Chardin, *op. cit.*, p. 264.

wooden mosaic. This work has been described previously.

3. The most common type of roofing in Central Persia is the vault, either barrel or dome. The Persian builder is a master in covering rooms of all shapes in this manner, and most of the work is done without any wooden form work at all. Light comes in from arched windows in the walls or through a glass pane set in the top of the dome.

Brickmaker

Burnt bricks were already made by the Babylonians in the fourth millennium B.C.[36] In Persia kilns have been unearthed in Susa and Siyalk dating back into the first millennium B.C.[37]

The maker of burnt bricks (*ājur-paz, ḫeštmāl, ḫešt-paz ḫeštgar, ḫeštzan, faḫḫār*) has his brickworks (*ājur-ḫāneh, ḫešt-kārī*) usually outside the town or village, close to a suitable clay pit. For the molding of the bricks he works in much the same way as the maker of mud bricks, but there are some differences. As his products are mainly used for face work on outside walls, he uses selected clay for raw material, and he has to slake and clean it of impurities. The clay (*gel, ḫāk*) is carried from the clay pit to the brickworks on donkey back and is tipped into a soaking pit (*ḫāk-šūrī*) together with one-fifth of its volume of a gray sand (*ḫāk-e siyāh*), also carried to the works on donkey back from a deposit nearby. The sand is added to make the clay lean and to result in light cream-colored bricks after the firing; they would otherwise turn red. The soaking pit is filled with water from a well (Fig. 170) or other water supply, and the clay is left in there for 24 hours for slaking (*gel šostan*). Next day the workers thoroughly mix (*maḫlūṭ kardan*) the mass with wooden shovels (*pārū*) first, and then they hoe it (*kašī-kaš, kaš zadan*). Since ample water had been added the mixture becomes rather liquid. It is lifted with a bucket and poured into a gutter from where it runs into a neighboring pit. There another worker passes it through a sieve (*qalbīl*, Fig. 171) that separates pebbles (*rīg*) and other coarse impurities from the clay. After the soaking pit has been emptied, the strained clay is left to settle. The surplus water is scooped off with a bucket after the first day, and after four days the clay is sufficiently dried to be molded and is shoveled out of the pit. The molder squats

Figure 170 Pit for Soaking Clay and Well

Figure 171 Straining the Slaked Clay

[36] R. Ghirshman, *op. cit.*, p. 166.
[37] C. Singer, *A History of Technology*, p. 396.

near the clay heap (Fig. 172) with some of the gray sand at his side. He puts a handful of the latter into the mold (*qāleb*), which is a cast iron box with four feet having two compartments for the narrower standard size bricks. He shakes the mold around so that the sand sticks to the wet surfaces and fills each compartment with a lump (*čūneh, mošt*) of clay, beats it in with his hands, and cuts the surplus off with a straight-edge (*šemšeh*) or a wire (*sīm*). He empties the mold by gripping it by two of its feet and turning it over (Fig. 173). The raw bricks (*ḫām-pūḫteh*) are left in the open for 24 hours for drying (*ḫošk šodan*), then they are turned on edge (*boland kardan*) and are left in that position for three days to achieve even drying and to prevent bending and cracking. Before they are put on donkey back to be carried to the kiln a worker goes over the edges with his hands to smooth them (*vākū kardan*). The kiln (*kūreh, kūreh-ye ājur-pazī*) shown in Fig. 174 is on the outskirts of Hamadān, and the method described is the one customary there. The base of the kiln goes 8 feet below the surface and forms the fireplace (*āteš-ḫāneh*), which is accessible by a number of steps leading down to it. A vaulted arch (*tāq-e kūreh*) over the fireplace has many holes, thus forming a kind of grate (*sambū-rak*). The charge is carried into the kiln on donkey back and is stacked over the grate. The first part of the charge enters through an opening on the front side of the kiln. At the back of the kiln is a second opening high above the ground with a ramp leading to it, and the remaining bricks are charged through this opening. All the bricks are stacked with spaces between them to allow the combustion gases through. The last row of bricks on top of the stack is laid very close, and the joints are smeared over with clay except for an area about 3 feet in diameter that serves as an outlet for the smoke. The entrances are likewise sealed up. The kiln described has a capacity of 50,000 standard bricks, 8 × 4 × 2 inches, or 25,000 bricks of an old-fashioned shape, 8 × 8 × 2 inches. Before World War II the fuel consisted of certain desert shrubs (*čār, tarḫā, tarḫān, Artemisia herba alba*) and wormwood (*dar-maneh, Artemisia santonica, A. maritima*).[38] They had been collected for weeks before the firing (*sūḫtan*) could begin and were deposited near the fire hole (*āteš-gāh*). These shrubs burn with a long and intensely hot flame. As they burned away

Figure 172 Filling the Brick Mold

Figure 173 Emptying the Brick Mold

[38] E. Gauba, "Botanische Reisen in der persischen Dattelregion," p. 43, and D. Hooper and H. Field, "Useful Plants and Drugs of Iran and Iraq," p. 87.

more shrubs were pushed into the fire hole with long forks, the men doing this work in relays on account of the strong heat radiation. Today this method has been widely replaced by the use of cheap black fuel oil (*naft, naft-e siyāh*), a by-product of the country's oil refineries. The fuel oil is mixed with chaff or the dry stalks of sugar beet (*pūš-e čoġondar*), and this mixture is shoveled into the fire hole. Firing of this large kiln takes 72 hours. Toward the end of this time a rather large quantity of the oil-chaff mix is shoveled in, resulting in a sudden lack of air, thus producing a reducing atmosphere that is also needed to obtain the cream color of the bricks. Immediately after the last fuel has gone in, fire hole and smoke outlet are sealed up with clay and the kiln is left to cool for 72 hours. The bricks are then taken out, again on donkey back, and taken straight to the building sites or stacked in the yard for sale. The bricks very close to the grate are usually overfired. They are put aside and are used for the construction of water basins (*ḥouż*) and cisterns (*āb aṃbār*), traditional features of every house in Persia.

As so often in Persia methods vary from province to province. The kilns in Ḫūzistān, where building relies exclusively on bricks, are much larger, usually having a capacity of 150,000 standard bricks. An unusual method of brickmaking has been observed on the high plain near Ābādeh in Central Persia. Here the permanent kiln consists of the fireplace and the vaulted grate above it. When stacking begins, there is first a pile of limestones erected in the center, and the raw bricks are stacked around it with sufficient space between them for the combustion gases to pass through. But there is no outer kiln wall (Fig. 175); the hot gases come out of the pile in all directions. After 24 hours of firing the bricks are allowed to cool. All of them except those on the outside are well fired. The good bricks are carried away to a building site and so is the burnt lime, which is just enough to prepare the mortar for this batch of bricks. The half-baked bricks are piled up again to be included in the next firing. When the writer discussed the economy of this method with the foreman he agreed that it was not very efficient but said that they could not afford a covered kiln and that they had always done it that way.

Brick and Tile Cutter

Between the tenth and twelfth centuries,[39] during Seljūq times, an ornamental

Figure 174 A Brick Kiln

Figure 175 An Open Brick Kiln

[39] E. Schroeder in A. U. Pope and P. Ackerman, *op. cit.*, p. 1036.

building technique became fashionable in Persia, and this has been a characteristic of Persian architecture ever since. This technique, ornamental brickwork, locally known as *hazārbāf* (meaning "thousand interweavings") appeared in Iraq as early as the eighth century A.D. The oldest building known is the Baghdad gate at Raqqa;[40] the fortified palace of Ukhaidir,[41] 120 miles south of Baghdad, is slightly younger, and almost contemporary is the caravanserai of ᶜAtshān near Kūfā.[42] All these early Islamic buildings are in a part of Iraq with many traces of pre-Islamic Persian (Sasanian) architecture. Yet, as ornamental brickwork was not a feature of Sasanian building technique, its origin in Iraq is rather shrouded.

The new technique began with the introduction of a great number of different brick bonds (Fig. 176), some of them having protruding bricks, thus giving light and shade effects and encouraging the use of writing as an ornament. The most remarkable example of this style is the small dome chamber in the Friday Mosque at Iṣfahān (Fig. 177), built under the great Seljūq vizir Niẓām ul-Mulk (1017–1092 A.D.).

During this time plaster joints came into use. The liking for ornamental enrichment led to the carving of these plaster joints, then to the insertion of carved plugs (Fig. 178) between the brick ends, and finally to the replacement of the plugs by wholly plastered surfaces incised with rich ornament. This technique reached its peak in the domes and vaults of the mausoleum of Oljaitu Ḫodābandeh at Sulṭāniyeh (about 1320 A.D.). In the mosque at Gūlpaigān this technique was already used in 1104 A.D., and it is dominant in the older parts of the Friday Mosque at Iṣfahān (about

Figure 176 Goṃbad-e Ālaviān at Hamadān, c. 1150 A.D.

Figure 177 Ornamental Brickwork at the Friday Mosque at Iṣfahān

Figure 178 Carved Plugs in Brick Joints at Sulṭāniyeh

[40] K. A. C. Creswell, *op. cit.*, p. 185.
[41] *Ibid.*, p. 197.
[42] *Ibid.*, p. 201.

1122 A.D.). It was still in use when the Friday Mosque at Varāmīn was built in 1326 A.D.[43] For the latter building it can be proved that plaster plugs were no longer carved but were cast in a number of different molds.[44]

Colored (glazed) brick faces mark another step in the development that led to the insertion of faience tiles (insets), at first in strictly geometrical forms according to the size of the brick face (Fig. 179). The beginnings of the use of glazed bricks in buildings are still obscure. In principle they can be traced back to the Babylonians, and they were used in Elam[45] during the second millennium B.C. They appeared on the Iranian Plateau in the Achaemenian buildings of Susa and Persepolis (fifth century B.C.).[46] There seems to have been no application of glazed bricks in Hellenistic, Parthian, and Sasanian times, but there was a revival in Baghdad under the ᶜAbbasid caliphs. When Ibn Rustah gave a description of Baghdad's Great Mosque in 903 A.D. he said that it was wholly ornamented with lapis lazuli glazed bricks. The tenth-century writer Yaᶜqūbī speaks highly of the green minaret of Boẖārā (then in East Persia).[47] The technique seems to be fully developed in Seljūq times (1037–1157 A.D.) although Niẓām ul-Mulk preferred plain bricks of quality to the rather showy colored tiles for the building of his Friday Mosque at Iṣfahān.[48] In the section on the development of glazes it will be shown that by the tenth century the potters of Persia had a thorough knowledge of glazes suitable for bricks and building tiles.

Pope[49] writes on the development of faience in building: "Insets appear first in the twelfth century, sparingly in the dome of the Masjid-e Jāmiᶜ at Qazvīn, but once the process was started, it developed swiftly and in a few generations whole buildings were bejewelled with investitures of fayence that herald a new epoch in architectural ornament."

Figure 179 Turquoise Tile Plugs in Brickwork at Sulṭāniyeh

The original form of application of colored faience was the insertion of small bricks with a glazed face in a bed of common though ornamentally arranged bricks. Principal colors were turquoise, cobalt blue, and buff. Most of the designs were geometrical patterns such as lattices, meanders, and polygons, but also rectangular, stylized inscriptions. A fully matured example of this type is the tomb tower of Muʾmina Ḫātūn at Naḫičevān in Āẕarbaijān, dated 1186 A.D.[50]

Toward the end of the twelfth century a new type of ceramic wall decoration appeared in Persia, i.e., the luster painted tiles. Such tiles had already been used in Iraq during the ninth century, especially in Baghdad and Samarra, from where the technique spread to Egypt, North Africa, and Spain on the one hand and to Persia on the other.[51] These luster tiles were

[43] A. U. Pope and P. Ackerman, *op. cit.*, p. 1288.
[44] *Ibid.*, p. 1322.
[45] *Ibid.*, Pl. 19*a*.
[46] *Ibid.*, pp. 321–325, 331; Pl. 19*b*, *c*; Pl. 72*a*, *b*.
[47] *Ibid.*, p. 1323.
[48] *Ibid.*
[49] *Ibid.*, pp. 1323–1324.
[50] *Ibid.*
[51] E. Diez, *Iranische Kunst*, p. 112.

mainly produced in the famous ceramic center of Kāšān in Central Persia and exported from there to many parts of the Near and Middle East. We distinguish two different types, first the flat painted tile in cross-and-star pattern, and second the much larger, embossed building panel, in most cases employed for the construction of the *miḥrāb* or prayer niches of the mosques. Both types of tiles were fired in a reducing atmosphere in which some metal oxides in the glaze deposit themselves on the surface in metallic form, giving the tiles a bright metallic luster (Fig. 180).

Figure 180 Fragment of a Luster Tile

Quite a number of these luster-tiled *miḥrāb* are signed by Kāšān artist-potters. One of the most famous was Abū Zayd, who built the *miḥrāb* of Persia's most venerated shrine at Mašhad in 1215 A.D.[52] Another Kāšān master, Yūsuf Moḥammad, designed, built, and proudly signed the *miḥrāb* of the shrine of ᶜAlī ibn Jaᶜfār at Qom in 1333 A.D.[53] Kāšān maintained the high quality of its luster tiles up to the middle of the fourteenth century.

By this time another technique in ceramic tiles had developed in East Persia, the faience mosaic. It is composed of differently shaped segments cut from monochrome tiles and arranged to form a previously designed pattern. It had several advantages over the luster tile: 1. Ordinary monochrome tiles could be made by the local potter, who had a sufficiently large number of good glazes and colors at his disposal. Though Kāšān held a cobalt monopoly for centuries, the relatively small quantities of cobalt oxide needed could be obtained everywhere through the ordinary trade. 2. The delicate and costly transport of ready-made tiles from Kāšān was avoided by the local manufacture of tiles. 3. By reverting to monochrome tiles the craftsman avoided the costly and uncertain firing process of luster tiles. 4. The faience mosaic is more adaptable to varying scales and sizes in architecture. It can be employed from a small rosette of one foot in diameter to the inside and outside covering of huge mosque domes (Fig. 181).

Faience mosaic apparently developed first in East Persia, where it achieved superior quality at the Timurid court of Herāt (today Afghanistan). During the fourteenth century the Herāt ceramic patterns were noble in design and robust in execution. The best examples of Herāt faience in Persia proper are in both Masjid-e Jāmiᶜ at Iṣfahān and Yazd. The latter is dated 1375 A.D.[54] A decided refinement in style and workmanship can be observed in the fifteenth century. By this time Kāšān had adopted the new technique too. In the Masjid-e Maidān at Kāšān the ceramic mosaic is signed by "Ḥaidār the tile cutter" (*kāšī-tarāš*), 1463 A.D.

The shift of the Timurid court from Herāt to Tabrīz took faience mosaic along with it, also in a superior quality. The best known example at Tabrīz is the Blue Mosque (Masjid-e ᶜAlī, finished 1522 A.D.) where we read: "Moṣaddeq the tile cutter designed this."[55] A peculiar con-

52 A. U. Pope and P. Ackerman, *op. cit.*, p. 77.
53 E. Diez, *op. cit.*, p. 109.
54 A. U. Pope and P. Ackerman, *op. cit.*, p. 1328.
55 *Ibid.*, p. 1332.

Figure 181 Faience Mosaic on the Dome of the Madreseh at Iṣfahān

tribution of the Tabrīz masters was to model their inscriptions in raised relief and leave them unglazed. The buff-colored brick stood out brightly against the dark blue background.

When the Ṣafavids transferred their capital to Iṣfahān at the beginning of the sixteenth century, Šāh Ismāᶜīl assembled craftsmen from all over his kingdom, and the many mosques, churches, and secular buildings of the Ṣafavid period prove that the previous high standard in design and technique could be maintained. An early master who decorated the walls of the mausoleum Hārūn-e Vilāya at Iṣfahān was Ustād Ḥosain (1512 A.D.).[56] In that period the tile cutter was already greatly assisted by artist designers, as we learn from the signatures of some work at the Masjid-e Jāmiᶜ at Iṣfahān: "Sayyid Mahmūd the painter [*naqqāš*] has written it."[57]

Since the seventeenth century, from the time of the great ᶜAbbās, painted polychrome tiles begin to replace cut faience mosaic. The polychrome glazing process, known as *haftrangī* (meaning "seven colors"), had developed in general pottery and was now applied to tiles. Good examples of this new technique are in the Masjid-e Šāh at Iṣfahān, side by side with faience mosaic, in the Masjid-e Luṭf-Allāh, also at Iṣfahān and the two Christian churches, St. Mary's and St. Elizabeth's, both at Julfa, opposite Iṣfahān, which Šāh ᶜAbbās had presented to the Catholic and Armenian communities of his capital. The tile work in the churches was designed by master miniature painters. It is of very good quality and is dated 1716 A.D. The art of *haftrangī* deteriorated, however, during the eighteenth and nineteenth centuries, and only with the revival of so many crafts under the late Šāh Reżā, i.e., since about 1930, can a marked improvement in *haftrangī* be observed again. The faience mosaic had a similar revival, caused by the need to repair the nation's artistic monuments. In this field the modern Persian ceramist has succeeded so much that the quality of his work is equal to that of the fifteenth-century masters.

The Technique of the Brick and Tile Cutter

The craftsmen engaged in ornamental brickwork (*hazāreh*, *hazār-bāfī*, *pārčeh*) and faience mosaic usually begin their careers as ordinary bricklayers. Those who succeed in doing work in face bricks well will specialize in this line, calling themselves brick cutters (*ājur-tarāš*). A further specialization takes place later, when the most skilled brick cutters are entrusted with tile or faience mosaic. Those who do this

[56] *Ibid.*, p. 1331.

[57] *Ibid.*, p. 1330.

work exclusively are called *kāšī-tarāš*, tile cutters.

Brick Cutting (ājur-tarāšīdan)

Once the design (*naqšeh*) has been decided, the brick cutter sets out to prepare his bricks (*ājur*). Since all bricks in face work have a ground front, he has to trim and grind at least one side of each brick. The untrimmed bricks (*zebreh*) are about ½-inch larger both in width and in depth. With the sharp edge of his hoe (*tīšeh*) he scratches a line (*ḫaṭṭ kašīdan, ḫaṭṭ gereftan*) along a marking ruler (*qadd, kašō*), which is a specially prepared piece of molded brick (Fig. 182). For the marking of corner bricks a square (*gūnīʾā*) is used. After a quantity has been marked he puts one brick after the other on edge (Fig. 183), and, following the scratch mark (*jazval*), he cuts the face clean with five or six strokes of his broad-edged hoe. Some cutters have a straight handle (*dasteh*) for this tool (Fig. 182); others prefer a crooked handle (*kāʾūl*).

After the trimming the cutter hands the bricks to his apprentice or assistant, who does the grinding (*sāvīdan, sābīdan, sāʾīdan*) of the faces with a coarse, wet, grinding stone (*sang-e sombādeh*, Fig. 184). All the bricks used for plain face work are prepared in this way, such as whole bricks (*ājur-e morabāʿ*), half bricks (*nīmeh*), and quarter bricks (*čārak*). Half and quarter bricks are made out of whole bricks with the broad-edged hoe, while the brick is held in the palm of the hand. Those used as coping stone or sill bricks (*gol-e nō*) are often cut to a special bevel (*fārsī*). Below the coping stone we sometimes find a molded profile brick (*pābaqal*) or one with a toothed face (*ājur-e dandāneh*).

The face brick wall is built with the bricks thus prepared, using a lime and sand mortar, the courses being either plain or zig-zag, but recesses are left on those parts of the wall that are designed to have an ornamental brick panel (Fig. 185) or a faience mosaic panel.

The design for such a panel (*naqšeh, tond*) is laid out on a specially prepared tracing surface (*taḫmin*, Fig. 186). For work in the traditional style a certain number of dif-

Figure 182 Marking Bricks for Edge Trimming

Figure 183 Trimming the Brick Faces

Figure 184 Grinding the Brick Faces

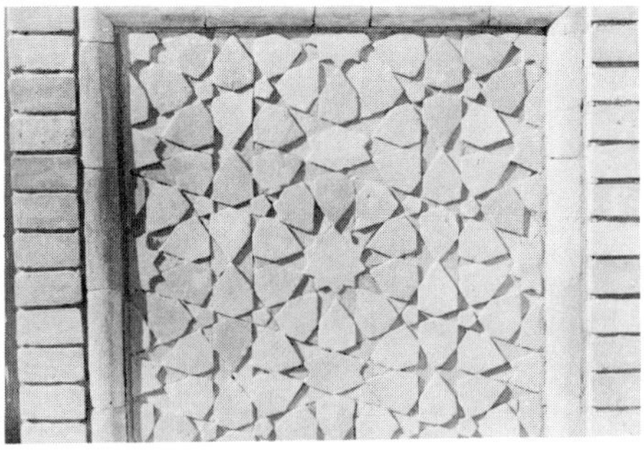

Figure 185 An Ornamental Brick Panel

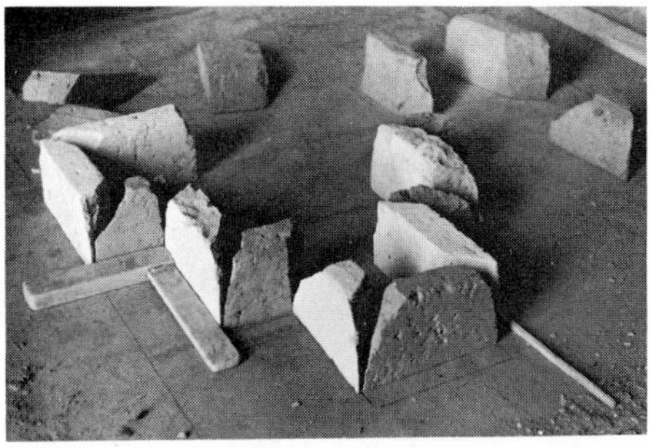

Figure 186 Cut Bricks Laid out on the Tracing Surface

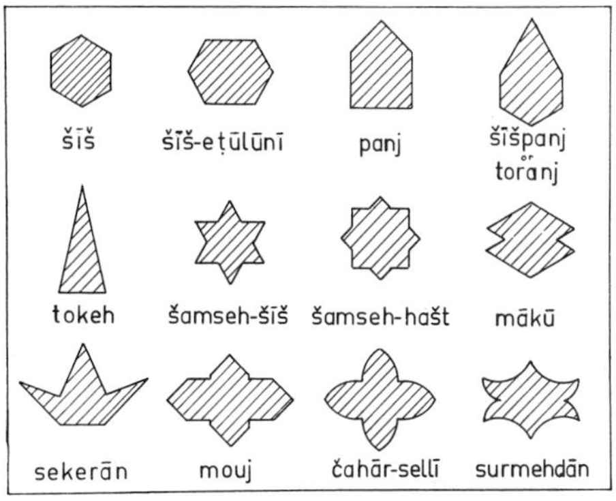

Figure 187 Names of Brick Profiles

ferently shaped brick profiles is used. The small section of a panel shown in Fig. 185 alone contains five different ones. Combined they form a distinct geometrical over-all pattern. Some of the commonly used profiles and their names are listed in Fig. 187. For the cutting of these profiles a smaller, narrow-edged hoe (*tīšeh-dam-e qalamī*) is used. These bricks show the exact profile on their face and are tapered toward the back (Fig. 186). As the pieces are cut they are arranged (*čārak kardan*) according to the design, but face down (*bar-ᶜaks*). The size of the panel is indicated by wooden straight-edges (*šemšeh-melāṭ*). Right angles within the pattern are checked with a square (Fig. 186). Meanwhile a rather sloppy mix of plaster of Paris and water (*dūġāb*) has been prepared and is now cast over the whole (*dūġāb rīḫtan*). The mix readily fills all the joints between the bricks with the tapered ends. This first mix is poured about ¾-inch thick. Immediately afterwards a thicker and coarser plaster mix (*gač-e seft*) is spread over the first one (*gač rūš rīḫtan*) up to the level of the brick ends. The cast panel (*pošt-baqal*) is then left to set and dry. After four to five days it is carefully lifted and attached to the wall (*be dīvār naṣb kardan*) into the previously prepared recess. Plaster mortar is used for this final stage of the work.

Tile Cutting (kāšī tarāšīdan)

The tile cutter (*kāšī tarāš*) does the ordinary tiling of walls as well as the more intricate faience mosaic. For wall tiling with square tiles the apprentice first grinds the spilled-over glaze off one edge and makes this edge straight (Fig. 188). The tiler then places his model tile over it as a stencil and marks the three remaining edges with a wooden stylus (*qalam*) that has been dipped into a paste of red Armenian bole (*gel-e armanī, gel-e māšī, jouhar*, Fig. 189). Resting the tile on one edge of a stone, the tiler trims the three sides marked with a few short strokes using the sharp chisel edge of a mason's hammer (Fig. 190). He checks his work with a

Figure 188 Grinding the Tile Edge

Figure 191 Checking Trimmed Edges

Figure 192 Gluing Stencils onto Tiles

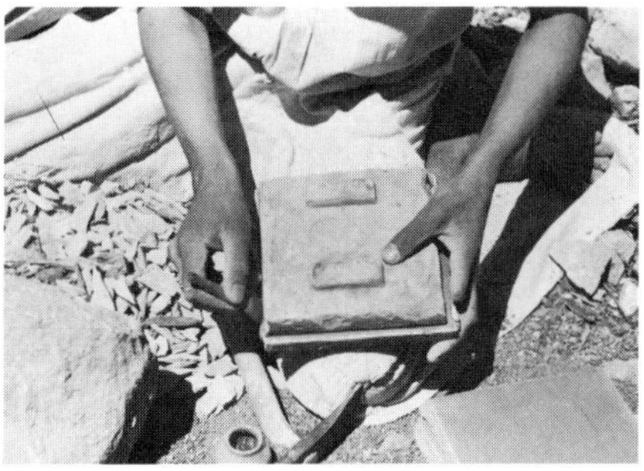

Figure 189 Marking Tiles for Squaring

Figure 193 Cutting Mosaic Pieces

Figure 190 Trimming Tile Edges

Figure 194 Composing the Mosaic Design

wooden square (*gūniyā*, Fig. 191). The tiles are now ready to be fixed to the wall with plaster of Paris.

The same type of monochrome tile is used for the preparation of faience mosaic. Tiles in those colors called for by the design are made by the potter in sufficient quantities: turquoise, cobalt and lapis lazuli blue, a light emerald green, several yellows from buff to saffron, white and black, occasionally a little red, and sometimes gold, either melted-on leaf gold or colloidal gold suspended in the glaze. For important work, e.g., in mosques and public buildings, a designer (*naqqāš*) prepares paper stencils for all the different shapes (*moʾarak*) of the mosaic and hands them to the tiler for cutting in specified colors (Fig. 192). The tiler glues the stencils to the tiles with a plant glue (*serešt*), and by exactly following their outlines he cuts each piece of tile to the required shape (Fig. 193). When this cutting with the chisel-edged hammer is finished, the tile edge is smoothed with a rasp and then tapered toward the back with a hoe. As in the case of the brick cutter, the design is laid out on a prepared surface, which is usually flat. If the covering of a dome is intended a special scaffolding is built, representing a section of the shape of that dome, the panels being laid on this curved surface. The master places the cut-out tile pieces face down on this surface to compose the design (*moʾarak čīdan*, Fig. 194). When a certain section of the work is so composed it is overcast with plaster of Paris in the same way as done for ornamental brickwork. The joints are so small that the plaster just shows enough on the surface to have the bright and glossy colors of the tiles separated by the dull buff of the Persian plaster. The panel sections are made to such a size that they can be lifted without breaking under their own weight. The transfer of the sections to walls, domes, or arches is similar to that of the ornamental brick panels. The design is continued through the different sections with such skill that in most cases it is impossible to tell from the finished work where the divisions have been.

Lime and Gypsum Burner

The use of gypsum for mortar and stucco-plaster began fairly early in the history of Persian building. The builders of the Achaemenian kings at Susa and Persepolis set their stone work without any use of mortar. The stones were cut to a high degree of precision and held together with bronze or steel clamps and dowels set in melted lead. Wherever walls of sun-dried bricks were built the brick courses were set in a mortar of the same composition as the bricks, i.e., mud and straw. There are, however, two places known in Achaemenian building where plaster was used: the floors of the palaces at Persepolis were covered with a very hard-set plaster-sand-gravel concrete,[58] and the brick walls of these buildings were rendered with a fairly thick coat of plaster, often beautifully painted with well-preserved earth colors.[59] Large quantities of plaster coating of the ninety-nine columns of the treasury hall, unearthed in 1937, indicate that the columns had a wooden core onto which the plaster was applied over a layer of reed rope coils.[60]

During the subsequent Hellenistic period the use of plaster must have fully developed, since the Parthian buildings show general use of plaster mortar for both stone and brickwork as well as for the rendering of walls with a fine plaster coat, a technique continually applied to Persian buildings ever since. The introduction of

[58] E. F. Schmidt, *op. cit.*, p. 53.
[59] *Ibid.*, p. 19.
[60] *Ibid.*, p. 54, Fig. 33.

lime mortar must have taken place later still, i.e., during Sasanian times. The early buildings of this dynasty, under Šāh Ardašir (224–241 A.D.), were erected with plaster for mortar. But a marked change in style as well as in technique took place under his successor Šāpūr I (242–272 A.D.). From then on the use of lime-sand mortar became general, a mortar that had already been used by the Romans for centuries.[61] This direct introduction of a new technique from Rome is not surprising after Šāpūr's victory over the Roman emperor Valerian in 260 A.D. Archaeologists, too, are convinced that the city of Šāpūr in Southern Fārs was built with the help of Roman artisans.[62]

Ibn Ḥauqal mentions that in his day they found gypsum of such superb quality at Qā'in near Nīšāpūr in Ḫorāsān that it was sent "to all parts."[63] Persia has unlimited deposits of limestone suitable for lime burning, and almost the same can be said of gypsum rock, so that both lime and gypsum burners can obtain their raw material from local quarries. Today lime burning (*āhak-pazī*) and gypsum burning (*gač-pazī*) are specialized crafts (*kūreh-paz*) in towns of sufficient demand. In smaller communities both are done by the same person, sometimes combined with brick burning.

The quarried limestone (*sang-e āhak*) and the gypsum rock (*sang-e gač*) are sent to the kiln (*kūreh*) by the quarryman (*sang-šekan*, *kūh-bor*) on donkey back. The same type kiln is used for both lime and gypsum burning. A most primitive form has been observed by the writer in Ḫorāsān. Here a shaft (*čā*) 3 feet in diameter was dug into the ground, about 8 feet deep. Next to it, but separated from it by about 2 feet, a pit (*páčāl*) was dug in steps, the lowest step reaching the depth of the shaft. A tunnel of 2-feet diameter connected pit and shaft and acted as a fire hole (*āteš-gāh*). The shaft was filled with the rock material up to ground level, and a fire was maintained in the tunnel for 12 hours, the fuel shrubs being pushed in from the pit with a rake (*kaš-bīl*). At the end of the firing the top of the rock stack was covered with one foot of earth, and the whole was left to cool. The more conventional furnace is in effect a smaller version of the brick kiln and often built on the sloping side of a hill (Fig. 195).

Figure 195 A Lime Burner's Kiln

Its hearth is dug straight into the hill and covered with a perforated brick arch (*tāqband*). The top of this arch has a flat, perforated surface (*sambūrak*) allowing the combustion gases to enter the kiln, which has a diameter of about 8 feet and is built by the rammed-earth technique, carefully dried during the construction to prevent cracking.

The raw material is stacked in the kiln and a fire is lit in the hearth. The lime and gypsum burner uses the same dry desert shrubs for fuel as already mentioned in the description of brickmaking. An intense fire is maintained for 12 to 24 hours for this size of furnace. The rocks packed into the kiln are about 15 inches in size at the bottom of the kiln, gradually diminishing in size to 4 inches, and sufficient space is

61 A. U. Pope and P. Ackerman, *op. cit.*, p. 427.
62 E. Diez, *op. cit.*, p. 72.
63 Ibn Ḥauqal, *The Oriental Geography of Ebn Haukal*, p. 314.

left between them to allow the free passage of combustion gases. When the firing is completed the kiln is given time to cool (*ḫonok šodan*) before its contents are taken out. Lime is sold to the builder for slaking as it comes out of the kiln, whereas gypsum is crushed to the size of hazelnuts with wooden mallets (*čakoš-e čūbī*) to be finally pulverized in an edge-runner mill. Sir John Chardin[64] described such a mill in 1665 as follows: "They take the stones (for the gypsum) out of the mountains in great plenty; they burn it, then pound it, or bruise it with a great grinding stone, thicker than a mill stone, but not so broad by two thirds of the diameter, it turns round on its back and a man always stands by, with a shovel, to throw the plaster under the grinding stone."

Quarryman

One of the more humble crafts in the building trade is that of the quarryman (*kūh-bor*, *sang-šekan*), although his is the important task of excavating suitably sized stones for the mason from their rock bed. He delivers the stones (*sang*) to the building sites as undressed rubble with just enough oversize for the stonemason to do his finishing work. The quarryman does not need many tools. Using a heavy steel crowbar (*dailam*), he and his assistant first make a series of holes into the rock in order to remove the less valuable upper rock layers by powder blasting. Ordinary black powder (*bārūt*) is carefully poured into the holes, which are closed with wads. The charges are ignited with saltpeter cords (*fatīleh*) as fuses. Once a sufficiently large horizontal bed has been cleared, the quarrymen work a vertical wall, again by blasting. All the waste fragments removed during these preparatory operations are sold either to the master builder, who needs large quantities of ballast stones for foundation building, or to the lime burner if the rock happens to be a suitable limestone.

[64] Sir J. Chardin, *op. cit.*, pp. 258–259.

Having prepared these two faces, the cutting of the rough blocks can begin. The quarrymen mark off the size of the blocks on the rock edge with a string (*rīsmān*) and red marking chalk, one line on the horizontal face, the other on the vertical. Using steel chisels (*qalam*) they cut a series of holes along the marked lines, spaced about 8 to 10 inches apart. When this rather tedious task is completed, a steel wedge (*gōveh*) is driven into each hole. When they are all set, they are gradually driven deeper and deeper until the rock breaks away from its bed, more or less along the line of the holes. Some quarrymen set wooden wedges and water them. The subsequent expansion of the wood is strong enough to break the rock from its bed.

A speciality of the Iṣfahān quarrymen is the production of huge slabs from a rather soft stone that splits easily in one direction. The slabs are about 4 inches thick and have a surface of about 3 × 5 feet. They are used as garden doors (Fig. 196). When the quarryman cuts them to size he leaves pivots (*pāšneh*) on the two ends of one side. Fitted into a hole in the lintel and another one in the threshold stone, these pivots act as hinges. Smaller stones are carried to the building site on donkey back while larger ones leave the quarry on horse-drawn carts.

The most common building stone of Persia, limestone, is of a fine-grained structure and blue-gray in color. If it is more whitish and veined it is referred to as marble (*sang-e marmar*). There are also some deposits of a pale green marble (*yaš*), mainly coming from the province of Yazd. This stone has been used for many of the Ṣafavid buildings in Iṣfahān, particularly for the interiors of mosques and palaces.

Figure 196 A Stone Door in Iṣfahān

Stonemason

The stonemason (*sang-tarāš*) belongs to one of the oldest and most respected crafts of Persia. Being fairly independent, he prefers to work on contract for a master builder. He works on the building site, as many of the stones have to be fitted to the proper dimensions as the building rises.

Having received the rough rubble (*ḫām*) from the quarryman he marks off (*ḫaṭṭ kardan*) his stone to the required dimensions. It is usually left to the assistant to cut all surplus material off with a heavy steel pick (*kolang*, Fig. 197). This squaring (*ḫām tarāšīdan*) brings the surface close to its final size. At this stage the master takes over. Using the widely spaced teeth of a mason's kernel hammer (*tīšeh-ye šāneh*) he hews the stone to an intermediate surface roughness (*tīšeh basteh kardan*). For the visible faces of the stone this process is followed by a further smoothing with the narrowly spaced teeth (*tīšeh čaġī kardan*, Fig. 198). In most cases this treatment is the last before the stone is placed into position with rather liquid sand-lime mortar (*dūġāb*). Only in special cases where highly polished surfaces are required is the stone brought to a bright shine by grinding it (*ṣaiqal kardan*) with a series of abrasive stones (*sang-e soṃbādeh*) of increasingly finer grain. When Tripoli sand and water are used in the final stage, a mirror-like surface is achieved.

Any line work or ornamental design is hewn in with chisels (*qalam*), first roughly with a heavy one (Fig. 199), followed by toothed kernel chisels (*qalam-e šāneh*) with edges similar to the kernel hammers. Finally the craftsman chisels his stonemason's mark (*ᶜalamat-e sang-tarāš*) into each stone. This is a special sign that he has chosen at the end of his apprenticeship and that he uses for the rest of his life. In comparing masons' marks of different ages it is striking to note how little these signs have changed over the centuries. Signs such as those on the stones of the palaces at Persepolis (*a* in Fig. 200) can all be found among the great number of such signs on medieval buildings as well as on the caravanserais and palaces of the seventeenth century (*b* and *c* in Fig. 200) or on present-day buildings. Little is known about the origin of these signs, which are also widely used by stonemasons of the Western world.[65]

Stone Sculptor

If the work of the stonemason is comparatively coarse, his colleague the stone sculptor (*naqqār*, *ḥajjār*) goes to an extreme of detailed minute work to chisel inscrip-

[65] The writer recognized a number of these signs on the stone walls of the old gaol in Sydney in Australia, built by English convict labor early in the nineteenth century.

Figure 197 Mason Roughing (Squaring) Column Base

Figure 198 Mason Smoothing Stone with Kernel Hammer

Figure 199 Mason Chiseling Flutes

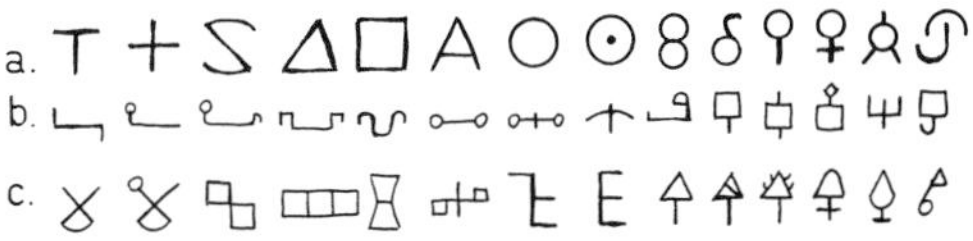

Figure 200 Stonemason's Marks. (*a*) Found in Persepolis (fifth century B.C.) and on Ṣafavid buildings of the seventeenth century A.D., (*b*) and (*c*) Found on the latter only.

tions and ornamental sculpture (*qalam-zanī, ḥajjārī-ye ẓarīfeh, monabbat-kārī rū-ye sang*) for mosques, tombstones of famous men, and walls of important buildings. He belongs to a craft that left masterpieces on the walls of the Achaemenian palaces at Persepolis and Susa, and there has been no period to our day without examples of his skill.

The country has an abundance of stones suitable for fine sculptural work, the white marble (*marmar*), fine-grained greenish marble (*sang-e gandomī*), the gray marble of Persepolis (*sang-e siyāh*), the soft green marble of Yazd (*yaš*), and fine-grained porphyry (*sang-e somāq*).

When the sculptor sets out to ornament for example a tombstone, he trims the raw block in much the same way as the common mason does, and he brings all surfaces to a bright shine. Next he copies the drawing (*naqšeh, naqš-e ḥajjārī*) onto the stone, tracing (*naqš kašīdan*) all the lines with Indian ink (*morakkab*). For the cutting (*qalam zadan*) of the pattern he has a steel hammer (*čakoš*) and a collection of sculpturing chisels (*naqqārī, qalam-e naqqārī*). They are made of hardened steel (*ḥoškeh*) and are about 6 inches long. The sculptor begins with tracing of the outlines, using a sharply pointed chisel (*mouj-e sūzanī, qalam-e sūzanī, naqqārī-ye sūzanī*), and continues with cutting the background away with various profiled hollow chisels (*dam-e qāšoqī*, Fig. 201). The cut-away background is smoothed with a set of bent,

Figure 201 A Stone Sculptor at Work

profiled files (*souhān-dastūr-dādeh*), a flat one (*souhān-e bārīk*), a round one (*souhān-e dom-mūšī*), and some with profiles at both ends (*souhān-e dō-sar*). A heavy one (*souhān-e koloft*) is used to smooth relatively large surfaces. The final polishing (*pardāḫt kardan*) is done with emery cloth (*kāġaẕ-e soṃbādeh*).

Stone Pot Maker

The carving of vessels from soft stone is a very old industry. Piggott[66] shows that even about 2800 B.C. there was an industry in the border region between Persia and India, in Balūčistān, which made and exported these stone vessels to Sumeria, Syria, and the Indus valley cities of Harappa and Mohenjodaro. There is a stone vessel industry still in existence in Austria, Bavaria, and Switzerland that is said to have been founded by the Romans.[67] The stone used there is known as Lavez (from Latin *lapis*) or Topfstein (meaning "pot stone") and is a composite of talc and chloride, very suitable for the purpose as it is both easily carved and fireproof in use. The writer also observed stone vessel makers in Central Anatolia. There they still make a few cooking vessels from soft stone for local use, but most of their work is now the making of alabaster vessels for the tourist trade.

The only large center of the industry in Persia today is at Mašhad. Just off one of the Pilgrim City's busiest streets is the quarter of the stone pot makers, who also call themselves *sang tarāš* or *ḥajjār* (Fig. 202). Their trade keeps over one hundred craftsmen busy with another hundred working in the quarries (*maᶜdan*) at the back of the "Stone Mountain" (*pošt-e kūh-e sang*) six miles out of town.

Over thirty mines are still in operation there. The miners (*kūh-bor*) first search for an outcrop of this stone, and in working the stones out follow the seam into the mountain, often more than 100 feet down. This mining technique is similar to the one applied by Persian metal miners for thousands of years, and it is probably just as old. With the seam of the gray stone in front of him, the miner makes holes (*čāl*) of about 1-inch diameter into it, using a heavy crowbar (*mīl, bairam*). From time to time he ladles the stone dust (*ḫāk-e sang*) out with a special long-handled spoon (*qāšoq*). When the right depth is reached,

Figure 202 A Stone Pot Maker's Stall at Mašhad

[66] S. Piggott, *Prehistoric India to 1000 B.C.*, pp. 105–117.
[67] L. Rütimeyer, *Urethnographie der Schweiz.*

the hole is filled with a charge of black powder (*bārūt*), a fuse (*fatīleh*) is attached, and the hole is closed with a wad (*moqavvā*). After the blasting the miner's assistant carries the rough stones weighing up to 1½ cwts to the top on his back, carefully climbing the steep steps hewn into the rock. Depending on the weather, a number of masons sit there in front of or inside humble huts and split these large stones into two to four parts, depending on the sizes ordered from the workshops. They then trim the resulting blocks (*angāreh*) with heavy picks (*kolang*) into shapes roughly approaching the future vessels. These roughed stone blocks are called *kolangī*, but if shaped to become the popular cooking pots (*dīzī*) their name is *qolveh*. Their further treatment takes place in the workshops in town.

Pots are either completely carved out by hand or turned on a special lathe. The former is done in the following stages:

1. The stone as delivered from the mine is trimmed from the outside to its approximate size with a heavy pick; the product is called *čalōr* (Fig. 203). The craftsman usually does a series of ten to fifteen at a time before he does the next stage.

2. The inside of the *čalōr* is roughed out with the heavy pick (*kolang*), followed by thinning of the walls with a smaller pick (*kōreh*).

3. Next comes the fine cutting of the outside with a coarse-toothed kernel hammer (*tīšeh-dorošt*), made of tool steel (*ḫoškeh*) with hardened teeth.

4. This is followed by a still finer cutting of the outside with a medium-toothed kernel hammer (*tīšeh-tāh*).

5. The last outside trimming is done with the finest kernel hammer (*tīšeh narm*), and then the product is called *zanjīreh*.

6. The inside is scraped out (*qalam zadan*) with a hooked scraper (*qalam*) about 2 feet long. The worker has his knee on the pot (Fig. 204), scrapes with heavy strokes, and moves the vessel on from time to time.

7. Finishing the outside (*lab kardan*) is the last stage and is done with a fine file (*souhān-e narm*). Lids for the pots are made in the same stages, and it is surprising how well they fit.

Figure 203 Trimming the Raw Stone

Cut by hand in the same way are the following other products of this stonecutter: hand mills (*āsiyā, dasteh-ās*) for the

Figure 204 Scraping the Inside of a Stone Pot

grinding of oil seeds, spices and pulse in the household, mortars (*hāvan-e gūšt-kūbī*) for the preparation of a kind of minced meat, basins for water fountains (*āb-bareh*) in the central courtyard of many Persian houses, and tombstones (*sang-e qabr*). Considering that many Moslems like to have their last rest in the Holy City of Mašhad it is obvious that there is quite a bit of work for the tombstone cutter.

A completely different way of handling these stones is the turning on a lathe (*dastgāh-e sang-tarāš*), which is similar to that of the wood turner though much stronger. This treatment gives the vessels a regular and very smooth surface. The lathe consists of a four-sided frame (*čār-čūbeh-ye dastgāh*) placed on the ground (Fig. 205). A fixed traverse beam (*langeh-s̱ābet*) and an adjustable traverse beam (*langeh motaḥarrek*) carry steel center points (*morġak, morġeh*). The movable traverse is kept square to the lathe axis by a wooden bar (*šamšīrak*) and is held in position by the outstretched leg of the operator; it can easily be opened when the work pieces are changed. A bar across the lathe acts as a tool support (*pīš-pā*). A wooden centering pivot (*kālū*) is cemented (*časbāndeh*) to the bottom of the roughed stone (*qolveh*) with hot pitch (*qīr, qīl*) and carries the string (*zeh*) of the operating bow (*kamāneh*). A point (*nōk*) is cut into the stone to form the opposite center. Pivot and point are greased, and the whole is placed between the two lathe centers (Fig. 206). The turner begins with the cutting of the outside (*pošt zadan*). The turning chisels are about 18 inches long, have hooked cutting point and wooden handles. He starts with a roughing chisel (*qalam-e kaptarāšī*) followed by an intermediate chisel (*qalam-e nīm-kāleh-pūš*), and the last one used on the outside is a smoothing chisel (*mofraz, qalam-e mofraz*). The stone turner has a good control over the movements so that he can even turn the area between the handles (Fig. 206)

Figure 205 A Stone Pot Maker's Lathe

Figure 206 Stonecutting on the Lathe

which have already been left in their places by the rough stone trimmer. Pot and pivot point are now changed over between the lathe centers and the inside of the stone is turned out, first with an inside roughing tool (*qalam-e dīzī*), followed by an inside smoothing tool (*qalam-e tah-sāvī*). The final shape of the wall is obtained with a broad, curved inside chisel (*šefreh*). The depth of cut is checked with a depth gauge (*sīḫ-e andāzeh*) and the outside diameter with calipers (*pargār-e andāzeh*). A center stem (*morġ-e dīzī*) is left inside the vessel (Fig. 207), and only after the smoothing of the whole with emery cloth (*soṃbādeh*) is the stem removed by undercutting it at the bottom of the vessel with a hooked chisel (*morġ-bor*).

Turned vessels are often rubbed with oil and obtain an almost black color. By partly removing this black surface with engraving chisels artistic effects are achieved, and especially flat dishes and plates are ornamented in this way.

The principal products of the stone turner are large cooking pots (*harkāreh*), smaller containers (*harkārečeh*), and small cooking pots (*dīzī*). Another product, selling well throughout the country, is the pipe cob for the water pipe (*sar-e qaliyān*).

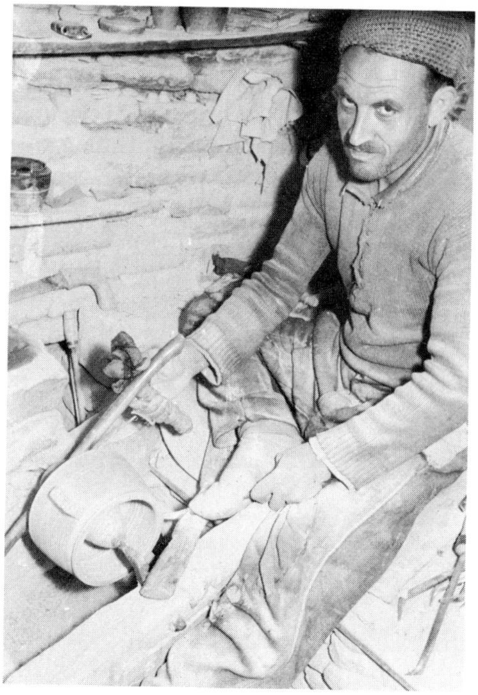

Figure 207 A Stone Turner Cutting the Inside of a Pot

Plasterer, Stucco Plasterer

In the section on the lime and gypsum burner it has been shown that stucco plaster as a building material can be traced back well over 2,500 years. Probably it was originally applied to unfired brick walls to protect them from the weather, but it also helped to mitigate bleakness of brick and rubble walls, and finally it provided a fine background for the application of decorations and ornaments.

Stucco plaster is not only cheap, easily handled, and capable of being efficiently secured to almost every construction material, but it also permits treatment with color pigments, relief and profile carving, and fine lattice work. The Persian craftsman with his gift for artistic design has brought this humble material to the high level of fine art in the form of his stucco work. No other craftsman, except perhaps the artists of Western Europe Baroque, has ever equaled him in this medium. Unfortunately the few fragments of Achaemenian, Hellenistic and Parthian stucco are only a shadow of their original polychrome beauty, and the stucco-decorated walls of the Sasanian palace ruins can only give a faint idea of the plasterers' craftsmanship.

But the architects of Islamic times continued to have their buildings decorated with stucco plaster right to the present time. There have been changes in style.

During the periods of ornamental brickwork and faience mosaic, stucco played a minor role, but there has always been a revival of it.[68] It was in the *miḥrāb*, the arched niche in a mosque indicating the direction of Mecca, that most stucco masters showed their greatest skill. One of the best preserved is the *miḥrāb* in the Friday Mosque at Iṣfahān (Fig. 208). The

Figure 208 Upper Part of the Miḥrāb in the Friday Mosque at Iṣfahān

English traveler G. Forster[69] mentions plasterwork in 1798: "All mosques are tiled with a plaster made of limestone burnt, which as soon as it is dry becomes so exceedingly hard that it rather resembles true stone than mortar, with which they do not only parget the outside of their houses and trimm it with paint after the Morisco manner but also spread their floors and arches of their rooms."

There are today two different craftsmen working in the field of stucco plaster, the difference being merely a degree of skill. We have the humble plasterer (*gač-kār, gač-gar, gač-bor*), who is only concerned with the rendering of walls and ceilings, and then there is the ornamental stucco plasterer (*nāzok-kār*) whose work is far more elaborate. It includes all kinds of architectural ornaments in plaster such as cornices, dadoes, profiled moldings, and richly carved decorations. Both craftsmen are using essentially the same tools.

The gypsum (*gač*) delivered to the building site often contains small, uncrushed particles. It must, therefore, be sifted first (*gač bīḫtan*). This is done by a laborer called *gač-bīz*. The Persian gypsum sets particularly rapidly after having been mixed with water, and this would prevent careful application and handling. To overcome this difficulty the soft gypsum-water mix has to be constantly stirred by the plasterer's assistant until it has lost most of its original setting power and has become rather creamy. This plaster is referred to as "killed plaster" (*gač-e kušteh*) and when applied to walls and ceilings can be handled with leisure and does not set hard for forty-eight hours. When it eventually does so it becomes just as hard and strong as our Western type of plaster.

Depending on the design, the plaster is rendered (*gač mālīdan*) to the wall in several layers. The plasterer has a quantity of "killed plaster" on a wooden float (*kopeleh*) from which he applies it to the wall with a steel trowel (*māleh*). Figure 209 shows how plaster is spread into the space

Figure 209 Spreading Plaster on a Wall

[68] A. U. Pope and P. Ackerman, *op. cit.*, p. 1291.

[69] G. Forster, *A Journey from Bengal to England*, p. 71.

Figure 210 Molding Plaster with a Board

between two previously prepared plaster edges. The wet plaster is then molded by a profiled board (*kašō*, Fig. 210). After the plaster has sufficiently set the surface is smoothed over (*pākīzeh kardan*, *rūsāzī kardan*), first with a trowel if the profile allows this, then with a wet cotton pad (*pambeh-āb*) or a fine-hair brush (*qalam-e mūhī*). If carved ornaments are to be applied the design is traced (*tarāhī kardan*) onto the previously prepared layers, and new plaster is built up sufficiently thick for the required ornament. This is often done with the aid of wooden molds or frames (*qāleb*). As soon as the plaster begins to set (*mohkam šodan*) the stucco plasterer starts cutting away (*borīdan*) any surplus plaster to bring out the required design (Fig. 211). For the cutting or carving he uses a series of differently-shaped knives (*kārd-e gač-borī*), i.e., a pointed knife (*dambor*), one with a round end (*būmgerd*), one with a concave end (*būmhwor*, *kārd-e qāšoqī*), and one with a square end (*naqālī*); another one with a hooked end (*kārd-e būm-konī*, *būm-konī*) is for cutting away the background (*būm*).

If columns are to be covered with plaster a straw or reed rope (*sāzū*) is wound around the column (*sāzū-bāz*, *pīčīdan be sotūn*). The coarse fibers of this rope give the plaster a good grip and also act as an elastic medium against cracking if the wooden core of the column expands and contracts due to changes in moisture.

For very fine stucco work the still wet plaster is dusted with a powder consisting of a blend of finely ground talcum powder and gypsum. Rubbed into the surface this treatment gives the plaster a high gloss. The powder is called "gold-leaf" (*zar-varaq*).[70]

If the plaster is later to be painted it is first soaked with linseed oil (*rouġan-e bazr-ʿalaf*), followed by a coat of sandarac oil (*rouġan-e sandarūs*), which is applied with a hair brush (*qalam-e mūhī*).

A speciality of the stucco plaster of the Ṣafavid period was the cutting of a lattice-work ornament from a plaster board and then filling the openings with stained glass. Such windows can still be seen in the palace of Čehel Sotūn at Iṣfahān, to which they have been transferred from the Darb-e Emām, a building erected in 1453.

Figure 211 The Carving of Stucco Plaster

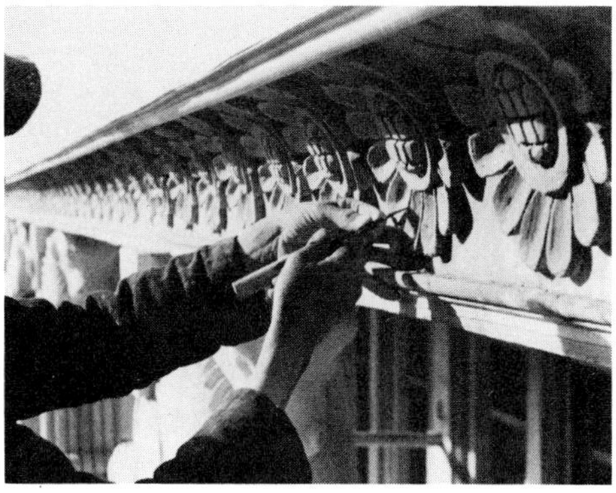

[70] Sir J. Chardin, *op. cit.*, p. 260.

Pottery and Ceramics

Clay, the raw material of the potter, is available in almost every country, and when early mankind abandoned a hunting life for animal husbandry and agriculture, earthenware pottery came into general use.[71] Persia's history of ceramics began in the fourth millennium B.C. Then most of the Neolithic peoples had settled for some kind of agricultural life and had developed forms of pottery, for daily use as well as for religious purposes. Only a few nations reached the summit of achievement and stayed there for long periods. The greatest of them are the Chinese and the Persians. The potters who produced the noble vessels of classical Greece confined themselves to very few styles and methods of decoration. They never used true glazes, and, magnificent as their products were, they were so only during a limited period in history. Chinese and Persian potters, however, exercised their craft from the very beginnings of ceramics, continued to work through prehistoric times to the present day, and they have applied all the techniques available to them to produce pottery of the highest standard. Apart from a considerable number of contacts and mutual influences the potters of the two countries went different ways in both style and technique.

Since pottery has this long and continuous record and since it expresses, more than any other craft, the Persian's ability to combine functional design with highly artistic adornment, and since it supplies almost every walk of life with its products, it may be proper to give here an outline of pottery technique in Persia from early Neolithic times to the present day. Most of the evidence for our knowledge of early pottery is due to the fortunate fact that, fragile as the potter's ware is, once the sherds were safely buried, they hardly deteriorated while waiting for the archaeologist to interpret their story. There is little written evidence on ceramics, except perhaps a few Babylonian and Assyrian cuneiform tablets from about 1700 B.C. and 650 B.C.,[72] in both cases giving a number of potter's recipes for colored clay bodies and glazes. In more modern times there are the recipe books written by a member of a famous Kāšān family of potters in 1301 A.D.,[73] and finally a number of signatures and short texts of potters and decorators on their products, some with dates, some without.

Tradition, literature, and archaeology have established some fifty centers in Persia where fine pottery has been made, and probably there existed many more engaged in producing utility ware. One pottery center merits mention above all others, i.e., Kāšān, where potters were already active in Neolithic times, became famous during the Middle Ages, and are still producing fine ware today, after 6,000 years of productivity.

A Historical Outline of Persian Ceramic Techniques

Prehistoric Wares: Clay Bodies, Pigment Painting, Early Glazes

Beginning with the middle of last century the spade of the archaeologist has brought to light a great number of ceramic vessels and other objects in an area reaching from East Persia to Mesopotamia, from the Caucasus to the Indus Valley. The prehistoric pottery found in this vast area

[71] H. Kühn, "Frühformen der Keramik," p. 128.

[72] C. J. Gadd and R. Campbell-Thompson, "A Middle Babylonian Chemical Text," pp. 87–96, and R. J. Forbes, *Studies in Ancient Technology*, Vol. 5, p. 135.

[73] H. Ritter, *et al.*, "Orientalische Steinbücher und persische Fayencetechnik," pp. 2–56.

is, with some variations, rather uniform in technique and style, and is of an astonishingly developed technical standard. Its first examples came from Susa in Elam, a very old settlement at the foot of the Iranian Plateau. Today Susa ware is a class name for pottery from Susa proper, but also from Tepe Mūsiyān, 100 miles west of Susa, from Sumer (Ur)[74] and Tel Halaf in Mesopotamia, from Northwest India and Balūčistān[75] or from the Iranian Plateau at Tepe Giyān, Tepe Ḥiṣār, Tūrang Tepe, Siyalk, or as far east as Anau, today in Russian Turkistan. Ware of what is known as Susa I has been dated for a period lasting from about 3500 B.C. to about 2500 B.C.[76] It should be noted here that people with a Neolithic culture also appeared in the Chinese province of Kansu,[77] and their ceramic ware has many features similar to Susa ware, in technique as well as in style.

The oldest pottery found in Persia is a black smoked ware[78] that is similar to the oldest pottery ever found anywhere.[79] The earliest earthenware vessels, dated by the carbon-14 method as belonging to the fourth millennium B.C., have been found in Mesopotamia. The oldest ones found in Persia belong to the same period. This rather primitive, hand-formed ware is followed by a red ware with black patches from crude firing. A number of technical improvements in the craft of the potter brought about a new style which was to last, with changes and interruptions, for over 2,000 years on some of the sites on the Iranian Plateau.

[74] E. Diez, *op. cit.*, p. 164.

[75] A. U. Pope and P. Ackerman, *op. cit.*, p. 194, and S. Piggott, "Prehistoric India to 1000 B.C.," p. 117.

[76] A. U. Pope and P. Ackerman, *op. cit.*, p. 180.

[77] H. Kühn, *Der Aufstieg der Menschheit*, p. 138, and G. Savage, *Pottery through the Ages*, p. 61.

[78] R. Ghirshman, *op. cit.*, p. 29.

[79] H. Kühn, *Der Aufstieg der Menschheit*, p. 26.

The most marked of the technical improvements are:

1. A very fine clay body which was obviously slaked. It burned in the firing to a buff, cream, yellow, pink or sometimes dark red color. The cream or buff colored sherds show a distinct zone produced by firing in a reducing atmosphere (see upper sherd in Fig. 212 where it measures $\frac{1}{16}$-inch in depth).

Figure 212 Pot Sherds from Siyalk

2. All vessels were formed to an even thickness. Those about 4 inches high were less than $\frac{1}{8}$-inch thick; the largest ones found were 12 inches high and only $\frac{3}{8}$-inch thick.

3. The perfect roundness and some turning marks suggest that at least a slow-moving turntable or tournette, the precursor of the potter's wheel, was already in use.

4. All vessels have been dipped in a fine slip of clay that gave them an extremely smooth surface.

5. A pigment paint made from powdered oxide of iron hydrate and manganese oxide was applied on this slip. In the subsequent firing the pigment burned to either a black or a dark brown color.

6. Before the end of the fourth millennium B.C. the slow-moving tournette had developed into a fully fledged potter's wheel. This has been proved at least for

Siyalk[80] in Central Persia and Tepe Ḥiṣār[81] in Northeast Persia.

7. At about the same time that type of kiln developed in which the combustion chamber is below the chamber for the ware, separated from it by a brick grate.[80, 81] It must have been this type of kiln that permitted the control of the atmosphere necessary for the production of buff and cream colored ware. This kiln type is still used by potters and brickmakers throughout the country, and they still prefer the buff color for pots and bricks.

8. Molded pottery has been found at Tepe Ḥiṣār and Tele Bakūn in South Persia.[81] A number of fired clay molds for the mass production of figurines, dated between 2500 and 1750 B.C., has been found on various sites (Fig. 213).

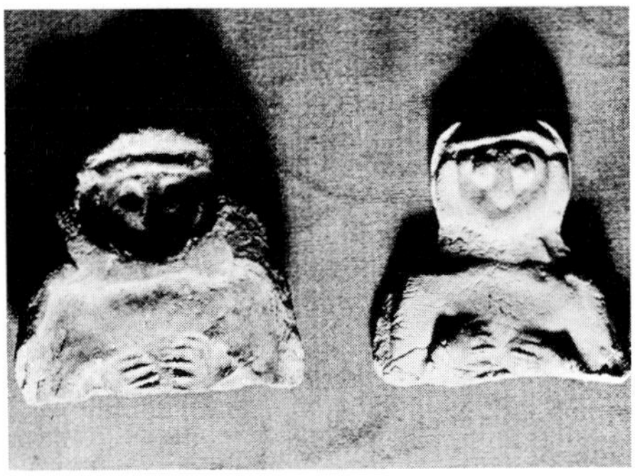

Figure 213 A Figurine Mold and Imprint from Tepe Giyān III, 2500–1800 B.C.

9. A gray-bodied pottery with a black shiny luster appeared first by about 2000 B.C. in Tepe Ḥiṣār and after 2000 B.C. at Siyalk. This too must have been fired in a reducing atmosphere, and it is the first luster ceramic of which we know. It may be of interest to mention here that the luster technique of the Middle Ages became famous at Kāšān, and Kāšān is only a few miles away from Siyalk.

All these technical advances made pottery an established craft in a relatively short time, and it has remained an established craft ever since. But the skill of the ancient potter was not only a technical one. The beauty of his products is extraordinary. The stroke of the brush applying the oxide pigments to the slip base is sure, the ornament using animal and plant forms bringing their essentials out in an almost geometrical design.

Most "oasis civilizations" of the wide area of "Susa Pottery" experienced interruptions and changes in the production of their ware. These were caused by the influx of new peoples, and by warfare; most of all, changes came about during periods of peaceful progress. Between 1750 and 1100 B.C. the great city civilizations of Mesopotamia, i.e., Babylon, Elam, and Assyria, made their presence felt from the west, and the Kassites, a hybrid nation of Central Asians and Indo-Aryan conquerors, exercised an influence from the east. During Kassite rule over Persia (1750–1170 B.C.), pottery became enriched by a further technique, i.e., glazing. This was the most important development after the forming of the vessel itself. It is generally assumed that the Kassites brought glazing to Persia from Babylonia, which they occupied for several centuries.

Glazing Techniques and their Development

1. Already during the fourth millennium the oldest known Egyptian civilization, known as Badarian, produced steatite beads covered with a blue to turquoise alkaline glaze. Steatite is a crystalline form of talc, hydrated magnesium silicate. Antique mines of steatite have been found in Egypt. The material can be easily carved and can be fired and glazed,

[80] R. Ghirshman, *op. cit.*, p. 36.

[81] D. E. McCown, "The Material Culture of Early Iran," pp. 430–432.

as A. Lucas has shown in a series of experiments.[82]

2. During pre-Dynastic times (4000–3400 B.C.) the Egyptians produced objects such as beads, scarabs, and tiles which were molded from ground quartz sand and about 5 per cent natron (sodium carbonate and sodium bicarbonate, naturally occurring in the Western Desert). This mixture was fused into a quartz frit and could also be glazed. Objects of this class have often erroneously been referred to as faience. They were made throughout the history of ancient Egypt and into medieval times up to 1400 A.D., and they were exported into most countries of the Near East.[83]

3. Since middle pre-Dynastic times solid quartz (rock crystal) shaped into beads and ornaments by grinding has been coated with blue glaze, which fused perfectly on to the quartz.

The essential ingredients of this Egyptian glaze were silica (from sand), an alkali (from wood ashes or natron), and a metal oxide (from a copper compound). It has been assumed by some historians of technology that quartz pebbles in a fireplace had been accidentally covered with these ingredients and a glaze was so produced. Another assumption was that the slags of copper smelting furnaces could be used to produce blue and turquoise glazes. Lucas[84] proved in laboratory experiments that neither of the two processes produced blue glazes. However, he knew from archaeological evidence that a certain copper ore, viz., malachite, had been used in ancient Egypt as an eye make-up. It was ground on a quartz stone with natron solution as a binder. Lucas took quartz pieces which he had used in this manner, fired them in a kiln, and obtained a brilliant blue glaze, very similar to the glazes on the ancient quartz frit, steatite, and quartz crystal. No glazes were applied in Egypt to earthenware until Ptolemaic times (second century B.C.). Then the glazes used were lead glazes, probably developed in Babylonia.

4. In Mesopotamia the manufacture of these blue alkaline glazes became generally known by about 3000 B.C., and they spread from there to the Indus valley civilization[85] through the numerous trade channels existing at that time. Interesting evidence is available on the later development of glazing in Babylon. As we will see, the discovery of the most important modern glaze, viz., lead glaze, took place there. In 1925 B. Meissner found a few Assyrian texts from the library of Assurbanipal (668–625 B.C.) that turned out to be chemo-technical recipes for the glaze technologists of that time.[86] In 1936 Gadd and Campbell-Thompson[87] published the translated text of some cuneiform tablets 1,000 years older (of about 1700 B.C.) containing a number of recipes for colored clay bodies and several alkaline and lead glazes. The discovery of these recipes came as a great surprise in finding the knowledge of glazes so well advanced in Babylonia and Assyria at that time. It is to be noted that we have here, for the first time, glazes on clay bodies and not on quartz frit as in Egypt. Excavations in Mesopotamia have shown that the knowledge contained in these tablets was widely used. At Nimrud in Assyria of the time of 750–612 B.C., building bricks often had a glazed face of $13\frac{1}{2} \times 4\frac{1}{2}$ inches in size. An analysis of the glazes[88] showed that then for the first time

82 A. Lucas, *Ancient Egyptian Materials and Industries*, pp. 178 ff.

83 *Ibid.*, p. 180, and W. J. Furnival, *Leadless Decorative Tiles, Faience and Mosaic*, pp. 34–36.

84 A. Lucas, *op. cit.*, pp. 198 ff.

85 G. V. Childe, *What Happened in History?*, p. 180.

86 B. Meissner, *Babylonien und Assyrien*, and R. J. Forbes, *op. cit.*, Vol. 5, p. 135.

87 C. J. Gadd and R. Campbell-Thompson, *op. cit.*, pp. 87–96.

88 W. J. Furnival, *op. cit.*, pp. 32–33.

known in history tin oxide was used to produce an opaque white. Pigments for the colors of the Nimrud tile glazes were antimoniate of lead for yellow, iron for brown, and copper for blue and green. The frit for these glazes mainly consisted of a silicate of soda aided by some lead as a flux. The most beautiful building of the new Babylon of Nebuchadnezzar (604–562 B.C.) must have been the great city gate dedicated to the goddess Ishtar, which was excavated between 1890 and 1917. It was completely covered with enameled bricks similar to those of Nimrud, the colors being deep blue, malachite green, sap green, yellow, cream, and white.[89]

5. During the 600 years' rule of the Kassites, much of the Babylonian knowledge of glazing technique must have come to Persia.[90] This influence continued during the Neo-Babylonian empire in Mesopotamia (1171–550 B.C.). Many glazed pots and tiles in the Babylonian-Assyrian technique of this period have been found in Susa. When the Achaemenians conquered the greater part of the Middle East from 550 B.C. on and Darius built new palaces for his winter capital in Susa and his summer residence in Persepolis, these buildings were adorned with multicolored relief bricks showing huge winged bulls, lions, and the immortal faithful ones. These friezes measured 36 × 11 feet, and all the work was done by Babylonian craftsmen as Darius describes in the foundation charter of Susa: "... the men who wrought the baked bricks were Babylonians ...."[91] Apart from these tiles very little glazed ware has been found in the Achaemenian palaces except one turquoise-blue jar in the large treasury hall at Persepolis.[92]

6. True glaze was not known to the Greeks,[93] and a glaze containing lead oxide came into general use in the Mediterranean world only during Ptolemaic times (second century B.C.).[94] This glaze was known to the Romans as Parthian glaze,[95] indicating that the Romans probably learned the process from their East Persian enemies with whom they had so many contacts in Syria and Mesopotamia. It is of course also possible that the Romans obtained their knowledge of glazes from the Phoenicians who, probably borrowing Babylonian techniques as a basis, established a flourishing glass industry in Sidon and Tyrus on the Mediterranean coast about 500 B.C.[96]

Lead glazes are brilliant, allow a wide color range, and melt at a low temperature. However, they tend to smudge and run and thus limit the scope of the ceramic artist.

During the second century B.C., i.e., during the time of the Parthian empire, lead glazes appeared in China[97] for the first time. Most authors today agree that the Parthians passed on their knowledge of lead glazes through the many trade contacts that had been established between them and the Han empire.[98] The Persian influence must have gone far beyond glazes only, since many Chinese ceramic objects of that time show Parthian horses, riders, and hunting scenes, all in a Scythian or Iranian style.[99] This would agree with an old Chinese tradition that lead glaze was brought to China by a Persian merchant.[100] There is strong evidence that the

[89] *Ibid.*, pp. 27–28.
[90] A. U. Pope and P. Ackerman, *op. cit.*, p. 186.
[91] R. Ghirshman, *op. cit.*, p. 166.
[92] E. F. Schmidt, *op. cit.*, p. 85.

[93] W. J. Furnival, *op. cit.*, p. 50.
[94] G. Savage, *op. cit.*, p. 24.
[95] A. Lane, *Early Islamic Pottery, Mesopotamia, Egypt, Persia*, pp. 8–9.
[96] R. J. Forbes, *op. cit.*, Vol. 5, pp. 143–148.
[97] G. Savage, *op. cit.*, pp. 62–63.
[98] A. U. Pope and P. Ackerman, *op. cit.*, p. 53.
[99] W. B. Honey, *The Ceramic Art of China and other Countries of the Far East*, p. 30.
[100] B. Leach, *A Potter's Book*, p. 136.

Persians sold the Chinese a ready-made glaze frit, known in old Chinese records as *liu-li*.[101] This would also explain why lead glaze disappeared from Chinese pottery after the breakdown of the Han dynasty in 220 A.D. It was firmly re-established during the T'ang dynasty, 608–906 A.D., and this was again a time of close trade contacts with Persia.

7. Lead glazes continued to be used during Sasanian times (224–651 A.D.). The next step in the development of glazes was the rediscovery of alkaline glazes by Persian potters during Islamic times, and this will be described when we reach that stage in the general history of pottery techniques.

Pottery in Achaemenian, Parthian, and Sasanian Times

With the arrival of the Achaemenians we have come to fully documented historical times. It is disappointing that very little pottery of that period has been found, when there was, at the same time, an abundance of products of other crafts, particularly in metal work and stone sculpture. The pottery vessels that have been excavated in Persepolis[102] and Susa are just a few unglazed water jars, some bowls and bottles, and large storage containers. They all seem to be purely utilitarian, and only one of the vessels found has traces of a turquoise glaze. There are the great colored tile reliefs from the two capital cities, but they had been made by Babylonians, as we know from the foundation charter already mentioned.[103] This obvious decline of the potter's craft can perhaps be explained by the general rise in the standard of living where gold, silver, and alabaster vessels were used in the royal households, copper and brass utensils in the average home, and only the poorest had to make do with the potter's products.

This status of the potter's craft, mainly to supply ware for daily domestic use, continued during the Hellenistic era and the Parthian empire. It should be remembered, however, that the Parthians brought lead glazes in many colors into general use. A peculiar new line of the Parthian potter was the production of glazed earthenware coffins, sarcophagi,[104] funereal urns, and many kinds of clay model gifts for tombs. Most of the vessels for daily use were thrown on the wheel; often they were carved on the surface before glazing; some were press-molded in carved and fired earthenware molds. There are also numerous finds of small stamps that had been used to decorate surfaces, in a manner somewhat similar to the Roman *terra sigillata* technique. Some of the finer products show decorations in what became later known as "Barbotine," a technique where a thin paste of fine clay was squeezed from a bag onto the surface of a vessel, forming lines and coils, not much different from the cake-icing of our pastry-cooks. Most of the vessels were glazed in one color, the color range comprising cream, yellow, brown, blue, and green.[105]

As mentioned before, there was not much development in the potter's craft during Sasanian times (224–650 A.D.). The potters continued the Parthian style, but their work does not compare favorably with the beautiful metalwork of the Sasanian masters. Parthian glaze continued to be used, often over a more richly carved or embossed surface. Some of the large storage jars from this period are over 3 feet high, unglazed but decorated all over by pressing a wooden carved stamp into the soft clay.

101 W. B. Honey, *op. cit.*, p. 32.

102 E. F. Schmidt, *op. cit.*, p. 85.

103 R. Ghirshman, *op. cit.*, p. 165.

104 *Ibid.*, p. 282, and A. U. Pope and P. Ackerman, *op. cit.*, p. 649.

105 R. Ettinghausen in A. U. Pope, *op. cit.*, p. 651.

Pottery in Islamic Times

When within a very short time the Arabs conquered the whole Sasanian empire, it did not at first greatly affect the work of the craftsman. But when in 750 A.D. the Persian House of Abū'l-ʿAbbās came to the throne of the caliphs in Baghdad, a great revival of all cultural activities took place. Islam forbade the use of luxurious metal vessels, especially those of gold and silver. Therefore the leading classes became once again the customers of the potter, and they were prepared to buy more elaborately decorated earthenware of a higher artistic standard. Gradually the potter's craft became well organized in the country's many ceramic centers, and master potters began to employ specialists. An inscription on the tiled prayer-niche (*miḥrāb*) for the shrine of Yaḥyā at Varāmīn near Tehrān gives credit separately to the potter, the ornament designer, and the calligrapher.[106] Other specialists occasionally mentioned are the ceramic engraver and the glazer.[107] Within a short time the Persian potter learned to apply a wide range of decorative techniques such as thumb marks, channels, and ridges worked into the soft clay and engravings from scraffito to carving. He applied the *champ-levé* process to clay, a process originally used in metalwork, and he worked with carved relief molds. He pierced walls of vessels and closed the holes with translucent glazes, and he also made attempts at luster glazes.

Historically we can distinguish three major Islamic periods:[108]

1. Early Islamic period up to the beginning of the eleventh century.
2. Middle Islamic period comprising the Seljūq and the Mongol dynasties.
3. Late Islamic period from the Ṣafavids to the present day.

Figure 214 A Press-Molded Jar from Istaḫr, Eighth Century A.D.

Early Islamic Period

During the first century of Islam the humble potter continued to produce his ware along Partho-Sasanian lines. He mainly made unglazed buff vessels, often formed and decorated in a press mold (Fig. 214), or vessels with a turquoise or blue lead glaze. Such press molds were made of unglazed clay with the ornament carved in before firing. There were usually several mold parts for one article, e.g., for a jar, one for the lower half, one for the upper half of the body, and a split mold for the neck. Figure 214 shows clearly how the parts were later joined together. In 1938 the writer unearthed such a mold at

[106] A. U. Pope and P. Ackerman, *op. cit.*, p. 1449.
[107] *Ibid.*
[108] *Ibid.*, p. 1465.

Figure 215 A Press Mold from Nīšāpūr, Tenth Century A.D. (*from C. K. Wilkinson, "The Kilns of Nishapur"; Metropolitan Museum Excavations, 1947*)

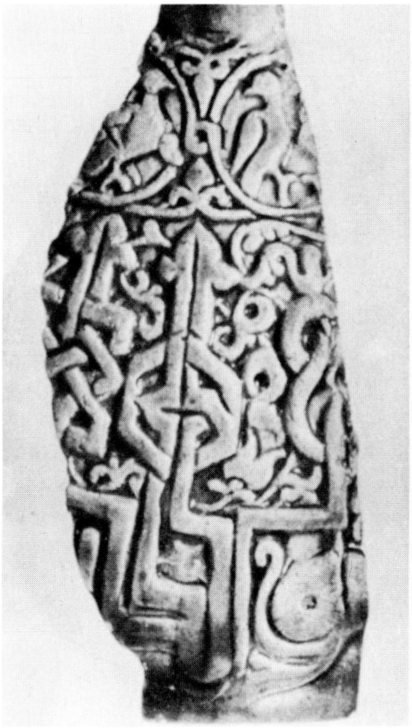

Figure 216 Pressing from Mold Shown in Fig. 215

Istaḫr in Fārs, a town famous in Sasanian and early Islamic times. That mold must have been used during the early eighth century A.D.

In 1947 a team of archaeologists from the Metropolitan Museum of Art at New York discovered a complete early Islamic workshop at Nīšāpūr in Ḫorāsān[109] and found many such molds and kiln wasters made in them. According to coins found near the same kiln site, the molds must have been in use right into the eleventh century A.D. Some of them have elaborate decorations. Close examination has shown that some of these molds must have been made by working clay over a carved wooden master model, as the imprint of the grain of the wood can be seen on some of the clay molds.[110] Other molds were thrown on the wheel—the throwing marks are still visible—and terra cotta stamps were used to produce a repetitive pattern. Figures 215 to 217 show a fragment of such a mold. It is obvious that the parts of this mold were temporarily held together by clay lugs (Fig. 217), making sure that they shrank equally during drying and firing. The lugs were later carefully cut and then served as register points.

During these early days of Islamic pottery, strong impulses for development came from China. The historians at-Taᶜālibī and al-Bīrūnī (d. 1048 A.D.) wrote about the various types of ware imported from China, and they were full

[109] C. K. Wilkinson, "The Kilns of Nishapur," pp. 235–240.
[110] *Ibid.*, p. 236.

Figure 217 Outside of Press Mold Shown in Fig. 215 (*note lugs*)

of praise for their quality.[111] Moḥammad ibn al-Ḥosain wrote that the governor of Ḫorāsān received twenty pieces of Chinese porcelain in 1059 A.D., that he had sent them to the caliph's court, and that the local potters were shown this ware and were exhorted to produce similar quality.[112] Indeed, a number of technical inventions were made during this time as a result of attempts to produce porcelain in the style of the T'ang. The Persian potters often succeeded in imitating T'ang ware so well that at first glance it was taken for genuine Chinese.[113] In particular they were good at producing what is known as splashed ware, popularly called egg-and-spinach ware. Two different hues of yellow were produced with chrome and antimony, and green was produced with copper. Later, other colors were added to the palette, brown from iron, purple and aubergine from manganese, and black from iron combined with manganese. These pigments were applied to a slip of an unusually white clay into which the vessel made of an ordinary red-firing clay had been dipped. The whole was covered with a clear lead glaze. The underlying metal pigments combined with this glaze and developed their color during firing. The clear glaze produced a porcelain-like appearance on the white slip. This slip was often carefully incised or partly carved away before the application of the glaze, thus giving the effect of Chinese scraffito ware.[114] Potteries having worked in these techniques have been found at Samarra, at Ray near Tehrān (the Rhages of the ancients), Susa, Tīz, Qaṣr Abū-Naṣr, Istaḫr, and Nīšāpūr.

The attempts at imitating Chinese porcelain by the Persian potters of the early Islamic period led to the rediscovery of tin-enamel glaze. In the section on early glazes the writer has shown that during the eighth century B.C. the Assyrians had already used tin-oxide in their lead glazes to produce an opaque white. Since the last use of this technique can be proved for the Near East on the glazed bricks at Susa and Persepolis during the fifth century B.C., we seem to be justified in speaking about a rediscovery after 1,500 years. This new glaze, which gave a perfectly white surface, eliminated the use of white slip. From Persia its use spread rapidly over the whole Islamic world, as far as Spain. There it formed the basis for the Hispano-Moresque pottery, ware from the Spanish island of Majorca. From there it came to Italy under the name of majolica, and soon Italy produced it too. From Italy it went

111 A. Lane, *op. cit.*, p. 31.
112 *Ibid.*, p. 10.
113 A. U. Pope and P. Ackerman, *op. cit.*, p. 1449.
114 G. Savage, *op. cit.*, pp. 26, 86.

to Germany, Holland, and England. In the two latter countries it became known as Delft ware.[115]

Another important innovation in the potter's craft was luster painting, which had already begun before 883 A.D.[116] Objects in this technique—never used by the Chinese potter—have been found near the old potteries of Fustat near Cairo and in Iraq, but most modern scholars agree that it is a Persian invention.[117] Luster, too, became known in Moorish Spain in the famous potteries of Paterna and Valencia;[118] it reached Italy about 1500 A.D.[119]

A great number of luster fragments has been found at Samarra, a pleasure resort built by the Caliph Muʾtasim, the son of Harūn ar-Rašīd, in 838 and abandoned in 883 A.D.[120] Another early application of luster painting is known in the tiles on the *miḥrāb* of the great mosque at Qairawān in Egypt, built between 856 and 863 A.D.[121]

In luster painting certain sulphuric pigments were mixed with dissolved gold, silver, or copper oxide and applied together with red and yellow ocher as an earthy vehicle or perhaps an oxidizing agent. This paint was applied onto an already fired smooth glaze. The piece was then fired a second time at a lower temperature, first in an ordinary, i.e., oxidizing, atmosphere, then toward the end of the process in a reducing atmosphere. During the latter stage the metal oxides were reduced to metals that were suspended in the glaze in colloidal form and appeared as a shining metallic film.

There are essentially three types of luster:[122]

1. Plain gold luster on white background.

2. Ruby luster on white background or together with other colors.

3. Polychrome luster in copper or silver metallic shine or, if the film is sufficiently thin, the luster appears to be yellow, brown, or olive, all on white background.

Luster painting was highly technical, and all depended on the skill of the potter. Some pottery centers otherwise famous for their achievements, e.g., Nīšāpūr,[123] have never successfully produced luster ware. However, in their efforts to obtain a luster effect these potters developed a new technique, i.e., underglaze painting.[124]

Luster painting reached its peak at Kāšān during Seljūq and Mongol times. Another development took place during the ninth and tenth centuries, but this was confined to East Persia: the potters of Samarkand discovered that colors under lead glaze, so apt to run and smudge, would stay fixed if the metal oxides applied were first mixed into a paste with fine white clay slip.

The potters of Nīšāpūr excelled in yet another form of decoration, the so-called manganese underglaze painting. Here a body of ordinary clay was dipped into a white slip, fired, and painted upon with manganese oxide suspended in water and grape syrup (*šīr-e angūr*). The whole was fixed in a second firing with a clear lead overglaze that produced a deep black with the manganese, strongly contrasting with the white slip of the background. In this technique the Persian calligrapher found an opportunity to apply his craft to pottery.

During the ninth and tenth centuries

[115] *Ibid.*, pp. 103, 106–107; also, W. J. Furnival, *op. cit.*, p. 82.
[116] A. U. Pope and P. Ackerman, *op. cit.*, p. 1469.
[117] *Ibid.*, p. 1490.
[118] G. Savage, *op. cit.*, p. 103.
[119] *Ibid.*, p. 107.
[120] *Ibid.*, p. 88.
[121] K. A. C. Creswell, *op. cit.*, p. 298.
[122] A. U. Pope and P. Ackerman, *op. cit.*, p. 1488.
[123] C. K. Wilkinson, *op. cit.*, p. 102.
[124] *Ibid.*

Chinese influence can be noted again in the imitation of the Ting-Yao ware of the Sung dynasty (906–1179 A.D.) The original Ting-Yao is a genuine porcelain with notched and scalloped rims. Here too it appears that the Persian potter did not for long merely try to imitate the Chinese style,[125] but modified it soon to the Persian taste and developed it into what is known as "graffito." On the Iranian Plateau we find a monochrome white graffito ware. A coarse red clay body carries a fine white slip; an ornamentation is engraved into it with a stylus. The whole is then covered with a transparent lead glaze. One bowl found[126] has the date (993 A.D.) and the name of the master: "made by Yaḥyā, the ceramist" incised under the glaze. In the Caspian province of Māzandarān we find the same ware but with an ivory or pale green glaze. The Ray potters produced graffito ware widely, but not as elaborately engraved as the former two, and theirs is covered with a turquoise clear glaze. In design all Persian graffito ware has a strong resemblance to chased metalwork, especially Sasanian. This is most marked in Māzandarān and is not surprising, because this province was the one where the Sasanian form of the Mazda religion survived right into the eleventh century.

Middle Islamic Period

During the Seljūqs' rule (1037–1147 A.D.), a remarkable upsurge took place in all the arts, crafts, and sciences. Although of Turkish origin, the Seljūqs adapted themselves closely to the Persian way of life. So far as pottery was concerned, this was the "golden age of ceramics."[127] It was the time when most of the then known techniques were applied: incised or in relief, pierced or embossed, painted over or under the glaze, gilded and lustered. It seems that it had become a regular practice at that time that painters and designers assisted the master potter with their skill. In Seljūq times also, Chinese porcelain appeared again in Persia—the Seljūq empire reached from the frontiers of China to the Mediterranean—and Chinese porcelain was still the ideal for the Persian potter. There are kaolin deposits in Tūs, Ray, Kāšān, and Iṣfahān. The potters' never-ending efforts to equal porcelain and its feldspathic glazes resulted in two new developments, i.e., the invention of the quartz-enriched soft-paste body and the rediscovery of alkaline glazes, last used in ancient Egypt. Pulverized quartz pebbles and an alkaline glaze frit, added to the clay, produced a fused, very hard, semi-transparent body after firing, similar to what became known during the eighteenth century in Europe as soft paste porcelain. As the same alkaline glaze, made up from powdered pebbles and potash, was used for the subsequent glazing, body and glaze fused excellently and no slip was needed. Analyses of such glazes[128] have shown that a new flux was introduced during the ninth century to obtain a low melting glaze. This flux was borax, of which Persia has abundant deposits and which she supplied to Europe during the Middle Ages.[129] The early ninth-century writer on mineralogy known as Pseudo-Aristotle[130] already mentions borax as an effective flux for glass and glazemaking. More details on the new flux are contained in the mineralogy of the Persian encyclopedist al-Bīrūnī (970–1038 A.D.).[131] In the chap-

125 A. U. Pope and P. Ackerman, *op. cit.*, pp. 1504–1505.

126 In the Chicago Art Institute. See A. U. Pope, *op. cit.*, Pl. 586*a*.

127 *Ibid.*, p. 1512.

128 L. J. Olmer, "L'Industrie Persane," p. 57.

129 B. Laufer, *The Beginning of Porcelain in China*, p. 503.

130 J. Ruska, *Das Steinbuch des Aristoteles.*

131 P. Kahle, "Bergkristalle, Glas und Glasflüsse nach dem Steinbuch des Al-Biruni," pp. 345–350.

ter on the composition of glass and glazes he says that a certain frit for glazemaking is made up from ground quartz, potash, and one of the boron compounds (*būra*, the local borax, or *tinkār*, the borax imported from Tibet) as a flux. His contemporary Ṣaharbūẖt, describing a similar glaze, states that its specific weight is $62\frac{19}{24}$ if ruby is taken as 100. Al-Bīrūnī further describes an enamel glaze containing borax and lead; for this glaze he gives the specific weight as $99\frac{1}{3}$ compared with ruby. Abūlqasim al-Kāšānī, a member of a well-known family of Kāšān potters, mentions in his book on the ceramic techniques of his time,[132] written in 1301 A.D., that the mineral *qamsarī* is used for glazemaking, and from the description it appears that it was probably boro-calcite.[133] Olmer found in 1908 that glazes from Kāšān and Nāʿīn contained approximately 10 per cent borax.[134]

Tin oxide was used if opaque glaze was required. The body was often carved and then covered with a clear glaze, a technique known as *laqābī*. A variation consisted in the covering of the white body with manganese and iron-oxide pigments, ornaments then being carved into the still powdery pigments, and the overcasting of the whole with a clear alkaline glaze. During the firing the remaining pigments turned into a deep black. Al-Bīrūnī wrote on this:[135] "Such vessels imitating porcelain (*čīnī*) are made from pure pebbles and clay." But we have a more concise description of many details of this and other pottery techniques of the time in the book of Abūlqasim.

The introduction of alkaline glazes resulted in completely new coloring techniques. Copper in lead glazes usually produces a turquoise shade or a vivid green,[136] but in alkaline glazes it results in a deep indigo blue. Cobalt (*lājvard-e kāšī*) produces a beautiful sapphire blue (*ābī-meškī*, *lājvardī*) in alkaline glazes. There are cobalt deposits near Kāšān and Qom,[137] and it is likely that the use of cobalt originated there. Abūlqasim quotes several cobalt minerals used at Kāšān for coloring glazes. During his time cobalt reached China (during the Yüang dynasty, 1260–1368 A.D.), and for a long time it remained there a commodity imported from Persia known as Mohammedan blue.[138] Other colors commonly produced in alkaline glazes were a bright turquoise, light green, maroon, purple red, and a mild yellow, often enriched by gold ornament. This was either melted-on gold or gold in colloidal suspension in the glaze. Al-Bīrūnī[139] describes the use of gold for the preparation of the famous ruby glass and ruby glazes and says that 1 part of gold in 50,000 parts of frit results in a deep ruby color, in 100,000 parts in a bright red.

In using this palette the Persian potter also developed two new glazing techniques, known as *mīnai* (enamel) and *haft-rang* (seven colors). For the *mīnai* the potter melted alkaline frit and pigments in a crucible into a glaze of the required color. After cooling the resulting block was powderized, and this glaze, when applied to a vessel, did not change its color any more during the subsequent firing. It offered the advantage to the decorative painter that he knew the outcome of the colors beforehand, and this fact encouraged him to use

132 MSS. Aya Sofia 3614 and 3613; see also H. Ritter, *et al.*, *op. cit.*, pp. 16 ff.

133 H. Ritter, *op. cit.*, p. 33.

134 European ceramists successfully introduced borax glazes in the ceramic industry toward the turn of this century. This was then regarded as an important discovery.

135 A. U. Pope and P. Ackerman, *op. cit.*, p. 1512.

136 C. K. Wilkinson, "Fashion and Technique in Persian Pottery," p. 103.

137 W. J. Furnival, *op. cit.*, p. 82, and L. J. Olmer, *op. cit.*, p. 56.

138 G. Savage, *op. cit.*, p. 82.

139 P. Kahle, *op. cit.*, p. 351.

a wide color range. The *haft-rang* process has been described by Abūlqasim in his treatise. The pigments for these colors were painted directly on the biscuit-fired ware, which was then dipped into a clear alkaline glaze. During the subsequent second firing the pigments developed into brilliant colors with the overlying glaze. Black outlines and supplementary colors, which during this firing would have produced unwanted color effects with the pigments already applied, were painted on after the second firing mixed with a vitreous flux of lower melting point and fixed in a third firing at a lower temperature, thus leaving the underglaze pigments undisturbed.[140]

As these alkaline glazes were less inclined to run, and as incompatible pigments were separated by the clear glaze, this technique was well suited for the fine detailed decorations in which the Persian artist has always been a master. This perhaps explains the strange fact that no attempts have been made by the potters of other Near East countries such as Egypt, Syria, Mesopotamia, and Turkey to introduce alkaline glazes. They probably did not have highly skilled artist-decorators requiring clearly separated colors.

It appears that *mīnai* glazes were already in use during the second half of the twelfth century,[141] and it is interesting to learn that Chinese technical essays of the end of the Sung dynasty give many details of the Persian color pigments and glazes.[142]

A modification of the *mīnai* developed during the thirteenth century in the so-called thin-brushed glazes. Here, vitreous glazes with a relatively high oxide content were brushed onto the already once fired body for the decorative lines. These colors developed in a second firing, and the ware was then dipped into an ivory or turquoise clear glaze and fired for a third time. Since the color pigments were so very thinly brushed on they did not run or smudge.

At the beginning of the fourteenth century the *mīnai* palette was enriched by a further pigment, likewise called *lājvar* (our lapis lazuli). This fine blue mineral is a silicate of aluminum, sodium, and calcium with sulfur as an impurity. It dissolves in alkaline glazes, giving them a warm blue color often called ultramarine. Pottery covered with lapis lazuli glazes and decorated with other colors has become known as lajvardina. Ware in this technique was mainly overglaze-decorated and often employed opaque glazes.

Centers producing high-class ware in these techniques were at Ray and Kāšān;[143] ᶜAlī ibn Yūsuf and Abū Ṭāhir Ḥosain were known potters from Ray.[144] From Kāšān, the most important Persian ceramic center of all times, we have complete genealogies of potter families, some of them beginning in 977 A.D. and continuing into the fourteenth century.[145] Although never the seat of a government, Kāšān developed as a peaceful industrial center, and its fame spread through the whole Islamic world. When the Mongol leader Hulagu Khan conquered Baghdad in 1258 the lists of booty made after the sack of the city particularly mention vases from China and Kāšān.[146] The North African-Spanish geographer Ibn Baṭṭūṭah (1307–1378 A.D.) tells us in his travel books[147] that the walls of the shrine of Imām Režā at Mašhad were covered with *kāšānī*, i.e., tiles from Kāšān, and that they were more brilliant and beautiful than those in his country. There is ample evidence that Kāšān tiles were exported all

140 A. Lane, *op. cit.*, p. 41.
141 G. Savage, *op. cit.*, p. 26.
142 *Ibid.*, pp. 26, 70.

143 A. U. Pope and P. Ackerman, *op. cit.*, p. 1560.
144 *Ibid.*, p. 1561.
145 *Ibid.*, p. 1566.
146 *Ibid.*
147 *Ibid.*, p. 1568.

over the Middle and Near East as far as Baku, Samarkand, Smyrna, and North Africa.[148] The Kāšān potters excelled in the making of *miḥrāb* or prayer niches. Previously these had been done in stucco work. The tile miḥrāb are splendid structures, composed of hundreds of large, closely fitting, often carved luster tiles. They too are the outcome of close cooperation between potter and painter-decorator. An inscription from the *miḥrāb* at the shrine of Jaᶜfar at Qom reads: "It was made on the 10th of Rabī II, 738 [November 6, 1337 A.D.] in Kāšān in the factory of Sayyid Rukn ud-Dīn, Moḥammad ibn Sayyid Zayn ud-Dīn al ġazāʾirī [the tile maker], the work of the venerated and respected Jamāl ud-Dīn naqqāš (meaning "the painter").[149] Two other painters who specialized in decorating the famous Kāšān star-and-cross tiles were Abū Rufaẓā, working about 1200 A.D., and Taḫr-ud-Dīn, who worked about 1263 A.D. One tile of the former has the following inscription: "It was made in the night between Tuesday and Wednesday on the last day of Ṣafar in the year 600 H" (November 1205).

Other provincial pottery centers producing ceramic ware of high quality were Nīšāpūr[150] in Ḫorāsān, Sāvā between Ray and Kāšān, Ṣultānābād in West Persia, and Ṣultāniyeh and Tabrīz in Āẕarbaijān. All these centers were using some of the techniques described, and it seems that master potters traveled widely and settled in places where their products were valued and paid for.

Late Islamic Period

When in 1501, after 850 years of foreign rule, Šāh Ismāᶜīl became the first king of the Persian dynasty of the Ṣafavids, two centuries of greatness began. They had their peak under Šāh ᶜAbbās the Great (1587–1620 A.D.). His glory as a powerful and politically active monarch spread to the European courts, and embassies from many countries arrived at the imperial residence at Iṣfahān. But Šāh ᶜAbbās was also a shrewd industrialist and businessman. He settled many skilled craftsmen from his vast empire in and around Iṣfahān, where he established a number of royal manufactures. He also sponsored individual craftsmen. When he learned from the traders and representatives of the Dutch East India Company, who had a base depot on the island of Hormuz in the Persian Gulf, that they traded large quantities of Chinese porcelain, he invited Chinese merchants to send their fine ware to his country overland for export to Europe, thus excluding the Dutch company. The Šāh himself was a great collector of fine pottery; his collection still exists in the shrine of the Ṣafavid Family at Ardabīl in Āẕarbaijān.[151] This renewed a strong Chinese influence, and local potters tried their hand at porcelain again and perfected the Kāšān process, using very fine white kaolin found near Nāʾīn and ᶜAlī-Ābād, which fused into a semi-translucent body with the alkaline frit glaze mentioned. Since this was clearly not true porcelain, Šāh ᶜAbbās invited 300 Chinese potters to Persia to instruct Persian craftsmen in the art of porcelain making. The chief of this technical mission was a man appearing in the Persian annals as Man-oo-har. European travelers of the time praise the quality of the locally made product.[152]

With the renewed Chinese influence came a vogue in blue underglaze painted

[148] *Ibid.*
[149] *Ibid.*, p. 1574.
[150] C. K. Wilkinson, "The Kilns of Nishapur," pp. 235–240, and "Fashion and Technique in Persian Pottery," pp. 99–104.

[151] A. U. Pope and P. Ackerman, *op. cit.*, p. 1649.
[152] Sir J. Chardin, *op. cit.*, p. 267, and J. B. Tavernier, *Les six voyages de M. J. B. Tavernier en Turquie, en Perse et aux Indes*, Vol. 2.

ware, for which Persia had almost unlimited supplies of cobalt. Pieces have been found dated as early as 1523, 1563, and 1592.[153] One of the masters of that period was Ḥajjī Moḥammad, "the painter," working in Tabrīz early in the sixteenth century.[154] The famous Chinese Celadon ware was also imitated at that time; a very smooth gray-green glaze was used to make it, but the design was true Persian. This ware was very popular during the seventeenth century.[155] Obviously under tutelage by Chinese masters, a new technique in monochrome incised ware, covered with a matt melon green glaze, developed in Kāšān.[156] Despite the emphasis on porcelain imitation all other techniques continued to be used, such as polychrome enamel (*mīnai*) and black painted ware. An incised and overglazed pseudo-porcelain produced in Nāʾīn between Kāšān and Iṣfahān should be mentioned here. It was sold to European traders at the Gulf port of Gambroon. As Gambroon ware it became fashionable in India and Europe, especially in England, during the seventeenth century.[157]

During Ṣafavid times the technique of mosaic tiling reached a high standard of perfection, completely eliminating the involved and expensive luster tiles. During the following centuries painted *haft-rang* tiles were often used instead of cut tiles, as *haft-rang* tiles were much cheaper to produce. Very fine tile work was achieved in the *haft-rang* technique during the eighteenth century.

Under the politically weak rulers of the late eighteenth and nineteenth centuries a general decline in most crafts took place, but the potters continued to produce remarkably fine ware so that after the rebirth of modern Persia under Reżā Šāh (1925–1941 A.D.) it was possible to restore most of the beautiful tile work on old mosques and shrines which had fallen into disrepair, in a quality equal to that of the Middle Ages.

In 1963 the writer collected samples of raw materials from the Kargez mountains, used by the potters of Natanz near Kāšān today for the manufacture of porcelain-like vessels and electric insulators. Analyses of these raw materials gave the following picture: Two materials are used. One is *sang-e čīnī* (meaning "China stone"), which is kaolinized quartz-porphyry and corresponds closely to the famous kaolinite of Cornwall, the base material of the English porcelain industry. It is mixed with *sang-e čaḫmāḫ* (meaning "flint"), a remarkably even-grained quartzite with the grains showing as a well-interlocked texture. This texture seems to be particularly suited for the changing of the quartz into tridymite during the firing process, a change largely determining the quality of the ceramic product. European porcelain connoisseurs have often expressed the opinion that the Persian potter, despite his skill in other ceramic techniques, has at the most succeeded in making a low-fired soft paste porcelain. This criticism can no longer be maintained on the grounds that suitable raw materials were not found in Persia. Olmer[158] described samples of feldspathic raw materials in 1908 that were then used by the potters of Nāʾīn. Whether they achieved true porcelain at that time was not quite clear. The other reason given for the Persian potter's not being able to produce porcelain is that he did not have the rising kiln like the Chinese; this reasoning is based on the assumption that the Persian kiln did not give a sufficiently high temperature. But we have no evidence that

[153] A. U. Pope and P. Ackerman, *op. cit.*, p. 1649.
[154] *Ibid.*
[155] *Ibid.*, p. 1658.
[156] *Ibid.*, p. 1660.
[157] *Ibid.*, p. 1661.

[158] L. J. Olmer, *op. cit.*, p. 56.

this was so; on the contrary, the previously mentioned porcelain raw materials do fuse in the local kilns. Therefore the writer feels entitled to assume that the Persian potter by the present day has learned to make porcelain.

The Working Methods of the Modern Potter

Today we can distinguish several branches in the trade of the ceramist (*faḫḫār*), i.e., the earthenware potter (*kūzeh-gar*), the maker of clay hoops (*kabal-māl, kaval-māl, kūl-māl*), the stone paste potter (*sangīneh-sāz, ᶜatīqeh-sāz*), the bead maker (*mohreh-sāz*), and the tile maker (*kāšī-paz, kāšī-gar*).

The raw material for ordinary earthenware (*sefāl, sofāl*) is clay (*ros, gel-e ros, ḫāk*). If the clay is reasonably free from impurities it is used as dug from the clay pit. However, if it contains too much foreign matter it is slaked (*taḫlīl*) with water in a soaking pit (*gelčī*) and screened (*bīḫtan, naḫl kardan, manḫūl kardan*) through a fine sieve (*ġarbāl, minḫal*), sometimes through a silk screen (*harīr*). The clay body for fine ware is always slaked. In most cases it is necessary to adjust the body to the correct composition (*tarkīb*) by adding finely ground quartz pebbles (*ḥaṣāt, šakar-sang, billūr, ḫiṣbāʾ*) or flint (*sang-e čaḫmāq, sang-e čaḫmāḫ*) to the slaked white clay or to a particularly valuable clay of pale green color (*ġażār*). Pebbles and flint are first crushed (*šekastan, rīzīdan, mofattat kardan*) with an iron bar (*sitām, miṭraqeh, ḥadīd*), then pounded (*madqūq, modaqqaq, moḥabbā*) in a stone mortar (*midaqq, midaqqeh, ṣilāyeh, ṣalāyat*) made of a basalt block (*siyāh sang*) to a granulate (*daqīq*) of the size of millet grains. This granulate is finely ground (*ṣaḥq, maṣḥūq, maṭḥūn, sābīdan, sāʾīdan*) in a hand mill or quern (*āsiyāb, āsak*, Fig. 218). Dry grinding (*ḫoškeh-sāb*) is applied in the first stage and wet grinding (*āb-sāb*) for the final stage.

Figure 218 A Potter's Dry Quern

The quern has a fixed bed stone (*zīreh*) with a hole in the center to let the axle (*mīl-e zīr*) through. This axle supports the runner (*rūʾī*) while the distance between bed stone and runner is controlled by a pair of wedges (*gōveh*). Figure 219 shows a tile-lined wet quern (*āsak-e āb-sāb*) where a wooden block (*qolfeh, kondeh, pārs*) is inserted as a support between axle and wedges. Small querns have a handle (*dasteh*) that is just a stick inserted into a hole near the circumference of the runner and is held in position by a wooden wedge (*čūb-e dasteh*), while larger querns have a

Figure 219 A Potter's Wet Quern

long handle bar (*nājī*) that is centered in a hole of the ceiling rafter and secured in the runner hole with a wedge. Slaked clay and ground pebbles, or if required slaked clay, ground pebbles, and flint are thoroughly mixed (*moḫtaliṭ, maᶜjūn*) and then left to settle. Surplus water is poured off and the sediment put in the open sun on a bed of fired bricks for drying. When it has reached the right plastic stage, the potter's assistant (*pīš-kār*) takes a large lump (*čūneh-ye gel*) and kneads it with his foot (*gel mālīdan, sirištan, gel varz dādan bā pā, pā zadan*, Fig. 220).[159] Subsequent wedging of smaller lumps by hand (*varz dādan bā dast, mošteh pīčīdan*) has been observed in several localities; the clay there apparently requires this second treatment to obtain the necessary plasticity. When the kneading is completed the lumps are cut into pieces (*mošt*) of the sizes needed for the objects to be formed, unless the potter prefers to center a large lump on the wheel in order to work piece after piece from this lump. To keep the clay moist it is covered with wet bags. Kneaded clay not immediately used is placed in a clay store (*aṃbar-e gel*). For the forming of the clay into the required shapes there are still three different methods applied: there is either free forming, mainly with clay coils, throwing on the potter's wheel, or forming in molds. The latter, however, is today confined to tile molding.

Figure 220 A Potter Kneading Clay

[159] This must have been the situation when Omar Khayyám wrote this quatrain:
For in the market-place one dusk of day
I watched the potter thumping his wet clay
And with its all obliterated tongue
It murmur'd "Gently, brother, gently pray!"

Coil-Formed Pottery

Figure 221 shows how the clay is formed in this age-old technique: the apprentice rolls handy lumps (*čāneh, čūneh*) of clay on a wooden board (*taḫteh*) into coils (*fatīleh*) and places them in front of the master, who fashions them into circles (*dāyereh zadan*), one on top of the other (Fig. 222). After about twenty layers the cylinder formed so far is smoothed (*mālīdan, bā āb ṣāf kardan*) with a spatula (*līseh*) or a small

Figure 221 Rolling Clay into Coils

Figure 222 A Coil Potter at Work

trowel (*māleh*). The coiling continues in this way until the object has reached its final shape and size. After the clay has become leather hard a second smoothing is done with a polishing stone (*sang-e mohreh*) or once again with a small trowel (Fig. 223).

The products of the coil potter include a great variety of vessels (*ālat*, *inā*ʾ) and builders' hardware. Most conspicuous are the bakers' ovens (*tanūr-e nānpazī*, Figs. 222 and 223), but there are also vessels (*lūleh-kaš*), large tapered ones of about 25-gallon capacity (Fig. 224) that are much used by various craftsmen for a number of processes such as fiber dyeing, leather tanning, or in the house for boiling syrup and cheese. Other coil-formed products are large water and storage jars (*ḫomreh*, *sabbā*, right bottom corner, Fig. 224), big and small drainpipes (*tambūš*, *kuluk*, *lūleh*, *mūrī-šoġal-rou*), water spouts (*nāvdān*), frames for the cup-shaped skylights in domed buildings (*jām-e ḥammām*), earthenware charcoal braziers (*manqal-e gelī*), and beehive frames (*penjeh*). The latter are rings of 10 to 12 inches in diameter and 8 inches in height, with an entry hole for the bees on one side. The inside of these rings is roughened with a toothed scraper (*šāneh*) to assist the bees when building the honeycombs. Three of these rings are usually put together to form a beehive (*kondū*) and are covered with an earthenware slab. Still more coil-formed objects are well-lining rings (*gom-e čāh*, *gom-e čāh-āb*, *lūleh-ye čāh-āb*, *kol-e čāh-āb*), grape-mashing vats (*čorūk-angūr-kūbī*), oriental-style toilet pans (*jūnou-mostarāḥ*), double jar stands (*jā kūzehgī*), and an unusual

Figure 223 Polishing a Coil Pot

Figure 224 Coil-Formed Vessels

product, a walking aid for little children (*tābū-bačeh*), a conic tube about 2 feet high, with no bottom, in which a child can stand without falling over.

Persia's underground water supply channels (*qanāt, kārīz*) are supported by earthenware hoops (*kabal, kaval, kavūl, kūl, nai, nār, gom, gūm, nāv-kārīz, dos*) where they pass through loose soil. Where the demand is not too great the coil potter supplies the well sinker with these hoops. In districts with a wide network of such channels there is sufficient work for a potter making nothing but these earthenware hoops. He is then called *kaval-māl, kabal-māl, kūl-māl, dos-sāz*. Sometimes this work is done by the well sinker himself or by one of his laborers. The hoops are made around an oval ring (*qāleb*) made of baked clay with handles (*dasteh*) at both ends. It is 6 to 8 inches high and has a major diameter of 46 and a minor one of 22 inches. The coil potter lays coils around the mold ring, smooths the outside with a trowel, lifts the mold ring up, and places it on the ground close to the hoop just made, thus having it ready to fashion another hoop. The specialized hoopmaker prefers to work with a mixture of clay and chaff (*kāh*) or clay and horse manure (*pehen*). Standing in front of a working bench (*dastgāh*), his assistant places a lump (*mošteh, čūneh*) of this mixture on a board which is as wide as the mold ring is high and as long as half the circumference of the mold. He spreads the mixture out (*pahn kardan*) about 1½ inches thick over the surface of the board. He then passes the board over to the molder, who places the clay slab against the mold ring, bending the ends around the mold (*dour-e qāleb*). Having provided such a clay slab on both sides of the mold he joins the ends (*sar band kardan*, Fig. 225) and lifts the mold with both hands, leaving the newly formed hoop on the ground for drying (Fig. 226). After three days of drying they are fired

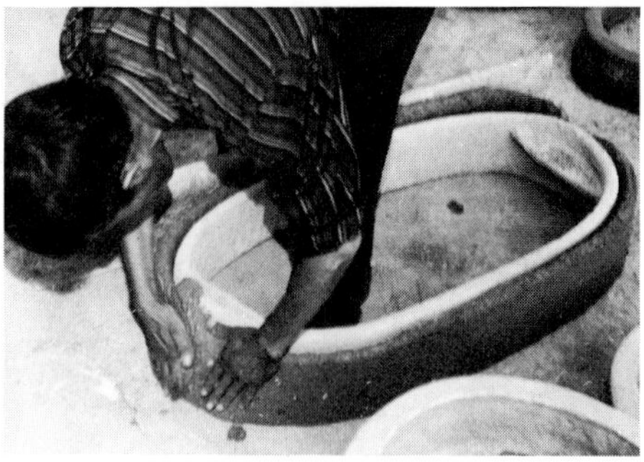

Figure 225 Placing Clay Around the Mold

Figure 226 Drying of Clay Hoops

(*pūḫtan*) for 24 hours. The kilns (Fig. 238, p. 159) have a capacity of 500 to 1,000 hoops; rejects (*talafāt*) amount to about 5 to 10 per cent.

Wheel-Formed Pottery

Whereas the two forming methods just described have a limited application and are used only for coarse ware, products made on the potter's wheel (*čarḫ, čarḫ-e kūzehgarī*) reveal the craftsman at his best.

The Persian wheel is a disk kickwheel (Fig. 227), not like the English wheel, driven by a crank mechanism. The Persian wheel is driven by means of a heavy treadle disk (*taman, pātaḫteh, čarḫ-e pā*) that the potter turns with his feet in an anticlockwise direction. The wheel shaft (*mīl*,

Figure 227 A Potter's Wheel

čūb-e āmak, tīr-e čarḫ) is made of wood. A three-pronged end (*seh-panjeh, seh-šāḫ*), made of forged steel, is attached to the top end of the shaft and carries the working table of the wheel (*sar-e kār, sar-e seh-panjeh, sar-e čarḫ*). A likewise forged thrust-end (*baltak, bāltak, mīḫ-e tīr, āhan-e tīr*) is fixed to the lower end of the shaft and runs in a thrust bearing (*šamak, zīr-mīḫ*) made from the shoulder-joint bone of a camel (*šāneh-ye šotor*) inserted into a stone block. A large horizontal beam under the round working table carries the bearing block (*qolfak, taḫteh*) for the upper bearing. The potter sits on a wooden board (*taḫteh-kūngāh*) and rests his feet on a beam (*pā-gāh*) above the treadle disk when he is not kicking. In Ḫorāsān the lower parts of the wheel, i.e., treadle and thrust bearing, are often built below floor level, and the potter steps down into a pit (*goudāl piš-e kār*) when he begins his work. For the throwing (*gel kašīdan*) the potter places a lump of clay on the wheel (*mošteh zadan*), centers (*laqaṭ zadan*) and holes it (*gel tūš pūk kardan*), and with a firm hand he brings the clay up (*bālā gereftan, bālā qabżeh gereftan*, Fig. 228). He throws as high as the length of his arm will permit, then thins the wall, at the same time bulging it in the center to form the body of the jar (*tan-e kūzeh*, Fig. 229), followed by the forming of the neck (*gardan-e kūzeh*) and the spout (*sar-e kūzeh*). The base of the jar (*pā-ye kūzeh*) is then shaped (*tarāšīdan*) with a modeling tool (*māleh*). A few simple linear decorations (*naqš*) are produced by holding a toothed modeling tool (*šāneh*) against the soft clay or by making incisions into it, and finally, the wheel still running, the jar is cut off with a wire (*sīm, bandak*), or a short steel peg (*sūzan*). During the throwing the potter wets his hands in a water dish (*dastdān-e āb*) that is handy on the working bench. While he throws the next jar his assistant takes the one just made into the drying room (*ambār-e żarfdānī*, Fig. 230) where the jars remain until they are leather hard (*nīmḫošk*). Only then the handles (*dasteh, gūšeh*) are put on. Handles are drawn (*gel gereftan*) from a roll of wet clay and attached (*gūšeh bastan, gūšeh časbāndan*) to the moistened and roughened surface with a mild pressure. Other earthenware vessels (*qadaḥčī*) produced by the wheel potter are dishes (*hasīn, qadaḥ*), smaller jars for drinking water (*kūzeh-ye āb-ḫworī, dūl-ābī*), chafing dishes (*kuluk*), jars for curdled milk (*gāv-dūšī*), and cobs for the water pipe (*sar-e qaliyān*). As these cobs have a long neck with a narrow hole in it they are thrown around a wooden centering tool (*čūb-e qaliyān-sāzī*) that is placed into a hole in the working table top before a lump of clay is put on for centering, and a number of water pipe cobs are drawn over this

Figure 228 A Potter Throwing at the Wheel

Figure 229 Throwing a Jar

Figure 230 Drying Room

centering tool, one after the other. Flower pots (*hasīn-e goldān*), plates (*qaṣ^{c}at*), mugs (*līvān*), and large cooking pots (*komājdān*) with lids (*makabbeh*) likewise belong to the wheel potter's ware, as well as a peculiar water jar shaped like a bird (*kaftar-e ābḫwori*). Many wheel potters make irrigation pipes in the same shape as those of the coil potter. In the Caspian provinces roof tiles (*sefāl, sofāl*) represent an important potter's product. They are thrown on the wheel in the shape of mildly tapered tubes. After cutting off from the wheel they are halved with a wire and carefully placed into a drying room until they have the right consistency for firing. While most of the ordinary jars and dishes have their final form when taken off the wheel, some of the better quality ware is turned (*tarāšīdan, tarāšeh-kūzeh*) after having become leather hard. For a vessel with a wide opening the potter places a lump of clay on the wheel top, shapes it to the approximate size of the inside of the vessel, thus forming a chuck (*qāleb-e tarāš*), places the vessel upside down (*bar-gardāndan*) over it, and turns its base to the required shape with a turning tool (*kār-tarāš, randeh*, Fig. 231). A number of jars commonly used in the household is shown in Fig. 232. The names of these have been recorded in the Alburz mountain village

Figure 231 Turning a Vessel

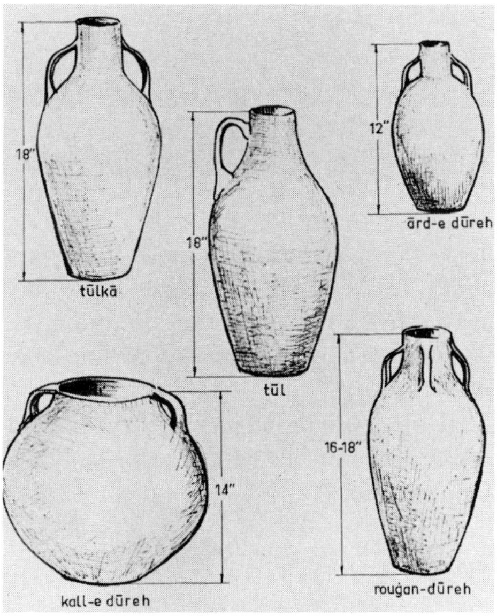

Figure 232 Earthenware Vessels Used in the Household (*from the Alburz village of Fašondak*)

of Fašondak[160] but the shapes are used throughout Persia.

The smallest of them, *ārd-e dūreh,* serves for the storage of flour. Slightly taller, but much larger in diameter, is the *kall-e dūreh,* handy for the transport of foodstuffs. The *rouġan-dūreh* is always well glazed inside and outside and is used for oil storage. Also for keeping oil, but often used for preserving pickles, is the *tūlkā.* For these purposes it is glazed, but if used to carry water from the well to the house it is left unglazed, like the *tūl,* which is always unglazed.

Mold-Formed Tiles

The tilemaker (*kāšī-paz*) usually works in the open air. His assistant prepares suitably sized clay lumps (*čūneh*). The master has a wooden mold (*qāleb-e kāšī*) in front of him (Fig. 233) and throws the clay lump into it with verve (*qāleb zadan*), beats it with his bare hands to force it into the remote corners of the mold (Fig. 234), folds the surplus up, and cuts it away with a wire (*sīm kašīdan,* Fig. 235). Then he empties the mold (*qāleb ḫālī kardan*) with a swift movement (Fig. 236). The assistant takes the tiles into the shade for the first stage of drying (*ḫošk kardan dar sāyeh*) and when they have sufficient strength he places them in a well-ventilated drying room (*otāq-e ḫešt-e kāšī*), face down on the flat floor, for the slow final drying (Fig. 237). The potters of Šīrāz work in a slightly different technique: The tiles are molded as described for the Iṣfahān tilemaker, are left in the open air for five hours, and are then placed into a slightly narrower steel mold (*qāleb-e felezzī*). A steel mold top (*darī*) is placed over the tile and is beaten with one stroke of a heavy hammer (*potk*). Thus a denser tile is achieved with less tendency to shrink and to warp. After the

[160] K. Hūšangpūr, *Fašondak*, pp. 90–104.

Figure 233 A Wooden Tile Mold

Figure 236 Taking Tile out of the Mold

Figure 234 Beating Clay into the Mold

Figure 237 A Tile-Drying Room

Figure 235 Cutting Away Surplus Clay

tile is taken out of this mold the edges (*aṭrāf*) are cleaned (*sāvīdan*) from any burrs. After a further period of drying the tile is dipped in a thin slip of fine clay (*ṣūrat-e lo*^{c}*āb*).

All tiles, when sufficiently dry, have a first (or biscuit) firing (*ḫām puḫtan*) in a common kiln.

Firing

To fire the potters' and tilemakers' products there is a great variety of kilns (*tanūr, kūreh, furn, barīz, šāḫūr, dāš, dam-ō-dāšt*). Their dimensions and construction depend on size and nature of the ware. The largest are the kilns for the firing (*ṭabḫ kardan, puḫtan*) of the well sinker's hoops and the coil potter's ware. Figure 238 gives details of this type of kiln. The fuel (*hīzum*) is thrown into the fire box (*kūreh*), the flames enter the room under the fire arch (*tāq-e kūreh*), through the fire hole (*darb-e āteš*) and pass into the kiln chamber through a network of small holes (*zaṃbūr*) in the fire arch. The flames are by now well distributed, pass upwards through the ware to the roof arch (*tāq*), and return to the sides, where five to six holes (*dūd-kaš*) lead the smoke into the open. Fuel for this type of kiln was dry brushwood (*čār, ḫār*), especially dry wormwood (*Artemisia herba alba, darmaneh*) but is today widely replaced by fuel oil (*naft*).

The writer has observed the most simple type of kiln in Gīlān. A beehive-shaped dome of 8 feet diameter and 5 feet high was built in ordinary mud bricks, leaving an entrance hole $2\frac{1}{2}$ feet wide at the bottom and a smoke exit 12 inches in diameter at the top. This kiln was used for very plain, mainly hand-formed, cooking pots (*gamej*). After charging, the entrance hole was walled up, and the firing was done through three or four small openings at ground level by pushing branch wood into them continuously. Since this type of fuel is amply available in Gīlān, the low efficiency of the kiln does not matter much.

The potters of Šāh-Reżā, a ceramic center near Iṣfahān, have a different type of kiln (Fig. 239). Here, two circular firing chambers (*falakeh*) 10 feet in diameter and 12 feet in height are built side by side. Each has an under-floor firing duct (*zīr-e kūreh*) that leads the combustion gases from a firing pit (*čāl, āteš-ḫāneh*) on the outside of the kiln into the firing chamber through a large hole in the chamber's floor. The roof of each chamber is formed by a cupola (*tāq-e kūreh*) with a hole (*ḥalqeh*) about 2 feet in diameter in

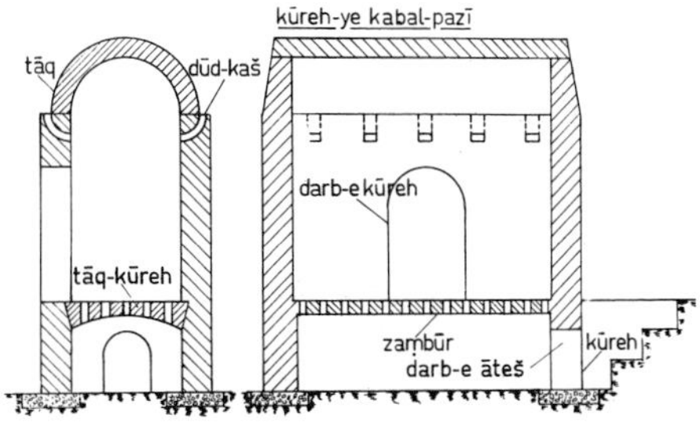

Figure 238 A Large Kiln (*section*)

the center. The unusual feature of this kiln is the large room above the two firing chambers, roofed by a single vault. This top room (*sar-e kūreh, dour-e kūreh*) is used as a drying chamber. The combustion gases rising from the firing chambers underneath pass through the ware stacked here before they finally reach the open air through a chimney (*dūd-kaš*) at the top of the drying chamber. When charging (*kūreh čīdan*) one of the firing chambers, an assistant passes the dried vessels from the top chamber to the master through the hole in the roof of that firing chamber. The discharging is done through a comfortable opening (*kāf-e kūreh*) in the front of each firing chamber, sealed during the firing process. One chamber is fired at a time, the firing taking 48 hours, while the

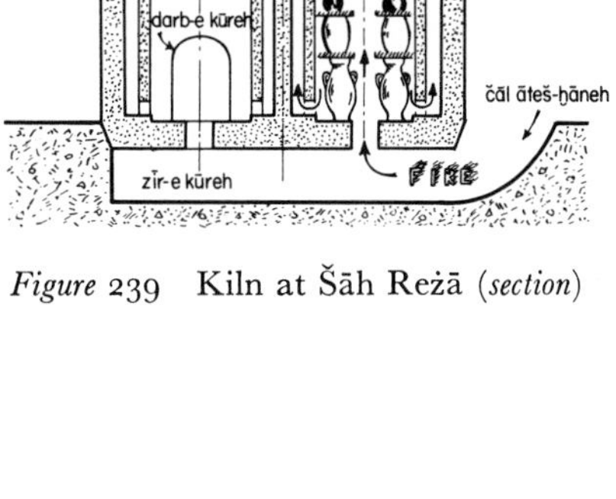

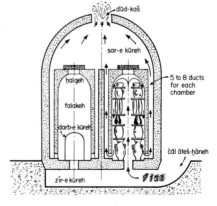

Figure 239 Kiln at Šāh Reżā (*section*)

other chamber is cooling down. Before firing one chamber begins, a large slab of burnt clay is pushed over the hole in the roof of the other chamber so that its ware is left to cool without being affected by the firing of the other chamber.

An almost modern, so-called down-draft kiln has been observed in Bīdoḫt in Ḫorāsān. Here the kiln was a square chamber with a vaulted roof (Fig. 240) having a fire pit (*čāh-e āteš-ḫāneh*) on one side. The fire burns on the bottom of the

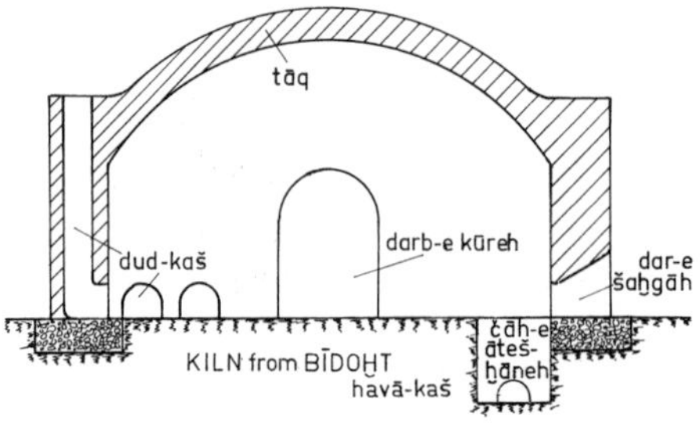

Figure 240 Kiln at Bīdoḫt (*section*)

pit and obtains primary air through an underground duct (*havā-kaš*). Firewood (*hīzum*) or brushwood (*pāteh*) is thrown into the pit through an opening (*dar-e šaḫ-gāh*) in the kiln wall. The walls opposite the fire pit have about a dozen openings at ground level that lead into as many chimneys (*mūrī, dūdkaš*) built into these walls. This means that the combustion gases first rise through the stacked ware to the vaulted ceiling and are then forced to descend to ground level in order to escape through the chimney openings. The speed of the gases is considerably reduced through the down-draft, and more efficient heating is achieved.

The most common type of potter's kiln, however, is one similar to the brick kiln, though much smaller. Kilns for finer ware have air holes (*darb-e havā*) at the sides of the combustion chamber for better control of the combustion, to achieve either oxidizing or reducing atmosphere as the ware may require. Abūlqasim of Kāšān[161] mentions that in his days the kilns had many shelves (*ṭabaqeh*) formed by ceramic slabs which rested on clay pegs (*mīḫ-e sefālīn*). Modern potters still place their products on such shelves for the firing of quality ware. These kilns used to burn wood, especially wild almond (*gauz*) and willow (*bīd*) instead of desert shrubs with which the brick kilns were fired. Abūlqasim[162] emphasizes that the potters then removed the bark from the wood to achieve a smoke-free flame, a practice still customary with the Iṣfahān potters before the general change-over to oil firing.

Glazemaking

It is common practice that potters and tilemakers prepare their own glazes (*rang, loʿāb, līqeh*). In places with a highly developed ceramic industry, however, such as Kāšān and Iṣfahān, there are men who specialize as glazemakers (*sujjāj*), selling their products in the required colors to smaller potters or working as employees in larger potteries.

The first step in the production of glazes is the preparation of a frit (*ābgīneh, bulūr, jouhar, šīšeh*), a kind of alkaline glass. The raw materials are quartz (*rīg, sang-e bulūr*), flint (*rīg-e čaḫmāq, čaḫmā, sang-e āteš*), and potash (*qalīʾeh, qilīʾeh, qaliyā, qaliyāb, kālā, keliyāb*). The preparation of the latter is done by the potash burner (*qallāʾ*). Many of them live in Qom and work on the fringe of the northern salt desert. Qom potash (*qaliyāb-e qomī*) is known for its high quality. For weeks the potash burners gather salt plants in the desert as long as they are not yet completely dry. The best

[161] H. Ritter, *et al.*, *op. cit.*, lines 233 ff. of MS Aya Sofia 3614.
[162] *Ibid.*, line 242.

of these plants is the common soda plant or saltwort (*Salsola kali, Salsola soda, Seidlitzia rosmarinus, ošnān, ošnūn*). Another one is *bandok, bondoq* (*Quilandia bonducella*). The burners collect all the plants in heaps and dig a pit (*čāl*) about 3 feet in diameter and 6 feet deep, start a fire at the bottom of it, and throw the plants into it so that they burn away, not with a hot and open flame, but rather slowly and smoldering. One donkey load after the other goes into the pit, and the ashes are left to cool overnight. They are collected next morning and taken to the burner's workshop. There he has a calcining furnace (*kūreh-rang*). It has a muffle that is heated from underneath. The saltwort ashes are placed in the muffle through a hole in its front wall in batches of 10 to 15 pounds. They are scraped back and forth over the muffle bottom with a scraping iron (*sīḫ*) until the potash has calcined. It is then taken out of the furnace and dropped into a pit at the feet of the operator. After cooling it is stored away in blocks (*šemš*) weighing about 10 pounds each.

Flint and quartz are usually collected in the dry river beds, unless there is a good quarry nearby, like those in the Kargez mountains near Natanz. The men charged with collecting the stones know how to distinguish quartzite pebbles (*rīg*) from limestone (*āhak*) and gypsum rock (*gač*). To make sure, all stones are broken up in the potter's workshop. Unsuitable stones are sorted out, and particularly white ones are set aside for glazemaking while brown varieties are used for making the ground quartz to be added to the potter's clay to give it the right composition. The crushing and grinding of the stones has already been described when discussing the raw materials used by the potter. The quartz for the glaze frit must be very finely ground and is usually filtered through cloth (*karbās, long*) after grinding. Fifty-five pounds of ground quartz and 65 pounds of potash are thoroughly mixed, and half a pound of manganese oxide (*maġn, maġnīsā*) is added to obtain a clear glaze frit.

The frit mixture is placed into a special frit kiln (*barīz*) that has a hollow hearth (*čāl*). Here the materials are heated (*puḫtan*) for eight hours and stirred with an iron ladle (*kafčeh-ye āhanīn*). When the mass has melted (*godāz šodan*) into a clear, bubble-free glass, it is taken out with the ladle and poured into a water-filled pit (*maġākī*) in front of the kiln. During this quenching operation the glass frit breaks up into a small granulate (*dāneh-dāneh*) that is subsequently pounded, ground, sifted, and stored for further use.

Preparation of Metal Oxides

Lead. The most important metal used in the preparation of glazes is lead (*sorb, usrub, arzīz*). It is added to the frit, to act as a flux, in the form of dross of lead (*murdāsang, ḫāk-e sorb*), as lead oxide (*šangarf-e zāvūlī*), as red lead (*sirinj, isrinj*) or occasionally as genuine white lead (*sapīdeh-zanān*).[163] Today potters are quite keen to buy old car batteries. Their lead is known as *sorb-e māšīnī* or *sorb-e bāterī*. They use the lead compounds of the plates directly after careful washing, and the remaining metallic grid of the plates is treated like ordinary lead, as will be shown.

Figure 241 shows a lead oxidizing furnace (*godāz*). Above the fire box there is a flat, dish-shaped refractory crucible in which the lead is melted (*tābīdeh kardan*) almost to red heat. There is a hole above the melt so that fresh air can reach the metal during the oxidizing process. The oxide (*gol*) forming on the surface of the melt is constantly skimmed off with a

[163] Meaning "White of Ladies," a name identical with the Latin term *blanchetum mulierum* for carbonate of lead.

Figure 241 An Oxidizing Furnace for Lead and Tin

scraper (*sīẖ-e āhan-sarkaj, mijrafeh*) until all the metal has turned into oxide (*ẖāk šodan*).

Tin. Lead oxide in any of the forms mentioned is used to obtain clear, transparent (*šaffāf*) glazes. If, however, a white, opaque (*moṣammat, moṣmat*) enamel glaze is wanted, tin (*qal*ᶜ, *raṣāṣ*) is added to the frit in the form of tin oxide (*sapīdāb, safīdāb*). Since many glazes also contain lead as a flux, it is common practice to oxidize lead and tin for these glazes in the same operation. Three parts of lead are melted (*godāz kardan*) first in the oxidizing furnace described above with a mild fire, and then one or two parts of tin are added. When this has been melted too the heat is increased and the whole is oxidized as explained for lead. This mixture[164] of oxides of lead and tin is likewise called *safīdāb*. For lead-free opaque glazes pure tin oxide is made in the same furnace.

Copper. This metal is the main coloring agent to obtain a blue (*ābī*) color in alkaline glazes and a bright turquoise (*fīrūzeh*) in lead glazes. It is added to the frit as a pigment in the form of copper oxide. The copper oxidizing furnace (Fig. 242) is charged with copper filings and lathe shavings (*tufāl-e mes, tūbāl-e mes, sūvāl-e mes, randeš*) bought from the coppersmith. The fire underneath brings the copper to red heat. As the flames pass through the shavings, additional air is drawn from the upper hole of the furnace, and the copper gradually turns into oxide. The furnace shown is charged with a hundredweight of copper. It takes eight hours to complete the oxidization. When cooled the oxide is carefully collected and stored as "burnt copper" (*naḥās, mes-e moḥarraq, tufāl*).

Iron. Iron oxide in clear glazes produces a yellow (*zard*) to pale green (*tariyākī*) color. Mixed with copper oxide it produces a bright green (*sabz*). There is no need for the potter to produce iron oxide, as the blacksmith collects more hammerscale (*tūbāl-e ḥadīd-e moḥarraq*) around his anvil than the potter can ever use.

Figure 242 A Copper Oxidizing Furnace

[164] Oxidization of lead and tin combined is already mentioned by Abūlqasim.

Gold. Pure gold (*zar, ṭelā*) is used by the Persian potter for high-class ware to produce a beautiful red to purple hue (*qermez-e parpar, yāqūtiyeh*) or a gilded surface (*moṭallā*) with the gold in colloidal suspension in the clear glaze. For each of these applications the gold is dissolved in a mixture of nitric, sulphuric, and hydrochloric acids. This mixture is produced by the potter in a genuine "alembic" (*aṃbīq*), probably the last remnant of medieval alchemy still in operation. The center of the alembic or still (*qarᶜaṃbīq*) is the retort (*qarᶜ*), a glass flask containing the chemicals (*davā, adviyejāt*) that are made up of pyrites or yellow vitriol (*zāj-e zard, zāq*), together with salt and saltpeter deposits (*šūreh*) and pure saltpeter (*namak-e turkī*). This retort (center in Fig. 243) is

Figure 243 An Alembic or Still

protected from the direct flame of the furnace (*kūreh-ye qarᶜaṃbīq*) by a heavy coat of mud mixed with the seeds of bulrushes (*gel-e lūʾīdār*). The acids (*jouhar, tīzāb*) developing inside the retort vaporize (*ᶜaraq kardan*) and condense (*čakeh kardan*) in the still head (*aṃbīq*), from where they run into the receiver (*šīšeh*). This crude form of aqua regia (*tīzāb*) is capable of dissolving gold. When added to the ground frit, the gold solution produces the effects mentioned.

Cobalt. The oxide of this metal, which played such an important part in the past, is still being mined near Kāšān and Qom, especially in the Kohrūd mountains between the villages Gujar and Kohrūd. The mines have been the property of a local family for centuries. Members of this family work the deposits by removing the oxides from small pockets in the rocks, known in English as cobalt wads. The cobalt oxide (*ḫāk-e lājvard, gel-e lājvard, sang-e lājvard*) is mixed with impurities, mainly clay and manganese oxide. Formed into balls (*qomčeh-lājvard*) of 1 *čārak* weight (1.5 pounds), the mineral is sold to a local "alchemist" (*isfarjānī, kīmiyā-gar*) who washes the impurities out and either sells the reasonably pure cobalt oxide to the potter or produces a glass frit of a high cobalt content that the potter can dilute with clear glaze to the desired strength.

Other coloring pigments. Apart from cobalt there are a number of other pigments that are mined as oxides or other compounds and can be used directly by the potter in the preparation of his glazes. The most important are antimony ore (*iṯmid, uṯmud*), antimony in the form of auripigment (*surmeh*) or as colyrium (*koḥl*), arsenic (*zarnīj*), and manganese oxide (*maġn, maġnīsā, maġnīsiyā*). A mineral known as *siyāh-qalam* consists of 85 per cent chromite, 10 per cent manganese, and 5 per cent magnesium silicate. It is used to paint the outlines of some designs and turns into a deep black after firing. Other pigments are verdigris (*zinjār*) and lapis lazuli or ultramarine, also called *lājvard.* Genuine lapis lazuli is rarely added as a pigment, if at all, then only to produce a deep ultramarine blue hue. Some of the hard mineral pigments are ground on a flat or slightly concave rubbing stone (*sang-e meškī, sang-e sehlāyeh*).

Glazing. For the final application of the glaze (*loᶜāb kardan*) to the biscuit-fired ware (*yak-āteš*) the potter or tilemaker mixes the frit with the pigments to obtain the required color (*bā rang maḫlūt kardan*), then adds pure white clay, potash, and some syrup of grapes (*dūšāb, šīreh-ye angūr*) or vinegar (*serkeh*). Potash, syrup, and vinegar might be a surprise to the Western potter, but Schumann,[165] while searching for the Greek vase painting techniques, has found by experiments that the Greeks added potash to the clay slip and that it acted as a "peptizer" or a means of preventing the extremely fine clay particles from coagulating into coarse clots. The addition of syrup, vinegar, or urine provided what Schumann calls a protective colloid, maintaining the suspension of all fine particles as long as possible.

All materials are carefully weighed, the correct proportions being known by tradition and from experience. Mixed with water, the materials are passed through a wet quern (Fig. 219, p. 151) several times; finally some gum tragacanth (*katīreh, katīrā*) is added, which acts as a binder for the fine glaze particles. The mixture is poured into a vat (*qadaḥ*). Figure 244 shows how a tilemaker (*kāšī-paz*) pours the glaze (*rang zadan, rang varkanī*), using a little pouring dish (*piyāleh*). Holding the tile at an angle, he tries to avoid the formation of air bubbles (*jūš*). Vessels are treated similarly or dipped (Fig. 245).

After the application of the raw glaze, the objects are placed in a special glazing kiln (*kūreh-ye rang-pazī, kūreh-rang, kūreh-ye loᶜābī*) or in a tile-glazing kiln (*kūreh-ye kāšī-pazī*). Such a kiln is shown in Fig. 246. It is a muffle kiln. Other potters use their ordinary kilns and place delicate ware into saggars (*qāleb-e saffālīn*) with lids (*makabbeh*). Many vessels are only fired (*ṭabḫ*) once, others twice, and others again a third time. Decorated tiles, for instance, are biscuit fired first, then fired with a

Figure 244 Pouring Glaze

Figure 245 Applying Glaze by Dipping

white opaque tin glaze for eight hours, cooled in the kiln for two days, and then handed over to a glaze-painter (*monaqeš, naqqāš*) for decorating (*naqašī kardan, taṭyīn*). The design for these decorations is transferred with a perforated paper stencil (*naqšeh*) and a small bag containing fine charcoal dust (*ḫāk-e zoġāl*) that penetrates

[165] T. Schumann, "Oberflächenverzierungen in der antiken Töpferkunst," pp. 408–426, and "Terra Sigillata und Schwarz-Rot Malerei der Griechen," pp. 356–358.

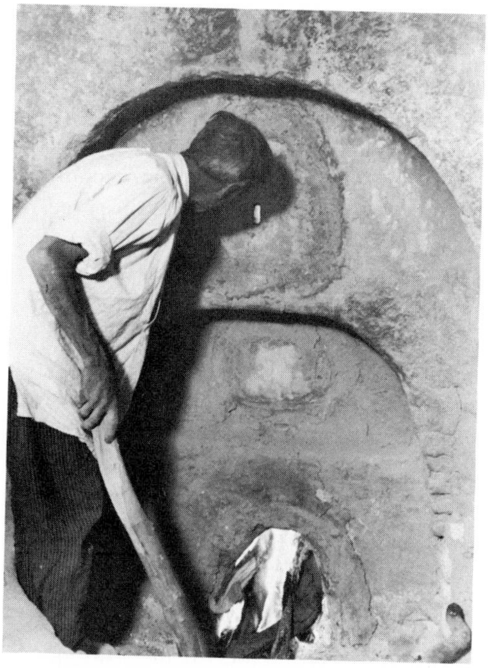

Figure 246 Firing a Tile-Glazing Kiln

Figure 247 Applying Decorating Glaze

the holes of the stencil and adheres to the ware in small spots. The painter applies a pigmented glaze (*līqeh-ye dō-āteš*) with a fine-hair brush (*qalam-e mū*) (Fig. 247), following the stenciled design. A third firing in the same kiln fixes these so-called overglaze paints.

Stone Paste Potter

It will be remembered from the introduction to this section that already in prehistoric times the potters of the Middle East made ceramic objects from a quartz-frit paste that was glazed over with an alkaline turquoise glaze. The art of making vessels in this technique is still alive, and those engaged in it are called *ᶜatīqeh-sāz* or *sangīneh-sāz*, meaning "stone paste potter." Ware of this kind is made in Iṣfahān, Natanz, Kāšān, and Qom. Most of it is sold in the latter town to the many pilgrims visiting the shrine of Fāṭimeh, as it seems to be an old tradition to take a vase or dish home from Qom, not to forget a number of turquoise stone paste beads for good luck.

The body (*gel, rīg*) is composed of 70 to 80 per cent white quartz or flint, 10 to 20 per cent of an extremely fine clay (*gel-e bōteh, gel-e safīd*), so fine that modern ceramists would call it bentonite, and 10 per cent frit of the same composition as described above for glazemaking. The most suitable type of clay is named *gel-čāhrīseh* after a village about fifty miles from Iṣfahān that has a large deposit of it. After quarrying it is soaked in water (*āb rūš rīḫtan*), thus turned into a thin slip and filtered (*ḫīš kardan*) through a cloth to separate any coarse material. Flint and frit are treated in the same way as for glazemaking. All components are carefully weighed, mixed and thoroughly kneaded. The mass is not as plastic as common clay but can be thrown on the wheel (*sāḫtan rū-ye čarḫ*). Whereas the common potter throws most of his vessels in one piece (*yak faṣlī*), the stone paste potter finds it easier to make most of his vessels in two pieces (*dō-faṣlī*) as shown in Fig. 248, or even in three. The pieces (*faṣl*) are thrown independently on the wheel and left to dry. When sufficiently dried the edges of the sections are moistened and the

Figure 248 Forming Stone Paste Ware in Several Pieces

sections cemented together (*časbīdan*, *časb kardan*) by adding some of the paste. After a further drying the joint (*band*) is smoothed over with a turning tool (*kārd-e tarāš*). To obtain a dense and even surface the whole vessel is dipped (*lāyeh var kardan*) into a slip or cast over with slip (*lāyeh dādan*) from a small dish. This slip (*lāyeh*, *rūʾī*) is made from 90 per cent extremely finely ground white quartz, 7 to 9 per cent bentonite clay, and 1 per cent gum tragacanth. For decorating, the outlines of the design are applied (*naqš kašīdan*) with a brush (*qalam*, Fig. 249). The pigment is a mineral containing chromite, manganese, and magnesium silicate coming from a mine near Natanz and is called *siyāh-qalam*. When the line work is completed, ground enamel glazes (*mīnā*) in different colors are applied (*rang āmīzī*) between the black lines, and finally the whole is dipped into a clear alkaline glaze that is made from 90 per cent frit, 9 per cent broken glass, and 1 per cent tragacanth. The vessels are left to dry well and are fired (*āteš dādan*) in a muffle kiln. The melting of the glaze (*loʿāb ṣāf šodan*) on the vessels is observed through a peephole, and the kiln is left to cool for three days after completing the firing in order to prevent glaze cracks (*ẖord*). With this precaution the glaze fuses well onto the surface, apparently on account of frit in the body as well as in the glaze.

A variation of this technique is the cutting (*kandan*) of relief work (*barjesteh*, *gol-barjesteh*) into the surface of vessels with a carving tool. An unusual technique to obtain relief work has been observed in Natanz. Here the painter (*naqqāš*) applied a sugar syrup solution (*časb-e šakar*) with a brush wherever the black outlines indicated flowers and other ornaments. The sugar hardened the surface sufficiently so that when the whole surface was brushed with a coarse brush (*boros*), the background, which was not hardened by the syrup, gradually crumbled away. The brushing was continued until the background had receded about $\frac{1}{16}$-inch. Then enamel glaze was painted over the flower work, and the whole was dipped into clear turquoise glaze. After firing, the glaze appeared somewhat deeper in color over

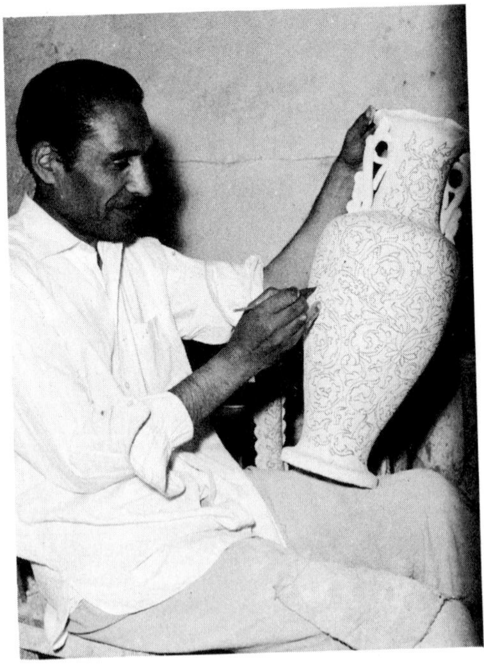

Figure 249 Applying Pigment to Stone Paste Ware

the brushed-away areas while the enamel colors were hardly affected by the glaze.

Apart from vessels the stone paste potters also produce glazed tiles in the paste technique (*ḫešt-e loᶜābī*) and, lately, electrical insulators.

Stone Paste Bead Maker

A real leftover from 6,000 years ago in the ceramic industry is the trade of the stone paste bead maker (*mohreh-sāz*), who produces nothing but turquoise colored beads (*mohreh*). One master observed in Qom employed a dozen assistants, and his annual consumption of potash alone was over fifty tons. The stone paste body was similar to the one used by the stone paste potter. Little children squatting on the ground filled tray after tray with balls $\frac{3}{4}$-inch diameter by quickly rolling small lumps of the paste in the palms of their hands. Other young assistants drilled holes (*sūlāḫ kardan*) through them on bow-operated simple drilling benches (*čarḫ-e mateh*). When dry, these beads were dipped into alkaline glaze containing copper oxide as a pigment. According to one master, freshly rolled and pierced beads, about two dozen at a time, were placed into a flat dish that had the bottom sprinkled with a dry mix of frit and oxide. The beads were shaken and rolled around in the dish and became evenly coated with the glaze powder. All these beads fired into a particularly bright turquoise (*fīrūzeh*). The Qom masters were reluctant about giving more details, for instance, how they fired the beads with the dry glaze powder on them. Probably they feared competition, as the manufacture of these beads has been a monopoly of Qom, from where they are sold all over Persia.

Glassmaker

It has been shown that in antiquity Mesopotamia was the leading country in the development of glazes for ceramic ware. Considering that glazes and glass are identical in their composition, it is not surprising to find a highly developed glass industry in Sumer, Babylonia, and Assyria. Archaeologists have proved that true glass (as different from the early Egyptian fused quartz or soda-lime glass) was already manufactured in Sumer during the third millennium B.C.,[166] and was imported into Egypt after 2000 B.C. but was not manufactured there before 1500 B.C. Babylonian recipe tablets[167] and especially Assyrian chemo-technical texts on glass technology of 625 B.C.[168] are proof of the high standard of the glass industry in an area close to Persia. From the Persian province of Ḫūzistān, the region of ancient Elam, we have evidence of a glass industry that must have flourished about the thirteenth century B.C. Ghirshman[169] has excavated many small glass bottles from the ziggurat at Čoġa-Zaṃbīl, as well as large quantities of glass tubes, with a $\frac{1}{2}$-inch outside diameter, $\frac{1}{4}$-inch hole diameter, and 30 inches in length. They are made of coiled black and white opaque glass and it seems that they have been used as window grills. A temple door contained inlaid glass mosaic; the colors too were white and black, and some pieces still had traces of melted-on gold and silver. And yet, little evidence of an extensive use of glass during Achaemenian times has come to light. Among rich finds in the Treasury of Persepolis[170] there are only a few glass vessels, mainly mold-blown, some with wheel-cut decorations, transparent and not tinted in any color. But an Athenian ambassador to the Persian Court of that

166 R. J. Forbes, *op. cit.*, Vol. 5, p. 113.

167 C. J. Gadd and R. Campbell-Thompson, *op. cit.*, pp. 87–96.

168 B. Meissner, *Babylonien und Assyrien*, and R. J. Forbes, *op. cit.*, Vol. 5, pp. 135, 200.

169 R. Ghirshman, "The Ziggurat at Tchoga Zanbil," pp. 68–81.

170 E. F. Schmidt, *op. cit.*, p. 84.

time mentioned that the Persians drank their wine from glass cups. Aristophanes (448–385 B.C.) also noticed this custom in his play *The Acharnians*.

During Hellenistic times a glass industry had been established by the Phoenicians on the shore of the Mediterranean near Sidon. Although Pliny credited the Phoenicians with the invention of glassmaking, it is believed today that they learned the art in Babylon. This corresponds to a Talmudic tradition[171] that the Jews learned glassmaking there during their second captivity. Phoenician and Jewish glass were both highly valued in preimperial Rome. From the many finds of glass objects that belong to Parthian and Sasanian times, it must be assumed that the art of glassmaking had spread to Persia almost at the same time. The skill of the Sasanian glassmaker was quite remarkable, especially in the art of decorating glass by wheel cutting. One of the best examples that has come to us is the cup of King Ḫosrou I, which is today in the Bibliothèque Nationale at Paris.

It appears that the glassmakers, like so many other craftsmen, continued to work in the Sasanian style during early Islamic times. Many glass objects have been found at Samarra and more still at Ray. Figure 250 shows such wheel-cut glass of the seventh to tenth centuries A.D. from Ray and Sāveh. Ordinary glassware, obviously pipe-blown, was clear white and undecorated. More valuable glass was blown first into a plain mold to give the object its general shape, then into a mold with straight flutes. While the glass was still on the end of the blow pipe and in its plastic state, the glass-blower must have given it a rapid twirling, thus producing spiral-fluted effects whenever these were what he wanted. Other objects have been blown

[171] R. J. Forbes, *op. cit.*, Vol. 5, p. 118.

Figure 250 Wheel-Cut Glass, Seventh to Tenth Centuries A.D. (*from C. J. Lamm,* Glass from Iran, *reproduced by permission of the publisher, the National Museum, Stockholm*)

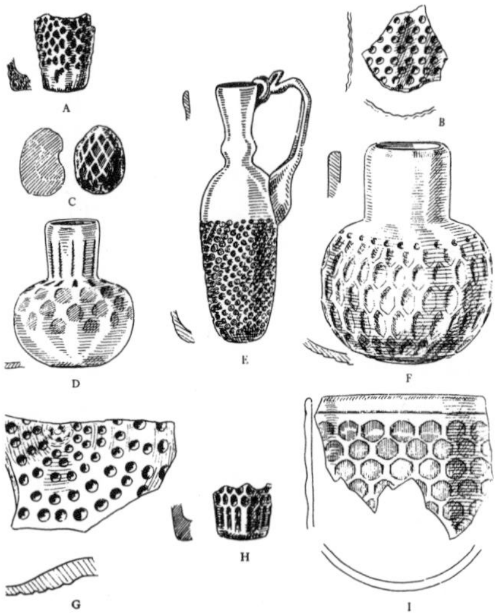

Figure 251 Ornamental Mold-Blown Glass, Sixth to Tenth Centuries A.D. (*from C. J. Lamm,* Glass from Iran, *reproduced by permission of the National Museum, Stockholm*)

into molds with honey-comb carvings or others with so-called pigeon-eye decorations (Fig. 251). Already very early in Islamic times the Syrian technique of decorating by applying glass threads, coils, and blobs in different colors can be observed. Many of these glasses have ornaments stamped onto the glass blobs; some carry the master's name and the place of manufacture.[172]

There must have been a general decline in the glassmakers' craft during the centuries after the Mongol invasion. When Chardin visited Persia between 1664 and 1681 he was not much impressed with their skill. After praising many other crafts he begins a new chapter:[173] "These are the arts and crafts the Persians do not understand: the art of glassmaking. There are glass-blowers all over Persia, but most of the glass is full of flaws and bladders and it is greyish . . . the glass of Shiraz is the finest in the country, that of Isfahan on the contrary is the sorriest, because it is only glass melted again." This is confirmed by Father Raphaël du Mans,[174] who saw Persia in 1660 and likewise observed that the glassmakers (*šišeh-gar*) of Iṣfahān merely remelted old glass, whereas those of Šīrāz made new glass. Despite an attempt by Šāh ᶜAbbās to revive the industry with the help of Italian artisans from Venice[175] the glassmaker did not rise much above a humble supplier of locally used common glass in the subsequent centuries. Polak,[176] who traveled in Persia in 1859, observed that "nearly every greater town has a glass melting furnace for local use, but glass from Qom and Shiraz is the best." Glass from there is shown in Fig. 252.

Figure 252 Fluted and Applied Ornament Glass from Šīrāz, Early Nineteenth Century

The Modern Glassmaker

The center of the glassworks (*šišeh-gar-ḫāneh, kārḫāneh-ye šišeh-garī*) is a large glass-melting kiln (*kūreh-ye šišeh-garī*, Fig. 253). The fire box is built below ground level and is reached by a number of steps. The fuel, desert shrubs until recently and mainly oil today, is fed through a fire hole (*kalāf*), and the flames pass through a relatively small grill (*zambūrak*) in the kiln floor into the kiln chamber. The floor of this chamber forms a ring-shaped pan (*čāl*) around the center grill. The pan is charged with broken glass (*ḫwordeh-ye šišeh*) through a door hole (*dahāneh*), and if not enough of this is available, with additional raw glass (*ᶜaiyar*). The raw glass for the Tehrān glassworks is made at Qom. To take a quantity of the melted glass

[172] C. J. Lamm, *Glass from Iran*, p. 11, Pl. 28.
[173] Sir J. Chardin, *op. cit.*, p. 275.

[174] Raphäel (le père) du Mans, *Estat de la Perse en 1660*.
[175] C. J. Lamm, *op. cit.*, p. 7.
[176] J. E. Polak, *Persien, das Land und seine Bewohner*, p. 179.

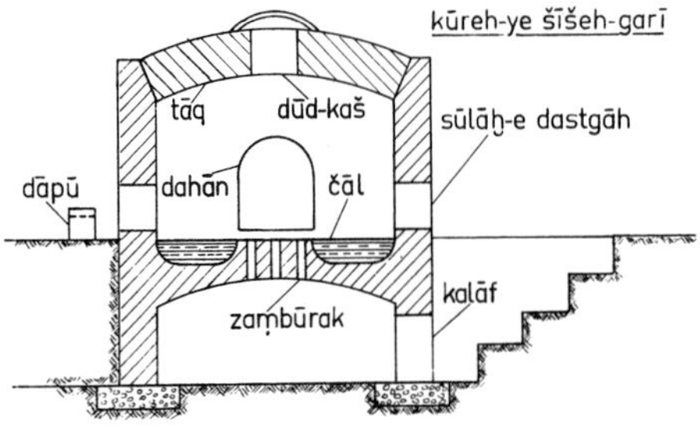

Figure 253 Glassmaker's Kiln near Tehrān (*section*)

(*giyūneh*) out of the pan the blowers pass their blow pipes (*dastgāh*) through a number of smaller working holes (*sūlāẖ-e dastgāh*) in the four walls of the kiln (Fig. 254). The flames leave the furnace through the same holes. In this way the glassmaker forces the fire to pass over the glass inside the kiln and keep it hot. At the same time he can reheat the glass blob at the end of his pipe in front of a working hole during the blowing operation (*bād kardan, fūt kardan, puf kardan*). A block (*dāpū*) made of a soft stone (*sang-e bargān*) is situated in front of each working hole. It takes the heavy weight of the blow pipe and serves as a general working bench for the glassmaker. When blowing is completed the object is touched with a cold form-iron (*vāgīreh*) and severed from the pipe. The manufactured glassware is placed in a cooling furnace (*garmẖāneh*) for 24 hours.

Glass objects today (*šīšeh, zujāj*) are undecorated and purely utilitarian. They include large bottles (*kūpeh-serkeh*), some with wide necks (*martabān*), small bottles with narrow necks (*tongī*), small bottles

Figure 254 Glass Blower Takes Melted Glass out of Furnace

with wide necks (*hoqqeh*), fruit-preserving jars (*morabbāʾī, bānkeh*), battery glasses (*šīšeh-ye qoveh*) for the old telegraph system, milk bottles (*šīrdān*), flower vases (*goldān-toq*), and glass insets (*golgūm*) for the skylights of domed buildings. Tehrān has modern glassworks operating with imported machinery, whereas Iṣfahān has its glassworks partly modernized insofar as the melted glass is taken out of the furnace manually, dropped into a press mold, and blown by compressed air.

4

TEXTILE CRAFTS AND LEATHER CRAFTS

Development and Diffusion of Important Textile Techniques

The Persian craftsman's contributions to progress within a craft can nowhere better be demonstrated than in the development of the textile industry.

An eminent research worker[1] in Persian textiles made the following remark:

> However little we may know of the other aspects of a civilization, if we find numerous and complex weaving techniques exacted with skill, we can infer that the community in question was highly involved and had advanced standards of living, and when the technical methods in this craft pass from one centre to another we may conclude that there was also a transfer in the same direction of other technical and artistic and quite possibly also intellectual, economic and political ideas.

Persia benefits largely from her central geographical position in the field of textiles, too. China in the Far East had great experience in fine silk weaving, the Central Asian pastoral people, making use of their wool, evolved the knotted rug, while the Syrians in the west were for centuries famous weavers of wool and linen, and India in the south developed cotton growing and its use in textile. Persia was able to draw from all these sources, but wherever the Persian weaver had adopted a new technique he rapidly assimilated it to his own style and tried to improve on it technically. If basic inventions originated outside the country, the most perfect realization was often achieved in Persia as we shall see, and supremacy in textile techniques has been maintained for well over 1,500 years.

Textiles in Persia can be traced back into the beginning of the Neolithic age. Excavations in the early 1950's in a cave near the Caspian Sea produced evidence of woven sheep's wool and goat hair, dated

[1] P. Ackerman in A. U. Pope and P. Ackerman, eds., *A Survey of Persian Art*, p. 2175.

by the carbon-14 method to about 6500 B.C. with a possible error of plus or minus 200 years.[2] Spinning whorls and warp weights have been found in early settlements on the Iranian Plateau dating from 5000 B.C.,[3] which indicates that the craft continued. Imprints of fabric on two copper axes, excavated in Susa, of about 3500 to 3000 B.C., show fine, even spinning and sheer, open weaving.[4] Tablet weaving can be proved for the turn of the third to the second millennium from finds at Susa[5] and continued uninterrupted to modern days. Tapestry, the kind of weave that later became so significant in Persian textiles, appeared west of Persia in the second millennium B.C.[6] Patterned shuttle weaving developed west of Persia from about 1000 B.C. in the form of a double weft weave. In this technique two wefts are carried simultaneously, one in plain cloth weave, while the second or pattern weft is brought to the surface only where it is wanted for the pattern, otherwise, it is carried floating at the back of the warp. This is the simplest form of compound cloth, the weft-patterned compound.

In China, however, a little later, a different type, the so-called warp-patterned compound cloth, had been developed. In this weave two warps of contrasting colors are used. A part of each warp is brought forward in accordance with the required pattern and is held there by a shoot of the weft that passes between the two warps without engaging in either. The next weft is then in normal cloth weave engaging both warps at once. Changes in the pattern are obtained by changing the warp threads brought forward. About the beginning of the Christian era[7] a second method of warp-patterned compound cloth appeared in China that differs from the previous one insofar as the binder warp engages in a weft twill while the pattern warp is left to float free. This produces a satin effect on the floating warp threads and a contrasting twill area on the remaining surface of the cloth.

In Parthian times both these Chinese compound weaves were already in use in Eastern Persia in their original Chinese technique. As the technique spread west, the Persian weavers adopted the idea of the two warps, but being accustomed to the weft pattern weave, they reversed the Chinese method and wove a compound cloth in which one or the other weft is on the surface according to pattern. Often, but not always, these two wefts enclose an alternative warp that engages no weft but is carried through in the interior of the fabric.[8] This new, combined method was generally used from the Sasanian period on (after 224 A.D.) and never ceased to be used in Persia, and in this form it passed on to Byzantium, Sicily, Italy, and northern Europe, where it became known as compound cloth.

During Sasanian times another weave appeared in Persia. The basis for this weave can be traced to Chinese fancy cloth of the second millennium B.C. It was proved to have existed in Han times from specimens dated to that period. It appeared in Central Asia in the second century A.D. and in Syria in the third century A.D. There it seems to have developed into a fully fledged compound twill. From Syria it went back to late Sasanian Persia and from there to China, where it became standard practice in the modified form since T'ang times (618–961 A.D.).[9] In Persia compound twill was even more used than compound cloth from Sasanian

[2] *Ibid.*, p. 3511.
[3] R. Ghirshman, *Iran*, p. 29.
[4] P. Ackerman, "Persian Textiles," in A. U. Pope and P. Ackerman, *op. cit.*, p. 3511.
[5] A. U. Pope and P. Ackerman, *op. cit.*, p. 2177.
[6] *Ibid.*
[7] M. Braun-Ronsdorf, "Silk Damasks," p. 3983.
[8] A. U. Pope and P. Ackerman, *op. cit.*, p. 2183.
[9] M. Braun-Ronsdorf, *op. cit.*, p. 3985.

times on, and it remains in use to the present day.

Development of Looms and Figure Harness

To produce advanced geometrical patterns a loom was required with at least four heddles or shafts for the twill binding and a minimum of a further four in the figure harness for the pattern. Since looms are made of wood, and perish, it is not possible to determine the equipment actually used for the regular geometrical pattern, unless we assume that it was similar to the one still in use in many present-day weaving shops.

Since Sasanian times, however, the design went far beyond geometrical patterns. It developed into free figures including animals, mythical birds, hunting scenes, and humans, usually framed by large rings. Such complicated designs can only be woven if it is possible to lift individual warp threads at will. The device for that action is the draw harness. When and where the draw loom was invented is still a point of argument, and various theories have been brought forward how it came to Persia. Some authors regard it as being a straight-out Chinese invention.[10] But then we know that the Sasanian kings employed captured Syrian weavers in their state weaving shops just about the time that the Sasanian free-figured weaving became famous in the Middle East. An answer to such an apparent contradiction lies in an analysis of fibers, spinning methods, and types of weave bindings used. This research work has been carried out by a textile technologist[11] and has resulted in the conclusion of a dual origin of the draw loom, both in China and in Syria, and a modification using features of both of them in Persia. Here is a summary of the argument:[12]

1. The silk fabrics of Han China mentioned in the preceding section, both the cloth weave and the twill weave, were woven with a loose warp and a tight weft. Patterns in both show threads in the warp while the thin, tight weft threads are hidden. Patterns on early fabrics that have come to us show the repeat exactly on the same warp threads. This is the best proof that a mechanical device to govern the warp has been used, viz., a kind of draw harness.

2. Syrian weavers who wove mainly in wool had for centuries produced their patterns in plain cloth weave with a thin, tight, and springy warp, and a thicker, loose weft thread that resulted in the disappearing of the warp threads, only the weft producing the pattern. At the beginning of the Christian era the Syrian tapestry weavers were the first to develop a third heddle to obtain surface variation in the form of a weft twill. In the subsequent century they used four and more heddles, which resulted in more complicated geometrical patterns, all in weft twill. During the third century A.D. patterns developed into free-figured design. Excavations in the then Persian city of Dura Europos on the Euphrates, which was destroyed in 256 A.D., brought many fabrics to light, of which, according to careful analysis, the ones with geometrical designs were clearly woven on multi-heddled looms and the ones with free-figured designs on draw looms. The geographical situation of Dura Europos makes it likely that the weavers there were the ones transplanted from Syria to Persia by the Sasanians.

[10] J. Needham, *The History of Science and Civilisation in China*, Vol. 1, pp. 6, 229, 240; and F. Orth, "Der Werdegang wichtiger Erfindungen auf dem Gebiete der Spinnerei und Weberei," p. 101.

[11] L. Bellinger, "Textile Analysis, Early Techniques in Egypt and the Near East," Parts 2, 3, 6.

[12] More details may be found in R. J. Forbes, *Studies in Ancient Technology*, Vol. 4, pp. 207 ff.

3. Considerable quantities of silk yarns and silk fabrics were imported from China into Persia during Sasanian times, and the Persian weavers saw for the first time complex patterns woven in a technique unknown to them. A simple copying of these designs on their own wool draw looms seems to have been out of the question. It has already been said that they were used to a tight, springy warp to produce tapestry weave in weft twill. They would have found considerable difficulty in handling a loose, unspun silk warp and in changing their harness from weft-figured to warp-figured design. What did the Persian weavers do to overcome this difficulty? First they spun the warp silk, which enabled them to have a tight warp similar to the wool warp; second they adopted the Chinese double warp but changed from warp-faced compound to weft-faced compound. All this could be done on the Syrian draw loom, and this was the loom that spread with the technique to Byzantium, Spain, Italy, and northern Europe. There the loom became most appropriately known as the damask loom. It was this loom that Charles Marie Jacquard, the Lyons silk weaver, mechanized in 1752, thus replacing the draw harness boy by an automatic pattern machine using punched cards.

4. After the Sasanians the weavers under the Omayyad and ʿAbbāsid caliphs continued to weave their fancy fabrics on these looms. Under the Seljūqs the weavers improved on them and refined some details. The resulting loom became known as the Persian loom. In that form it reached China for the production of the so-called *k'o-ssu* tapestry. Not only did the Chinese weavers change over from warp-figured to weft-figured twill for this type of fabric, but they also used spun and plied silk threads for the warp like their Moslem colleagues, after unspun warp threads had been used in China since time immemorial.

5. There are other aspects that have been brought forward by the research worker previously mentioned to determine the origin of the draw loom technique. These include direction of spin, type of pattern repeat, and the influence of other materials such as linen and cotton on the technique. An elaboration on this, however, seems to exceed the aims of this study.

Gold and Silver Textiles

The development of free-figured silks included an extensive application of gold and silver threads, a refinement known as brocade[13] or lamé. Precious metal threads woven into the material for priestly robes and royal garments are mentioned in the Middle East at an early date. Exodus 39 describes how Bezalel made Aaron's vestments: "... he made a mantle of gold blue and purple. . . ." To do this he had to cut up gold leaf and spin it into threads so that it could be worked into the rest of the colored weft. Xerxes is said to have presented the citizens of Abdera with a tiara interwoven with gold.[14] Of a later date are details of the garments of King Darius III (337–331 B.C.) "... and a mantle gleaming with gold on which were depicted two hawks, beak to beak."[15] The sacred book Avesta[16] mentions gold-woven rugs.

The Chinese annals Liang mention as something special that in 520 A.D. Persian gold brocade was sent to the Emperor Wu and that the garments of the kings of

[13] Brocade in the original sense means any fabric with a raised pattern. Modern English usage seems to imply a fabric with inwoven metal threads.

[14] Herodotus, *The Histories*, viii.120.

[15] Quintus Curtius, *Opera*, iii.3.

[16] *The Zend Avesta*, Yašt xv.2.

Persia were made from this material.[17] The Chinese traveler Hwan T'sang, who saw Persia early in the sixth century A.D., praises the skill of the Persian weavers in producing beautiful fabrics in wool, silk, and silk brocade.[18] Weaving centers during Sasanian times were at Susa, Šuštar, Jūndīšāpūr, and Baṣinnā. Here, and at the eastern centers in Ḫorāsān, brocade weaving became a major industry. Many precious fabrics woven there found their way into medieval Europe, where they were used for wrappings of relics, church vestments, and coronation garments of kings. Those that have survived to our day form the basis of our knowledge of Sasanian weaving skill. When the Byzantian emperor Heraclius seized the Sasanian palace at Duftgird in 627 A.D., he found there vast quantities of silk garments, royal robes woven with gold thread.[19] From then on Persia became the main country producing brocade fabrics. The industry flourished during the Middle Ages, reached a technical and artistic peak during Ṣafavid times, and has kept producing to the present day.

Technically we distinguish four different kinds of gold and silver threads:

1. *Beaten, drawn, and rolled gold.* In this process, known in the Middle Ages as "aurum battutum," the precious metal is drawn and rolled into a thin flat wire that is wound spirally around a silk or linen core. This type of metal thread gives the most brilliant luster and is very wear-resistant. However, it needs considerable quantities of the precious metal, and the fabric therefore becomes heavy and expensive. The gold spinner still is a specialized craftsman in Persia. This craft must have followed the brocade weaver across to northern Europe as we find guilds of gold and silver spinners in Paris in 1250 and in Cologne recorded since 1347,[20] about the same time that brocade weaving became established there.

2. *Gilded gut thread.* A much more economical way of making gold thread developed in Byzantium,[21] where it was used extensively in the state weaving shops. From there it spread to Cyprus, and the new gilt thread became known in Europe as *aurum cyprese.* It consisted of narrow strips of animal gut gilded with leaf gold before cutting. While still moist, these strips were spun around yellow silk or linen threads and adhered firmly because of the gluten content of the gut. These threads were surprisingly flexible and easy to weave, brilliant and nontarnishing in the same way as the spun gold threads, and kept their luster reasonably well. The technique spread through Italy and northern Europe and became standard practice there, side by side with spun gold. Gilded gut thread never found its way into the Persian weaving industry.

3. *Gilded leather thread.* A similar method producing silver and gold threads originated in China, but instead of guts the Chinese used previously gilded thin leather. From the twelfth century A.D. on, China became a major producer for brocade containing gilded leather thread. During the Mongol conquest the technique came to Persia, where it was used for centuries.[22]

4. *Gilded paper strips.* During the fourteenth century Chinese weavers gilded a relatively strong mulberry bark paper on both sides, cut it into strips, and interwove it with their silks in this form, or they spun it into a paper cord and then used it for weaving. It proved to be surprisingly durable but the technique did not survive

17 B. Laufer, *Sino-Iranica*, p. 488.
18 *Ibid.*
19 A. U. Pope and P. Ackerman, *op. cit.*, p. 692.

20 M. Braun-Ronsdorf, "Gold and Silver Fabrics from Mediaeval to Modern Times," p. 4.
21 O. von Falke, *Kunstgeschichte der Seidenweberei*, Vol. 2, p. 23.
22 M. Braun Ronsdorf, "Gold and Silver Fabrics from Mediaeval to Modern Times," p. 7.

in Persia much longer than the Timurid period. It probably depended entirely on the supply of Chinese paper.

Velvet Weaving

This is another technique that should be mentioned here, as it seems to have developed in Persia from the beginning of the eleventh century on. Hand-knotted rugs had come to Persia from Central Asia and were then already known for centuries. It seems that the Persian weaver in an attempt to mechanize his loom for pile weaving first adapted the loom for loop weaving and then designed a cutting device, known in the industry in Europe as a fustian knife. A twelfth-century Persian velvet[23] is an elaborately woven multicolored fabric that indicates that the industry was already fairly advanced at that time. Toward the eleventh century A.D. the Saracen rulers of Sicily established a velvet industry at Palermo where the fabric was produced under its Persian name, *ṭīrāz*. A century later the industry spread through Italy, reached France in the sixteenth century, Germany, the Netherlands, and Britain through Huguenot refugees from France during the seventeenth and eighteenth centuries. Between 1413 and 1566 a velvet industry flourished in Turkey, centered at Brussa.

Textile Fibers used in Persia

Wool (*pašm*) is the oldest fiber used in Persia for textiles. Domestication of the sheep (*gūsfand*) probably began on the Iranian Plateau and goes back to Neolithic times.[24] Three species of wild sheep seem to have been involved, the mouflon or mountain sheep (*ovis musimon* and *ovis orientalis*), the steppe sheep of the vigneus group (*ovis vignei* and *ovis arkal*) and sheep of the argali group (*ovis ammon* and *ovis poli*). Traces of wool from varieties and crossbreeds of these species have been found in Persia, Mesopotamia, Egypt, and northern Europe. Babylonia of the time of Hammurabi (1948–1905 B.C.) was called the "Land of Wool," and had already two main breeds, a sheep for wool and a sheep mainly grown for its meat. The same still holds in Persia of today, to which we can add the Boḫārā sheep that is grown for the lamb skins.

The Persian wool is rather coarse compared with Australian merino, but because of its hardness and shine it is well suited for its main application, i.e., carpet weaving. Considerable amounts of other animal hair are grown in Persia, e.g., the underhair (*kork*) of the goat (*boz*), known in the West as mohair, its Persian-Arabian name being *moḫayyar*, meaning "choice." It is used for the weaving of fine shawls and a warm and smooth cloth (*tarmeh*) for the cloaks of the Moslem clergy. Other hair of economic importance is camel hair (*pašm-e šotor*). In springtime, when the camels shed their warm winter fur, the caravan drivers pluck (*kandan*) the winter hair as they walk alongside the animals on their voyages and stuff it into bags attached to their saddles.

The fine goat hair is carefully combed (*šāneh kardan*) from the goats when the shepherds look after their animals in the evening camp. They make sure that as little as possible of the straight, hard top hair is combed out, since the weavers of Nāʾīn northeast of Iṣfahān pay good prices for clean mohair only.

The sheep are usually shorn (*pašm borīdan, pašm čīdan, boreš kardan*) with a pair of shears (*qaičī*). Plucking the wool, a practice of former times, is today only applied to sheepskins going to the tanner, in order to obtain the carcass wool (Fig. 255). Carcass hides are often soaked in lime water before plucking, and carcass wool (*ṭabaḫī*) is therefore of a lower quality.

[23] Now at the Musée Historique des Tissus, Lyons. See also A. Latour, "Velvet," p. 3451.
[24] R. J. Forbes, *op. cit.*, Vol. 4, p. 2.

Figure 255 Plucking Carcass Wool

Another textile fiber that has been in use in Persia since Neolithic times is linen (*katān, šīr-kanaf*). Flax (*linum usitatissimum, ʿalaf-e katān*) grows today chiefly in Māzandarān and Gīlān, but has also been cultivated in most parts of the Plateau during medieval times.[25] A considerable quantity of hemp (*cannabis sativa, kanaf*) is grown in the Caspian provinces and is mainly used for the manufacture of ropes and sackcloth.

A relative newcomer to Persia among the textile fibers is cotton (*Gossypium* spp.). First used in India, where cotton fabrics have been found in Mohenjo-daro (dated to about 3000 B.C.),[26] it was already mentioned in the sacred book Rigveda, which had been written about 1500 B.C. Cotton must have come to the Middle East before 700 B.C., since King Sennacherib is known to have planted cotton in Mesopotamia in 694 B.C.[27] Pliny saw cotton growing on the Persian Gulf island of Tylos.[28] The Sanskrit name for cotton, *karpasa*, is still retained in the Persian name for cotton cloth (*karbās*), thence Hebrew *kirpās* (Esther I, 6), Greek *carbasos*, and Latin *carbasus*. Our modern word "cotton" is derived from Arabic *quṭn* (from Old Babylonian *kitinnu*, which originally meant linen). The modern Persian word for cotton, *pambeh*, goes back to a Middle Persian word, *pambak*, which was much used in Parthian times; thence the Greek *pambax* and Latin *bambacium*. Cotton spread from Persia eastward rather late. Marco Polo saw much cotton growing in Persia, some in Turkestan, and in the Toledo manuscript of his works it is mentioned[29] that some cotton was grown in Fukien in China, but not enough of it. It must have come into general use in China about the thirteenth century,[30] a time of intense interchange with the West. In Persia today cotton is still grown in many parts of the country for home consumption as well as for export.

The finest of all the textile fibers, silk, has been known in Persia for a long time. Originating in China, silk was traded to the West mainly through Persia. When Herodotus called silk fabrics "Median"[31] he did not realize that they were only imported via Media. From the days of Alexander on, the silk fiber was called "serica" in the classical world after a not clearly defined people, the Seres. Their country "Serinda" may have been the Tarim basin in Central Asia, Soġdiana, the Iranian land between Oxus and Jaxartes, or Ḫotan. Whoever the Seres were they must have made considerable profits from the silk trade, especially after the Seleucids had established a safe land route between China and the Mediterranean. Their successors, the Parthians, were also vitally

[25] Al Balkhi (*Description of the Province of Fars*, trans. G. Le Strange, p. 55) mentions extensive flax cultivation and fiber treatment near Qazvīn and Māhrūbān during the twelfth century.

[26] S. Piggott, *Prehistoric India*, p. 155.

[27] R. J. Forbes, *op. cit.*, Vol. 4, p. 45.

[28] H. B. Brown, *Cotton*, p. 8.

[29] P. Pelliot, *Notes on Marco Polo*, p. 428.

[30] L. C. Goodrich, "Cotton in China," p. 408.

[31] Herodotus, *The Histories*, i.135; iii.84; vii.116.

interested in the silk trade. Mithridates II sent two successful embassies to China in 128 and 115 B.C., aiming at a better organization of the silk road and direct contacts with Chinese silk merchants. The Sasanians inherited the silk trade monopoly, and when during the wars between Persia and Byzantium (about 530 A.D.) silk yarn supplies to Byzantium came to a standstill, many of the Byzantian and Syrian silk weavers migrated to Persia. The Byzantian emperor Justinian, in search of the precious fiber, according to Procopius,[32] accepted an offer made by two Christian monks to smuggle some silkworm eggs out of Ḫotan in West Turkestan where a Chinese princess one hundred years previously had introduced silk cultivation.[33] From there it had spread to Yarkand, Fergana, and the Caspian provinces of Persia. According to Theophanes[34] it was a Persian at Byzantium who showed the birth of the silkworms from eggs that he had smuggled out of Serinda. In the early seventh century A.D. Byzantium was able to produce enough silk for its own industry and for export to Europe.

The geographer Ibn Ḥauqal (about 977 A.D.) wrote that silk was grown in his day in most parts of the Plateau but that it was originally transplanted from Central Asia into Ṭabāristān on the Caspian Sea, and that the cultivators still sent to Merv for the supply of silkworm eggs.[35] A traveler of the seventeenth century, Thomas Herbert, gives a vivid description of silk cultivation in Māzandarān,[36] and another, Sir John Chardin, estimated that the annual silk production of Persia was eight million pounds in 1670.[37] The industry declined after the downfall of the Ṣafavids, but by 1864 it had recovered, encouraged by good prices and improved export routes to France and Italy via Baku and Batum. In that year the production was two million pounds of cocoons.[38] A succession of poor seasons following disease attacking the silkworms brought production down to one-tenth of that figure within a few years and made Gīlān one of the poorest provinces. Through the introduction of selected eggs from Brussa in Turkey in 1890 a strain of silkworm free from disease marked the beginning of a revived silk industry for the Caspian provinces. In 1937 the government established a silk monopoly. Eggs for rearing the worms are issued to the farmers, and the cocoons must be sold to the agents of the monopoly, which has cocoon-handling factories at a number of places along the Caspian coast. The production in 1958 was 2.5 million pounds of cocoons but has since gone down owing to low prices offered to the farmers.

Fiber Preparation

Most fibers need preparation before they can be spun. In many parts of Persia it is customary to comb (*šāneh zadan*) the sheep to free the fleece from dirt and burrs and to wash the animals with soap (*ṣābūn*) or potash (*qalīʾeh*) before shearing. In other districts the combed fleece is shorn and the shorn wool (*pašm-e fīrīz*) washed (*šostan*) afterwards.

The cotton pods (*jouzaq*) are picked by hand, and women free (*kūʾeh-kaš*) the cotton bolls (*vaš*) from the hard capsules (*kuzeleh*, *pūst-e kuzeleh*), also by hand. A mechanical cleaner (*kulzebuzeh*) described

[32] Procopius, *De Bello Gothico*, iv.17.

[33] B. Laufer, *op. cit.*, p. 537.

[34] Theophanes of Byzantium, *Photios Myrabilion*, p. 64.

[35] Ibn Ḥauqal, *The Oriental Geography of Ebn Haukal*, p. 216.

[36] W. Foster, *Thomas Herbert's Travels*, p. 171.

[37] Sir J. Chardin, *Travels in Persia*, p. 281.

[38] H. L. Rabino, "Silk Culture in Persia," p. 455.

by nineteenth-century travelers[39] is no longer in use, since modern cotton varieties are not suitable for this rotary, crank-driven device. The cotton seeds (*toḫm-e pambeh*) are removed (*vaš kašīdan*) from the bolls by means of a cotton gin (*čarḫ-e vaškanī, čarḫ-e lōhanān*). Whereas the cotton gin in India and the Far East works with two rollers of equal diameter joined by a pair of helical gears, the Persian gin shows three rollers and, as a new feature, has a fly wheel (*ṣad-par*). The largest of these rollers is about 3 inches in diameter, is driven over a large crank handle (*dasteh*, Fig. 256), and is called *tīr-e čarḫ*. It runs in

Figure 256 A Cotton Gin

a pair of bronze bearings (*bālešmak*) that are housed in square wooden bearing blocks (*bālešmak-dān*). Roller and bearing blocks are placed between two vertical columns (*pāyeh*), both fixed to a horizontal board (*kondeh*). Loosely playing above this wooden main roller, but guided in slots in the columns, is a thin steel roller of only ½-inch diameter (*mīl*), which carries the fly wheel and is driven through friction from the main roller. Pressure between these two rollers can be adjusted by means of two wedges (*zīr-e ḥarakī*) below the bearing blocks. The cotton is inserted between these two rollers and the fibers pass between them while the seeds remain in front of them and drop to the ground. The third roller (*pošt-mīl*), also a steel roller of ½-inch diameter, rolls freely on top of the main roller and behind the fly wheel roller. Its purpose is to divert the cotton fibers away from the main roller. The ginning (*faḫmīdan*) is sometimes done by the peasants, especially if they do their own spinning, but more often by a specialist, the cotton ginner (*ḥallāj*), whose job it is also to loosen the ginned cotton (*bandak*) prior to spinning, by bowing (*kamān zadan, pambeh zadan, vāčīdan, ḥallāj zadan*). Some bowers work in their workshops all the year round, but others doing bowing only, then called *pambeh-zan*, take their tools to the clients' houses and loosen the fibers there, mainly cotton, sometimes wool or mohair. The tools of the bower are a rod (*šafteh*) for a preliminary beating of the fibers, the bow (*kamān-e pambeh-zanī, lōr, lūrak*), and a mallet (*čak, mošteh*). The bow (Fig. 257) consists of a round bow shaft (*kamān*) that is made up of laminations of poplar wood (*čūb-e kabūdeh*) or willow wood (*čūb-e bīd*) glued together with a fish glue (*serīš-e māhī, serešt-e māhī*), popularly called *jīd*. The top of the bow (*sar-e kamān, sar-čang*) is shaped like the neck of a harp, the foot is formed by a board (*taḫteh-ye kamān*) that is inserted into the slot of a round board carrier (*ḥāmel-e taḫteh*), and the whole is attached to the shaft by four gut strings (*tang-kaš*). The tightening is achieved by inserting two wedges (*čūb-e gōveh*). A strong bowstring (*zeh, zī, čelleh*) prepared from four individual guts (*rūdeh-gūsfand*) runs from the bow top to the end of the footboard of the bow. At the top it is attached to a peg (*mīḫ bā gereh-ye zeh*), runs over strips of soft leather (*soġārī, čarm zīr-e zeh*), and around the corner of the square footboard, where

[39] H. C. Brugsch, *Die Reise der königlich preussischen Gesandtschaft nach Persien 1860–61*, p. 45.

Figure 257 A Cotton or Wool Bow

it divides into two guts on each side and is wound around the foot of the bow shaft. Rough tightening is achieved by twisting a toggle peg (*čūb-e čahār zeh*) through the strings. Final adjustment is made by pushing a block (*pūlak*) made from a roll of hard leather between string and footboard. A smaller tightening string (*kamānčeh, komak-e sāz*) wound by a peg (*tāb*) provides the proper tension. The bower usually carries a spare string (*kafan-e kamān, ziyādeh*) wound around the shaft. A bundle of cotton yarn (*kalāfeh*) is fastened to the bow shaft near its center of gravity. In operation the bower passes one hand through this sling (*jā-ye dast*), which at the same time protects his hand. The bow is then placed over the fibers (Fig. 258) and is beaten with a round mallet (*čak, mošteh*) made from ash wood (*čūb-e zabān-e gonješk*). The ridge at the end of the mallet grips the bowstring, and when the latter's tension becomes too high it slips off the ridge, causing a strong vibration. As the string is kept in contact with the fibers these vibrations loosen them and throw them away from the bower. To take the weight off the bow it is either suspended from the ceiling by a string or, when working in the open, the bower places a thick cushion (*čaṃbareh*) between the bow-holding arm and his knee. After the bowing the cotton is rolled (*pīcīdan*) into large balls (*gondal, gondaleh,* see background, Fig. 258).

If wool to be bowed is too long, especially wool for fulling, it is cut in half by gripping some of it with both hands and drawing it over a broad knife having a cross handle that rests on the ground (Fig. 259). The fibers to be bowed are placed on a reed mat (*kazveh, ḥasīr*) to keep them clean. Some of the bowed fibers (*kuls*) to be used for spinning are wound (*pīčīdan*) onto distaffs (*čulleh*). It may be mentioned here that considerable quantities of fibers are bowed for the mattress, quilt, and cushion makers.

Figure 258 Beating the Cotton Bow

Figure 259 Cutting Wool

Bowing, which is done everywhere in the Middle East and in China, appeared in Venice during the fourteenth century,[40] and its introduction in Germany caused some trouble between the wool and cotton working guilds.[41]

Efficient as this method of loosening fibers is, women in the country who prepare wool for spinning prefer combing (*šāneh mīk zadan*) to obtain loose and parallel fibers. Figure 260 shows a comb (*šāneh-mīk*). It consists of a base (*pāyeh*) on the ends of which the comber kneels during the combing and two upright boards (*taḫteh*) which, where they join, hold two rows of sharp steel teeth (*dandeh*). The comber takes a small quantity of wool into her hands, draws it into the teeth, and by pulling her hands apart separates the fibers. If necessary she repeats this process several times until the fibers are more or less parallel. They are then loosely placed together and slung into a coil (*kalāfeh*) ready for the spinning process.

Figure 260 A Wool Comb

One of the less important fibers is hemp (*kanaf*). When matured in October it is about 7 feet high, and the stems (*čūleh*) of the plant are cut and placed into water (*āb kardan*), usually into ditches branched off from the irrigation canal. After about a week the stems are sufficiently softened so that the fibers can be peeled off (*kanaf az čūleh savār kardan*). The baled fibers are sold to ropers and sack weavers at Rašt.

Preparation of the Silk Yarn

The peasants (*ra^{c}iyyatī*) of the provinces of Gīlān and Māzandarān who are engaged in the rearing of silkworms (*pīleh-abrīšam*) buy the eggs (*nouġān, toḫm-e nouġān, toḫm-e kerm, toḫm-e abrīšam*) from the nearest agent of the silk monopoly (*edāreh-ye abrīšam, edāreh-ye nouġān*) in the middle of March. The eggs are sold in boxes (*ja^{c}beh*) containing 100 grams of them. The average producer buys 5 to 10 boxes.

The rearing of the silkworms is done in the silkworm nursery (*telembār*), one of the open barn-like wooden structures typical for this region. The walls are formed by lattice work. The eggs are placed (*gozāštan*) on wooden trays (*sīnī-ye čūbī*), each carrying a layer of a strong-scented herb, *^{c}alaf-e būdār*. The trays are kept in a warm spot (*jā-ye garm*), preferably on the sunny side of the nursery. When after a few days the silkworms (*kerm-e abrīšam*) begin to hatch (*zendeh šodān*) leaves (*barg*) of the

[40] C. Singer, *A History of Technology*, Vol. 3, p. 194.
[41] *Ibid.*, p. 195.

white mulberry tree (*Morus alba, tūt-e safīd*) are strewn over them. The leaves have been collected in the forest and from hedges and have been cut up (*ẖword kardan*) with a knife (*kārd*). Every 10 hours fresh leaves are placed on the trays. On the seventh day the worms are transferred to a clean tray. In between they have periods of rest (*ẖwāb dāštan*), after which they cast their skin. During the seventh week whole branches of the mulberry tree with their leaves are placed on shelves in the nursery (*taẖt*). The worms are transferred there and eat the leaves greedily so that the branches have to be replaced every four hours. Soon afterwards they begin to spin (*bastan*) their cocoon (*pīleh*). When this is done the cocoons are sold by weight to the cocoon-handling factory (*kārẖāneh-ye abrīšam*) of the monopoly, where the encased chrysalis is killed in a modern steam or hot air apparatus (*sīkātūr*). Experts at the factory select a certain quantity of the cocoons that are allowed to complete their life cycle and become silk moths (*parvāneh*), which lay the eggs for the next season.

The killed cocoons are classed (*nomreh-bandī kardan*) into four standard grades numbered from 1 to 4 and two substandard grades, *šelleh siyāh* and *kar*. The producers obtain a uniform price for the standard grades but a reduction is made for substandard qualities. Women do the sorting (*tamīz kardan*) and put the cocoons into the appropriate bags (*kīseh*). Those for export are sent to Tehrān while the silk (*abrīšam*) used locally is sold at Rašt, already wound from the cocoons into skeins (*naqādī kardan*). The latter, mainly used in the manufacture of high quality carpets, is marketed in three grades; *dāneh* is the finest and is used in the carpet industry for the knotting of the pile; *haštī* is a medium grade and is spun into yarn for warps of silk and high grade wool pile carpets; *pūdī* is a coarse grade, and is likewise spun and used as weft between rows of piles of silk carpets.

The preparation of silk yarn consists of a number of steps beginning with the unwinding of the skeins. This is done in Yazd and Iṣfahān as a cottage industry, usually involving several members of the family who call themselves silk winders (*abrīšam-tāb*). These are the steps involved:

1. Transferring the thread from the skein to a large cage spool (*māsūreh, kalāfeh, kūpī*). A four-legged stand (*naqāṭī*) is formed by four rods, each one placed into a stone base (*kūn-e bīnī*). The silk skein is placed over the rods, which can be arranged in such a way that they hold it fairly tight (Fig. 261). The thread is guided through an eyelet (*gūšeh, ḥalqeh*) suspended from a separate stand (*bannīy*) to the cage spool. The silk winder, holding this spool by its handle, turns it rapidly, thus winding (*kalāf kardan, kūpī kardan*) the thread (*rīsmān*) onto it from the skein.

Figure 261 Winding Silk from the Skein to the Cage Spool

2. Transfer from the cage spool to a bobbin (*čarī*). The cage spool when full is handed over to another person, who places it opposite a spool winder (*čarẖ-e kalāfeh*). The spindle of this wheel is and tapered

carries a small wooden bobbin on which the silk thread is wound. If a thicker, twined thread is required, a twining wheel (*čarẖ-e tābī*) is used that is similar to the simple winder except that the spindle carries a flyer (*parreh*) and the threads are drawn from two cage spools. The threads on the bobbins may be used for wefts, in which case they are transferred onto still smaller shuttle bobbins, or they may be used for the preparation of warps (*čelleh, tān, tūn, tār*). In the latter case another step is necessary.

3. Transfer from bobbins to warp spools (Fig. 262). This illustration shows a warp spool winder. In the right foreground it has the spool holder (*dūk-ẖāneh*) capable of holding eight warp spools (*dūk*). Each one is driven by a pulley (*qorṣ, gāvdom*), the power coming over a transmission cord from a hand-driven large wheel (*čarẖ*). An upright bobbin carrier (*čarī-ẖāneh*) with provisions to hold 32 bobbins is visible between this winding wheel and the spool holder. Threads from one to four bobbins can be wound onto each one of the warp spools, the number of bobbins taken depending on the thickness of the warp threads required.

Figure 262 A Warp Spool Winder

Figure 263 A Warping Frame

4. Winding of the Warp. A warping frame (*čelleh-tūn, čelleh-dādanī*) is prepared on the longest wall of the house, often on an outside wall facing the courtyard and covered by a short sun roof. A sufficient number of warping pegs (*mīẖ-e čelleh-tūn*) has been fixed into the wall to provide for the required length of the finished warp (Fig. 263), two special pegs being placed close to the first peg. These so-called cross pegs (*damgāh*) are necessary to produce the lease or warp cross (*eśdī, bāft, čap-ō-rāst*). Opposite the warping frame is the spool stand (*rīgdān*), capable of holding a large number of warping spools in a vertical position (Foreground, Fig. 263). A long bar carrying a thread guide for each warp thread is fixed above this stand. The warp winder begins his work by attaching all the threads to the commencing peg, then alternately leading one warp thread under, the next one over the cross pegs, and so on, until the whole strand of the warp is laid at the cross. Then the strand is guided over all the warping pegs on the wall. If the weaving process requires a protection of

the warp, a glutenous size (*šumāl*) is applied to the warp strand at this stage, the warping room having its name (*šumāl-ḫāneh*) from this process. After the drying of the size, the threads are cut off at the end, tied to a wooden peg (*čelleh-pīč*), and secured with a cross peg (*ḫār, sīḫ*). The warper then winds the whole warp strand into a ball (*čelleh, tūneh*) onto this peg. When he comes to the cross near the starting peg, he carefully secures it with a loop of string. After that he begins with a new strand as before until he has about 12 to 15 strands wound on to warp balls, this number being necessary for a complete silk warp of about one yard width.

The Iṣfahān warp winders also use rotary warp winding frames (*čarḫ-e čehel tābī*).

Spinning of Wool, Cotton, and Flax

This process involves three steps: the drawing of the fibers from a bag, a sliver, or a distaff and attenuating them in a more or less parallel order; the twisting of the fibers into a thread; and the winding of the thread into a ball or onto the spindle. Two methods of spinning (*rīstan, rīsīdan, rīḫtan*) are customary in Persia, the spinning with a hand spindle (*dūk, dūk-e jalak, pīl, pīlī, parreh*) or with a spinning wheel (*čarḫ-e nāḫrīsī, čarḫ-e rīsandehgī, čir*). Although the division is not quite rigid, nomads and wandering shepherds prefer the hand spindle while people with a fixed abode generally spin on the wheel.

A hand spinner (*dūk-rīs, rīsandeh*) draws fibers (*ḫāmeh*) from a bag (*kīseh*) which he holds strapped over his shoulder or under his arm. Other hand spinners just draw wool or cotton from their wide coat sleeves (Fig. 264) or they have some fibers wound around their hand. The spindle type commonly used for wool and cotton is the suspended spindle. It consists of a slightly tapered wooden or iron spindle rod

Figure 264 A Hand Spinner Drawing Wool from his Sleeve

(*mīl, čōl, čoul*) with a notch or hook (*čōl-e gīreh, dandeh*) at the upper end, weighted for better twisting momentum by a whorl (*langar, dūk-sareh*), which may be just one or two pieces of wood or two pairs of wooden or iron arms (*šāḫ, fōq*, Fig. 265) pushed over the spindle rod. Some spinners use properly turned wooden spindles where the upper part near the hook is sufficiently large and heavy to act as a whorl. The spinner attaches the fibers to the spindle end, gives the spindle a sharp twist, and while it is freely suspended and rotating he draws more fibers and keeps on doing so until the spindle reaches the ground. He then lifts it and winds the thread (*rīsmān, naḫ, qatmeh*) around the whorl in the form of a ball (*gūrūp*) or around the spindle rod. Since cotton washes better when Z-spun,[42] owing to the natural twisting of its fibers when moistened, it is customary in most parts of Persia to spin it in that direction. Even wool spinners (*pašm-rīs*) to whom it would be immaterial have adopted this spin.

Figure 265 A Hand Spindle with Iron Whorl

[42] A yarn has Z twist if, when held in a vertical position, the spirals conform in direction of slope to the central portion of the letter "Z" and S twist if the spirals conform in direction of slope to the central portion of the letter "S."

Flax spinning is always done from a distaff, and the turned wooden spindle is not of the suspended but of the grasped type. The spinner holds the spindle at the handle end while he whirls it round, at the same time drawing, with his other hand, fibers from the distaff for as long as his arm can reach. Then, with a sudden twist, unhooking the thread from the spindle end, he winds the yarn onto the spindle shaft. As the natural twist of moistened flax is always in S-direction, S-spinning is common practice in the flax region for all fibers.

Those using a spinning wheel claim that it allows faster work, produces a more uniform thread, and permits other operations with the same device such as bobbin winding and doubling of threads. Figure 266 shows such a wheel built by the local carpenter. The base (*čūb, pāyeh*) carries on one side two wooden columns (*pāyeh buzurg*) between which the main or driving wheel (*parreh, pāl*) operates. This wheel consists of two groups of spokes (*parreh*) that are fixed to the driving axle (*tīr, kūndeh*) and two strings (*zeh, vaṣl-e parreh*), one slung across the free ends of the spokes, thus forming the circumference of the wheel and the other one tightening this circumference. A crank (*tīr-e vaṣūl, kolāneh*) carrying the operating handle (*dasteh, dasteh-čarḫ*) at its end is attached to the axle. Two horizontal bars (*vaṣleh*) connect the main wheel stand with the spindle stand, which is formed by two shorter columns (*pāyeh kūčīk*), each of them carrying a spindle bearing (*souveh, gūšeh*) made of thick, tallow-soaked leather. In the Nāʾīn-Ardestān region the bearings are formed by the holed seeds of a melon (*toḫm-e hendevāneh*) that are placed in slots in the columns, last several days, and are easily replaced. The spindle (*dūk, mīl*), made of steel or wood, runs through both bearings and is driven from the main wheel by a transmission cord (*naḫ, rīsmān, rū*).

Figure 266 A Spinning Wheel from Kalārdašt (*Alburz; note comb left of the wheel*)

For the spinning on the wheel (*riḫtan bā čarḫ*) the spinner draws about 15 inches of fibers from the sliver, twists their ends around the hooked end of the spindle (*dandeh*), and begins to turn the wheel handle with one hand, at the same time drawing fibers away from the spindle as far as the other arm can reach. When this arm is relaxed so that the newly spun thread can return to the spindle it winds itself around the front end of the spindle (Fig. 267). When the spindle is full the yarn has to be transferred. It is wound onto a winding stick (*hazeh-gard*, foreground Fig. 266), the yarn being released from the spindle by turning the wheel backwards. The yarn can be taken off this winding

Figure 267 A Spinning Wheel from Ardestān

stick as a skein (*kalāf*). When used for knitting it is then wound (*pīčīdan*) into a ball (*gol nēkā*). When it is intended for weaving it is wound from the skein onto a bobbin (*māsūreh*). This is done by placing the skein over a reel, also called *hazeh-gard*, whose axle stands in a lump of dried clay (*gel-moč*), pushing a bobbin over the spindle head, and winding the yarn from the skein onto the bobbin. In households with more than one spinning wheel a bobbin is slipped over the spindle head of the second spinning wheel and the yarn is wound onto this bobbin (*māsūreh kardan*, *māsūreh pīčīdan*) straight from the full spindle. (Figure 268 shows the full spindle in the center foreground.)

Textile Dyeing

The dyeing of textile fibers has been a highly developed craft in Persia for many centuries. Even today, when modern textile mills use synthetic dyestuff exclusively, the old craft of the dyer using animal and vegetable coloring agents is still alive.

When at the end of the last and the beginning of this century the first aniline dyestuffs were used in the manufacture of Persian carpets, they lost much of their original character, partly through an unsuitable color range, partly owing to the inability of the simple cottage weaver or nomad to apply the complex recipes for these dyes. The government and the carpet manufacturers then realized the danger to this important industry, and for years synthetic indigo became the only dye which obtained import permits. Later, with the improvement of synthetic dyestuffs and the increasing ability of the Persian dyer to use them properly, more and more of these products were allowed to be imported, so that today urban dyers too use many synthetic dyes.

Like authors who tried to investigate the

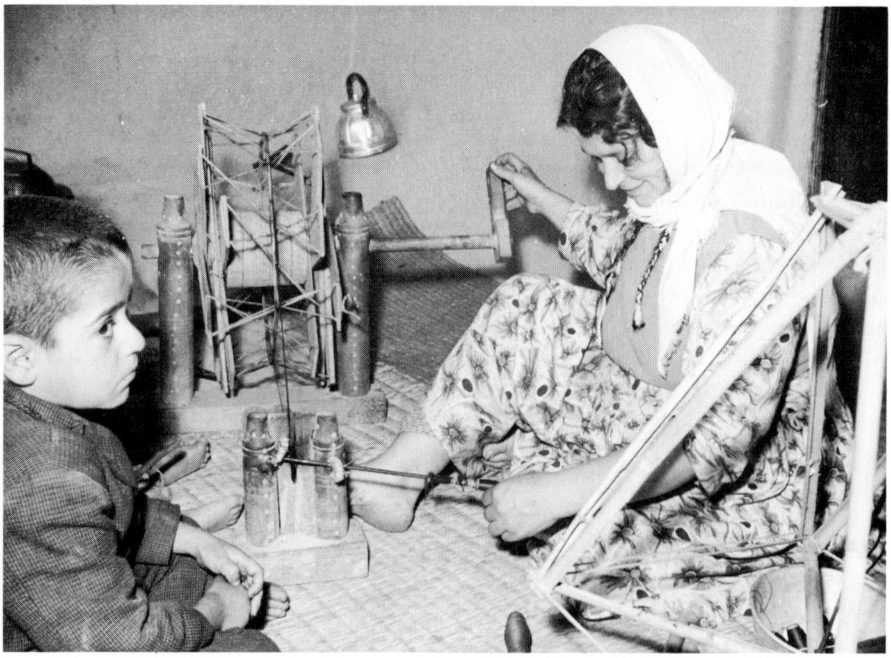

Figure 268 Using the Spinning Wheel for Bobbin Winding

dyer's craft, the nature and application of his dyes, the writer found it extremely difficult to obtain full technical information. For many centuries recipes have been passed on from father to son, understandably so because a good dyer is relatively well paid and a respected person in the community.

Mordants. For the full development of the colors and for the fixing of the dyes to the fibers, most of the dyestuffs described in the following pages need a mordant or fixer that in Persia is mainly alum (*zāj*), principally in the form of ammonium alum, aluminum sulphate (*zāj-e safīd*), potassium alum (*zāj-e qalīʾeh*), and chromium alum. Sometimes certain iron and copper salts are used. Often combined with the above, some astringents with a high content of tannic acid are applied, partly to act as fixers, partly to provide darker hues through the formation of dark iron-tannic compounds. Some such astringents are extracts from the leaves of the turpentine tree (*Pistacia terebinthus, saqiz-e safīd*),[43] others from the leaves and galls of the wild pistachio tree (*jift, jaft, Pistacia intergerrima, Pistacia khinjuk*) or the leaves and husks of the cultivated pistachio tree (*Pistacia vera, pasteh*). The galls on the leaves of *Pistacia intergerrima* and *Pistacia khinjuk* are caused by the sting of the insect *Pemphigus utricularius*. They contain 40 per cent tannic acid. In Kurdistan other galls are collected from the leaves of an oak (*Quercus infectoria*). These galls (*māzū, affaz*) are traded as Aleppo galls and contain 50 to 70 per cent tannic acid. They are caused by the sting of the insect *Cynips gallae tinctoriae*. Quite common in Persia are the galls from the leaves of *Quercus lusitanica* where the stings of *Cynips insana* and *Amdricus lucidus* cause the formation of the galls. For the preparation of such extracts, dried leaves and gall nuts are ground, either in a hand mill or on an edge runner (*sang-e narm*), boiled with water in large copper vats for several hours, and strained through a piece of cotton fabric.

Some of these mordants cause an undesired darkening of the colors owing to the presence of unduly high quantities of iron in either the water or the alum. In these cases it is important for the dyer to use rain water, if available, and pure alum. In early times the dyers already treated natural aluminum sulphate with urine. When concentrated by boiling and subsequently cooled, pure ammonium alum crystallized out. This process came to Europe in the middle of the fifteenth century.[44]

Commonly Used Natural Dyestuffs

Red Dyes. The most beautiful and highly valued red dye is cochineal (*qermez-dāneh*), which is processed into crimson or carmine lake.[45] It is produced from the female bodies of the insect *Coccus cati*. Already mentioned by Sargon II (714 B.C.) as coming from northern Persia and Armenia, the production of cochineal continued in that area where the insect breeds on *Aelupus leavis* and *Dytylis litoralis*. The dried bodies of the insects are crushed and the coloring matter, carminic acid, is mordanted with alum, tin, or calcium salts.[46] A variety of cochineal is Armenian red and is obtained in northern Persia from the insect *Porphyrophora Hamelii*.

The Persian dyers with their limited

[43] Many of the species used in the dyer's trade have been identified with the aid of D. Hooper and H. Field, "Useful Plants and Drugs of Iran and Iraq."

[44] C. Singer, *op. cit.*, Vol. 2, p. 368.

[45] A lake is produced when the actual coloring matter is allowed to precipitate as an insoluble substance that is then filtered out and used as a pigment, instead of being deposited onto fibers.

[46] Most of the historical and chemotechnical information in this section is taken from R. J. Forbes, *op. cit.*, Vol. 4, and C. Singer, *op. cit.*, Vol. 2.

entomological knowledge cannot be blamed when they often confused true cochineal with the dyestuff kermes (*qermez*) obtained from the insect *Kermococcus vermilio* (formerly called *Coccus ilicis*). It lives on the stalks and branches of the kermes oak (*Quercus coccifery L.*). The use of this dye goes back to prehistory; Persia has been a well known producer through the ages and still is to this day. Kermes was introduced into Assyria about 1100 B.C. and spread to Greece, Rome, and Spain in classical times. It derived its name from the Persian word for worm, i.e., *kerm*, from which our "crimson" and "carmine" have derived. An older Persian word for it is *sakirlāt*, which became *scarlatum* in Latin and "scarlet" in English. Kermes is produced from the female insect. The harvesting takes place about May or June. Women and girls scratch the insects from the leaves with their fingernails at the rate of about 1 kg per day. The insects are killed by holding them over the vapors of vinegar or by immersion into vinegar. Dried and crushed, they yield the dyestuff; its coloring matter, kermesic acid, is soluble in water or alcohol and is fixed with alum or urine. As a color it is not as bright as cochineal but a pleasant one and also very fast (*rang-bast*).

Another red dye and most important in the carpet industry is madder (*rūnās*, *rūniyās*), obtained from the roots of *Rubia tinctorum*, a shrub reaching three feet in height. This was already known about 3000 B.C. at Mohenjo-daro in the Indus valley from where it spread to the Middle East at an early date. There it was cultivated extensively and spread to Central Asia and Russia in historical times. Although known to Greek and Roman dyers, madder went out of use in Europe at the end of Roman rule and only came back during the Crusades as Turkey red. The Dutch became the leading European producers of madder. When France wanted to become independent of Dutch imports it secured the services of J. Althen, an Armenian from Iṣfahān, who became the founder of the madder industry around Avignon.[47]

In Persia madder is produced as follows: When the plants are at least two years old the roots are dug up in autumn after the leaves have fallen. The seven-year-old plant yields a maximum of dye and one of a deep purplish color, whereas the dye from the younger plant gives a terracotta red color. The roots are dried, beaten to remove dirt and the skin, and finally they are pulverized. They contain ruberythric acid which when moistened splits into sugar and alizarin (*lizārī*), the latter being the actual coloring agent. Mordanted with pure alum it gives a beautiful and fast red color; when iron alum (*zāj-e zard*) is used it yields a brownish red hue. A particularly bright red is obtained from madder root when dried yoghurt (*dūġ*) is added to the extraction water. This color is known as *dūġī*. The Venetian traveler Barbaro,[48] who saw Persia in 1471, wrote that Persian dyers travel with large quantities of madder to India where they exercise their craft as red-dyers. Today principal trading centers for madder are Šīrāz and Iṣfahān.

Cinnabar (*ḫūn-e siyāvūš*) is a red-to-orange dye that was often used in conjunction with other dyestuff, according to older recipes. It is a resin imported from Zanzibar via India under the name of dragon blood. It is an exudation from the leaves of *Dracaena cinnabari*, which is soluble in alcohol and is also used as a stain in varnishes.

Kamela (*qaṃbīleh*) is another red-to-orange dye especially for silk. It is obtained

[47] G. Schaefer, "Der Anbau und die Veredelung der Krappwurzel," p. 1718.

[48] *Travels of Venetians in Persia*, p. 165.

from the glands of *Mallotus Phillipinensis.*

Another red-to-purple dye is extracted from the roots and plants of *Onosma echioides* (*rīšeh havah-ye čūbeh*) and *Onosma Hookeri* (*rang-e pādšāh*), English ratanjot.

A particularly warm red hue is obtained from the dye shellac *rang-lāk*, *lākī*, which is a by-product in the preparation of the well known shellac gum, an exudation of the Banyan tree caused by an insect. It is a very fast dye and is imported from India.

Yellow Dyes. A wide range of yellow dyes in many shades is available. The most important one is safflower (*gol-e rang*). The coloring matter, carthamic acid, is extracted from the petals and florets of *Carthamus tinctorius.* It is cultivated in Persia as a field crop, the petals being collected, dried, and pounded. When used the powder is steeped in water; after the addition of fuller's earth and potash the dye goes into solution, the colors ranging from orange-red to yellow.

One of the finest yellow dyes is saffron (*zaʿfrān*), which is extracted from the stigmas of *Crocus sativus.* It was known in the Middle East, Egypt, Crete, and Phoenicia since ancient times, being extensively cultivated in Persia right through the Islamic period. It came to Spain with the Arabs during the tenth century. Today saffron is cultivated in the fields around Qāʾen in Ḫorāsān. It is a rather expensive dye and is mainly used for silk dyeing.

A widely used yellow dye is turmeric (*karkum*, *zard-čūbeh*), the so-called Indian saffron. It is produced from the shoots and roots of *Curcuma domestica* and *Curcuma longa*, which have both been cultivated in India, Persia, and Mesopotamia from ancient times on.

The leaves of *Rhus coriaria* give the valuable yellow dye, sumach (*sumāq*). Already known to the Sumerians, the sumach tree is cultivated in Persia, Afghanistan, and Central Asia. The dye solution also contains 15 to 30 per cent tannic acid. Its main application is in the dyeing of silk and the tanning and coloring of leather.

The extracts from pomegranate rinds (*pūst-e anār*) are a useful combination of dye, mordant, and tanning agent resulting in a mild yellow coloring agent. Known for this purpose in Mesopotamia since 2000 B.C., in Egypt since 1500 B.C., the rinds are collected when the peasants turn their surplus pomegranate juice into syrup, and are dried, and ground to powder. The active substance is extracted with water.

A dye mainly used for silk, but mixed with other dyes also for wool, is extracted from the flowers of the yellow larkspur (*Delphinium zalil*), a weed growing abundantly in Ḫorāsān. This dye is known in Persia as *isparag*, *esperek*, *asparg*, or *zalil.* When used with pomegranate rind or alum as a mordant it yields a bright and fast yellow, but mordanted with copper sulphate the color turns into a pleasant green known as *ābī sangar.*

A rather intense yellow, often more toward orange, is obtained from the dried unripe berries of *Rhamnus infectorius*, a member of the buckthorn family. The coloring matter, rhamnetin, is extracted by boiling in water. Alum as a mordant gives a yellow hue, whereas tin mordant yields a stark orange. This dye is very fast.

Still another, likewise very fast yellow dye is *gandal*, obtained from the malodorous herb *gandalāš.* It grows in the Baḫtiyārī mountains northwest of Iṣfahān and is sold dried in the Iṣfahān bazaar. For dyeing it is boiled for 10 hours and mordanted with alum.

In autumn a pleasant yellow dye is extracted from the yellow leaves (*barg-e mou*) of the grapevine. The leaves are dried in the sun. For use as dye they are boiled for 4 to 6 hours and fixed with alum. This fast color is known as *barg-e mou.*

Blue Dyes. Blue is almost exclusively produced from indigo (*nīl*, *rang-e kermānī*, *rang-e vasmeh*). The dye is obtained from the leaves of *Indigofera tinctoria*, grown in Ḫūzistān near Šuštar and Dizful. The ground leaves (*rang-e sābīdeh*) are steeped in water by the Persian dyer, and after twelve hours fermentation the water containing the colorless *glucisid indoxyl* is drawn off. The fibers are immersed in this solution and exposed to air until through oxidization the soluble indoxyl turns into the blue insoluble indigotin, the actual coloring agent. Coming from India this dye, Skr. *nīla*, was already known in Egypt about 2500 B.C., was introduced into Mesopotamia during the seventh century, into Palestine during the second century B.C., but never came to Rome, where the same color was obtained from the less effective woad (*Isatis tinctoria*). When indigo is deep blue, almost black, it is called *surmehʾī*, when only light blue its name is *ābī*.

Turnsole (*barg-e qīṭarān*) is a purple-blue dye extracted from the leaves of *Chrozophory tinctoria*. When mordanted with urine a fresh turquoise blue is achieved.

Green Dyes. The so-called Chinese green is obtained from two other members of the buckthorn family, i.e., *Rhamnus chlorophorus* and *Rhamnus utilis*. The berries, known in England as Persian berries, give a brilliant green.

The green obtained from *Delphinium zalil* when mordanted with copper sulphate has already been mentioned in the section about yellow dyes.

A wide range of green is achieved by double dyeing. Indigo provides the blue component while yellow from the aforementioned *Rhamnus infectorius* or *Delphinium zalil* go well with it. The shades obtained through this combination are known in the carpet trade as "Prophet's green" (*sabz-e nabī*). Most of the other yellow plant dyes are also suited for double dyeing with indigo.

Brown and Black Dyes. A pleasant hue of dark brown (*qahvehʾī*) can be obtained from the green rinds of the walnut (*Juglans regia*, *pūst-e gerdū*). This color is often brightened by double dyeing with madder, the resulting hue is known as camel color (*rang-e šotorī*). Another brownish dye also called *rang-e šotorī* is made from the skins of acorns (*pūšt-e ballūṭ*) and ground pomegranate rind. The mixture is boiled for several hours and the fibers are added without any other mordants. Since many of the sheep in Persia are brown or black, dyeing is often unnecessary, or the dyer uses some of the tannic acid extracts in combination with iron vitriol (*zāj-e zard*) to correct the natural brown to the desired hue. A deep black is obtained if this process is applied to fibers previously dyed dark blue with indigo.

Two varieties of indigo, *Indigofera anil* and *Indigofera linifolia*, are grown near Bam in Balūčistān. The plants are dried and ground. They are used for black dyeing in the following way: The fibers are first dyed in henna (*Lawsonia alba*, *ḥennā-ye barg*), then in an extract of one of these indigo varieties. The result is a deep black. The process is suitable for hair tinting too.[49]

A medieval Persian from Tabrīz who worked in India as a dyer took with him a book of recipes, some of which follow:[50]

Birbul's Blue. Take cinnabar, indigo, and alum, grind and sift lighter than the dust on the hills, soak for ten hours, keep stirring, put in the wool and soak for many hours. Boil for three hours, wash in curd water in which curds and whey have been well beaten up, leave for three hours, then wash and beat again in water.

A fine Indigo Blue. Take indigo, soak it in water for twelve hours, grind it into a fine paste

[49] L. J. Olmer, "L'Industrie Persane," p. 80.

[50] Harris in W. A. Hawley, *Oriental Rugs*, pp. 40–41.

in a mortar, add some Terminalia citrina,[51] pomegranate rind, and alum and mix thoroughly. Boil, put the wool into the hot bath and keep stirring till cold. Now mix in some iron filings water and boil steadily for another two hours, wash with a beating, and dry.

Ruddy Brown Grey. Take sulphate of iron, *Terminalia citrina*, oak galls and alum, mix well, dry, then steep for twenty-four hours. Put in the wool, soak it for twenty-four hours, then boil it for two to three hours. Dip in a soda bath, wash and dry.

Cinammon. Take oak galls, acacia bark, cinnabar, and alum and steep for a night. Put in the wool and soak for twenty to thirty hours, boil the water for two to three hours and give a soda water wash. Dip in acidulated water and wash again with beating.

Crimson. Take lac color and cochineal. Steep for from four to six days in the sun, in hot weather for a lesser time, stirring constantly till a rich deep color comes where some has stood for a few minutes in a thin glass bottle and settled. Then strain through two cloths and put in pomegranate rind and iron filings water. Add mineral acid, steep wool for thirty-six hours, then boil for three hours, wash well, and dry.

Pale Greyish Green. Take verdigris, asparg, and alum. Mix well with any hot water, not boiling, soak wool for eighteen hours, then boil for three hours. Give a bath with water acidulated with some limes and dry in the shade.

Old Gold and Rich Yellow. Take tumeric and asparg, cinnabar and alum. Soak all night. Steep wool for twenty-four hours, boil for four hours, wash with a beating, and dry in the shade.

Rose Color. Take ratanjot, a thought of cochineal, madder (*Rubia tinctorium*) or lac color a very little, and cinnabar. Add water, soak them for twelve hours, put in wool and steep for thirty-six hours, boil for three hours, then bathe the wool in alum and wash well, afterwards dry in the shade.

Persian Scarlet. Take lac color and if you choose, a little cochineal for richness, and soak from four to six days, strain it in two cloths, and add alum and a little tumeric, let it stand for three hours. Put in wool and steep for twenty-four hours, then boil for two hours. Take out the wool and add mineral acids, re-enter wool, and boil an hour more. Wash fifteen minutes when cold and dry in the shade.

Saffron Yellow. Take tumeric, cinnabar, and soda, add water, and keep for a full day. Then add some alum, make the dip, and soak the wool for thirty hours. Boil for several hours and dry in the shade after beating and good washing.

Rich Yellow. Take asparg and tumeric, soak for a night in water, steep the wool for twenty-four hours, add alum, shake out, and dry in the shade.

After having learned about the wide range of dyestuffs and dyeing methods the Persian craftsman had at his disposal, one can understand the advice given by Richard Hakluyt of the Middle Temple to Morgan Hubblethorn, a dyer who was sent to Persia in 1579:[52]

> In Persia you shall find carpets of coarse thrummed wool, the best of the world, and excellently coloured: those cities and towns you must repair to, and you must use means to learn all the order of dyeing of those thrumms, which are so dyed as neither raine, wine nor yet vinegar can staine. . . . For that in Persia they have great colouring of silks it behoves to learn that also.

The Dyer's Workshop. In the absence of a modern water supply system the dyers (*rang-raz, rang-rīz, ṣabbāġ*) have their dye houses somewhere near the water, e.g., in Iṣfahān on the banks of the Zāyandeh-Rūd, in Šīrāz near a water supply canal (*jūb*). Most dyes require boiling (*puḫtan*) for the preparation of the extracts as well as for the actual dyeing (*rang kardan, rang afgandan*). The dye houses usually have a long row of built-in boilers (*pātī, pātīl, pātīleh, dīg*) along one wall. They are made from either copper or cast iron, depending on the affinities of the particular dye. Each one of these boilers has a fireplace (*kūreh-ye pātīl*) underneath. Opposite the row of boilers there is usually a row of likewise built-in vats (*qadaḥ, toġār*), generally

[51] An astringent (*halīleh-ye zard*).

[52] R. Hakluyt, *The Principal Navigations, Voyages and Discourses of the English Nation*, p. 202.

of glazed earthenware (*lūleh-kaš*) for the preparation of the dyes (*rang, ṣibāġ*) and the cold soaking and rinsing of the fibers. The tall fermentation vats (*ḫomreh*) for the indigo process (*nīl-kārī*) are placed together in a group, each one secured by a wooden stand. These vats are covered with basketry lids (*sabedī*) to give access to the air. Most of the dyer's work is skein-dyeing (Fig. 269); very little woven fabric is dyed in the piece. The natural fat of wool fibers has to be removed prior to dyeing. This is done by rinsing (*qaliyāb kardan*) the yarn in a solution of potash (*qaliyāb*) in warm water. From the potash vat the wool skeins are transferred to the dye vat for boiling (*jūšīdan*) to apply the dyestuff (*rang zadan*). The skeins (*kalāf*) are dipped into the vats or boilers and turned over (*gardāndan*) with wooden rods (*čūb, zīrāb*). Heavy wooden pegs (*mīl-e čūbī*) are let into the wall above the vats. The skeins are suspended on these pegs to drip out and for exposure to the air where the process requires oxidization. The largest vats are those for rinsing (*āb dādan, āb ḫwordan, šostan*), from which the skeins are finally taken out into the yard (*bīrūn kardan*) and hung there over heavy poles for drying

Figure 269 A Dyer Dipping Wool Skeins into a Vat

(*āftāb ḫwordan, āftāb dādan, dādan be tāb*, Fig. 270). The dyers work on contract for the weavers; the price per skein is based on the weight of the yarn treated but varies for the different colors.

Figure 270 Wool Skeins Drying outside the Dyer's Shop

Weaving

In few of the industrial arts is the principle of divided labor carried as far as in the textile crafts. In addition to the four servicing crafts, viz., bower, silk winder, spinner, and dyer, there are still three more independent crafts engaged before the weaver can throw his shuttle. These are the reed or beater-comb maker, the warp winder, and the heddle or heald maker. This is only true for the organized craft-weaver. Home weavers and weaving nomads have to rely on their own skill.

Reed Maker

The reed maker (*šāneh-sāz, šāneh-bandī*) is in effect a specialized wood worker. His clients are the master weavers in towns and villages. Figure 271 shows a reed maker on his way to a country weaver. He and his donkey carry a number of commonly used reeds (*šāneh*), but also the parts to make new reeds of nonstock dimensions and spare parts to repair worn ones if necessary. The main rods (*tīr, pīšō*), made from split bamboo, are in the saddle bags. The reed maker carries properly shaped end battens (*qolfak, badūmak*) and large quantities of split bamboo to form the reed blades (*ālat, dandāneh, sīm, nai*) and several grades of cotton thread (*naḫ*) for winding around the rod halves, thus keeping them together and the reed blades in between, the distance determined by the thickness of the thread. The wound-on parts of the reed are later dipped into a hot mixture of wax and pitch that fixes everything in position. The end battens are then reinforced by gluing cloth strips (*kohneh*) over them. The adhesive is the commonly used plant glue (*serīš, serešk*). The average width of a silk loom is about 32 inches. The reed for such a loom would carry 800 to 1,000 bamboo blades, which means about 25 to 32 blades to the inch. A finished reed is shown in Fig. 277, p. 199, second from the top.

Figure 271 A Reed Maker

Warp Winder

The functions of the warp winder vary with the requirements of the local weavers. It has already been shown that the silk winder includes silk warp winding in his work. There we saw that the warp was wound onto a warping frame. Warp winding (*tān pīčīdan*) in its simplest form is shown in Fig. 272. Here a village weaver has driven a number of warp pegs (*mīl*) into the ground, two side by side, wherever a warp cross (*gazuk*) is intended. The warp yarn has been wound onto bobbins (*mašūreh*). The warp winder takes two of them and slips each one over a warp-winding stick (*tān-tāb, tanestik*) on which the bobbin can freely rotate. The bobbins are prevented from falling off by little cross pegs at the end of the sticks. The warp winder attaches the ends of these

Figure 272 Village Warp Winders

two threads to the first warp peg and walks around the two rows of pegs (*naḫ*), leading one thread to the right and one to the left of the cross pegs. After reaching the end peg the winder leads the two threads back to the starting peg in the same way as he came. He starts a second run, etc., until the warp has all the threads required. The length of this warp will be about 70 to 100 yards. Cotton warps are then sized to reduce friction and avoid damage to the threads during weaving. The size (*āhār*) is made from a boiled mixture of wheatmeal (*ārd-e gandom*) and bran (*sabūs, sūs*).

A highly specialized worker is the warp winder (*vartāb*), preparing the warps for the carpet industry in such centers as Kāšān, Iṣfahān, Kermān, Šīrāz, and many others. The carpet weavers require strong warps, obtained by plying up to sixteen spun threads into one. The material for these warps is either cotton or silk. The latter is used for pure silk carpets as well as for finely knotted wool carpets.

The work of the carpet warp winder is done in two stages, the plying (*tābīdan*) of the warp threads and the warp winding proper. The former operation is done on a twisting wheel (*čarḫ-e vartābī*, Fig. 273) that is situated at one end of the long and narrow warp-winding shop (*kārḫāneh-ye vartābī*). This intriguing machine is driven over a hand-operated main wheel (*parreh*) that runs on an axle attached to a sturdy tripod (*pāyeh čarḫ*) over a horizontal cross beam. A spindle box (*dūk-dān*) containing 24 hooked spindles (*dūk*), each one having a small pulley, extends from the tripod in the opposite direction. Twenty-four transmission cords (*band-e čarḫ*) connect the 24 pulleys with the main wheel, the velocity ratio being about 1 in 50. The winder begins his work by transferring the yarn from a skein to a cage spool (*rū kūpī pīčīdan*). This cage spool (*kūpī*) rotates freely on a stick that the winder guides with his hand and that rests in a belt socket (*pīš-band*) tied to his waist (Fig. 274). Next he attaches a thread end from this cage spool to the first hook (*čangāz*) on the spindle box, and guiding the thread with the other hand walks along the full length of the workshop, about 150 feet, to the opposite wall where a board with 24 hooks is fixed. He slings the thread around the first hook, walks back to the spindle box, guides the thread over the second hook and so on until 48 threads have been stretched (*bār kardan*) between the 24 pairs of hooks. From time to time a new skein of yarn (*sar-kūpī*) has been wound onto the cage spool. Now the winder moves behind the machine and turns the handle of the main wheel about 10 times, thus causing each spindle hook to revolve about 500 times, producing 24 two-ply threads (*dōlā*). Next the winder places them in pairs onto the hooks, both at the spindle box and the fixed end, and turns the handle again 10 times but now in the

Figure 273 A Thread-Twisting Wheel

opposite direction. This done he has 12 threads of four-ply (*čahār-lā*). This is repeated once more resulting in 6 threads of eight-ply (*hašt-lā*), a grade used for most carpet warps. Strangely enough the weaver refers to it as ten-ply (*dah-lā*).

Now we come to the warp winding proper. The warp pegs are inserted in the long wall on one side of the workshop, one near one end, and two, the cross pegs, near the other end of this wall. When the last twisting is completed the winder transfers each thread to these warp pegs. He carefully leads them over the cross pegs and has now 6 warp threads on the wall. The whole twisting process is repeated four times, thus, working for eight-ply threads the warp strand so far consists of $4 \times 6 = 24$ warp threads. The crosses of this warp strand are tied up with string, and the strand is wound (*pīčīdan*) onto a warp-winding stick (*kār-pīč*, Fig. 275) and finally

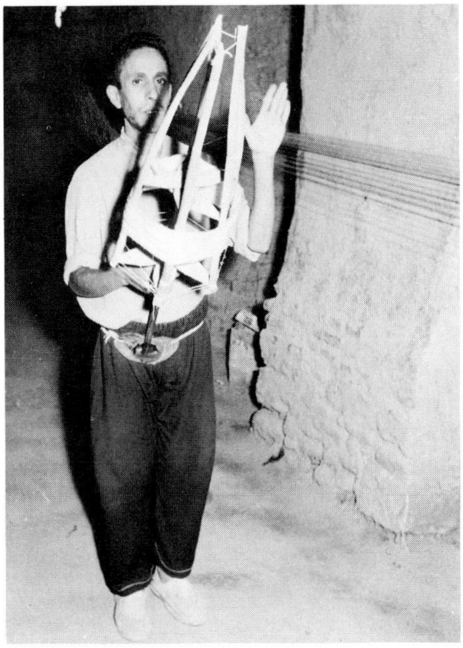

Figure 274 A Warp Winder

transferred to a simple reeling wheel, and then tied up in the form of a bundle. If the carpet weaver, for example, needs 240 warp threads for the full width of a carpet, he will order ten of these bundles from the warp winder.

Figure 275 Winding the Warp onto a Stick

Heddle Maker

The heddle maker (*ṭarrā'ī*) not only makes the heddles (*vard*, *gurt*) but also enters the warp threads into them. For this purpose he receives from the weaver a complete, balled-up warp, the reed, and instructions regarding the number of heddles and the sequence of entering the warp threads for the required pattern. A glance at Fig. 282, p. 203, showing a mounted loom with 12 heddles, leaves no doubt that the heddle maker must be a well-trained textile craftsman. He does his work in the following steps:

1. Kneeling behind a heddle-making device (*taḫt-e gurt-čīnī*, *taḫt-e gurt-bāfī*, Fig. 276) he places the upper heddle rod (*jūjeh*) on the beam of the device and ties the rod on both sides to the beam. A movable wooden block (*ḫarak*) rides over rod and beam and supports a string leading from one end of the beam to the other. The heddle cord is wound around beam and rod, forming loops. To keep them separate the heddle maker winds the first loop passing the cord under the string, the second over it, and so on. When the required number of loops has been made, the rod with the loops is slipped off the beam and suspended above it.

2. Having fixed the lower heddle rod below the beam, the heddle maker winds the second half of the heddle, passing the cord through a loop in the suspended upper half after each turn of the cord around the beam and the lower rod, thus forming a mail for a warp thread. A finished heddle is shown at the top of Fig. 277.

3. The heddle farthest away from the weaver is hung into the warp-entering frame. All the warp threads to be lifted by this heddle are entered through the mails formed by the intertwining loops; the rest of the warp threads are entered in between the loops. This finished, the heddle is taken from the frame and carefully placed on the ground.

4. The next heddle is then attached to the frame, and those warp threads that are to be lifted by this heddle are entered through its mails, whereas all other warp threads will again be led in between the loops. This heddle is also taken down after completion, and the process is repeated until the last heddle has its warp threads entered.

5. Then all warp threads are passed through the reed, which is also fastened to the warp-entering frame (Fig. 278). Warp,

Figure 276 A Heddle-Making Device

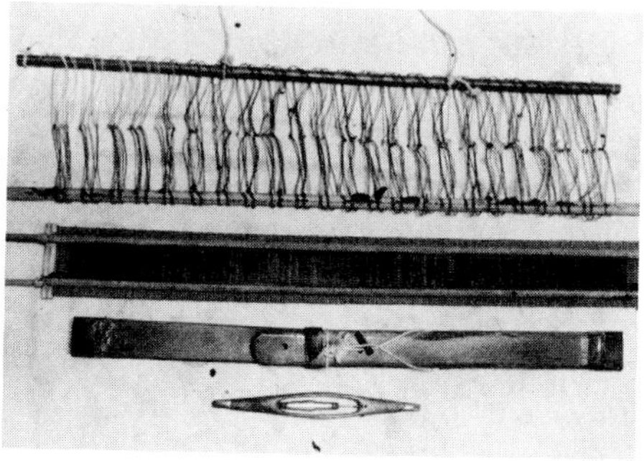

Figure 277 A Heddle, Reed, Temple, and Shuttle

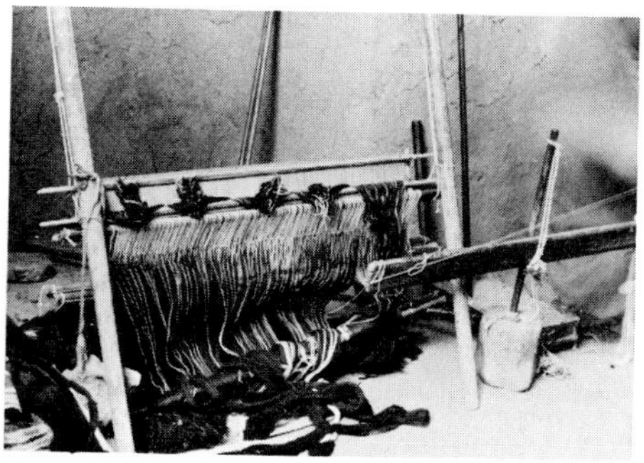

Figure 278 A Warp-Entering Frame

heddles, and reed are now bundled up and delivered to the weaver, ready to be mounted on the loom.

The Looms

A great variety of looms can still be found in Persia ranging from the horizontal ground loom of the nomads, which can be traced back to the third millennium in many places in the Middle East,[53] to the multiheddled compound weave loom, and finally to the picture-weaving draw loom, the forerunner of the European Jacquard loom.

With regard to the construction, we find horizontal and vertical looms, the latter being for carpets (*qālī*), tapestry (*gelīm*) and the so-called *zīlū* mats. We find two-beamed looms as well as warp-weighted one-beam ones. Most of them are heddled, but tablet weaving is still practised by some nomadic tribes for the production of webbing and ribbons.

The Horizontal Ground Loom

This simple loom of the Persian nomads is easily set up wherever the camp is pitched and can be rolled together again and packed on a mule's back when the tribe moves to the next camp. The tent fabric loom (*dastgāh-e tōn-bāfī*) shown in Fig. 280 (p. 201) can be taken as typical for a variety of similar looms. The warp (*naẖ*) is stretched over two beams, each of which is secured in its place by two pegs (*mīẖ-e pūtī*) driven into the ground. The warp is usually wound over the two beams in the form of an endless belt. In its simplest form, without any heddles, this loom is used by the women of the nomadic tribes for their *gelīm* weaving, a kind of gaily patterned tapestry. In *gelīm* weaving the weaver makes a shed by lifting every alternate warp thread by hand, but only to the width required by the design, inserts wefts for this area with a bobbin,

[53] C. Singer, *op. cit.*, Vol. 2, p. 427.

opens a new shed next to the previous one, and inserts another color, thus developing the pattern over the whole width of the warp. From time to time the wefts are compacted with a beater comb. A certain difficulty arises when a line in the design runs parallel to the warp. For such a boundary line between two colors there will be no actual connection by means of wefts, and we talk about slit-tapestry, very common in Persian *gelīm*. To avoid the formation of slits some weavers resort to dovetailing the wefts over the boundary line or avoid lines parallel to the warp altogether and use staggered lines instead. This technical requirement gives the *gelīm* its typical style. *Gelīm* weaving permits a great flexibility in design but actual weaving is slow, and many tribal people have abandoned it in favor of the more profitable piled carpet.

If plain or striped fabrics are to be woven, this simple tapestry loom is easily converted into a heddle-rod loom. The threads on the upper part of the warp are divided into two groups of which the odd ones are lashed to the heddle rod (*gūleh, kōjī, gord, gurt*) with string loops (*naḫ-e gūleh, naḫ-e kōjī*, Fig. 279). When this rod is raised and held in suspension from a tripod (*seh-pāyeh*) by a rope (*ṭanāb-band*, Fig. 280) it lifts half the threads (Fig. 279, top diagram), and, leaving the other half of the warp straight, a space, the shed

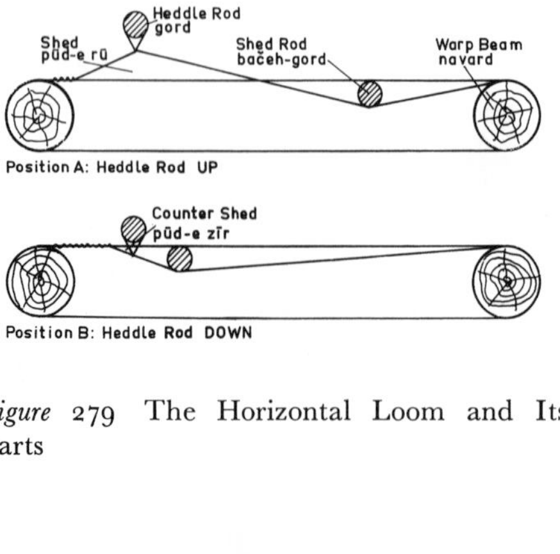

Figure 279 The Horizontal Loom and Its Parts

(*radīf, pūd-e rū*), is formed through which the weft (*pūd, pūt*) can be passed. Note that during this phase a heavy pole between the two halves of the warp, the shed rod (*pošt-e gūleh, pošt-e kōjī, bačeh gord*), is pushed back as far as the weaver can reach. In the next phase (Fig. 279, lower diagram) the heddle rod is let down from its suspension and the shed rod is drawn close to the weaver, thus forming a counter shed (*radīf-e dōvom, pūd-e zīr*) for the passage of the next weft. This way of changing the shed is still widely used for the carpet loom where the change does not occur so often. For the weaving of tent fabric (*tōn, palās*) this would be too cumbersome. On the loom in Fig. 280 we see the first step toward the treadle mechanism. Here heddle rod and shed rod are attached to ropes and connected to a short piece of wood that rests on a horizontal beam (*gīreh*) and acts as a heddle support (*dam*). For the position "heddle rod up" the weaver pushes it back so that its end drops down, letting the shed rod down too. For the next weft it is "shed rod up," so the weaver pulls the support forward, thus bringing the shed rod up and the heddle rod down. The wefts are compacted by beating them with a flat batten, the sword beater, or with a beater comb (*šāneh, dastak*). To keep the fabric at a constant width iron broad holders (*pahn-kaš*) are hooked into the freshly woven material and are attached to a peg driven into the ground with a bit of string. When the weaver has woven a number of wefts and the shed gradually moves too far away from the breast beam, the warp is loosened by being slipped off the ground pegs and moved toward the weaver, so that the material already woven disappears under the beam. The warp is then tightened again, ready for the weaving of another 20 to 24 inches. Many nomad looms have the warp just stretched out between two beams (*navard*). At the beginning of the weaving,

Figure 280 A Tent Fabric Loom from Sīstān

the tripod with its heddle rod and shed rod is placed at one end of the warp and as work progresses the tripod is moved forward from time to time.

It should be mentioned here that this heddle rod loom is not only used for plain weaves like those of the tent fabric weavers (*tōn-bāfī*) shown in Fig. 280, but this principle is also applied to all carpet and tapestry looms, regardless of whether they are horizontal or turned upright and mounted on two posts, the only difference being that in carpet weaving a row of piles is knotted-in before the next weft is passed through.

The Band Loom

A loom in many aspects similar to the one just described and yet different in others is the band loom (*dastgāh-e jājim-bāfī*) used by the nomads for the weaving of gaily colored bands (*jājim, jājīm*). Figure 281 shows a narrow warp stretched out on the ground, the heddle rod suspended from a tripod by ropes. The shed rod, however, is no longer a round pole but a flat board with rounded edges. In the "heddle up" position it is lying flat and pushed back. After the insertion of the weft the board is pulled forward, acting as a beater for compacting the weft. It is then turned on edge for the "heddle down" position, thus producing a comfortable counter shed. Before pushing it back it is used as a beater again. A close inspection of Fig. 281 shows that the woven fabric has a pronounced pattern design, part of it coming from the striped warp, but another pattern-forming feature is the repeated appearance of some of the warp threads on the surface. Those warp threads that are to flotate are carried over a separate stick in front of the heddle rod.

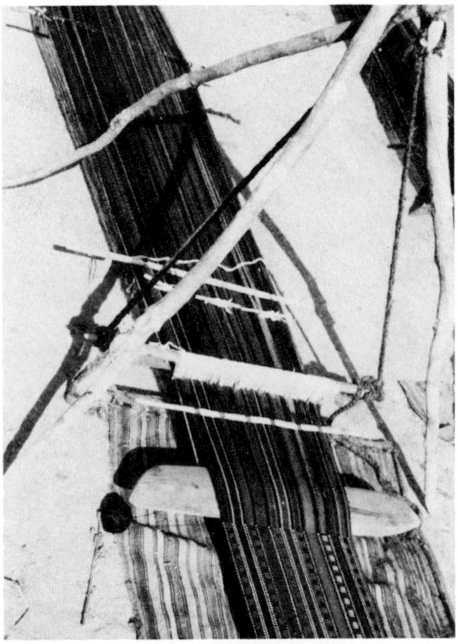

Figure 281 A Band Loom

These warp threads that would otherwise go down with the shed rod are kept up by the stick and show on the surface of the fabric. For those parts of the pattern where the loom is to revert to normal binding, the stick is pushed back.

It should be noted here that even a simple loom with a heddle rod can be used both for weft pattern weaves like tapestry or for warp patterns like *jājīm*, and further that the introduction of a stick to control some of the warp threads is the first step toward a multiheddled loom. In Southeast Asia the control of the warp design by sticks to achieve complex patterns has been developed into a fine art. The writer observed in Laos that up to forty sticks were used to produce one pattern. The stick system seems to have been the precursor of a genuine draw loom.

The Horizontal Multiheddled Loom

The development from the rather primitive horizontal ground loom with just one heddle rod to a loom with more than one treadle-operated heddle must have taken centuries, but only a few steps of the development have been traced so far. Whereas for a long time the Greeks and Romans used a vertical loom with a weighted warp instead of the warp beam, treadle-operated heddles are known to have existed in Egypt from the second century B.C. on.[54] At a sixth-century A.D. monastery excavated near Thebes, loom pits have been found that were clearly designed to provide space for the treadles to control the heddles of this loom. The fulcrum for the pedals can still be seen in some of these pits.

Warp-weighted vertical looms have been in use in the Middle East since Neolithic times, as evidenced by many warp weights found by archaeologists,[55] but whereas the Greek, Roman, and North European looms had the cloth beam up and the warp with its weights hanging down, forcing the weaver to work upwards, in Persia we find a loom that seems to have developed from the horizontal loom with its two beams by two modifications:

(*a*) By leading the warp around a deflecting pole (Figs. 282 and 283), at an angle toward the ceiling, then vertically over warp suspension pulleys (Fig. 284), a much longer warp can be placed into the loom by balling it up and having it suspended under constant tension by weights. We now have a loom that is conveniently horizontal but has the advantage of having warp weights.

(*b*) By introducing an easily operated treadle mechanism enabling the weaver to handle a greater number of heddles in a predetermined sequence, as described below in the following paragraph. In Egypt as well as in Persia the treadles were placed in a pit, where they still are in

[54] R. J. Forbes, *op. cit.*, Vol. 4, p. 215.
[55] *Ibid.*, p. 199.

Figure 282 A Horizontal Warp-Weighted Loom

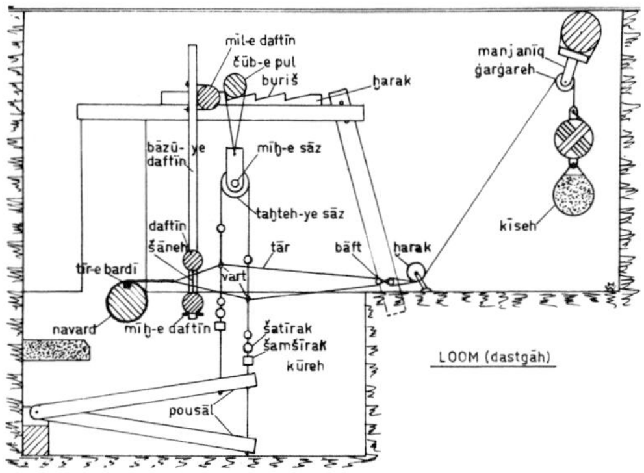

Figure 283 Elements of the Horizontal Warp-Weighted Loom

many parts of Persia, e.g., in Iṣfahān, Yazd, Kermān (see Fig. 283). Even if looms are built completely above ground level, the former existence of a pit for the treadles is still reflected in the name, *pāčāl*, for the whole loom in Māzandarān, literally meaning foot-pit. Similar developments of a treadle mechanism must have taken place in China and India,[56] but clear priorities have so far not been established.

In the following description some technical details are given of a loom at Yazd, the home of Persia's silk-weaving industry since medieval times. The warp (*tār, tūn, čelleh, čelūn*) has been prepared on the

Figure 284 Warp Suspension

warping frame (*čelleh-tūn, čelleh-davānī*) by the silk winder. The weaver (*nassāj, nāsij, bāfandeh*) had given it to the heddle maker, and he strings it now to the loom (*dastgāh*, Fig. 285) by knotting the warp thread

Figure 285 A Twelve-Heddled Loom

[56] F. Orth, *op. cit.*, p. 92.

ends in strands to a stick (*tīr-e bardī*) that fits into the slot of the breast beam (*navard, nouvard, nouhard, kāġazak, qāzak*). The beam has an iron shaft (*mīḫ-e kāġazak*) that runs in bearings (*kavījak*) attached to the side walls of the loom pit (*kūreh*). The breast beam is locked with a peg (*dar andāz, bar andāz, dailam*) and can be rotated with a lever (*pahlū-kaš*). Following the warp threads we see them passing through the reed (*šāneh*) that the weaver inserts into the batten (*daftī, daftīn*), a quadrilateral frame that oscillates and beats the reed against the weft (*pūd*). The batten has two vertical arms (*bāzū-ye daftīn, bāʾū-ye daftīn, bābak*), and it swings about a horizontal axis (*mīl-e daftīn*) that runs in a pair of bearings (*qāz*). The reed is held inside the batten with a pair of pegs (*mīḫ-e daftīn*) and the batten arm is kept tight with a tourniquet (*tāb-e pīč, tou-pīč*). After leaving the reed the warp goes through a series of heddles (*vard, jūjeh*) that are suspended over balancing pulley blocks (*taḫteh-ye sāz, ʿarūsak*). They run on iron axles (*mīḫ-e sāz*) and are well balanced against each other, finally ending up in two large pulleys suspended from a beam (*čūb-e pol*). The position of this beam can be adjusted by placing it into different notches (*buriš*) on the adjusting board (*ḫarak*). On the lower end the heddles are connected, over balancing levers (*šatīrak*) to jibbet levers (*šamšeh, šamšīrak*) which, in turn, are linked to the treadles (*pā, poušāl*, Fig. 283). A shed (*čārak-kār, radīf, dahāneh, čar*) is formed each time the weaver presses one of these treadles down in a predetermined sequence, and a weft is passed through with the shuttle (*mākū, mākūk*). The latter is often made of the wood of the persimmon tree (*ḫormālū*), has a smoothly pointed end (*ṭouq*), and the weft thread is supplied from a bobbin running on an iron peg (*mīl*) inside the shuttle. The weft thread leaves the shuttle through a bone-eyelet (*mastūreh, masūreh*). To prevent over-running of the bobbin, a pair of springs (*par-e mākū*) acts as a brake. A broad holder or temple (*mātīz, mītīz, matīt*, third from top, Fig. 277) on the woven part keeps the cloth at a given width. Following the warp still further we come to the cross or lease (*bāft, ešdī, čap-ō-rāst, pīš*) originally made by the warp winder and now held in position by two rods (*jūjeh, nai*). Hereafter the warp turns around a strong deflection pole (*ḫarak*) that is attached to the ground over a shackle. Beyond this pole the warp rises in strands at an angle toward the warp suspension frame (*manjanīq*), which is tied to a heavy beam on the ceiling carrying a number of guide pulleys (*ġar-ġareh, ġarġar*). The strands run over these pulleys and drop perpendicularly down, ending in the warp balls (*qalambak*) on wooden pegs (*sok*) that are weighted with sandbags (*kīseh*). As the work proceeds and the woven cloth is wound around the breast beam, the warp balls with their weight bags rise. When they approach the pulleys the weaver lets their warp strands off until the sandbags are close to the ground again, and the loom is set for the weaving of a further 5 to 6 feet of fabric.

The Čādor-Šab *Loom*

In the Caspian provinces of Gīlān and Māzandarān, with their high rainfall figures, it must have been difficult to keep the treadle pit dry. Here the whole loom (*pāčāl*) is above ground level (Fig. 286). It consists of a rectangular frame (*čārpāyeh*) with two short columns holding the breast beam (*nōrd*), and two longer columns holding at their upper end a warp-diverting beam (*sar-gāh*) and further down the warp beam (*nōrd*). The loom is used for the weaving of the *čādor-šab*, a cloth traditionally worn around the waist by the women of these provinces. The warp

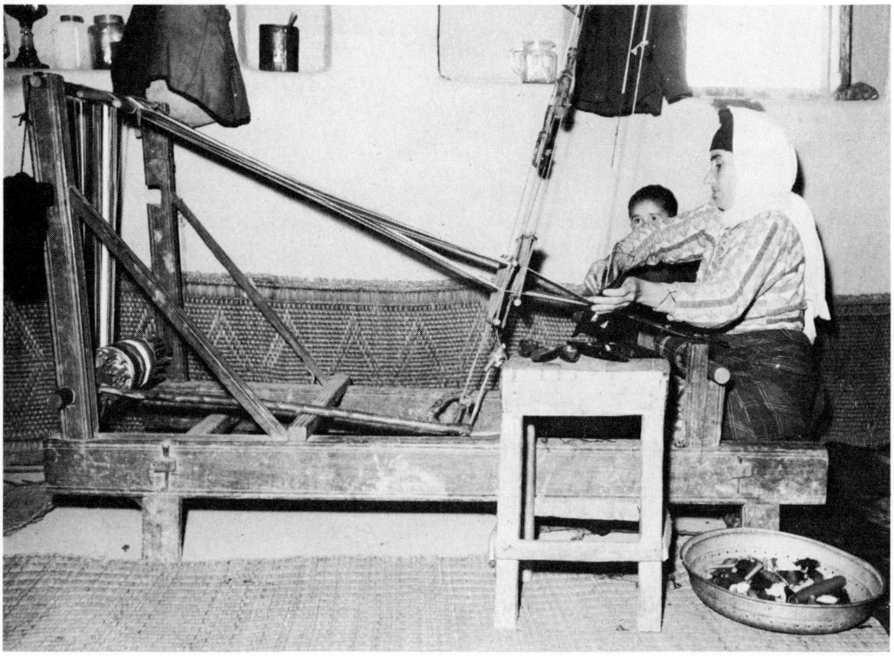

Figure 286 A Čādor-Šab Loom

(*rišteh*) is prepared by a specialist who, with the advice of the weaver (*čādor-bāf*), winds the warp, makes the heddles, and threads the warp into the heddles and the reed, all this preparatory work being referred to as *rajeh kardan*. The material mainly used is a silk thread made from broken-up (*porz kardan*) silk cocoons. This silk is combed over a wool comb and spun on a wheel. The warp ends are knotted to thin steel blades (*ġaibeh*) that are inserted into slots in breast and warp beams. The warp cross (*lāh-e gāzkon*) is tied to the warp-diverting beam. The heddles (*vard*), two in the loom shown, but often more for complex patterns, are suspended from the ceiling over a pair of pulleys (*čarḫ*) and connected to the treadles by thin ropes. By pressing the treadle lever (*pā fešār dādan*) the weaver forms a shed (*kār-dahān*), throws (*īlāk dādan*) the shuttle (*mākū*) and compounds (*pārčeh šāneh zadan*) the weft with the reed (*šāneh*). The width of the cloth is maintained by a toothed broad holder (*arreč*). The shuttle bobbins (*māsūreh*) are filled from a winding reel (*kalāf-pīč*). After a certain length of fabric has been woven the weaver loosens the warp beam with a release lever (*nōrd-gardān*) and winds the woven cloth on the breast beam, turning it with another lever (*dast-kaš*).

The Draw Loom

The looms described so far limit the weaving of patterned design to geometrical figures whose complexity depends essentially on the number of heddles used. Free-figured design is only possible on a draw loom whose harness permits the control of every one of the warp threads. The development of this loom has been shown in the introduction to this chapter, and it is this loom that is described in the following paragraph in the form that still

Figure 287 A Draw Loom

existed at Iṣfahān and Tehrān in 1963 (Fig. 287).

The draw loom (*dastgāh-e naqšeh-bandī, dastgāh-e naqš-bandī, dastgāh-e zarī-bāfī*) has basically the same construction as the multiheddled loom, but in addition has a number of features needed for the weaving of free-figured patterns.

1. Instead of a single warp the draw loom has two, an upper warp (*čelleh-rūʾī*) and a lower warp (*čelleh-zamīneh*).

2. It has the same set of standard heddles as the ordinary cloth loom, here called binder heddles, operating on the binder or ground warp, but in addition it has a draw harness (*naqšeh, dastūn*) that operates on the figure warp only (Fig. 288). The latter consists of a large number of vertical drawstrings (*dastūr, mošteh*) that converge on a wooden support (*čūb-e dastūr, qalambok*) near the ceiling. At its lower end each drawstring is connected to a horizontal gut string (*zeh*) in a cross harness (*čelīt, šelīt, šīlīt*). The purpose of this cross harness is to reduce the number of vertical drawstrings to a fraction of the number of warp threads to be lifted, or to see it from the pattern, the cross harness permits the brocade weaver (*zarī-bāf*) to weave several repeat patterns across the width of the fabric with the harness outfit for one pattern only (Fig. 289). This drawing and Fig. 290 show that, with the lifting of the one drawstring, the cross harness gut string is lifted and with it, in this case, eight mails (*roḫ, vard*) attached to eight warp threads; the resulting pattern will therefore be repeated eight times. Each of the vertical drawstrings continues below the warp, carrying at its end a metal weight (*langar-e vard*) to draw the harness back into its original position when released.

3. When the brocade weaver sets the

draw harness for the required design he places one circular loop (*gūšvareh*) around all those vertical drawstrings that will have to be lifted for the weaving of the first figure weft. This loop is carefully hung over one side of the extension of the string-supporting rod. The combination of strings to be drawn for the next figure weft is likewise surrounded by a loop that is placed next to the previous one, and so on until all drawstrings are grouped for the complete figure (top of Fig. 291).

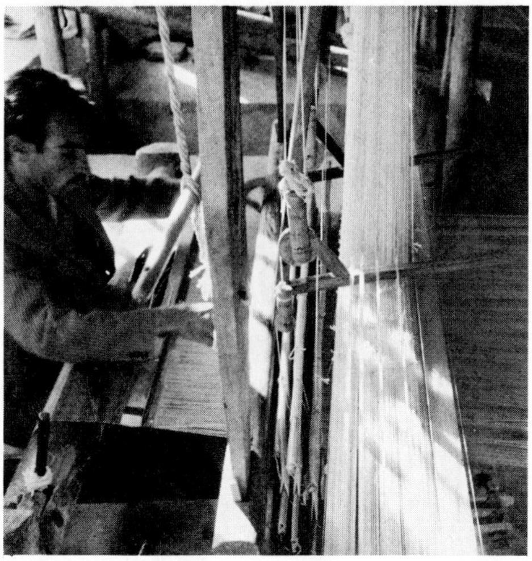

Figure 288 Draw Harness and Cross Harness

Figure 290 Warp, Cross Harness, and Draw Harness

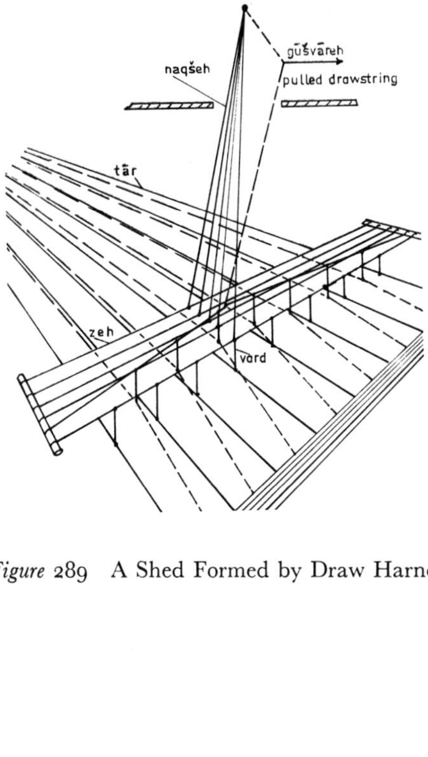

Figure 289 A Shed Formed by Draw Harness

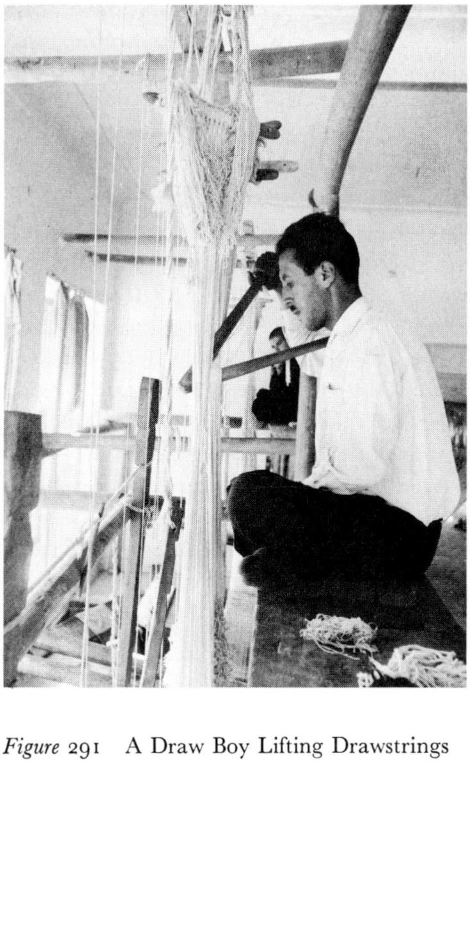

Figure 291 A Draw Boy Lifting Drawstrings

4. A draw boy sits on a board on top of the loom right in front of the draw harness (Fig. 291), and he works to the following rhythm: The weaver forms a shed by pressing the treadle for the binder heddles and throws the shuttle across (*mākū andāḫtan*), thus placing a standard weft into the shed. He then releases the treadle, brings the heddles into a neutral position, and beats the weft in with the reed. At this moment the draw boy pulls the first loop (*gūšvāreh kašīdan*, Fig. 292) and shakes it, thus separating the strings to be drawn from those which stay untouched. Then he grips the drawn ones with one hand, takes a branch hook (*šāḫeh, kalak*), slings the bunch of strings in his hand around it, gives the hook a twist (*pīčīdan*) with his hand while one end of the hook rests on his shoulder (Fig. 291), and signals the master with a short shout. The latter quickly places two suspended angle hooks (*čalak, kalak*, Fig. 293) under all the gut strings of the cross harness that have been lifted by the draw boy, thus keeping the figure shed open. The weaver throws the shuttle with a gold thread (*golābetūn*) or a colored thread across and withdraws the two angle hooks; the boy above the loom releases the drawstrings, and hangs the first draw loop over the opposite end of the string-supporting rod. Meanwhile the master opens a new binder shed with his treadle and throws the second standard weft across while the boy draws the strings secured by the second loop, and so on. When all the loops have been used, one full figure pattern is completed. If it is intended to repeat this pattern all loops have to be placed back into the position where the boy started. If it is intended to weave a mirror image of the original pattern the draw boy can operate all the loops in the reversed order, beginning with the loop last used. This technique is typical for Persian brocade since Sasanian times, i.e., since the beginning of free-figure weaving in Persia, and it is a case where an artistic principle originates from a mere technique. In medieval Europe the draw loom has been known as the damask loom since the crusades. Its draw harness, however, was guided over rollers to the side of the loom

Figure 292 A Draw Boy Pulling Harness Loops

Figure 293 Placing Angle Hooks under the Cross Harness

so that the drawer could stand at the side of the weaver.[57]

The Velvet Loom

The velvet weavers (*maḫmal-bāf*) of Iṣfahān, Kāšān, and Tehrān employ several technical features of the draw loom just described for the weaving of a piled fabric. One is the use of a double warp; the other is the application of the draw harness to produce embossed velvet.

For the weaving of velvet two warps are used in the following arrangement: the first or main warp (*čelleh, būm*) consists of silk threads for the weaving of the basic fabric. This warp is stretched horizontally between a ware beam (*navard-e pīš*) and a rear beam or warp beam (*navard-e būm, būm-kār*). The warp is kept tight by means of a heavy weight (*langar*) that acts on a lever of 2-foot length placed in capstan holes in the rear beam. The second or pile warp (*ḫwāb*) stretches likewise from the ware beam but is guided upward over a diversion pole (*samak-e ḫwāb*) that is suspended from the ceiling. In going down again it crosses the main warp, is led under a second diversion pole (*samak-e pāʾin*) near ground level, and goes up into strands over a group (*manjenīq*) of warp rollers (*ġarġareh*), similar to those of the multiheddled loom. From the rollers the warp strands are led down, ending in warp balls (*qalambak, qalambeh, ġalambeh*) wound around wooden pegs and weighted with sandbags (*kīseh-ye ḫwāb*). The harness consists of six heddles (*vard, jūjeh*), four of which operate the main warp and two the pile warp, all six being connected to treadles (*pā*).

The velvet pile (*kork, kolk*) is produced in the following way: After a few plain wefts have been woven, employing the heddles of the main warp, the weaver produces a shed with the pile warp heddles, and instead of a thread he introduces into it a brass wire (*maftūl, mīl*) having a diameter of about 1 mm and being provided with a fine groove (*ḫaṭṭeh*) over its whole length. To show the position of the groove the wire is bent up at one end in the direction of the groove so that it can easily be placed pointing up. To prevent damage to the main warp during its insertion, the other end of the wire carries a polished knob (*sar-mīl*) made of camel bone (*kaʾūn-e šotor*). The weaving-in of the wire is followed by three plain wefts shot into the sheds of the main warp. These wefts are compacted with a reed (*šāneh*) whose frame (*daftīn-e sorb*) is weighted with about 90 pounds of lead for greater impact. After this the weaver takes a small pile-cutting knife (*tīġ*), inserts it carefully into the groove of the woven-in wire, and following the groove he cuts (*borīdan*) the loops open that have been formed by the pile warp threads, thus producing a pile. This done the wire is removed, the fabric compacted once more, a new pile shed opened, the wire inserted again, and so on. The product is a plain, surprisingly smooth velvet.

The weavers' customers often ask for some kind of ornamented velvet. One way to achieve a surface variation is the pressing of the piles into a wavy pattern (*mouj kardan*). This work is done by a finisher (*mouj-kār*), one of the weaver's assistants. He takes the woven fabric from the loom (*dastgāh-e maḫmal-bāfī*) and places it on a smooth wooden board (*taḫteh-mouj-dahī*). He has a number of wooden tools (*mouj-dahī*) about 18 inches long with highly polished ends of different profiles. While pressing one of them firmly on the velvet and giving the tool a backward and forward twist he moves right across the width of the material, bending some of the piles over, leaving others as they were before, thus producing a pleasant surface

[57] *Ibid.*, Fig. 37.

effect. He treats row after row of the velvet in this way until the whole length of the fabric has been ornamented.

A far more sophisticated method to produce fancy velvet is the weaving of embossed velvet (*maḫmal-e barjesteh*). It is a material where only ornamental patterns appear on the surface as pile whereas the background of the patterns is plain cloth weave. Embossed velvet is woven on a true draw loom that has the two warps, but is arranged for velvet weaving as described in the previous paragraph, i.e., the main warp is heddled to produce the basic fabric, and the second warp's heddles produce the pile. But this second warp is controlled through a draw harness. The weaver, with the assistance of the draw boy, by using the pile wire method, produces a free-figured velvet pattern in accordance with the sequence of the draw harness.

The Zīlū *Loom*

The draw loom described before is mainly used for the production of silk fabrics and is therefore warped with a great number of fine silk threads. There is a counterpart to it where free-figure weaving with a draw harness is similarly employed, namely in the manufacture of a soft, blanket-like floor covering, the so-called *zīlū*. Until the last century *zīlū* used to be made either of wool or of cotton. Today, however, they are made of fairly heavy, usually blue and white or red and white, cotton threads only. *Zīlū* are often found in mosques as prayer rugs for larger congregations. The writer has seen *zīlū* 15 to 18 feet wide and up to 30 feet long. In smaller sizes they are used in homes as floor coverings too. Though woven in two colors only, the patterns in most cases are intricate, sometimes in the form of Qorʾān inscriptions and geometrical designs, thus satisfying the Persian's demand for rich ornamental detail. For this reason a draw loom is employed instead of a multi-heddled standard loom.

The *zīlū* loom (*dastgāh-e zīlū-bāfī*, Fig. 294) is always vertical, two columns (*pahlū, pāyeh, ostā*) carrying the warp beam (*navard-e bālā, navard-e čelleh*) on the upper end and the cloth beam (*navard-e pāʾīn*) on the lower end. The beams are blocked with pegs that are removed when about 18 inches of material have been woven, and are rotated with long wooden levers (*ahrām, tang*) to wind the material onto the cloth beam. A double warp (*tūneh*) of two different colors is stretched between the beams, the two colors alternating. One color is threaded to a pair of heddle rods (*šemšeh, bīl-e dasteh*) with heddle loops (*gord*). These rods are suspended from the ceiling with ropes (*gūšvāreh*). The threads of the other color are connected to a draw

Figure 294 A Zīlū Loom

harness (*šelīt*) by means of short draw-strings. Forty to 60 of these strings are sufficient for most of the designs. For the weaving of the ordinary cloth binding, the heddle rods are operated by two weavers, one of them standing near each selvage, each moving a wooden lever (*kamāneh*) which slides up or down behind a heavy horizontal beam (*pošt-band-e kamāneh*) attached to the wall behind them. These levers are connected with the heddle rods through a pair of ropes (*pārčeh-band*). After the first shed has been opened with the heddles, the weft (*pūd*) is thrown in by one of the weavers and caught by his companion. They do not use a shuttle but an elongated ball of cotton yarn (*māšūreh*) wound around a stick (*qāleb*). After the two weavers have released the heddles, they beat the weft in with a beater comb (*panjeh*) similar to the one used in carpet weaving. Now they pull the first group of strings being part of the figure harness (*šelīt-e naqšeh*). They separate them by means of draw loops similar to those of the draw loom and slip the bundle (*maj*) of separated strings over strong wooden hooks (*kālī, kelī*) that are also attached to the beam at the back by means of ropes (*ṭanāb*). The draw harness strings hold the figure weft across and the other catches it. For less complicated patterns the weavers have fewer cross harness strings, and they do not need any loops for separation, knowing by heart which ones to pull for the next step in the pattern. It is customary to cut the weft threads about 2 inches outside the selvage and to weave in this extra end (*naḫ-e rūš*) together with the next weft so that the selvage becomes stronger than the remainder. A weaver's temple (*pahn-band*) digs into the selvage with its sharp teeth (*mīl*) and keeps the *zīlū* at a uniform width during the weaving.

Once in a while a *zīlū* weaver may have to weave a *zīlū* with a complicated pattern, possibly with a band of writing included in the design (Fig. 295). But normally he would be satisfied to produce some of the more popular and simpler designs that are known in the Iṣfahān and Kāšān bazaars as *mosallasī, naqšeh-gereh, gačkeneh, pīleh, pateh-tūreh,* and *zanjelō*.

Figure 295 Part of a Zīlū

The pattern of the *zīlū* loom is produced by changing the two colors of the double warp, whereas the standard draw loom works on the weft-faced pattern principle. An interesting piece of wool fabric is shown in Figs. 296 and 297, the former showing the front surface of a section of the pattern, the latter showing the reverse side of exactly the same section. Similar to the *zīlū*, it is a double cloth produced on a double warp with two contrasting colors, but the difference as compared with the *zīlū* is that the two contrasting colors have also been employed in two independent wefts so that in effect there are two fabrics, one behind the other but combined on all those points where one warp changes from the front to the back and the other comes forward, and vice-versa. While, however, warp-faced patterns and weft-faced patterns have floating threads, this double cloth pattern has none. This fabric has been woven by nomadic tribespeople of the province of Fārs.

Figure 296 Double Cloth Woven by Fārs Nomads (*front*)

Figure 297 Double Cloth Woven by Fārs Nomads (*reverse*)

Carpet Weaving

The Development of the Carpet Weaving Technique

There is no field in the industrial arts in Persia that is as important as carpet weaving, and yet little is known about its early development.

When discussing carpets here, the kind of woven fabric meant is that which, in addition to warp and weft, has a third dimension in the form of the knotted pile. In Europe, historical interest in Persian carpets began about 1870 when a collection of sixteenth- to nineteenth-century carpets was established,[58] all those woven before that time being classified as "earlier carpets" with the assumption that nothing was older than fourteenth-century, and that the technique had come from the Turks of Central Asia. This oversimplified classification, still found in most books on carpets, can no longer be maintained in the light of modern research.

The Greek Historian Xenophon (430–359 B.C.) mentions in his *Kyropaidaia* that the Persians had carpets (*psilotapis*) that "yielded" and on which only the king was allowed to walk. The old Persian sacred book, the Avesta, also mentions soft floor coverings. Since there is no specific mention of a knotted pile, these rugs are not necessarily the ancestors of the pile carpet. However, excavations at a *kurgan* (a royal tomb) at Pazyryk in the Altai mountains in Central Asia have brought textiles and felt to light of which a piled wool carpet 6 × 6 feet in size was the most important.[59] This tomb belonged to the Scythians, an Iranian people, cousins of the Persians. The burial place belongs to the fifth century B.C. and has been under a perpetual ice cover, a fortunate circumstance which has preserved the textiles in texture and color. This carpet is of an extremely fine texture, having 520 knots per square inch, as compared with 80 knots for coarse woolen carpets and 800 for the finest silken ones known today. The knots are genuine Ghiördes (Fig. 298), so-called Turkish knots. If we consider that Scythians and Turks were neighbors in Central Asia, the question arises whether the Turks or the Iranians were the originators of carpet weaving. Design details of the Pazyryk carpet are undoubtedly Iranian.

The next documented step in the development of the pile carpet was the finding of carpet fragments at Noin Ula and Loulan, both east of Persia in what is today

[58] K. Erdmann, *Der orientalische Knüpfteppich*, p. 10.

[59] J. Wiesner, "Zur Archaeologie Sibiriens," pp. 44–50.

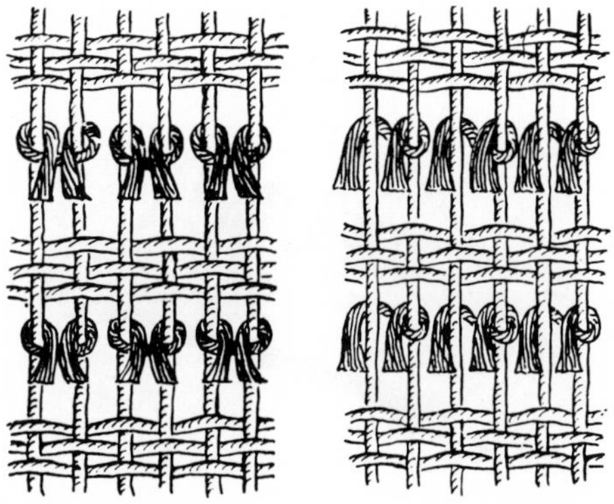

Figure 298 Ghiördes Knot (*left*) and Sehna Knot (*right, from K. Erdmann,* Der orientalische Knüpfteppich, *reproduced by permission of the publishers, Wasmuth Verlag, Tübingen*)

Mongolia. The Noin Ula samples were found in a dated lacquer box, the date being equivalent to 3 A.D.,[60] whereas the Loulan fragments belong to a period not later than fourth century A.D. Both these carpets have a thick, knotted pile, held together with weft bands. Beginning with the fourth century A.D., knotted pile textiles were manufactured in Dura Europos in Mesopotamia and Fostat in Egypt with linen as pile material[61] and one to six wefts between each row of knots. Knotted wool carpets have also been found in an oasis settlement in East Turkestan excavated by Sir Aurel Stein and by the German Turfan expedition.[62] Nestorian and Manichaean refugees from Syria and Persia are known to have lived there between the third and sixth centuries A.D.

We have no carpets of this time from Persia proper, but when the Byzantian emperor Heraclius sacked the Sasanian town of Dastjird in 628 A.D., he mentioned in the booty lists carpets (*tapis*) that were fleecy (*nakotapētes*). As according to Laufer[63] the name for carpet weaver in Byzantian Greek (*tapi-dyphos*) is of Persian origin, it may be assumed that the craft could have come to Byzantium from Persia.

In early Islamic times carpets with Persian inscriptions in the palace of al Mustansir (861 A.D.) were mentioned by the historian al-Masᶜūdī,[64] and the Caspian province of Ṭabāristān must have been an early production center as its annual tribute to the caliphs was 600 carpets.[65] Only from the eleventh century on do we have actual samples of Seljūq carpets, and from the twelfth century on the existence of a Persian carpet industry is firmly established. The basic technique has not changed to this day, and the development is mainly one of design, amply treated in numerous books on art history.

Materials Used in Carpet Weaving

Warp. Nomad carpets have woolen warps, as this fiber is immediately at hand in abundance from their herds. For sufficient strength the woolen warp threads must be thick, resulting in a coarser design. Carpets woven in town weaving shops normally have twined cotton threads for their warps that allow a much finer design, and occasionally they use a spun and twined silk warp for still finer knotting. The Persian weaver counts the fineness in *reġ*, which is the number of knots counted along the distance of one *gereh* ($2\frac{3}{4}$ inches) of warp length. The coarsest nomad rugs would have 20 *reġ* (corresponding to approximately 61 knots per square inch); 35 *reġ* (approximately 162 knots per square inch) would be average. The famous Ardabīl carpet in the British Museum has 52 *reġ* (360 knots per square

[60] A. U. Pope and P. Ackerman, *op. cit.*, p. 2437.
[61] *Ibid.*, p. 2438.
[62] K. Erdmann, *op. cit.*, p. 12.
[63] B. Laufer, *op. cit.*, p. 493.
[64] A. U. Pope and P. Ackerman, *op. cit.*, p. 2276.
[65] *Ibid.*

inch), and 75 *reġ* (800 knots per square inch) would be the finest known, with silk warp and silk pile. Carpet weavers in villages mainly make their warps with their homespun wool, but they sometimes work to order for city merchants who then frequently supply the yarn for a cotton warp.

Pile. The most typical material for the knotted pile is wool. Its quality differs with the region of its origin. The finest white wool, needed for the light tones, comes from Northwest Persia, especially the region around Lake Urūmiyeh, Ḫōʾī Mākū, Salmas, and Sauj-Bulāq. Tabrīz, however, the capital of this region, is known to use a lot of the dull carcass wool from its slaughter houses. Excellent carpet wool comes from Kurdistān and the region around Kermānšāh in the west and Ḫorāsān in the east. A rather coarse wool, but well suited for carpets because of its shiny surface, is that of Fārs in the south. Town weavers usually buy the spun wool from the herdsmen passing through on their annual migration round. To produce most valuable carpets with brightly shining surfaces silk piles are knotted into silk warps. Contrary to repeated statements in carpet handbooks, camel hair is not used for carpet weaving. What is called *šotorī* is naturally brown sheep wool, *šotorī* meaning "camel-colored." Very little use is made of goat hair for carpet weaving. *Kork*, which could mean the underhair of the goat, is also the name for the fine belly wool of the sheep. The Kermān carpets are famous partly because weavers there use this selected wool.

The Carpet Loom

There are two types of carpet looms (*dastgāh-e qālī-bāfī, dār-e qālī, kār-gāh*) in use, which are identical in function. They differ only in their position, viz., they have their warp either horizontal (*rū-zamīnī, kār-gāh-e zamīnī*) or almost vertical (*dīvārī, kār-gāh dārī*). Both have the warp (*tār, čelleh*) stretched between two beams (*navard, nebārd-nāv*) and use a rod heddle (*šamšeh, gord*) and a shed rod (*bačeh-gord*) to produce a shed. Figure 299 shows a horizontal carpet loom of the type generally used by the nomads. Here the heddle rod is suspended from a tripod. To lift it the weaver twists the suspension ropes with a pair of mouflon horns, thus keeping the heddle rod up while the shed is being used. The loom is pegged down to the ground and can easily be packed together and transported to the next camp.

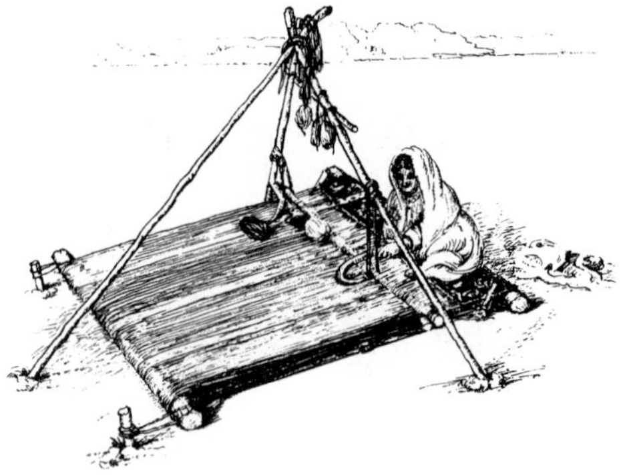

Figure 299 A Horizontal Carpet Loom

The most common carpet loom, however, is the vertical one where the upper beam (*navard-e bālā*) and the lower beam (*navard-e pāʾīn*) run between two upright posts (*pahlū, nebārd*). In Central Persia, where timber is scarce, the beams often run in holes in opposite walls of the workroom.

Preparing the Warp

The work of the specialist warp winder (*čelleh-davān*) has been described in the section on cloth weaving. He not only supplies the shuttle weavers with their warps but also some of the carpet manufacturers. There is another way of warp winding (*tār bastan, čelleh kašīdan*) that is done by the carpet warp winder (*tār-bandeh, čelleh-kaš, pūd-tāb*) or by the carpet weaver himself. He climbs on the upper beam, attaches a balled-up warp thread to it at one end, and drops the ball to his assistant who, sitting in front of the lower beam, takes the ball around that beam and throws it up again to his colleague, always making sure that it passes alternately in front of and behind a string stretched between the two warp posts about half way between the warp beams. This is done to obtain a warp cross (*čap-ō-rāst*). Skillfully maintaining the proper distance and the right tension they continue until the required number of warp threads has been wound on. Then the rod heddle (above the weaver's head in Fig. 302, p. 216) is formed by winding a strong cotton twine in continuous loops (*band-e gord*) around a horizontal pole and every second warp thread. A second horizontal pole is inserted to form the shed rod (behind the rod heddle in Fig. 302). The length of the complete warp corresponds to the length of either one large carpet or two smaller ones, which are often woven as a pair (*joft*), always leaving sufficient warp length for the knotting of the fringes (*rīšeh, hāšiyeh*) at the beginning and the end of each carpet. The lower beam slides in slots in the upright posts, and the warp can be tightened by inserting a pair of wedges (*tang*) and loosened by removing these wedges.

Knotting the Pile (bāftan-e qālī)

There are two kinds of knots (*ġond, ḫeft*) used in carpet weaving. One, the Sehna knot (right in Fig. 298), also called the Persian knot (*fārsī-bāf, yak-gereh*), is used in most of the town carpets. It results in a rather soft and flexible rug, and the knots appear small in size from the back. Most of the tribes of Turkish origin and the weavers in Ḫorāsān, however, tie their carpets in the Ghiördes or Turkish knot (*turk-bāf, dō-gereh*, left in Fig. 298), which shows the knots much coarser at the back. The Sehna knots permit a more minute design.

After a few inches have been woven in plain tapestry weave[66] (*pūtān-e pūbīleh*), the weaver begins with the knotting (*bāftan-e qālī*). In Āẕarbaijān he grips two adjacent warp threads with the hooked point (*sar-e qolāb*) of a special knife (*qolāb, tīġ*), in the southern provinces with his fingers, draws them toward him, and slings a thread of pile wool (*gorūk*) behind these two warp threads and forward again in the form of the required knot (Fig. 300).

Figure 300 Knotting the Carpet Pile

Then he pulls the knot tight and cuts the thread ends with the sharp edge (*dam-e qolāb, dam-e tīġ*) of the knife to a length of about 2 inches. The carpet weavers of Kāšān and Iṣfahān have a blunt point at the end of the knife blade used to remove faulty knots; the weavers of Šīrāz have an ordinary knife. The pile material in balls of all the colors needed is suspended from an overhead beam. Village and nomad weavers work their traditional designs without any drawing or plan. Many of the designs are passed on from generation to generation, and the sequence of colors is

[66] Tapestry is a type of cloth weave with less warp than weft threads to the inch.

chanted while the work goes on. Some of the villagers and some nomads work for town dealers or manufacturers, and in these cases it is quite common to give sample carpets (*vāgīreh*), i.e., part of the center medallion, one-quarter of the field, and one corner of the border, to such weavers. It is interesting to see how they rarely copy them mechanically but take the samples merely as guides. In town manufactures, design cartoons (*naqšeh*) drawn on graph paper, every square (*ḫāneh*) representing one knot, are placed in front of the weavers. These drawings have been prepared by specialized carpet designers (*naqšeh-kaš*) who in many cases have been skilled weavers before. It is customary that the foreman or forewoman weaves the design outlines, whereas younger weavers fill in the rest. When one row of knots (*pū*) has been completed a number of tapestry weft threads is woven in (Fig. 301), usually three, with a change of the heddle after each weft. For the "heddle up" position the weaver pulls the heddle rod toward himself and presses it against a pair of wooden brackets (*zīr-sarī*) that are attached to the uprights (position shown in Fig. 302). For the "heddle down" position he releases the rod, which then rests on these brackets. Next he compacts (*šāneh zadan*) wefts and knots with a beater comb (*šāneh, daftīn, yarkid*, Fig. 302).

Figure 301 Weaving in the Tapestry Wefts

Figure 302 Compacting a Row of Knots

A weaver in an organized weaving shop is expected to make 14,000 knots a day, for which he is paid his wages, regardless of the time worked. Good weavers manage to do this in five hours, which amounts to three knots in four seconds. Very seldom do they continue after completion of this norm; rather, they relax or do other work around the house.

Finishing the Carpet

From time to time the weaver cuts the overhanging piles shorter to be able to see the design more clearly, but he does not cut down to the final length of the pile. After this preliminary cut he loosens the warp beams (*šol kardan*) by removing the wedges from the slots in the uprights, and with the aid of a large lever (*ahrām*) the beams are turned so that the whole warp is moved forward (*gardāndan*), so that the woven part gradually disappears behind or underneath the loom. This will be done several times until the beginning of the carpet eventually will show above or in front of the weaver, which means that the knotting is completed. Another short piece of tapestry weave is now woven in, and after this comes the time for the most skilled man in the team, the finisher (*pardāḫtčī*). He first trims (*čīdan*) one section of the pile with a pair of scissors (*qaičī-qālī-bāfī*) having offset handles (Fig.

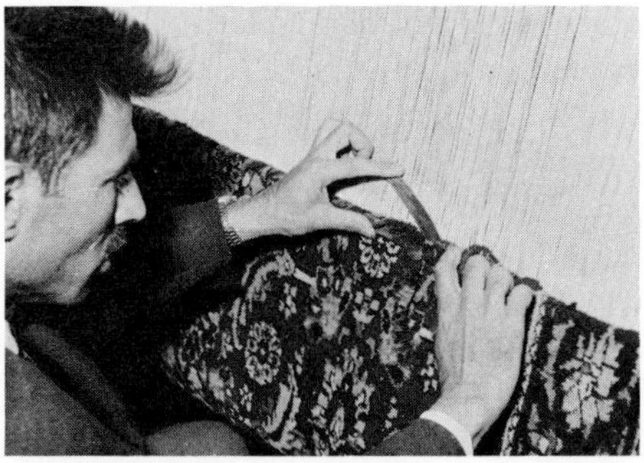

Figure 303 Trimming the Carpet Pile with Scissors

Figure 304 Finishing the Carpet with a Trimming Knife

303). After he has treated this section of the carpet in such a way, he performs the final shaving (*pardāḫt kardan*) with a broad and very sharp trimming knife (*kārdak*, Fig. 304). Then the carpet is again moved over the warp beams so that the next section to be trimmed and shaved comes within the reach of the finisher, and so on until he has gone over the whole carpet. Finally the remaining loose warp threads are cut in half and knotted (*gereh zadan*) into bundles of ten to fifteen warp threads each, which form the fringes. They not only protect the end wefts from becoming undone but also enhance the appearance of a carpet. It should be mentioned here that most carpets have one or two extra-strong warp threads on the outsides of the warp over which the weft ends are woven as described for the *zīlū*, so that this strong selvage (*band-e kenāreh*) acts as a side protection of the delicate knotted pile.

Embroidery

In his well known desire for rich ornament the Persian has often turned to embroidery (*sokmeh-dūzī, naḫ-dūzī, golābetūn*). As it is generally not an industry or a craft but work done by women in the house, little is known about its development. It has been suggested that the ornaments on the garments of the nobles and guards shown in the bas-reliefs on the palace walls of Susa and Persepolis were embroidered ones. Numerous other rock sculptures and silver vessels show persons with richly embroidered dresses. All these may have been embroideries, but in the absence of any archaeological evidence this question must be left open, as it is likewise possible that the fabrics of the garments were tapestry or pattern-weave.

The first sample of actual embroidery that has come to us belongs to the Seljūq period (1037–1157 A.D.), and a strong Chinese influence can be noticed in design as well as in technique.[67] The Chinese often used plain as well as pattern-weave silk fabrics and applied embroidery to them for ornamentation, mainly using the satin-stitch that became known in Persia as *ṭirāz*. Chinese influence became stronger still during the Mongol and Timurid dynasties in the thirteenth and fourteenth centuries. It is known that Timur had Chinese embroiderers working at his court in Samarkand.[68] The Chinese style in embroidery had another great revival under the Ṣafavids.

During the twelfth century, so-called Persian-style embroidery came to Sicily

[67] P. Ackerman in A. U. Pope and P. Ackerman, *op. cit.*, p. 2066.
[68] *Ibid.*, p. 2158.

together with silk brocade weaving. One of the finest examples of woven brocade further enriched with embroidery, made in Sicily, is the coronation cloak of the German emperors, originally made for the Norman king Roger II.[69] It is decorated with Arabic inscriptions and dated 1133 A.D.

Marco Polo mentions that at Kermān women were producing excellent gold embroidery.[70] A regional group with a style of its own were the embroiderers of Northwest Persia, where an industry flourished during the sixteenth and seventeenth centuries around Ardabīl, the home of the Ṣafavid dynasty. The Victoria and Albert Museum in London has a fine collection of these embroideries,[71] which are mainly worked in cross-stitch, others in darning stitch. The style of their design indicates connections with the people who produced the so-called Caucasian carpets. Another style of embroidery, *melīleh-dūzī*, was worked during the sixteenth and seventeenth centuries all over Persia. Materials used were colored silk and metal threads worked onto colored silk satin. Most of this work was applied to divan covers. A feature of these covers was the provision of wide brocade and embroidered borders. More confined to the south, worked in centers such as Iṣfahān, Kāšān, Yazd, and Šīrāz, were embroideries applied to divan covers, prayer mats, and bath rugs mainly worked in chain-stitch.[72] The richly embroidered women's trousers of nineteenth-century Persia became well known in Europe as *gilets persans* or *nakshe*, the latter word simply meaning "ornament." Iṣfahān was the main center producing them.[73] Still famous for its fine embroidery (*gol-dūzī*) is Rašt in Gīlān, where men and

women decorate saddle cloths (*ᶜaraq-gīr*), cushion covers (*rūbāleš*), table cloths (*rūmīz*), wall hangings (*rūdīvārī*), and bed quilts (*rūleḥāf-e dārāᵓī*) as well as garments.[74] The embroiderers (*gol-dūz, golāb-dūz*) of Rašt hold the cloth (*māḥūt*) in a wooden clamp (*gerīdeh, jerīdeh*) that rests on one of their legs while they press it down with the other (Fig. 305). The design has been traced on the cloth with chalk (*naqš bā rang kašīdan*). The embroiderer takes a crochet hook (*golāb, sūzan*) with a wooden handle and pierces it through the cloth (*forū kardan*). Holding the embroidery thread (*naḫ*) on the reverse side of the cloth, he grips it with the crochet hook (*naḫ pīč kardan*) and pulls a loop formed by it to the front (*naḫ az dast-e čap gereftan, bālā raftan*), and with this thread loop still around the hook, pierces through the cloth

Figure 305   An Embroiderer

69 O. von Falke, *op. cit.*, p. 120.
70 B. Spuler, *Die Mongolen in Iran*, p. 437.
71 *Persian Embroideries*, p. 3.
72 *Ibid.*, p. 5.
73 Tehrān, Mūseh Honarā-ye Tazᵓīnī.

74 H. Brugsch, *op. cit.*, p. 89.

again, gripping the thread underneath, and pulling the next loop up, and so on, thus producing the chain-stitch (*pīč*). Much of the surface of the cloth is covered in this way. Often the design includes differently colored pieces of cloth applied to the base material with these stitches.

Between the two world wars a home industry was revived in Iṣfahān where traditional designs were applied to home-made or imported materials in old and new techniques.

The most commonly used stitch is the chain-stitch (*pīč*, *zelleh*, *naqšeh*, *golāb*). Embroidery in chain-stitch only is known as *golāb-dūzī*. Other stitches used are the cross-stitch (*naḫ-andāzī*), which is still very popular with the Zoroastrians in Central Persia for the decoration of their traditional white garments, the fillet or darning stitch (*goldūz*) applied to fillet nets (*tūrī*), and the hemstitch (*šabeh-kaš*), which is just as popular in Persia as it is with the European needleworker.

Today quite a number of embroiderers work for export, the foundation material being mainly linen (*katān*, *ᶜalaf-e farangī*) or cotton fabric (*karbās*). In Iṣfahān a coarse cotton material called *mitqāl* is extensively used. Many of the more frequently used elements of the pattern have popular names, e.g., a pair of wavy lines (*bōteh*), a star (*setāreh*), a zig-zag line (*dālbor*, *dālbort*), a double zig-zag (*dālbor-e dōbarī*), and a number of small circles (*čašmeh-bulbul*).

Mat Weaving, Basket Plaiting, Rope-making

The plaiting of reeds and grass into mats and baskets is an activity even older than weaving. Specimens found in Iraq must have been made about 5000 B.C., and grain baskets from the Badarian period of ancient Egypt revealed 4500 B.C. as their date of manufacture.[75]

Mat plaiting (*būriyā bāftan*) is still an important craft in Persia, the plaited mats (*būriyā*) being used in the ceiling construction of mud-roofed houses. The mat plaiter (*būriyā-bāf*) buys the raw material, bamboo (*ḫaizarān*, *nai hindī*), or rushes (*nai*), in bundles (*bōġeh*, *bōġčeh*, *basteh*, *ᶜadl*). The first operation is the trimming of the stems by cutting the seed tops and the root ends with a sharp, hooked knife (*dās*, *nai-šekāf*). Bamboo has to be softened (*narm kardan*) by pouring water (*āb pāšīdan*) over it before the plaiter's assistant can beat (*kūbīdan*, *kūftan*) the stems flat with a mallet (*nai-kūb*). Rushes are trimmed but need not be softened before beating. Both rushes and bamboo are split open (*šekāftan*) after beating. Working on the ground (Fig. 306), the plaiters spread a number of

Figure 306 Bamboo Mat Plaiters

the flattened and split stems out next to one another and plait a "weft" of bamboo or rushes across at right angles, using a kind of twill binding, or, as the plaiters put it: "We take two and leave two" (*dōtā mīgīrīm dōtā veleš konīm*). The ends of the "weft" stems are turned in (*pīč ḫwordan*), thus forming a strong edge. The average size of these mats is 12 × 24 feet; they are

[75] R. J. Forbes, *Studies in Ancient Technology*, Vol. 4, pp. 178–179.

Figure 307 Mat Plaiter's Work Place

tied into rolls and sold to the builders (Fig. 307). A well known center of this industry is Zarġān near Šīrāz, where the rushes are cut in the nearby swamps of the Pulvar river. The cutting and bundling of these rushes is a source of additional income for many peasants there. Zarġān employs more than a thousand people in mat plaiting. Other centers are Borūjerd, Nahāvand, and some villages around Hamadān, all obtaining their supply of bamboo from the plains of Ḫūzistān.

Mat weaving (*ḥaṣīr-bāfī*), i.e., the making of mats by weaving thin reeds into stretched-out warps of cotton thread, has not changed much since old Egyptian days. The mat loom (*dastgāh-e ḥaṣīr-bāfī*, Fig. 308) used today in Persia is essentially the same as the one shown on a wall of the tomb of Kethy at Beni Hasan (2000 B.C.).[76]

Figure 308 Mat Weaving

The strong cotton twine warp threads (*rīsmān, tān*) are stretched between two wooden beams, one at the far end of the warp called *sar-e kār, sar-e dār*, the other *pas-e kār, čūb, čūb-e poštband*, where the work commences. These beams are tied to wooden pegs (*čangām*) driven into the ground. The mat weavers (*ḥaṣīr-bāf*), usually three, thread the reeds (*ḫong, lī, liyān, gālī*) under and over alternate warp threads by hand (Fig. 308). Where the outer reeds meet the middle ones, two warp threads have been doubled during the warp winding, a measure necessary to strengthen the overlapping joint (*bast, sarband*) of the reeds. When threading the reeds in, the ends of the outer ones are left to stand out for about 2 inches, and these ends are turned in with the next weft, thus reinforcing the selvage (*kenār-e kār, šīrāzeh*). After each weft the reeds are compacted with a comb (*baš, māš, šāneh*), a wooden pole with a number of holes through which all warp threads are running. When 12 to 18 inches have thus been woven, the weavers support the woven part with a board (*šipā, taḫteh-nešastan*), and squat on the mat (*ḥaṣīr*) above it. The warp is kept tight by a wooden beam (*pādār*) underpinned by a number of bricks. Both supporting board and tightening beam are moved forward as the work advances. When the end of the warp has been reached, the mat is cut off from the warp beams, and the ends of the warp threads are knotted around the first and last wefts. This type of mat is commonly used as a floor mat in the poorer homes or as an under-carpet mat to protect the carpets from the coarse gypsum floor.

In Māzandarān the mat warps are made of hemp (*kanāf*) and the reeds are twisted into a kind of thin rope on a reed winder (*kotolām*). The resulting mat is rather thick and durable.

Another type of mat is used for blinds or curtains (*pardeh, tejīr*) in front of doors and

[76] *Ibid.*

windows. These mats are made of a particularly light cane (*nai-tejīr*). The blind weaver (*pardeh-bāf*) has a loom (*kār-gār*) as shown in Fig. 309. Here the warp threads (*rīsmān*) are twined around the canes with the help of a horizontal board supported by two vertical posts in working height.

Figure 309 Blind Weavers

The warp threads are wound into balls around stones of fist size or cast-iron balls (*delgerān*) and are arranged in pairs so that one ball is in front of the supporting board and the other one behind it. After having laid a cane over the full length of the board, the weaver, beginning at one end, throws the first warp ball from the front to the back and its pair from the back to the front, doing the same with the next pair and all the others until they have all changed positions. Then he places the next cane on the board and repeats this procedure, thus entwining one cane after the other. When the warp threads are used up he unwinds some from the balls so that they hang down nearly to the ground again (*delgerān pāʾīn kašīdan*). The canes for curtains or blinds are cut off at the ends to an equal width. Sometimes this loom is also used for the weaving of mats from fine reeds (*ḫong*), then the overhanging ends of the reeds are turned in to strengthen the selvages. The blind weaver usually weaves the cane blinds to a width ordered by his customer. After he has completed the weaving he reinforces the edges by lining them with cotton webbing (*karbās-e pardeh, pārčeh*) that he sews on by hand.

The calling of the basket plaiter (*sabad-bāf, sabadgar, sabadčī, zambīl-bāf*) is often combined with that of the mat weaver. The only tools used for basket plaiting are a wooden block (*kondeh*) and a curved knife (*kārd, čāqū*) serving to split and cut the reeds, rushes, or canes. The plaiting of baskets (*zambīl, sabd*) is done freehanded. The basket maker also makes brooms (*jārū, jārūb*). If he makes brooms exclusively, he is called a broom maker (*jārū-bāf*).

There is a certain similarity between basket plaiting and ropemaking in Persia, since a good deal of rope (*ṭanāb*) is plaited or braided from the coarser goat hair. Hemp (*kanaf*) and cotton (*pambeh*) ropes, however, are twisted on a ropemaker's walk with a rope-spinning reel. The ropemaker (*ṭanāb-tāb, ṭanāb-bāf, ṭanāb-sāz, rīsmān-bāf*) has in fact two reels similar to the one used by the carpet warp winder (Fig. 273), each mounted on a strong wooden frame (*čahār-pāyeh*). A light reel (*čarḫ-e rīsmān-tāb*) is for the twisting of the individual threads into strands (*rīsmān*) that will make up the rope, and a heavy reel (*čarḫ-e ṭanāb-tāb*) serves for twisting these strands into ropes. The center part of each of these reels is the spinning head (*čahār-qolāb*), consisting of four individual spindles, each ending in a hook (*qolāb*). These spindles are driven from a large wheel (*čarḫ*) over a belt cord (*band*) and four pulleys (*qarqarī*). The tension of the belt cord can be adjusted with a tourniquet (*tang*) tightened by a wooden peg (*čūb-e tang*). The spindles run at the end of a strong board (*taḫteh*). To operate the lighter reel the ropemaker attaches himself with a cord to an endless belt, which runs between the driving pulley on the large wheel and an idling pulley on the wall at the far end of the workshop. When he walks away from the reel toward the idling pulley he sets the large wheel in motion, and the spindle hooks rotate with it. To make a strand he stretches four threads between the spindle hooks and four hooks on the wall at the far end of the workshop. Having attached himself to the endless belt, he walks away from the spinning head, causing the spindle hooks to turn round rapidly, thus giving each thread a twist (*tāb*). When he has reached the end of the walk he detaches himself from the endless belt, grips the four threads tightly, unhooks them, making sure that they do not lose their twist, and inserts their ends into a wooden mold (*qāleb, mohreh*) that has carved-in guiding grooves corresponding to the profile of the strand to be made. The ends are attached to one hook on the wall, and while he firmly guides the mold (*qāleb kardan*) he walks back toward the spindle head. In doing that he forms the threads into a strand. The larger reel, constructed similar to that of the carpet warp winder, is driven by the ropemaker's assistant, who turns the large wheel with a handle. It has heavier hooks to which are attached four strands, which the ropemaker forms into a single rope in a similar way to that described for the strand, using a larger mold.

Fulling

Felt, one of the so-called nonwoven textiles, is formed in the presence of pressure, moisture, and preferably heat. The felt formation is based on two properties of wool, viz., crimp and scaliness. When wool crimps in moist heat and its fibers interlace, the scales prevent the fibers from sliding back. This interlacing process produces an irregular fabric that becomes stronger if so-called fulling agents (such as alkalines and fuller's earth) are applied to intensify the natural properties of wool. Mechanical working, called hardening, accelerates the integration of the fibers.

Very little is known about the origin of felting except that it has been closely linked with wool-growing people since Neolithic times. Chinese records of 2300 B.C. refer to felt mats, armor, and shields.[77] Felt has been found in a Bronze Age grave in Germany dating back to 1400 B.C. The classical authors, from Homer on, mention felt and significantly link it with Persia. Scythian kurgans of the fifth century B.C. found in ice-covered parts of Central Russia have yielded many felt objects such as wall covers, mats, rugs, saddle cloths, and blankets.[78] Turkish tribes coming from this region, and Persian tribesmen too, are to this day masters in the ancient art of fulling. Not only do they produce complete cloaks in felt with sleeves and hood, all made in one piece, but they are also experts in decorating the felt with fulled-in patterns of dyed wool. The technique used by these nomads was simple and has persisted to this day.

Hat Fulling

Wool (*pašm*), often mixed with goat underhair (*kork, kolk*), is degreased with potash, rinsed, and after drying combed (*šāneh zadan*) on a wool comb (*šāneh*) or loosened with a bow (*kamān zadan*, Fig. 310). A circular layer of this wool, a so-called bat (*angereh*), about twice the size of the finished hat, is spread (*vāz kardan*) in even thickness over a shallow copper dish (*tāveh, touveh*, Fig. 311) that is mildly heated from underneath by a charcoal fire. The fuller (*gāzūr, qaṣṣār, namad-māl*), or *kolāh-māl* if he is a hat fuller, sprinkles this bat with a thick soap solution (*āb-e*

[77] Sustmann, "Felt," p. 25.
[78] *Ibid.*, p. 23.

Figure 310 A Fuller Bowing Fibers

Figure 312 A Fuller Hardening the Felt

Figure 311 A Fuller Preparing the Wool Pad

Figure 313 A Fuller Opening the Hat

ṣābūn) from an earthenware dish beside him. While wool and soap water warm up, he presses the fibers with his hands, first gently, then harder, and releases them again. As soon as the felt begins to form he places a flat cotton pad into the center of the bat, approximately the size of the required diameter of the hat. He lays a second bat of beaten wool, smaller in size than the first one, over the pad and folds the surplus of the larger one over, thus joining the two halves (*lab gereftan*), then saturates the whole in soap water. After he has squeezed it mildly for a while he places it on a piece of cotton fabric and rolls both, prefelted bats and fulling cloth, into one roll, thus preventing interfelting. He puts this roll back in the dish with warm soap water, where he rolls it backward and forward with both hands and one foot (Fig. 312). This hardening (*namad mālīdan, mālīdan*) operation takes about 10 to 15 minutes, after which the fuller carefully unrolls the felt, tears the center of the bat apart, widens the opening (*bāz čīdan*, Fig. 313), takes the cotton pad out, and forms the opened part into a rim (*gūšeh*). From time to time he pulls the felt over a wooden block (*qāleb zadan*), perfects the rim, and places the whole back into the hot dish for further shrinking (*mošteh šodan*) until it obtains the shape of a hat and the required density. During the process thin patches are overlaid with little wool bats and these are worked in. If the fuller works in a small village he immediately proceeds to finish this raw felt into a hat, but in larger communities this is left to a specialist, the hatter. His work will be described in the following section.

Large felt rugs, tent coverings, cloaks, and blankets are worked along similar lines, except that the large wool bats are placed on the ground (*ham kardan*) and are sprinkled with soap water, after which the fullers walk over them to achieve the first interlocking (*pašm gereftan*), usually several of them walking side by side and working the wool with their bare feet. The mildly compacted bat is rolled up in a canvas or reed mat (*ḥaṣīr*) and is placed in a long earthenware mold built into the ground and heated from underneath. In Ḫorāsān they pour boiling water (*āb-e jūš*) over the roll. Several men walk on this roll (*pūk kašīdan*) and turn it over with their feet while they lean against a wooden bar at waist height. For large rugs and tent covers it often takes several hours before the felt is sufficiently dense. Most of the nomadic people like their felt rugs with colored ornaments (*gol*). They dye (*rang kardan*) the wool prior to fulling, do the first stage of the fulling in one color, open the roll, and place wool in different colors according to the ornaments planned onto the base felt, often with different patterns on front and reverse, and continue with fulling. The ornaments become an integral part of the felt. After the fulling, soap and fuller's earth (*sang-e qibṭī*) are washed out, the felt is dried, and, if used for tent covers, waterproofed with animal fat.

Hatter

Felt hats (*kolāh*) have always been popular in Persia, as we can see from the bas-reliefs at Susa and Persepolis. This is understandable because they are an ideal protection in the wide range of temperatures between deep winter frosts and the burning heat of summer. The hatter (*kolāh-dūz*) takes the raw hat felts that he obtains from the fuller, pulls them over hat blocks (*qāleb, qālūb*), of which he has a number in various sizes, and first trims the surface of the felt by shaving away (*tīġ tarāšīdan*) with a sharp knife (*tīġ*) any surplus wool that stands out. The next step, the scraping (*šāneh kardan*) of more surplus wool from the surface with a finely toothed scraper (*šāneh*), is followed by grinding (*pardāḫt kardan*) the felt with a pumice stone (*sang-e pā*). The hatter then dips the hat, while it is still on the block, into hot soap water in a dish (*sāj*) similar to the one the fuller has and rubs the felt surface smooth with a burnishing wood (*čūbeh*), followed by further smoothing with a polished stone (*mohreh*). Both these operations are in effect continued fulling processes. When the required surface smoothness has been achieved the rim is stretched out or, as in the case of the typical Qašqāʾī hats, the two flaps (*dō-jā*) are bent over and cut to size with a pair of scissors. Then the hat is washed, dried, and dipped into a thin solution of gum tragacanth (*katīreh, katīrā*) that acts as a size. During the final drying stage the surface of the hat is burnished once again with the polished stone to obtain the last finish.

Textile Printing

The production of colored designs and patterns on textiles with stamps or blocks seems to have originated in India during the fourth century B.C.[79] Chinese chronicles report that printed cloth was brought from India to China in 140 B.C. Indian origin of the art is indicated by the Persian word for printed calico, namely *čīt*, which is of Hindi origin.[80] About the beginning of our era the Roman historian Strabo wrote that in his time printed textiles were imported from India into Alexandria.

[79] R. J. Forbes, *Studies in Ancient Technology*, Vol. 4, p. 137, and G. Schaefer, "Die frühesten Zeugdrucke," pp. 854–856.

[80] F. Steingass, *A Comprehensive Persian-English Dictionary*, p. 405.

Finds in Egypt have shown that printed calicoes were marketed there up to the fourth century A.D. During the Sasanian period textile printing had developed in Persia into one of the major techniques for the decoration of woolen, linen, and silk fabrics.[81]

The earliest printed textiles in northern Europe have been found in the grave of St. Caesarius of Arles (about 543 A.D.). They were made in the eastern technique. When block printing was eventually established in northern Europe, it differed essentially in technique from the oriental method. The medieval European printer, from the thirteenth century on, transferred a colored pigment mixed with a binder, in other words a paint, from his wooden block to the textile. This color pigment did not penetrate the fiber but stayed on its surface. The oriental printer, on the other hand, uses true textile dyestuffs that stain the whole fiber. Three different methods that may be applied individually or combined can be distinguished today:

1. The printer stamps a resist (wax or certain gum pastes) onto the fabric. When the cloth is dyed, the resist-stamped portions of it are not affected by the dye. The resist is later washed out, and the process can be repeated with different colors, often partly overlapping the previous one, thus permitting a great variety of effects. This method has been and still is used in Persia for some patterns.

2. The printer stamps a mordant (alum, vitriol, plant extracts) onto the fabric. When dyed with certain dyestuffs that develop only in the presence of these mordants, the pattern appears on the mordant-stamped portions of the cloth while the undeveloped dyestuff is rinsed out from the rest of the fabric. This method is the most important and commonly used in Persia to this day for two of the colors in the printing process.

3. The printer stamps the dyestuff directly onto the cloth. Some of the old natural dyes can be used in this way, and a number of the modern synthetic inks, too, are suitable to be applied directly, and the Persian craftsman uses them for two other colors.

Most of the Persian textile printers employ a printing block cutter or are associated with one who prepares and maintains the printing blocks (*qāleb, qālūb*) needed for each pattern.

The system used today by most of the printers (*čīt-sāz, qalamkār-sāz*) of Iṣfahān, Kāšān, and Yazd is the so-called four-color printing. The design (*naqšeh*) is carefully divided into sections, such as center piece, border, corner, and so forth, to provide the printer with conveniently sized blocks. As all sections will be printed in the four colors black (*meškī*), red (*qermez*), blue (*ābī*), and yellow (*zard*), four blocks have to be prepared for each section. Figure 314 shows a complete set of blocks used for the printing of the border of a shawl. The printing is done in the following way:

1. The first color, *rang-e avval*, is black. The block for dyeing it is called *qāleb-e meškī* or *siyāh*. It shows the outlines of the design (top, Fig. 314). The substance printed with this block is iron vitriol (*zāġ-e siyāh*), which, acting as a mordant, turns madder into a black and fixed color.

2. The second color, *rang-e dōvom*, is red and is printed on with the block shown in Fig. 314, second from top. It is called *qāleb-e qermez* or *lāb*. The areas to be printed red are usually wider, and to assure an even distribution of the mordant the block cutter hollows them out and inserts strips of felt. These act as stamping

[81] R. J. Forbes, *Studies in Ancient Technology*, Vol. 4, p. 137, and G. Schaefer, "Die frühesten Zeugdrucke," pp. 854–856.

pads absorbing the mordant. The mordant used for this stage is alum (*zāġ-e safīd*), which fixes madder into a bright red.

3. The third color, *rang-e sevom*, is blue. The block used (third from top in Fig. 314) is called *qāleb-e ābī* or *dōt* and prints the dyestuff indigo in its undeveloped state, glucisid indoxyl, on the textile.

4. The fourth color, *rang-e čahārom*, is yellow, another one of the nonmordanted traditional dyestuffs or, increasingly today, a directly applicable synthetic yellow. Figure 314, bottom, shows the block for yellow (*qāleb-e zard, zardī*).

The actual printing process comprises the following stages:

(*a*) The fabric used today is a hand-woven calico (*karbās-e dastbāf*). If it is part of the color scheme previously outlined that the background for the design should not be white but fawn (*zard*), the fabric is boiled in a solution of pomegranate rind (*pūst-e anār*), rinsed, and dried.

Figure 314 A Set of Textile Printing Blocks

(*b*) The printer has the dry calico in a stack in front of his workbench, which is a low, heavy wooden table (*taḫteh*). The printer draws a piece of calico onto the workbench, takes the first printing block, and moistens it with iron vitriol from an earthenware dish (*qadaḥ*) at his side. The mordant is thickened with gum tragacanth (*katīreh*) to prevent it from running during the printing process. A piece of cloth (*pārčeh, šāl*) is stretched over the mordant dish and fastened around its rim with a string in such a way that it just touches the surface of the mordant, thus giving the printer always the right amount of mordant for his block. He places the moistened block onto the fabric, and pressing it down with his left hand, and using his right hand as a hammer, strikes the block with one blow. His right hand is protected by a pad (*tarm*) made from folded-up woolen cloth or felt. He moistens the block again and places it back on the cloth, carefully joining marks on the edge of the block with repeat marks (*ḫāl*) left from the previous print, and so on.

(*c*) After he has completed all the prints with the different black blocks, he applies the mordant for the red areas with the red blocks in the same way, carefully observing all repeat marks (Fig. 315).

(*d*) When he has printed all the pieces of cloth from the stack with the black and red mordants, he takes the whole stack to the dye house (*rangraz-ḫāneh*), where he lowers one sheet of fabric after the other into a boiling solution of madder (*rūniyās, rūnās*). In one bath the iron vitriol-stamped lines turn black and the alum-stamped ones become red. During the subsequent washing (*šostan bā āb*, in Iṣfahān near the banks of the river Zāyandeh, Fig.

Figure 315 A Textile Printer Applying Dyestuff

316) the surplus madder solution is rinsed out, the fabric is dried in the sun, and sent back to the printer.

(*e*) Taking indigo dye with the blue block from the cloth over the indigo dish in the same way as he did with the mordants, the printer applies it as the third color.

(*f*) The last step is the stamping on of the yellow dye in the same way as the blue, thus completing the actual printing process.

(*g*) The fabric is taken to the dye house for a second time, where it is boiled in water, during which process both dyestuffs develop and, when subsequently exposed to the air, gain their full color strength.

Another way of obtaining the fawn background referred to in step (*a*) is the following: After thorough moistening, 20 to 30 printed and dyed calicoes are spread on the ground, all on top of one another, each one being sprinkled with finely ground pomegranate rind before the next one is placed over it. More water is poured over this pack and it is left alone for several hours. After a final rinse in fresh water the cloths are dried in the sun. This process also serves as an additional color fixer. In the printing centers of Iṣfahān, Kāšān, and Yazd, where large series of each design are printed at a time, the printers work in teams, each team member handling all the blocks of one color and then passing the fabric to a colleague for the next color.

Figure 316 Dyers Rinsing Printed Textiles

Quilt Making

Although Persia now has an efficient modern textile industry, including in its products good woolen blankets, people still like to cover beds with the traditional quilt (*leḥāf*), and bazaars of even small towns have at least one quilt maker (*leḥāf-dūz*). The quilt covers are usually sewn together from pieces of colored cotton fabric; popular designs have the field (*būm*) of printed cotton, a center diamond (*mouj*), and a wide border (*kenāreh*) of plain cotton in a contrasting color or viceversa. The cover is filled with cotton (*pambeh*) or wool (*pašm*) that the quilt maker has loosened with a carder's bow at the back of his workshop. After the filling and sewing up of the cover the fibers inside it are evenly distributed by being beaten with a wooden stick (*čūb-e dōšak-ṣāf-kon*). This is followed by the quilting (*duḫtān-e leḥāf*), with a needle 3 to 4 inches long (*sūzan*) and strong cotton or linen yarn. The needle is dipped into a pincushion filled with tallow (*kohneh-pī*, *bāleštak*, *bālešak*) from time to time. The tallow eases the sewing and also protects the needle when not in use. The quilter's finger is protected by a strong iron thimble (*angoštar*, *angoštāneh*). The Persian quilt makers indulge in fanciful ornamental quilting patterns that they are able to sew in without any drawn-on design. They usually start by sewing large circles into the four corners of the cover, and by adding more concentric and eccentric circles and wavy lines they gradually secure more and more fibers in their places.

After years of use some of the quilting threads wear through and the filling forms lumps. There are some quilters who go into the people's homes and, sitting in the courtyard, open such old quilts, re-bow the fibers, fill them in again, sew the cover up, and finish their work by requilting a different pattern.

Cloth Shoe Making

Little is known about the development of the humble craft of cloth shoe making. The historian al-Balḫī[82] mentioned in 1105 A.D. that Ġundījān (modern Jamīleh) in Fārs was known for its cloth shoe industry, which was still flourishing when the geographer Mustoufī saw it in 1340 A.D. The finest cloth shoes in modern times come from Ābādeh on the High Plateau between Iṣfahān and Šīrāz.

The Persian cloth shoe (*gīveh*, *malekī*) is comfortable to wear and well suited for the climate, but completely different from a Western type of shoe. It consists of a cloth sole (*šīveh*) of remarkable strength and endurance and a cotton upper (*rūvā*, *rūʾā*, *rūveh*, *rūʾeh*).

[82] G. Le Strange, *Mesopotamia and Persia under the Mongols in the 14th Century*, p. 69.

Figure 317 Making a Cloth Shoe Upper

Three people are involved in the manufacture of cloth shoes. The uppers are made (*rūʾeh čīdan*) by the women at home from a strong, twined cotton thread (*naḫ*) with a heavy needle (*sūzan-e gīveh-bāfī*) in a kind of blanket stitch, but not applied to any fabric (Fig. 317). The sewer starts at the tip of the upper with a few stitches slung around the end of her sewing thread, and then adds row after row of stitches, gradually extending at both sides according to the shape of the article. Having reached the required length of the flat part of it, she forms the heel by working about one inch from the edge, turning, working back to the edge, working the next row half an inch longer, turning back to the edge again and so on six to twelve times, depending on the size of the shoe. Having formed the other half of the heel on the opposite side she forms the piece of material she has made so far into a circle and continues stitching around this circle for the last twelve rows, thus forming the ankle part of the shoe. Making such an upper of average size and thread thickness takes about two days. The best Ābādeh *gīveh* are made from a fine cotton twine and have beautiful geometrical patterns consisting of small holes left in the course of stitching. They take much longer to make.

The second person involved in cloth shoe making is the sole maker (*pāreh-dūz, taḫt-kaš*). The soles (*taḫt*) are made from strong linen or cotton rags (*kohneh, latteh-kohneh*) that are cut into strips about 1 inch wide with a knife (*šafreh*) kept sharp on a lapping stone (*sang-e iskāf*). The strips are sized in a solution of gum tragacanth (*katīreh*), placed on a wooden block (*kondeh*), their edges turned over so that they meet in the center, and beaten flat with a handleless mallet (*mošteh*). Owing to the sizing the strips then stay folded and flat. Their length varies with the width of the sole. At the widest part of the sole each strip is about 5 inches long. When the strips for one complete sole are ready, the sole maker takes about a dozen of them at a time onto the block, and with a flat-pointed awl (*derafš-e šīveh*) he pierces flat holes through the center (Fig. 318) and through each side of the bundle of strips, about ½ inch from the edge. Next he prepares a number of hide strips of ½-inch width. They are made of cowhide tanned in lime. Like the cloth strips these leather strips are pierced with the flat awl, then placed aside to be used as reinforcements of heels (*pāšneh, naᶜlekī, pas-pīš*) and tips (*pūzeh, damāġeh*). When all this is completed, cloth and hide strips are threaded onto a strong hide lace (*dūvāl*) that runs right through the center of the sole. Likewise another pair of laces (*park*) is threaded through the holes near the edges. The sole maker uses a long and flexible awl (*sīḫ-e gerd*) for this threading. He pulls the hide laces tight with a pair of flat-nosed pliers (*gāz*) and then secures them by sewing them through the tip and heel hide reinforcements; then he cuts the sole to shape with a sharp knife. When the third cloth shoe craftsman, the actual shoemaker (*gīveh-dūz, gīveh-kaš, malekī-dūz*), takes the soles over from his colleague, his first job is to sew a strong hide welt (*kamar, doureh, bāneh, čarm*) around the edge of the sole (Fig. 319), piercing welt and sole with a heavy awl (*derafš, derouš, dorōš*). He makes sure that every stitch is taken around the edge lace previously inserted by the sole

Figure 318 Piercing the Cloth Strips

Figure 319 Cloth Shoe Soles

maker. During this operation the shoemaker keeps the sole straight by attaching a stick (*čūb-e poštband*) temporarily to the underside of the sole (right sole in Fig. 319). When the welt has been attached he places a wooden last (*qāleb*) onto the sole, slips the upper over the last (Fig. 320), and sews it against the welt. The holes for sewing are pierced into welt and upper with a short, round awl (*tīġ-gerd*). The overhanging ends of the welt are turned over the tip, sewn together and onto the upper with a needle (*sūzan*), thus forming a protection (*sangbar*) for the tip (center, Fig. 320). Similarly the welt ends at the back are sewn to the upper above the heel. There is a variety of cloth shoes that have a broad band (*šīrāzeh, kamar, baġal*) made by women with the same technique as the uppers sewn to the rim of the sole instead of the welt. The upper is then sewn on without a last (Fig. 321). Some cloth shoes have a narrow tip (*pūzeh bārīk*); others have a wider one (*pūzeh pahn*); better quality shoes are lined with cotton cloth (*kohneh, āstar*) and have a leather heel lining (*tūpāšneh*); others have reinforced toe caps (*pīš-panjeh*).

Because there is an almost unlimited supply of used car tires, many craftsmen now make cloth shoes with soles from such cut-up tires, a practice that has resulted in a marked decline of the craft. Many of the poorer peasants just buy a pair of such rubber soles and make the upper with thick cotton thread in the technique described above, starting with the first row of stitches around the edge of the rubber sole and adding row after row of stitches, shaping the upper as they go.

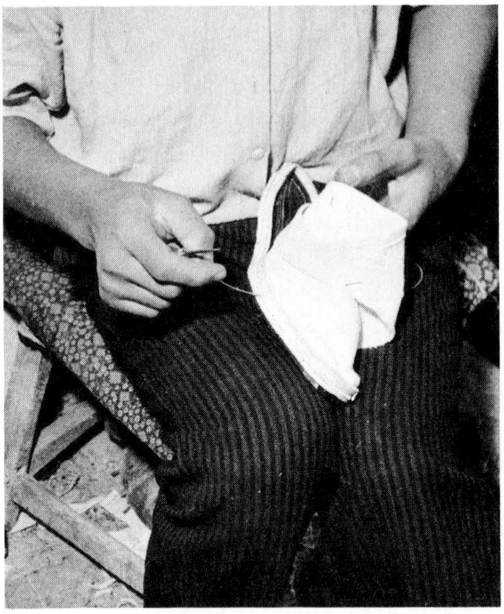

Figure 321 A Shoemaker Sewing Sole to Upper

Figure 320 Uppers and Lasts

Leather Crafts

Tanning and Leather Grinding

The use of leather is certainly older than spinning and weaving, and yet the technique of preparing the hides has not changed much. A historian of technology[83] claims for northern Europe "that leather techniques remained static from the earliest ancient times till the nineteenth century," and the same was the case in Persia until recently, when modern tanneries began to operate.

[83] C. Singer, *op. cit.*, Vol. 3, p. 753.

Medieval tanners were well known for the fine leather they produced. Ibn Ḥauqal, who visited Ḫorāsān in 950 A.D., praised the fine goat leather (*seḫtiyān*) made by the tanners (*dabbāġ*) of Gūrkān near Merv, whose products were sent all over the country.[84] Sir John Chardin classified tanning and leather craft as one of the "Mechanick Arts which the Persians know best," and he gave some details on the tanning of shagreen leather that Persia exported in his days (1665 A.D.) to India and the Near East.[85]

Today there are two ways in use for treating hides (*ḫām*, *čarm*), the preparation of sheep and goat skins into tawed leather (*čarm-e zāqī*) with alum and salt, and the tanning (*dabġ*) of cow, ass, and horse hides. The latter is done in the following steps:

1. *Soaking the Hides* (ḫāmrā āb zadan). Dried hides brought to the tanner from outlying districts have to be soaked in large watering pits (*houż*) for three to six days, depending on hide thickness and fat content. Hides bought locally (*čarm-e būmī*) from the skinner (*jellād*) at the abattoir (*qaṣṣāb-ḫāneh*) do not have to be watered.

2. *Liming and Depilation.* The dry hides, after having been sufficiently softened by the soaking, and the fresh unsoaked hides are placed in lime pits that are glazed earthenware vats (*lūleh-kaš*) let into the ground (Fig. 322). Quicklime (*āhak*) is sprinkled over the hides, and the vats are filled with water. After four to six days the lime water has opened the texture of the hides and softened the hair. The hides are taken out of the lime pit, and each one is hung over a wooden beam (*tīr*) and depilated (*ᶜorām-kārī*) with a special knife (*kārd-e ᶜorām*) that is kept sharp on a honing stone (*sang-e ᶜorām*).

[84] Ibn Ḥauqal, *op. cit.*, p. 221.
[85] Sir J. Chardin, *op. cit.*, pp. 267–269.

Figure 322 Liming Vats

3. *Swelling* (ārd-e jou kardan). Each hide, after the depilation, is transferred into another vat and sprinkled with barley meal (*ārd-e jou*). When a sufficient number of hides is in the vat it is filled with water, and a fermentation process begins that causes swelling of the hides to make them susceptible to the tanning agent, partly loosens superfluous flesh, and neutralizes the lime from the previous treatment. This process takes about 15 days in summer and 20 in winter. After the hides have been cured (*puḫtan*) they are taken out of the vat, each one is placed over an almost upright beam (*ḫar-e čūġ*), and any superfluous flesh is removed (*ḫāmrā dās kardan*) with a double-handled fleshing knife (*dās*, Fig. 323). That done the hides are placed back in the swelling vats for a second curing.

4. *Salting* (namak pāšīdan). When after three to four days the second swelling has been completed the hides are placed into round tubs (*qadaḥ*, Fig. 324), each hide being sprinkled with salt, and they are left there for three to four days.

5. *Tanning* (māzū-kārī). The hides are now ready for the actual tanning and are placed into deep, brick-built pits lined with wooden daubes (*goud-e čūb*, *sīleh*, center, Fig. 324). Each hide, when placed in the pit, is sprinkled with finely ground gall nuts (*māzū*) or the ground bark of the salam tree (*Acacia* spp.). The tanner has

Figure 323 Removing Superfluous Flesh

Figure 324 Salting Tubs and Tanning Pit (*center*)

the grinding done by one of his assistants on a hand mill (*dastās*, *ārčī*) similar to that used by the potter, or he can obtain these tanning agents from the bazaar where they are crushed and ground on an edge runner. The hides stay in the tanning pit for four to five days. They are daily turned over and trodden down again (*lāgad zadan*).

6. *Grinding* (kāšī-kārī). When the tanning is completed, the hides are dried in the sun (*ḫoškandan dar āftāb*) and then placed on a polishing board (*taḫteh*) supported by a trestle (*kursī*). With the flesh side up the hide is ground smooth with a pumice stone (*sang-e pā*).

7. *Dyeing* (rang rīḫtan). Dyestuffs such as *gel-e varz*, *jouhar-e golī*, and *ṣābūn-e safīd* are suitable for leather staining, and they are applied to the outside (*rū*) of the hide at this stage.

8. *Burnishing* (ṣaiqal zanī). For this final operation the hide is again placed on the polishing board and burnished by moving a highly polished stone (*ṣaiqal*, *mohreh*) over the surface under heavy pressure. In larger tanneries grinding, dyeing, and burnishing are done by the leather trimmer (*čarm-sāz*, *čarmgar*).

Fur Garment Making

A very useful garment for the cold Persian winter is a long sheepskin coat known as *pūstīn*. The skin is prepared as chamois leather, worn with the fleece inside. An important center for the manufacture of quality garments of this kind is Mašhad, but many regional bazaars too have masters working in this craft.

The main product of the fur garment maker (*pūstīn-dūz*) is the above-mentioned long coat, others are a short jacket (*nīmtaneh*) and a sleeveless vest (*jeleqeh*). In this trade the following stages are involved from the raw skin to the ornamented garment:

Between 20 and 30 sheepskins (*pūst-e gūsfand*) are treated at a time. For pickling one moistened skin is placed on the ground, fleece down, and about 12 ounces of coarse rock salt (*namak*) are sprinkled over it. The next skin is placed on top of the first one but fleece up and so on, pair after pair, forming a stack. After two days they are taken out into the yard and dried in the sun. Next day they are taken to the river or a water course on donkey back, and all surplus salt is washed away (*tar kardan*). Still wet, the skins are taken back to the shop where a mixture (*āš*, *ārd-ō-namak*) of barley meal (*ārd-e jou*) and salt (*namak*) has been prepared for the swelling process. The first skin is placed in a large earthenware vat (*ẓarf-e sefālīn*), again fleece down, after having been covered with the flour–salt mixture that has been thoroughly rubbed in (*mālīdan*). A second skin, after having been treated in the same way, is placed over the first one, leather down, and so several vats are filled with pairs of skins, and water is sprayed over them. For eight to ten days the skins are daily taken out, stretched (*kaš-ō-gīr kardan*) by hand in all directions, placed back into the vats and covered again with the wet mixture. From the eighth day on the master can tell from the stretching when the skins have matured (*rasīdan*). After the swelling they are taken out to the river again, are well washed, and are spread out for drying. Brought back to the shop they are sprinkled with the mixture and moistened for the second time, this time by spraying water over each leather side with a broom (*jārū*) before stacking them in pairs once more. They are left for two days, washed in water, and dried again. The skins are then stretched out on a work-bench (*taḫteh*) and scraped (*tarāšīdan*) with an iron scraper (*āhan*) to remove any superfluous flesh. When clean (*pāk*) the leather sides are sprinkled with the ground rind (*pūst*) of the wild pomegranate (*anār-e jangalī*), sprayed over with water, and the skins are again packed away in pairs, leather to leather, and kept wet. After a few days the rind is removed with a scraper, the skins are stretched, and fresh pomegranate rind is applied. After two days, when this rind is removed, the leather side of the skins has taken on a pale yellow color from the rind that at the same time acts as a mild tanning agent. Next the leather sides are rubbed with a mixture of sesame and castor oil known as lamp oil (*rouġan-e čerāġ*). The skins are finally dried in the sun and stretched several times over a sharp edge during the drying to soften them (*molāyem kardan*). Attention is then given to the fleece, which is combed (*šāneh kardan*) and beaten with a stick to remove any remnants from previous treatment. The master selects matching skins for each garment, cuts them (*borīdan*), and assistants do the hand sewing. Women take them over in contract work at home to decorate the garments with cotton threads in satin-stitch embroidery (*abrīšam-dūzī*). This name suggests that some of the embroidery has been done or may still be done with silk threads. The traditional color is yellow, but embroidery in other colors is also found (Fig. 325).

Figure 325 An Embroidered Sheepskin Vest

Packsaddle Making

One of the principal users of leather, the saddler (*zīn-sāz, zīngar, sarrāj*), has not been recorded, but a few details are available on the work of his humble brother, the packsaddle maker (*pālān-dūz, pālāngar, pālānī*). Since the pack horse and the donkey play an important role as beasts of burden, particularly in remote, roadless mountain areas, packsaddles are still much in demand. Horse hair and straw are packed around a wooden frame and covered with hand-woven woolen bagging and webbing. The sewing along the edges is done with an ordinary pack needle (*javāl-dūz*) that is pressed through with an iron palm (*kafī, kafdastī*) inside the hand. For the through-stitches holes are pierced with a heavy iron awl (*siḫ*) about 4 feet in length, and strong woolen cords are passed through the holes and taken up at the other end with an iron hook (*šāḫ*, foreground, Fig. 326). The horsehair and straw packing is beaten into position with a short, handleless iron mallet (*mošteh*) (left foreground, Fig. 326).

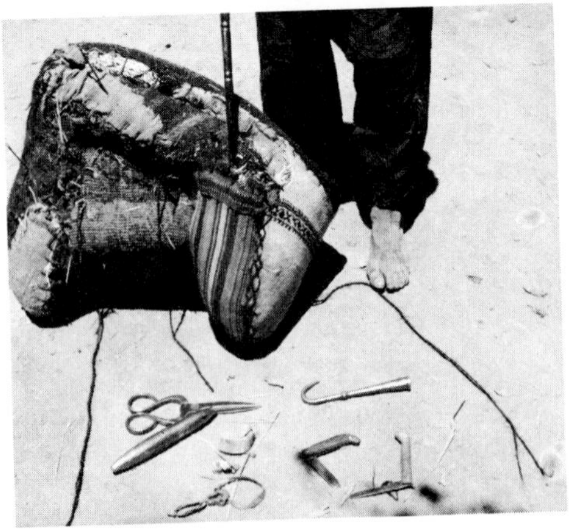

Figure 326 A Packsaddle Maker

Leather Shoe Making

It has been shown before that the cloth shoe was the footwear generally worn in Persia. Leather shoes are a later arrival, the trade being strongly influenced from Russia. At his best the shoemaker (*kaffāš, kafš-sāz*) works with Western methods and is therefore not interesting for the purpose of this study; at his worst he applies a hybrid technique of some traditional and some Western methods which becomes particularly poor in style when the soles are cut from disused automobile tires. With the increased use of leather shoes, the shoe repairer or cobbler (*kafš-dūz*) established himself as a new craftsman.

Making of Leather Buckets

A humble but quite busy craftsman in the bazaar is the maker of leather buckets (*dūl-dūz, dūl-sāz*). Large leather buckets (*dūl, dālī, dāleh*) are used to draw water from the well. They are cylindrical, made from the whole skins (*pūst*) of sheep or goats with the leg holes sewn up and a sewn-in round bottom. To give the bucket rigidity at the top, an iron hoop (*āhan-e dūl*) is sewn to it carrying the handle (*dasteh-ye dūl*). This craftsman also makes leather drinking-water containers (*dūlčeh-ye ābḫwọrī*), a peculiar feature in Persian houses. They consist of a tapered leather bucket (*mašk*) supported by three wooden feet (*čūb-e dūl*, Fig. 327) that are sewn to the bucket with leather lace, sometimes with colored lace to form a decorative edging (*maġzī*). When filled with water, the pores of the leather let a certain amount of water through, which evaporates and keeps the water inside the container cool. The container is closed with a wooden stopper (*sar-e dūlčeh, dar-e dūlčeh*). Both feet and stopper are supplied by the local wood turner and are often gaily painted.

Sieve Making

The women of the nomadic Koulī tribe, kinsfolk of the gypsies, specialize as sieve makers (*ġarbāl-band, ġarbāl-bāf*), whereas

Figure 327 A Drinking-water Container

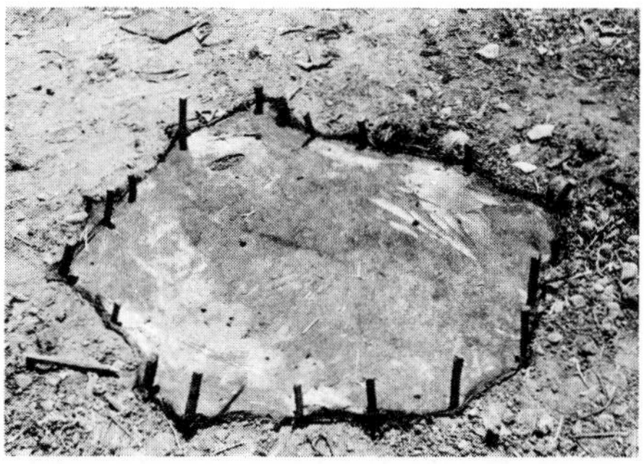

Figure 328 Drying a Skin in the Open Air

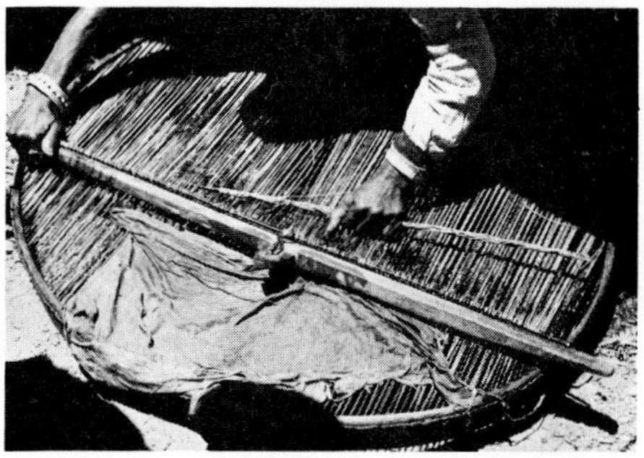

Figure 329 Warp and Heddle inside a Sieve Hoop

their men are well known as wandering blacksmiths and tinkers. For ordinary sieves (*ġarbāl*) the women clean sheep and goat skins in the open air and dry them by pegging them to the ground (Fig. 328). When dried the skins are rubbed with tallow to keep them pliable. Going around a skin with a sharp knife (*tīġ*), the women cut a narrow strip called *rūdeh* which they roll between hand and thigh, making it look like a gut. Only for very good sieves do they use genuine sheep gut (*rūdeh*). In the meantime their men have prepared wooden hoops (*kūm, kām*) with holes all around the edge. The women stretch a warp (*rūdī*) inside these hoops (Fig. 329), place an iron rod across it, and tie every second warp strip to it, thus forming a rod heddle. This heddle is attached to a wooden bar (*sīḫ-e bošak*) by means of an iron hook, and when turned over this bar lifts the rod heddle and forms a weaving shed. The weft strips are wound around an iron spit (*sīḫ-e dast*) that is inserted into the first shed. The strip is moved into place with a shed rod (*sīḫ*). For the next weft the wooden bar holding the rod heddle is turned forward, thus releasing the rod heddle; the shed rod is pushed forward and placed on the edge of the hoop, thus forming the alternate shed. During the weaving warp and weft are kept moist with a wet rag (*kohneh*). When the last weft has been put across, the rod heddle ties are cut and the leather strips dry and become very tight.

These sieves are made with coarse meshes (*ġarbāl-e dorošt*) or with fine ones (*ġarbāl-e rīz*) and are used for the sifting (*bīḫtan*) of grain, pounded plaster (*ġarbāl-e gač-bīzī*), or sand (*ġarbāl-e šen-bīzī*), besides many household purposes. The Koulī women also weave wire sieves (*ġarbāl-e sīmī*), mainly used for flour sifting. In that case they are called *alak*. The sieve wires are drawn by the men of the tribe from soft steel wire. When passing through towns and villages on their wanderings the Koulī sell these goods.

Figure 330 shows a sieve that is also made of leather strips but braided instead of woven. This type of sieve is commonly used in North Persia for grain sifting during harvest time.

Figure 330 A Braided Sieve

Making of Water Pipe Hoses

One more leather craftsman should be mentioned here, the maker of water pipe hoses (*nai-pīč*) who produces the flexible hose (*nai*) for the water pipe (*qalyān*) so commonly used for tobacco smoking. He first winds a thin cotton thread around a wooden stick that acts as a mandril. Next he winds a thick, twined cord over the cotton in the form of a screw thread. On this he glues, with fish glue, very thin parchment that has been soaked in water. Before it dries the craftsman winds another thinner twine over the parchment in such a manner that this twine presses the parchment between the threads of the cord underneath, thus forming the parchment into the shape of folding bellows. Before the glue sets, the thin cotton twine is removed and the flexible hose is taken from the mandril and hung up for drying.

Bookbinding

Before we come to the bookbinder's craft it seems necessary to explain that papermaking as a craft has been omitted because no paper has been manufactured in Persia for more than one hundred years. This is all the more regrettable as Persia played a key role in the transmission of the art of papermaking from China to the West. While the Achaemenians used clay tablets for writing up to the end of their empire through Alexander, it has been proved that the Parthians, from the second century B.C. on, wrote on parchment[86] for which they used the Greek name *diphthéra*, a word still alive in the Persian word for copy book, *daftar*. About 650 A.D. the Sasanians began to import Chinese paper made from the bark of the mulberry tree, but used it exclusively for important state documents.[87]

Although varying dates are given for the conquest of Samarkand and the commencement of papermaking there, it can be proved from Arab chronicles and is confirmed in Chinese annals that it was in July 751 when the ʿAbbāsid governor of Ḫorāsān sent his lieutenant Ziyād ibn Ṣāliḥ against two Turkish chieftains who had rebelled against the Moslems and had obtained Chinese military assistance. In the battle of Aṣlah on the Ṭarāz river the Turco-Chinese army was defeated, and among the prisoners of war were Chinese papermakers who were taken to Samarkand and encouraged to start a papermaking industry.[88] It is interesting to note

86 B. Laufer, *op. cit.*, p. 563.

87 *Ibid.*, p. 559.

88 R. Hoernle, "Who Was the Inventor of Rag Paper?" pp. 663 ff.

that the paper produced in Samarkand and later in every part of the Moslem world was not the mulberry bark paper first invented in China but another paper made from linen rags, hemp, and so-called China grass, also a Chinese invention made about 105 A.D.[89] Microscopic and chemical investigations carried out with early Samarkand paper have proved[90] that the Persian papermakers (*kāġaẕ-sāz*) never made mulberry bark paper. The same investigations also showed that the tradition carried through our historic reports on paper, viz., that the early Persian paper was made of cotton, is not true. No cotton fiber can be proved for any Islamic paper.[91]

Early Arabian chronicles confirm that for some time Chinese masters directed the paper industry of Samarkand before Persians took over. Already by 794 the first paper mill was erected in Baghdad, and it produced a fine paper, second only to that of Samarkand. Syria, Egypt, and North Africa were further stations in the spread of the industry, and in 1154 A.D. the Arabs established the first mill near Valencia in Spain,[92] and as late as 1390 the first paper mill began operating at Nuremberg in Germany.

The chemical investigations also proved that the Persian papermakers at Samarkand made an important contribution to paper technology by introducing paper sizing to make it more suitable for writing with ink and a reed pen. The size first used was made of wheat starch (*našāsteh*), later also size made from gum tragacanth or the boiled bulbs of asphodel was used.[93]

Regarding the history of bookbinding we are in the fortunate position of having three detailed descriptions of the bookbinder's craft. The oldest of them is by Ibn Bādīs (1031–1108 A.D.),[94] who had a practical knowledge of the processes involved in bookbinding. The second account is that of Qalqašandī, who died in 1418. He gives a detailed description of bookbinding materials and tools.[95] The most comprehensive is the book by Sufyānī, who wrote about 1619.[96] He was a master bookbinder himself and described his craft in full for fear that his apprentices might forget his teachings and neglect the craft.

Many technical aspects of these books have recently been critically investigated.[97] This and the writer's own records of the craft's present situation in Persia show that it has not changed much since the Middle Ages and that modern good hand binding even in the West is essentially the same if we disregard the use of paper-cutting machines.

The bookbinder (*ṣaḥḥāf, jeldgar*) obtains the sections (*jozv*) of the book (*ketāb*) from the printing press, aligns them (*bāham kardan*) in the right order, and puts them into a screw press (*tang, fešār*). The old press where two boards were pressed together with a tourniquet at each end has gone out of use. When sewing against cords (*mīl*) is intended, cuts are inserted with a saw (*arreh kardan*). For tape sewing, pressing and cutting are not required.

Sitting in front of the bookbinding frame (*dastgāh*) with cords or tapes in position, the bookbinder places a folded endpaper (*āstar, badreqeh*) behind the tapes and sews (*dūḫtan*) it onto the tapes, together with the first section. Sewing from

89 B. Laufer, *op. cit.*, p. 563.

90 J. Wiesner, "*Mikroskopische Untersuchungen alter ostturkestanischer Papiere.*" Vienna, 1902, pp. 9 ff.

91 J. Karabacek, "Das arabische Papier," pp. 43–50.

92 *Ibid.*, p. 40.

93 J. Wiesner, *op. cit.*, pp. 9 ff.

94 Ibn Bādīs, *ᶜumdat al-kuttāb.*

95 A. Qalqašandī, *Ṣubḥ al-ᶜaša.*

96 Sufyānī, *Ṣināᶜat tasfīr al-kutub* (*The Technique of Bookbinding*).

97 K. G. Bosch, "Islamic Bookbinding from the 12th–17th Centuries," pp. 41–82.

left to right for this section and returning for the second and so on, he completes the whole book, including another endpaper with the last section. This done, cords or tapes respectively are taken from the frame, and the work is put into a press for gluing (*časbīdan, serīš kardan*) of the spine. The glue commonly used for this work is leather glue (*serīšom*), boiled from leather scraps, or fish glue (*serīš-e māhī*), made by boiling the swimming bladder of the sturgeon. After drying (*ḫoškīdan*) of the glue the book is trimmed (*boreš dādan*) with a bookbinder's knife (*kārd, šefteh*). During the trimming, the edge to be trimmed is held in a trimming press (*qaid, gīreh*). In a few modern binderies the trimming is done with a guillotine (*māšīn-e boreš*). After this the headbands (*šīrāzeh, golābdūzī*) are glued to the ends of the spine. Next the binder cuts the cardboards (*moqavvā*) for the case (*jeld, rūyeh*) to size on a marble block (*sang-e marmar*). A variety of cover materials is commonly used. The cheapest is cloth binding (*sotūnak*) or embossed cloth (*gālingōr*). Next in quality comes half case (*abrī, jeld-e maᶜmūlī*), a type widely applied, consisting of a cloth cover and a leather spine. Valuable books are still bound as full leather case (*rūyeh-ye mīšeh, rūyeh-ye čarmī*). With a vegetable paste (*serīš, sereš*) made from the glutinous bulbs of *Asphodelus ramosus* or *Eremurus aucherianus* the case boards are glued to the tapes and the cover material, and endpapers are glued to the boards. Then dry decoration or tooling is applied to the case. In its simplest form it is blind tooling, i.e., pressing lines (*ḫaṭṭ andāḫtan*) into the cover material with a wooden lining tool (*maḫaṭṭ*) but without the application of gold leaf. A considerable number of books are gold-tooled (*ṭelā-kūbī*). Lettering (*ḥurūf*) and tooling brass (*gol-e kilīšeh*) are placed into a form (*gīreh*) and are warmed over a charcoal brazier. Meanwhile a thin coat of shellac solution (*lāk-e alcol*) is applied to the cover. The form is taken from the brazier, pressed onto a sheet of gold leaf (*varaq-e ṭelāʾī*), and the form is pressed onto the book case (*ḥurūfrā andāḫtan*) and beaten mildly with a wooden mallet (*mošteh*). Ornamental corners and center panels are applied in the same way. Rich embossing of the leather and the application of miniatures is no longer done to book cases, but has survived in the souvenir trade. Books of the past embellished in these techniques are kept in many of the great museums and bear witness to the high standard of the Persian bookbinder's craft.

Pen Box Making

A craft in some respects similar to that of the bookbinder and using some of his materials is that of the pen box maker (*qalam-dān-sāz*). His product is a box containing a small ink pot, several reed pens, and a penknife. The larger ones of these are made in papier maché (*ḫamīr-e moqavvā, ḫamīr-e kāġaẕ*) while the smaller boxes are made from layers of paper glued together (*kāġaẕ rūham časbāndan*).

For both processes the pen box maker has wooden molds (*qāleb*) that represent the inside of the pen container and the cover respectively. The papier maché mass (*ḫamīr*) is prepared by pounding paper (*kāġaẕ*) together with asphodel paste (*serīš, sereš*) in a stone mortar (*hāvan-e sangī*). The mass for about 100 boxes takes 2 to 3 days to pound (*kūbīdan*). First the molds are rubbed with soap (*ṣābūn*) on the outside, the soap from Qom being regarded as the best. Rubbing with soap (*ṣābūn kašīdan*) is done to prevent the papier maché or the paper from sticking to the mold. The pen box maker starts with the mold for the container (*zabāneh-qalamdān*) by applying the papier maché around the sides and the bottom of the mold. When the mass has dried on the surface he rubs it with a wooden burnisher (*mohreh*) to smooth and compress it. After further drying he applies a second layer of papier maché and treats it similarly. Now taking the mold for the pen box cover (*ṭableh, ṭableh-ye qalamdān, jeld-e qalamdān*), he applies papier maché, this time all around the mold, also in two stages. When the mass is completely dry he cuts the cover open with a special knife (*abzār-e qāleb-borī*). The cut (*kalleh-borī*) runs about 1 inch from one end of the cover and thus takes a cap off it. This cut, vertical along the sides of the cover, is executed in such a way that it produces either a semicircle (*nīm-dāyereh*) on top and bottom or follows a zig-zag line (*dahān-e aždarī*). The cut-off cap and the remainder of the cover are both withdrawn from the mold sideways, which is not difficult thanks to the effect of the previous soaping. The container is likewise removed from its mold and the cap is pushed over one end of the container and glued on. When the cover is pushed over the rest of the container it matches with the cap and closes the box.

For the manufacture of the smaller boxes only one mold, that for the container (*qāleb-zabāneh*), is used. After careful application of soap as described before, the pen box maker places a strip of paper around the sides of the mold and one underneath, folds (*tā kardan*) any overhanging edges (*zāviyeh*) over, applies asphodel paste, glues a second paper strip on, and so on, each time pasting a cut-off of the paper on his bench to keep count of the number of layers pasted on. After every three layers he beats (*fešār dādan*) the paper with the flat side of a file. The cuts (*āj*) of the file compact the moist paper and the paste. After that he burnishes the surface with a wooden tool. After 28 layers the gluing is completed and the work is left to dry. In preparation for the making of the cover the thoroughly dried paper surface is well rubbed with soap, and then the laying of the paper strips begins, this time covering the whole surface of the soap-rubbed core. As before there is beating and smoothing after every third layer, and with 28 layers the cover is completed too. When it is dry the master carefully cuts the end cap off in the same way as for the papier maché boxes, this time using a tool whose cutting edge is just as deep as the cover is thick so that he does not cut into the container underneath the cover. Cover and cap are then slipped off the core, the mold of the container is removed and the cap is glued to one end of the container as before.

When fully dried, both the papier maché pen boxes and the laminated paper pen boxes are varnished with a lacquer (*rouġan-kamān*). It is prepared by boiling one part of sandarac resin (*sandalūs*) in three parts of linseed oil (*rouġan-e bazrak*). Then miniature paintings and ornaments are applied (*naqqāšī kardan*) to the cover in oil paint, and a final varnish for the protection of the decoration completes the work.

5

AGRICULTURE AND FOOD-TREATING CRAFTS

Ever since the time when, seven to eight thousand years ago, the Neolithic settlers began to grow crops and raise sheep, goats, and cattle on the Plateau, Persia has been primarily an agricultural country. Today the value of Persia's agricultural output is about four times that of its entire oil industry,[1] and 75 per cent of the total population of 21 million work on the land. But only 10 per cent of the country's area is at present cultivated, about 40 per cent is used by seminomadic tribes for grazing, 15 per cent is forested, and the remaining 35 per cent is desert and waste land.[2]

Climatic Conditions

The factor dominating the peasant's work is the climate, which in Persia is one of extreme contrasts.[3] During winter the general air circulation over the northern hemisphere brings a series of low pressure centers from the Mediterranean and the Black Sea over the Iranian Plateau. These depressions cause most of the annual rainfall. They are often combined with warm southerly winds that result in the melting of snow in the highlands. Many of the country's river beds carry water only at this time of the year. Between two depressions, however, the pressure rises fairly high with a clear sky and warm days but extremely cold nights, particularly in the desert basin. If, however, a depression in the south attracts cold air masses from Turkmanistan and Siberia that enter through the gap between the Alburz ranges and the Hindukush, the temperature may drop to

[1] Mohammed Reza Shah Pahlavi, *Mission for My Country*, p. 195.

[2] *Ibid.*, p. 196.

[3] G. Stratil-Sauer, "Iran, eine länderkundliche Skizze," p. 180.

−20°F during the day in Ḫorāsān and Āẕarbaijān, or in South Persia to +14°F. Snow in the mountains is regarded as the most important water storage. Perennial snow can only be found on the higher ranges of the Alburz, on a few peaks near Tabrīz, and on the Zagros ranges west of Iṣfahān. Most of the northern half of the Plateau is covered with snow for several months, in some of the mountain ranges up to 12 feet deep. In the center of the Plateau the snow is about a foot high for 4 to 6 weeks and in the south snow, if any, may only stay for a day.

Spring and summer weather develop when the large high pressure zone over the Azores and the South Atlantic grows and air masses are shifted over Northwest India, Balūčistān, and Southern Arabia, where they warm up and pass over the Iranian Plateau. The daily temperature rises gradually until it reaches between 100 and 115°F by the end of May. When between June and September high pressure develops over Central Asia, the famous "wind of the hundred and twenty days" blows over Ḫorāsān and Sīstān day and night with unabated intensity. Warming up as it comes south, it makes the Lūt desert one of the hottest spots on earth. During the summer months the relative humidity is rarely more than 4 per cent in most parts of the Plateau, with a few occasional showers in the south from the northern edge of the Indian monsoon. During October the period of the depressions moving eastward marks the beginning of winter.

Seen in the form of climatic regions Persia can be divided into the following five zones:

The northern slopes of the Alburz and the Caspian provinces may have rain at any time of the year when southward moving, rain-laden clouds are prevented by the mountains from entering the Plateau. The annual rainfall in the Caspian provinces averages 80 inches. On the Plateau the climate is primarily determined by the altitude. At 8,000 feet above sea level in the north and at 10,000 feet in the south begins what the Persians call the *sarḥadd*, i.e., the upper limit, a region of purely alpine pasture during summer. It is above the tree line and is covered with snow throughout winter.

Quite the opposite to this is the *garmsīr*, i.e., the hot region or lowlands, comprising the province of Ḫūzistān, the littoral of the Persian Gulf and the mountain slopes running parallel to it up to about 2,500 feet altitude. The *garmsīr* never has any snow; it has sufficient pastures in winter and allows some farming early in spring before its inhabitants, in seminomadic fashion, move to the *sarḥadd* into their summer quarters (*yailāq*).

Between these two extremes there is the *sardsīr*, i.e., the cool region or uplands. It has snow and frost in winter for some months and moderately warm summers. At the lower reaches of the *sardsīr*, viz., below 4,500 feet in the north and 6,000 feet in the south, there is a zone of subtropical climate in which most of the important towns of the Plateau are situated. There one finds moderately cold winters with snow for a few days or weeks and very warm but dry summers. The typical oasis cultivations on the alluvial flats between mountain ranges, such as Qom, Iṣfahān, and Šīrāz, belong to this zone. Annual rainfall on the Plateau averages 10 inches in the north, gradually decreasing to 6 inches in the south.

Agricultural Crops and Notes on Their History

By far the most important crop grown in Persia is wheat (*gandom*), followed by barley (*jou*). Annual production of the two is about 3 million metric tons. Archaeologists have established[4] that agriculture began on the Iranian Plateau before it developed on the irrigated lowlands. Charred grains found at the excavated Neolithic village of Geoy Tepe near Lake Urūmiyeh[5] prove that wheat of the variety *Triticum aestivum* must have been grown more than 5,000 years ago. Wheat and barley are both indigenous to Persia, where they still grow wild, and their cultivation is believed to have spread from there to Mesopotamia, Egypt, and Europe.[6] The wheat variety *Triticum durum* is the one mainly grown today. With its high gluten content it is well suited for the Persian type of bread that forms the staple food throughout the country.[7] Both wheat and barley are grown in dry-land cultivation in Āẕarbaijān, Ḫorāsān, and the high valleys of the Zagros mountains. They are sown there soon after the melting of the snow and depend on the spring rains for maturity. In the south both grains are grown on irrigated land. For dry regions barley has a great advantage in that its roots deeply penetrate the soil in search of moisture. Barley is mainly used as animal fodder, though some is grown for export and for the country's small brewing industry. Rye (*čādār*, *čavdār*, *čoudār*, *dīvak*) is grown in the high valleys of the Alburz mountains and is used for bread and fodder. Rice (*berenj*) is grown on irrigated land, principally in the Caspian provinces. The variety grown there is known as *aṃbārbū*. Some is grown in southern Fārs under the name of *čaṃpeh*. Only grown to the extent of 0.4 million metric tons per annum, it has never become a staple food although it is much enjoyed by those who can afford it, mainly in the form of *pilāv*. Historically, too, rice is a relative newcomer. No word for it is contained in the Avesta, and Aristobulus, one of Alexander's companions during the conquest of Persia, wrote in 285 B.C. that rice was cultivated only in Babylonia, Susiana, and Bactria but not on the Plateau.[8] This negative evidence is confirmed by the early Chinese traveler General Čaṅ K'ien, who reported about rice cultivation only in Ferġana and Parthia, then the easternmost provinces of Persia. Later Chinese travelers reported that during Sasanian times Persia had no rice, and only from Islamic times on has rice been grown in Persia, its cultivation then being practised, according to early Islamic geographers and historians.[9] Other grain crops (*ġalleh*) are millet (*arzan*), introduced from India, and maize (*ẕorrat*), a latecomer from America via Europe.

Sugar (*šakar*) is refined in Persia from beet (*čoġondar*) and cane (*ḫūz*). At present the greater part of the annual sugar production of 100,000 tons is extracted from beet grown on the Plateau, introduced early this century by Europeans together with modern refineries. Only a small part of the sugar production comes from the cane of Ḫūzistān, but its cultivation has been modernized and is expanding again after a lapse of several centuries. Of Indian or Southeast Asian origin, sugar cane played an important role in Sasanian Persia. This is first mentioned by the Armenian archbishop and historian Moses of Chorene, who wrote in 462 A.D. during the reign of the Sasanian King Peroz: "In Elam near Gundešāpūr precious sugar is grown." A story by Ibn Ḫalliḫān containing an account of how King Ḫosrou I (531–579 A.D.) was given a cup of sugar cane juice to drink[10] is further evidence

[4] E. E. Herzfeld and A. Keith, "Iran as a Prehistoric Centre," pp. 43–44.

[5] T. B. Brown, *Excavations in Azarbaijan, 1948*, p. 50.

[6] R. Ghirshman, *Iran*, p. 35.

[7] Already so in Achaemenian times; cf. Herodotus, *The Histories*, iii.22.

[8] B. Laufer, *Sino-Iranica*, p. 372.

[9] *Ibid.*, p. 373.

[10] N. Deerr, *The History of Sugar*, p. 68.

that sugar cane must have been known at that time. A Western source is the account of the Roman emperor Heraclius, who mentions sugar among the valuables taken as booty after the capture of Dasteragad, the palace of Ḫosrou II, in 627 A.D. The Chinese Sui-šū annals,[11] which were written during the time of Ḫosrou II (590–628 A.D.), attribute the refining of sugar syrup into hard sugar to the Sasanians. Although the Chinese had annual tributes from Tonkin and Cambodia paid in sugar cane, they had regular imports of hard sugar from Persia.[12] The seventh-century writer Moṅ-Šen praised Sasanian sugar consumed in Szechuan. However, when the Chinese wanted to learn the secret of sugar refining they sent a mission to Maghada in India in 647 A.D. to study the sugar boiling process. The Indian method was then adopted by the cane growers of Yaṅ-čou.

The early Arabian historians and geographers Ibn al-Fakil (about 900 A.D.), Al-Istaḫrī (about 950 A.D.), and Al-Idrisī (1099–1154) all mention two regions in Persia where sugar cane was grown, Makrān, which is part of Balūčistān, and Ḫūzistān, meaning "land of the sugar cane." Considering that Makrān has been an important link between the Indus valley civilization and Mesopotamia it is not hard to see how the sugar cane traveled from India.

The Arab conquerors took great interest in cane growing and sugar refining, and they disseminated both cultivation and refining methods to Palestine, Syria, Egypt, North Africa, and Spain.[13] The Persian sugar industry declined after 1300 A.D. and remained unimportant until it was revived in our times. It will now expand further with the introduction of modern irrigation and more dams in Ḫūzistān.

The fodder plant lucerne (*aspist, yōnjeh*) was already an important crop in ancient times, especially for the feeding of horses. It seems to be indigenous to Persia, and its history is so well established that it is of interest to follow its spread over the world. The earliest mention known to us is in a Babylonian text of about 700 B.C.,[14] where it appears under its Persian name, *aspastī* (meaning "horse fodder"), on a list drawn up by the gardener of King Marduk-Balidin. In 424 B.C. the Greek dramatist Aristophanes[15] mentions lucerne as horse fodder under the name of Mēdikē, and Strabo says that the Greeks call this excellent fodder this name because it grows in abundance in Media. In the Sasanian land tax schedule of Ḫosrou I the tax on lucerne is the highest one on any crop, a sign of its high valuation.[16] The Arabs who had obtained the plant (together with its name, arabicized *isfist* or *fisfisa*) from the Persians, spread the cultivation of the new plant throughout the caliphate as far as Spain, from where it reached northern Europe and later the Americas.

We are fortunate in having full records of how this useful plant came to China. The desire to obtain the taller and stronger Persian horses led the Chinese emperor Wu (140–87 B.C.) to send trade missions to Persia at regular intervals. Their leader, the general Čaṅ K'ien, soon found out that the imported horses did not thrive as well on Chinese fodder as on Persian lucerne. He carried some of it home on his next mission. In 126 B.C. it is reported that wide tracts of land near the Imperial palace were covered with the

11 B. Laufer, *op. cit.*, p. 376.
12 *Ibid.*
13 *Ibid.*, p. 377.

14 C. Joret, *Les Plantes dans l'antiquité*, Vol. 2, p. 68.
15 Aristophanes, *Opera*, v.606.
16 B. Laufer, *op. cit.*, p. 209.

new plant, which from then on is mentioned in many annals.[17]

Clover (*haft-čīn, šabdar*) is another fodder plant and is extensively grown in the valleys of the Alburz mountains.

Of the many fruit plants that grow in Persia the grapevine (*raz, mou, tāk*) is perhaps the oldest and best known. Plant historians seem to agree[18] that the grapevine is at home in the region south of the Caucasus, in Armenia, and North Persia. Although the grapevine was already known in Egypt and Mesopotamia by 3000 B.C., Greek and Roman writers associated wine drinking first with the Persians.[19] The same Chinese general Čań K'ien who introduced lucerne to his homeland wrote after he had seen the eastern provinces of Persia, viz., Fergana, Soġdiana, and Bactria: "They have wine made from grapes, and the wealthy store wine in large quantities up to ten thousand gallons which keeps for several decades. The Persians are as fond of wine as their horses relish lucerne."[20] The envoys took grapevine cuttings to China, and later travelers noted extensive plantations near the Imperial palace. Other annalists record the importation of different varieties of grapevines from Persia and Syria.[21] Today fifteen varieties of grapes are grown in the province of Fārs alone, having a wide range in taste and appearance. The first to come to the market in May are the ruby grapes (*yāqūtī*) with berries tasting like muscatels; the last of the year are the *mehrī*, ripening in the month of *mehr* (September–October). Economically the most important are the sultana grapes (*kešmešī*). Other varieties are *rīš-e bābā* (father's beard), *šast-ᶜarūs* (sixty brides), *ṣāḥibī* (the lordly), *nabātī* (the confectionery), *mādar-ō-bačeh* (mother and child, on account of the different sizes of berries in the same bunch), *askarī*, *mesqālī*, *ḥalīlī*, *munegā*, *kalāčeh*, and *šīrāzī*.

Another instance of royal interest in the development of agriculture is a letter from Darius the Great to his satrap Gadates in which he exhorts him to transplant eastern plants and trees to Asia Minor and Syria.[22] It is therefore not surprising to find a number of fruit trees introduced from China into Persia, thence to the West. The peach (*Amygdalus persica*) and the apricot (*Prunus armenica*) were the earliest to go this way. It is known that the Chinese were the first to cultivate these fruits, and it is assumed that their transmission westward followed the silk route. Theophrastus of Alexander's staff, who gives so many details on other plants, does not mention them,[23] but they appeared in Persia during the second century B.C. and were later grown in Armenia, from where the Romans took them to Greece and Rome during the first century A.D. The Persians do not have original names for these fruits, but as they so often do with things imported, apply a descriptive name, viz., *šaft-ālū*, meaning "large plum," for the peach and *zard-ālū*, meaning "yellow plum," for the apricot. A similar development took place at the Indo-Scythian court in the Panjab where Chinese hostages introduced the peach, known there to this day as *čīnānī*, "fruit from China," and the pear, *čīnārājputra*, "crown prince of China."[24] Later there was, so to speak, a return of compliments when in 647 A.D. the Persian province of Soġdiana presented the T'ang emperor T'ai Tsuń with plants of the golden apricot, a variety

[17] *Ibid.*, p. 211.

[18] A. de Candolle, *Origin of Cultivated Plants*, p. 192.

[19] B. Laufer, *op. cit.*, pp. 223–224.

[20] *Ibid.*, p. 221.

[21] *Ibid.*, p. 228, and Grumm-Grjmailo, "History of the Introduction of the Grape Vine to China."

[22] R. Ghirshman, *op. cit.*, p. 182.

[23] B. Laufer, *op. cit.*, p. 539.

[24] *Ibid.*, p. 540.

that had been developed there over the centuries and whose fruits were said to be as big as goose eggs.[25]

A fruit tree that spread from Persia to Europe on the one hand and to China and India on the other is the almond tree (*bādām*), still known in Tibet under its Persian name *ba-dam* and in China as *p'o-tan*.[26] The pistachio tree (*pisteh*) is another native of Persia and was already observed there by Theophrastus.[27] Galenus and Dioscorides, both second-century A.D. scientists, saw it in Syria; Vitellius had introduced it into Italy in the first century A.D. while his friend Flaccus Pompeius had brought it to Spain. During the eighth century A.D. the fruit became known in China as the "hazelnut of Persia." Similar spreads and developments can be shown for the fig (*anjīr*)[28] and the pomegranate (*anār*), the latter having been introduced into China by General Čaṅ K'ien.[29]

All these fruits still play an important role in the diet of the people and the economy of the country, together with dates (*ḫormā*) and a number of vegetables (*baql, baqūlāt*), including a kind of lettuce (*kāhū*), beans (*lūbiyā*), onions (*piyāz*), and garlic (*sīr*). Other crops comprise a variety of pulse (*ḥabūbāt*) such as peas (*noḫōd*) and broad beans (*baqaleh, bāqelā*), both known in China as of Persian origin.[30] Of the seeds producing edible oil we must mention here cotton seed, poppy seed, linseed, rape, mustard, and sesame. The latter used to be the principal source of edible oil in Babylonia,[31] apparently introduced there from India, and became known in Persia during Achaemenian times. Sesame was introduced into China together with flax during the second century B.C.[32]

Tea and tobacco as crops are of more recent origin, but Persia grows enough of both to satisfy its own requirements.

Irrigation

Considering the annual rainfall on the Plateau as outlined before, it is astonishing that agriculture is possible at all. Areas with similar climatic conditions, e.g., the "dry heart of Australia," Lake Eyre, and inland South Australia, have no agriculture whatsoever. That it is attempted at all in Persia can only be explained by the existence of much more favorable conditions in earlier times and a gradual drying up, mainly through deforestation and loss of fertile soil by erosion, circumstances that forced the inhabitants to devise a number of ingenious methods for preserving enough water to grow sufficient food, although today this may often only be at subsistence level. From detailed descriptions of many geographers and historians of the ninth to the eleventh centuries it is evident that the country then must have had a flourishing irrigated agriculture. Much of it was destroyed during the devastating invasions by the Mongols and Turks, and it is only now that Persia has begun to reconstruct its agriculture with modern methods.

Already in the Avesta, the sacred book of the ancient Persians, irrigation (*ābyārī*) was a good deed in the eyes of Ahūra-Mazda: wasteland and deserts were described as haunted by Ahriman and his demons. The Achaemenian kings granted exemption from land tax for five generations to all who made land cultivable through the construction of an irrigation system.[33] From Sasanian times on,

[25] *Ibid.*, p. 379.
[26] *Ibid.*, p. 406.
[27] *Ibid.*, p. 246.
[28] *Ibid.*, p. 410.
[29] *Ibid.*, p. 276.
[30] *Ibid.*, p. 305.
[31] Herodotus, *The Histories*, i.193.
[32] B. Laufer, *op. cit.*, p. 288.
[33] H. H. von der Osten, *Die Welt der Perser*, p. 11.

throughout the Islamic period, there have been many laws, regulations, and customs governing the building of irrigation channels and water supply systems, their maintenance, and equitable distribution of the available water.[34] Modern governments since Reżā Šāh have spent considerable amounts of the budget and foreign aid on the building of new dams, on the reconstruction of old ones, and on mechanical pumping to overcome limits imposed by the level of the water available. In doing this, great care has been taken not to rely solely on modern engineering schemes but to improve and extend the traditional system,[35] which is still so highly valued that the Soviet Union, for example, has paid particular attention to the "Fergana System" for the planning of irrigation work in the Kazakestan Republic, formerly an East Persian province.[36] The magnitude of the system may be illustrated by the fact that there are 85 principal channels between Panjkand and Denjiz in Transoxania alone, with a total length of 1,600 miles.

Technically, irrigation water may be obtained from dams (*band, band-e āb, sadd*), underground channels (*qanāt*), and wells (*čāh*). In describing the water supply systems in this order we follow traditional Islamic classification.

Irrigation by Dams

Most of the rivers (*rūd*) in Persia do not carry water all the year round. Throughout history dams and weirs have therefore been built to store the surplus of spring water and raise it to a level where it can be taken directly to the fields in supply channels (*jūy, jūb*). Some of them are still functioning, although generally at a reduced storage capacity, being badly silted up. Figure 331 shows the dam at Band-e Amīr in Fārs, built about 960 A.D. by the well-known Buyid ruler ʿAżod ud-Douleh, probably on Achaemenian foundations.[37] The historian Muqaddasī wrote

> that the ruler brought engineers and workmen to the place to build this dam in stones set in mortar, reinforced by iron anchors which were set in lead. Upstream and downstream the river bed was paved for several miles and the supply canals extended for over 10 miles, serving 300 villages in the Marv-e Dašt [the fertile plain of Persepolis]. Ten water mills were built close to the dam whose crest was wide enough to allow two horsemen abreast to ride across it.[38]

Figure 332 is a present-day aerial view of this dam and its canal net. During his travels General Houtom-Schindler saw five major dams upstream from Band-e Amīr, among them the one of Ramjird that was almost as large as Band-e Amīr. Five more were downstream, the last one, Band-e Qaṣṣār, only a few miles from the salt marsh. An imposing structure, even by modern standards, is the Band-e Farīdūn in Ḫorāsān, 40 miles southeast of Mašhad, a solid dam in stone masonry built during the eleventh century to a height of over 120 feet and a length of 280 feet, the crest having a width of 24 feet. A great number of minor dams can still be seen in the valleys of several of the smaller rivers.

Another feature in irrigation is the use of weirs across the major rivers. The one often mentioned by historians is the Šāẕūrvān, built by the Sasanian king

[34] A. K. S. Lambton, *Landlord and Peasant in Persia*, pp. 210 ff.

[35] Mohammed Reza Shah Pahlavi, *op. cit.*, p. 209.

[36] M. A. Savickaja, *Ukazatelʾ Literatury po irrigacii i melioratii Sredne-Aziatskich republik i Kazakstana.*

[37] A. Houtom-Schindler ("A Note on the Kur River in Fars," pp. 287–291) thinks that the original dam was already built under the Achaemenians, an opinion orally confirmed to the writer by Dr. E. F. Schmidt, the archaeologist who investigated the structure in 1936.

[38] Al Balkhi, *Description of the Province of Fars*, trans. G. Le Strange, p. 65.

Figure 331 The Dam at Band-e Amīr in Fārs

Figure 332 Band-e Amīr, the Head of an Irrigation System in the Marv-e Dašt (*courtesy of the Oriental Institute, University of Chicago*)

Figure 333 Remnants of a Sasanian Dam at Dizfūl

Šāpūr with the aid of prisoners of war after the victory over the Roman emperor Valerian in 260 A.D. The builders used granite blocks set in mortar and anchored, as at Band-e Amīr, with steel clamps cast in with lead. It took three years to build while the Kārūn river was diverted through two bypass channels. It raised the water to the level of the city of Šūštar, which lies on a hill. This dam is still partly in use (Fig. 333) and is listed for reconstruction under the government's Seven Year Plan.

The Zāyandeh river is banked up at Iṣfahān by a structure known as *pol-e ḫwājū*, built by Šāh ᶜAbbās II (1642–1666) on the foundations of an earlier weir. It is a combination of a weir with sluice gates, flood arches above these that are high enough even at flood times, and a permanent roadway. A masterpiece of stone masonry and fine brickwork, it is ornamented with inlaid colored tiles and is completely intact.

The Ṣafavid Šāh Ṭahmāsp attempted to divert the headwaters of the Kārūn river to the course of the Zāyandeh. The springs of the two rivers are separated only by a narrow mountain ridge. The work involved the construction of a dam 100 feet high and 300 feet long to bank the Kārūn river up and a deep cut into the mountain ridge on a base length of 6,000 feet. The work continued under ᶜAbbās the Great and his son ᶜAbbās II, but was abandoned after the latter's death, when only 100 feet of the cut into the mountains had been completed.[39] Recently this work, known as the Karkunān scheme, has been completed with modern engineering methods and on a wider scale with an increased intake, with the result that the water

[39] A. K. S. Lambton, *op. cit.*, pp. 213, 215.

supply for the Iṣfahān oasis will be satisfactory for a long time to come.

A rather original irrigation system is widely used in Ḫorāsān. There the smaller rivers and water courses in the alluvial flats of mountain valleys are banked up from time to time with low level dams built from stone and earth, and the water is led into manmade ponds (*ḫandaq*, *goudāl*, Fig. 371, p. 269). These river beds are dry through most of the year and carry water only in spring or after heavy rain. The series of dams and ponds along their courses serve the double purpose of preventing the formation of devastating torrents and of storing the water in the ponds from where it is led into the fields for watering the spring and early summer crops.

The "Qanāt" System

While dams and weirs are methods for water conservation known in many countries, it is the *qanāt* system that is a special feature of Persia. *Qanāt* are underground channels dug into the alluvial fans rising from the valleys toward the slopes of the mountains. A head well (*madār-čāh*) or a gallery of them tap the aquifer (*āb-deh*) at a depth between 50 and 300 feet and, by using less slope for the conduit tunnel (*pusteh*) than that of the surface of the fan, water is eventually led to the open (Fig. 334). The length of such a *qanāt* from the head well to the outlet may be only a mile or two; often it is 10 miles[40] and occasionally much more, e.g., the *qanāt* from Māhūn to Kermān is 18.3 miles long.[41]

The *qanāt* system is used all over the Plateau, and throughout Balūčistān[42] and Afghanistan, where it is known as *kārīz* or *kahrīz*, often as *qah* in place names, such as Qah-Jāristān or Qah-Davījān. It is also known in Pakistan, where conditions are similar to those in Balūčistān, as well as in Soviet Russian Transoxania, Fergana, and Sogdiana, and still further east as far as the Chinese oasis settlements of East Turkestan, and westward in Iraq and neighboring Syria under the name *fuqarā*. In

[40] P. H. T. Beckett, "The Soils of Kerman, South Persia," p. 29.

[41] A. Smith, *Blind White Fish in Persia*, p. 142.

[42] A. Gabriel, *Durch Persiens Wüsten*, pp. 239, 247.

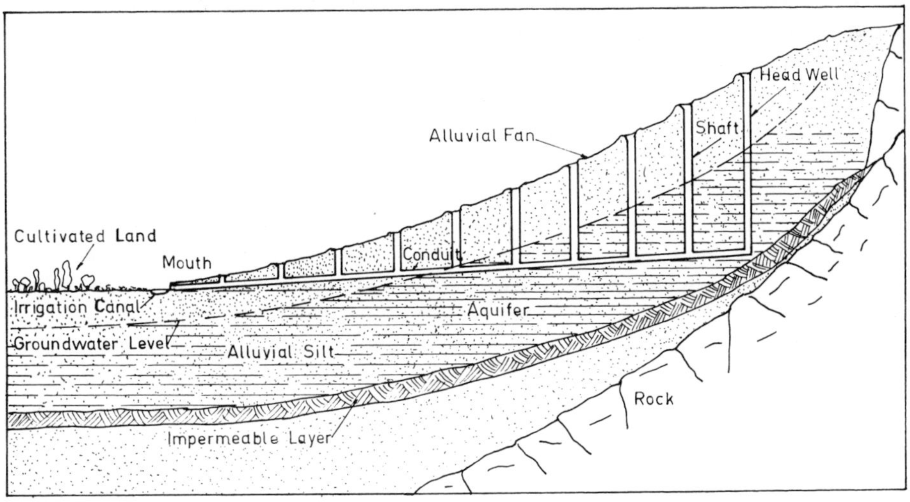

Figure 334 Sectional View of a Qanāt

Arabia and Yemen it is called *šarīz*. The system spread from the Near East to North Africa, Spain, and Sicily in Roman times, followed by a second wave of activity in this field after the Arabic conquest. In Tunisia and Algeria a number of oasis settlements are still irrigated by these *foggariur*; in the Sahara region of Taut alone, 1,200 miles of them are in full working condition.[43] The *qanāt* are known as "Persian work" to the Touareg, who live on the southern fringe of the Sahara.[44]

Roman participation in the westward spread has led some observers to the conclusion that the Romans invented the system. This theory, however, is not tenable in the light of so many written records now available. We know that the Assyrian king Sargon II (722–705 B.C.) claims that he learned the secret of tapping underground water during his campaign against the old mining country of Urartu around Lake Urūmiyeh in Northwest Persia.[45] His son, King Sennacherib (705–681 B.C.), undertook a great irrigation scheme around Nineveh which included underground conduits, according to the commemoration plaque at the exit. The same king built a true *qanāt* for the water supply of Arbela.[46] Recent translations of Egyptian inscriptions[47] revealed the nature of some irrigation work carried out by the Persian admiral Scylox in the oasis of Kargha after Darius I had conquered Egypt. The inscription says *inter alia* that Scylox applied the Persian method of irrigation to bring water to the oasis in underground conduits. From then on the Egyptians were no longer hostile toward the conquerors, built a temple of Ammon, and conferred the title Pharaoh on Darius. Remnants of these *qanāt* that still function have been investigated, and it appears that they tap the underground water table of the Nile and lead the water into the oasis, which is a depression 100 miles away from the Nile. Polybius gives some more details on the *qanāt* in his description of the war between Antiochus the Great and the Parthian king Arsaces III (212–205 B.C.):[48]

> For in that tract of Media there is no water appearing on the surface, though there are many subterranean channels [*hyponomoi*] which have well shafts sunk in them, at spots in the desert unknown to persons not acquainted with the district. A true account of these channels has been preserved among the nations to the effect that, during the Persian ascendancy, they granted the enjoyment of the profits of the land to the inhabitants of some of the waterless districts for five generations, on condition of their bringing fresh water in; and that there being many large streams flowing down Mount Taurus, the people at infinite toil and expense constructed these underground channels through a long tract of the country in such a way that the very people who use the water now are ignorant of the sources from which the channels were originally supplied.

The Greek geographer Megasthenes saw the system operating in North India where government overseers inspected the conduits, ordered maintenance work, and supervised water distribution.[49] The first historian on technology, Vitruvius (80 B.C.), gives us much technical detail on the *qanāt* system.[50]

When the Caliph Hišām in 728 A.D. built a garden palace some distance away from Baghdad, water for it was obtained through a *qanāt*.[51] Likewise, when the Caliph Mutawakkil (847–866 A.D.) constructed the water supply for the newly

[43] M. A. Butler, "Irrigation in Persia by Kanats," p. 70.

[44] H. Goblot, "Le rôle de l'Iran dans les techniques de l'eau," p. 48.

[45] R. J. Forbes, *Studies in Ancient Technology*, Vol. 1, pp. 153 ff.

[46] *Ibid.*, Vol. 2, pp. 21–22.

[47] *Ibid.*, Vol. 1, p. 153, and M. A. Butler, *op. cit.*, p. 70.

[48] Polybius, *Historiae*, x.28.

[49] R. J. Forbes, *op. cit.*, Vol. 1, p. 153.

[50] P. Vitruvius, *De Architectura*, viii.6.3.

[51] K. A. C. Creswell, *A Short Account of Early Muslim Architecture*, p. 120.

built residence at Samarra he must have relied on Persian engineers.[52] Recent excavations there showed that the water was obtained from ground water of the upper Tigris and conveyed to Samarra in *qanāt* conduits totaling 300 miles in length. The governor of Ḫorāsān, ᶜAbdullāh b. Ṭāhir (828–844 A.D.), found that the "traditions of the Prophet" did not refer to the *qanāt* system and the distribution of water, and asked the jurists of the province to write a book on the subject. Known as "Kitāb-e Quniy," it was still in use during the eleventh century.[53] A technical treatise written about 1000 A.D. has fortunately survived to our day and has been republished recently.[54] Written by Moḥammad ibn al-Ḥasan al-Ḥāsib, author of several other books on engineering and mathematics, it gives surprisingly good details on the finding of the water level, instruments for surveying, construction of the conduits, their lining, protection against decay, and their cleaning and maintenance.

Although the Persian *qanāt* system is of such venerable age it is to this day by far the most important source for water. Recent estimates by a United Nations expert[55] show that 75 per cent of all water used in Persia comes from *qanāt*, and that their aggregate length exceeds 100,000 miles.[56] The city of Tehrān alone has 36 *qanāt*, all originating from the foothills of the Alburz 8 to 16 miles away with a measured flow of 6.6 million gallons in spring and never below 3.3 million gallons in autumn.[57] An eminent authority on groundwater[58] is convinced that the *qanāt* system undoubtedly is the "most extraordinary method to develop groundwater."

Qanāt *Construction*

As considerable capital outlay is involved in the building of a new *qanāt*, and as the future flow of water, determining any financial return, depends on so many factors, it is customary for a landowner to engage an expert surveyor for the preparatory work. This expert, usually a former *qanāt* builder with great field experience and a keen power of observation, carefully examines the alluvial fans from which the *qanāt* is to draw its water during autumn, looking for traces of seepage on the surface, often only for a hardly noticeable change in vegetation, and decides where a trial well (*gumāneh*) is to be dug by a team of *qanāt* builders (*muqannī, kahkīn, čāh-ḫū*). They set up their windlass (*čarḫ*, Fig. 335)

Figure 335 A Winch Bringing the Spoil to the Surface

[52] F. Krenkow, "The Construction of Subterranean Water Supplies during the Abbaside Caliphate," p. 23.

[53] A. K. S. Lambton, *op. cit.*, p. 217.

[54] *Inbāt al-Miyāh al-Ḫafīa* (*The Bringing to the Surface of Water*). See F. Krenkow, *op. cit.*, p. 24.

[55] R. N. Gupta, *Iran, an Economic Survey*, pp. 46–50.

[56] E. Noel, "Qanats," p. 191

[57] M. A. Butler, *op. cit.*, p. 71.

[58] E. W. Bernison, *Ground Water*, p. 124.

on the upper slope of an alluvial fan, and two *muqannī*, working with a broad-edged pick (*kolang*, *kaland*) and a short-handled spade (*bīl-e kār*), dig (*ḥafr kardan*) a shaft about 3 feet in diameter. The spoil (*ḫāk*, *gel*) is placed in large leather buckets (*dūl*, *čarm-e gāv*) and two laborers on the surface haul them up and empty them in a heap (*karvar-čāh*) around the mouth of the shaft (*sar-e čāh*). The leather buckets, taking about 60 pounds of spoil, are kept open at the top by a strong circular iron hoop (*čaṃbar*, *čaṃbal*) suspended from an iron hook (*golāb*).

The trial well is sunk until the *muqannī* reach the aquifer (*āb-deh*). They proceed slowly from the top (*sar-sū*) of the aquifer until they reach the bottom (*zīr-sū*) of the water-bearing stratum, usually characterized by an impermeable layer of clay or sedimentary calciferous conglomerates. For the next few days the inflowing water is hoisted up in the leather buckets and the quantities are noted, while at the same time any depression of the aquifer is observed. This helps the surveyor to decide whether they have reached genuine groundwater (*āb-e ḫarī*) or just some water trickling in from a local clay or rock shelf. This so-called *āb-e ʿaraq-e zamīn* would be of no value. If necessary more trial wells are dug to find a genuine aquifer or to determine the extent of the one already found and its yield. The shaft with the highest yield and yet with its bottom sufficiently high above the fields to be watered is then chosen as head well (*madār čāh*). In some cases all trial wells are later linked with a conduit, thus forming a water-yielding gallery.

For the next step, the determination of the course, gradient, and outlet of the underground conduit, the surveyor is consulted again. A long rope is let down the head well to the water level, and a mark is made on it at surface level. Looking toward the proposed mouth (*darkand*, *maẓhar*) of the *qanāt*, he marks a point about 30 to 50 yards away from the trial well for the next ventilation shaft (*čāh*, *mīleh*), where a laborer is placed with a stave. Using a level (*tarāz*), the surveyor measures the fall on the surface and puts a second mark on the rope. The length of this rope from the lower end to this mark indicates the required depth of this second shaft. Although some surveyors are satisfied by extending a string between the head well and the spot for the next shaft and regard it as being horizontal when water splashed against its center no longer runs along the string one way or the other, leveling instruments are used for more important work. Already in the *kitāb-e quniy*, a tubular water level and a large triangular leveling device with a plumb are described for this kind of work.[59] Thus proceeding from each point of a future ventilation shaft to the next one, the surveyor marks the drop of surface level on the rope each time until he reaches the lower end of it. Thus he has reached the point on the surface, even with the water level of the head well. For the mouth of the *qanāt* he now chooses a place on the surface below the level point but still above the fields. He then divides the drop from the level point to the mouth by the number of proposed ventilation shafts and adds this amount to the previously surveyed depth of each shaft. In this way he determines the gradient of the conduit, which is usually 1 in 1,000 to 1 in 1,500. Too much gradient would mean too rapid a speed of flow and result in excessive washout and damage to the conduit.

After completion of the survey, a number of guide shafts, about 300 yards apart, are made under the supervision of the surveyor. Then the rope with the marked length of each vertical shaft is handed over to the *muqannī*. He now begins to work

[59] F. Krenkow, *op. cit.*, pp. 28–30.

with his assistants by driving the conduit (*pusteh*, *kūreh*) into the alluvial fan, beginning at the mouth. To protect the latter from storm-water damage it is often carefully reinforced with a stone lining (*sangāneh*, *sang-čīn*, Fig. 336), the lined end (*haranj*) being 10 to 15 feet long. The first section of the work takes place in the dry stratum (*ḫošk-e kār*), viz., above the natural water table. Figure 337 shows several teams of *qanat* builders at work: two *muqannī* are digging at the head of the conduit (*pīš-kār*), the spoil made by them being hauled to the surface by their team mates through the nearest shaft. They keep the conduit straight by sighting over a pair of burning oil lamps. A second team is busy sinking another ventilation shaft. At the extreme left is one of the finished guide shafts dug by the surveyors.

The conduit measures about 3 by 5 feet. When it passes through reasonably hard soil (*dum*) or well-packed coarse conglomerate, the work can proceed fast, but if the *muqannī* strikes soft, friable soil (*šūrat*) he is working under an unsafe roof (*bad-dum*), and baked clay hoops (*nai*, *nār*, *gum*, *gūm*, *kabal*, *kaval*, *kavul*, *kūl*) have to be brought down for lining. They are oval in shape, 2 by 4 feet and about 8 inches deep (Fig. 338), and are packed in position with gravel and broken hoops. The loose soil may be of the sandy type (*riḫvai*, *masteh*) or a soft clay soil (*rūst*). In each of these cases the conduit has to be continued as a lined stretch (*nārestān*) until better soil is met. Collapsing roofs (*gusain*) are the greatest danger in the *muqannī*'s work. If they meet a rock or a bowlder during their progress they have to build a diversion tunnel (*kungūrt*, *baġal-bur*), and after its completion they have to find a new bearing, an operation in which they show a good deal of skill, partly relying on their sense of direction, partly listening to the noises made by the diggers of the nearest ventilation shaft. During the work they

Figure 336 The Mouth of a Qanāt

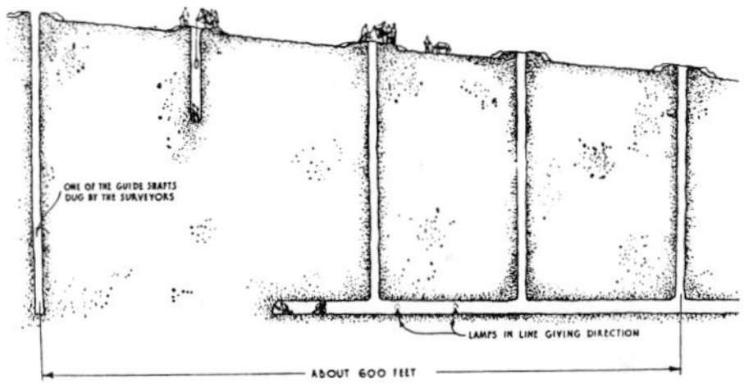

Figure 337 Stages in the Construction of a Qanāt (*from A. Smith,* Blind White Fish in Persia, *reproduced by permission of the publishers, George Allen & Unwin Ltd., London*)

Figure 338 Qanāt-Lining Hoops

carefully watch their oil lamps (*čerāġ-e rouġanī*), as these are the best indicators of poor air and vapors (*dam*), going out long before a man is in danger of suffocating. When the workers enter the aquifer they face another danger, viz., a sudden flow of water (*ġarq-e āb*) from a water-filled vein in the subsoil. Therefore, when working in this area they proceed slowly to prevent a sudden break-through. Similar care is taken when approaching the head well, which is often emptied before the break-through. But if a *muqannī* misjudges the distance and taps the full head well he may be washed away at the moment of break-through. It is for all these reasons that *qanāt* are often referred to as "the murderers." Nobody will ever force a *muqannī* to go into a *qanāt* if he thinks that it is his unlucky day, and he always says a prayer before entering.

When the head well has been reached it will soon become obvious whether a continuous flow can be maintained, the *qanāt* then being called *qahrī*, or whether the water runs only a short time in spring (*bahār-āb*) or is depending on heavy rains (*āsmān-negāh*). In many cases it is possible to construct a branch (*qanāt naḫ*) into another alluvial fan, a practice saving the duplication of the *qanāt* from the branch point to the mouth. Sometimes it is necessary to correct a level conduit (*pasgod*). Before a *qanāt* is handed over to the owner the craters of spoil around the tops of the shafts are carefully arranged so that no storm water running down the surface may enter the *qanāt*, causing great damage. Sometimes these craters are protected by chimney-like hoods (*kelilai-band*) that prevent water from entering but let enough air in for ventilation. All the *qanāt* need constant attention. Owing to the continuous flow, silt (*ẕarat*) is washed out from the aquifer and the conduit walls and is deposited on the floor of the conduit. Another cause of trouble is the occasional caving-in of the roof and the blocking of the flow. So for a good deal of the year the *muqannī* is occupied with cleaning work (*lat-rōbī, lā-rōbī*) and repairing.

Two recent observers[60] investigated the cost and concluded that a medium length *qanāt* of about six miles requires $13,500 to $34,000 to construct and, allowing 0.5 per cent for maintenance, gives a return in crops and sale of water of 10 per cent. Two larger *qanāt* of 10 and 15 miles respectively cost $90,000 each and yielded returns of 15 and 25 per cent. The considerable variation is due to differing local conditions, yield of aquifer, depth of head well, etc. Ten to 20 gallons of water per second could be regarded as an average yield; 50 gallons per second would be the flow in a number of well-planned and well-maintained *qanāt*; 110 gallons per second is an exceptional yield, and has been measured in spring.

Water Distribution

The distribution of irrigation water, especially that of *qanāt* water gained after so much effort, is regulated by custom and law, often going back to pre-Islamic times and early Islamic codification.[61] Even if the water belongs to a single landowner—by no means always the case—it has still to be distributed equally among the tenants. The cycle during which water is allocated is usually divided into a number of shares (*firzeh, šabāneh-rūz*), corresponding to the number of tenants participating in it. The cycle starts with the beginning of the agricultural year, i.e., early October, and whoever obtains the first allocation has the right to obtain water (*ḥaqq-e āb*) again when everybody else has had his share and

[60] P. H. T. Beckett, "Qanats Around Kerman," p. 56, and E. Noel, *op. cit.*, p. 199.
[61] A. K. S. Lambton, *op. cit.*, p. 217.

the cycle starts again. The actual watering time for each tenant depends largely on the amount of water available and on the ability of the soil to absorb and hold the water.[62] If a *qanāt* has a high yield the water is often split into different channels and led to different users simultaneously. In this case the *qanāt* water is first led into a distribution basin (*maqsam*, *gūšiyeh*, *ḥouż*) where the outlet side is divided into ten equal gaps by a number of squarely hewn stones (*dastak*). Since the basin is deep the water loses its speed and turbulence, so that the same amount of water passes through each gap. This quantity, the tenth of the total, is referred to as *sang-āb* and corresponds for example in Šīrāz to 160 gallons per minute and in Tehrān to 215 gallons. Depending on his rights or arrangements with the owner, each peasant is allocated one or more "stones" (*sang*) of water, which is led to his plot through an open channel. This system is known as *pāšūreh*. In regions where the share (*sahm*) of water allocation (*taqsīm-e āb*, *taqsīm kardan*, *lāt kardan*) does not vary, the whole width of the distribution basin (*ḥouż*) is dammed up by a hewn stone weir (*lāt*). Several partition walls (*dastak*) begin at the weir (Fig. 339), so that the width of the orifices is proportional to the allocated share. The division of water for the region of Sehdeh west of Iṣfahān, to quote an example, has not changed since the time of Šāh ᶜAbbās (1587–1629 A.D.) and is 8 shares for each of the villages of Dastgerd and Parvār and 9 shares for Karton. The orifices at the rim of the weir (*lab-e ḥouż*) are 8 spans wide for each of the first two villages and 9 spans for the last one. In Āẕarbaijān and Ḫorāsān another system is operating. Here the outlet of the basin is formed by a stone slab or a heavy wooden board into which a number of holes of uniform size has been drilled. The holes can be closed with wooden pegs, and the amount of water flowing through such a hole is called *bast*. As usually several *bast* are allocated to one recipient, a larger unit is introduced for the counting, the *finkāl*, one *finkāl* equaling 10 *bast*.[63] The time during which the water is allocated varies. In some cases the peasant obtains water during 24 hours (*sahm*). This period may be subdivided into smaller units called *dāng*, 12 *dāng* corresponding to 2 hours, one *dāng* therefore being 10 minutes. In other districts the *sahm* is divided into 120 *finjān*, the latter unit thus being equal to 12 minutes. Still other time units in use are a *fain*, 20 minutes, a *sabū* or *jurreh*, both locally varying between 8 and 11 minutes. In each case these short times are measured (*tašteqeh kardan*) with a kind of hourglass in the following way. The water bailiff (*mīr-āb*, *āb-māl*, *āb-bargardān*, *ābgar*, *lāvān*, *pākār*, *qāsem*, *qāsem-āb*, *bārāndār*), who supervises the distribution from a hut near the distribution basin, has a large bowl (*kūzeh*, *tašt*) filled with water near him on the floor. When he begins to time he places a small dish (*taštak*, *piyāleh*, *finjān*, *finkāl*, *peing*) on the surface of the water so that it floats. Water gradually enters this dish through a small hole (*sūrāḫ*, *lūbeh*) in its

Figure 339 A Water Distribution Weir

[62] *Ibid.*, p. 219.

[63] E. Wiedemann, "Zur Technik und Naturwissenschaft bei den Arabern," p. 309.

bottom until it eventually sinks down with a noise. This marks one time unit. As most customers are allocated a number of time units, a pebble is transferred from one jar into another each time the dish has gone down. When the last pebble has been transferred the customer's time is up and the water is directed to another channel. In other areas the water allocations are so determined as to irrigate a plot of a certain size during 24 hours, e.g., one *jarīb* or 32 square yards. The office of water bailiff is an important one, as he must have the trust of all concerned. It is often hereditary[64] or the bailiff is appointed by the village head man (*kadḫodāh*). In some districts he is elected each year from among the peasants, or the whole distribution is left to the peasants, and only in years of water scarcity do they appoint a bailiff.[65] The remuneration for the bailiff is usually a certain share of the crops of each villager. In other cases the landowner allocates to him a certain share of water free of charge, whereas the peasants obtain their water under a crop-sharing arrangement with the landowner. In districts with extensive irrigation there are often overseers (*sar-mīrāb*, *mādī-salār*, *sar-tāq*) appointed to have control over a number of bailiffs. In case of any dispute these men may refer their quarrel to a district overseer (*mobāšir*) or they have their case decided by a flow-measuring expert (*moṣaddeq*, *mojaddeh*).

Wells and Cisterns

The description of water conservation in arid Persia would not be complete without mentioning two further methods, viz., animal- and man-operated wells and storage cisterns. They do not provide as much water as rivers and *qanāts* do,[66] but they supply or supplement the needs of homes, small orchards, and garden plots, and in dry years even save the crops of larger holdings.

Wells

In most of the alluvial plains of the Plateau, where the majority of towns and villages are situated, the level of the underground water table varies between spring and autumn but it rarely dries up. In Iṣfahān its level averages only 15 feet below the surface, in Šīrāz about 50 feet, and in Yazd and Kermān 150 to 200 feet. Many houses and gardens have their own well (*čāh*, *čāh-ābī*, *āb-kašī*) built by a professional well sinker (*čāh-kan*), whose work is similar to that of the *qanāt* builder. In the Caspian provinces, where the water level is high and the soil can become rather soft in heavy rains, the wells are usually lined with logs of wood and the water is lifted with an earthenware jar (*kūzeh*) attached to a pole (*gerd-e ḫālī*). On the Plateau, however, wells are unlined except for the last 2 or 3 feet near the top. In the fields such a well is usually equipped to be operated by two water drawers (*āb-kaš*) and two animals, oxen or mules, and is called *gāv-čāh* or *gou-čāh*, *gāčeh*. It has two brick-built pillars (*sotūn*, *jarz-e čāh*) above the well mouth (Fig. 340), or just two heavy upright posts (*čūb-e sarḫak*), connected by a wooden scaffold (*māšūn*, *pūreh*). Two pulleys (*čarḫ*) run on axles (*masrī*) attached to the scaffold. They have a wooden hub each (*gelū*) from which two rows of spokes (*parreh*) radiate. Boards, morticed over the spoke ends and tied to them with strips of rawhide (*zeh*), form the circumference of each pulley, over which two ropes (*band*, *ṭanāb*, *ṭā*) run into the well. The ropes are made of cotton, in southern Fārs of the fibrous bark (*parīčeh*) of the palm tree or the fibrous thin stems of certain rushes (*ḫong*).

[64] A. K. S. Lambton, *op. cit.*, p. 222.

[65] *Ibid.*, p. 223.

[66] One per cent of all irrigation water, according to the *Oxford Regional Economic Atlas*.

Figure 340 The Mouth of a Water Well

The well end of the main rope (*ālat-e bālā*) is attached to a hook (*ḥalqeh*) and a ring (*čambal*) carrying a wooden cross (*jūġ*) from which a large leather bag (*dalv-e ābkašī, dūl-ābkašī, dūl-e ābī*) is suspended. The bag has a capacity of about 15 gallons and runs out into a narrow spout to which the auxiliary rope (*ālat-e zīr*) is attached. A draft animal is attached to the other end of both ropes by means of a breast harness (*žī, gelōʾī, zī-berevān*). A runway (*gāv-rāh, gou-rō, gou-čū*), beginning at the well head, descends at an angle of about 20 degrees (Fig. 341). When the animal walks up the runway the bag is let into the well; the auxiliary rope, being a little shorter than the main rope, lifts the spout up and holds it in that position while the bag runs into the well over a pair of guide rollers (*qaltaq, qaltāq, bērak*, lower foreground, Fig. 340). While the bag fills with water the water drawer lifts the animal's harness so that it can turn round, and he then drives it down the slope, thus lifting the full bag from the well. When the bag has reached the surface the auxiliary rope draws the spout over a stone basin (*mambeh, ḥouż, čāhrak*) in front of the well, and the bag empties itself into it (Fig. 340). At that time the animal has reached the end of the runway where two mangers (*āḫereh, āḫor*) are built-in that are filled with fodder (Fig. 342). The animal is allowed to eat a little hay while the bag empties. The water drawer places a small pebble from one bowl into another for counting, turns the animal again and walks up the slope with it. As the weight of the rope would draw the harness over the animal's head, the man takes over with a smaller harness (*pošteh, bazdarak*) that runs from his shoulder or waist to the rope end. Leaning back the man is increasingly assisted by the rope's weight during the ascent. As soon as man and animal have reached the well head they turn round again while the bag fills for the next run. Two hundred and fifty

Figure 341 The Runway of a Water Well

Figure 342 The Lower End of the Runway

runs for each man would be a good day's work; at 15 gallons per bag this represents 7,500 gallons, just enough to water a number of plots growing summer crops (*ṣaifī-kārī*) in rotation.[67]

A similar type of well, though hand-operated (*čāh-dastī*) with only a single rope, a pulley, and a bucket, is used in southern Fārs for the water requirements of the household. There is no runway but sufficient standing space under the pulley to draw the rope. The pulley is fastened on either a scaffold or a rafter if the well has a little protecting roof. A more comfortable way of lifting well water for the household is the windlass (*čarḫ-e čāh*), shown in Fig. 343. Here the water drawer sits on a stone bench, pulling the horizontal bars (*dastak, bām*) of the windlass toward himself with his hands and pushing the opposite ones away with his feet at the same time. The windlass is similar to the one used in the building trade and by the *qanāt* builders. Its iron axle (*māsūn*) runs through the center of a wooden shaft (*dīrak*) and is supported by two wooden bearings (*jā-ye māsūn*) on top of the well column. The rope (*band-e čarḫ, sāzū, band-e āb-kaš*) is usually made of cotton, carrying a much smaller leather bucket (*dalv, dūl*) that the water drawer empties into a stone-built basin (*ḥouż*) under his seat. From there the water is led either into the garden or into the cistern of the house.

Figure 343 A Household Well with Windlass

[67] A windmill of the type commonly used for boreholes in Australia would do the work without the efforts of two men and two animals.

Cisterns

In an endeavor to store as much as possible of the precious water while it is available, many cisterns have been built throughout the country that serve a number of purposes. Almost every house has a storage tank (*āb-ambār*) in its basement. It is built of fired bricks and lined with waterproofed mortar (*sārūj*), a mixture of lime, sand, wood ashes, and the seed of rushes. This tank and the traditional pond (*ḥouż*) in the garden of almost every Persian house are filled from the *qanāt* whenever the householder has his turn. In dry years the needs of house and garden must often be supplemented by well water.

Surplus rain water is often led into huge cisterns (*birkeh, burkeh, burqā, istaḫr*), domed circular structures (Fig. 344) 50 to 70 feet in diameter and reaching 15 to 20 feet, often more, below the surface. In some cases such a cistern is supplied from the

Figure 344 A Cistern near Naʾīn

Figure 345 A Persian Wheel Operating at the Bank of the Indus River

spring surplus of a *qanāt*; in others an underground spring discharges into it. Famous in early Islamic times was the tank in the city of Istaḫr near Persepolis built by the Buyid ruler ᶜAżod ud-Douleh (949–983 A.D.). The historian Ḥamdullāh Mustoufī[68] tells us in the Nuzhat-ul-Qulūb that the insertion of bitumen-soaked canvas between masonry and the rendering made the walls impermeable, a rather modern approach to the problem. The basin was so deep that 67 steps led down to its floor, and in one year when 1,000 men used the water the level dropped only by one step. Several rows of columns in the tank supported a roof so that the water was protected from the effects of the weather. The English traveler John Fryer[69] was quite impressed by many of the cisterns he saw in 1672. He said that some of them were built by the charity of well-meaning people, and others were constructed at the "common charge." His countryman Thomas Herbert[70] saw a cistern at Band-ᶜAlī in southern Persia of which he said that it was as deep as the span of its vault and that its water kept sweet to the last bucket.

The Ṣafavids built an interesting storage basin, the Šāh-göl, near Tabrīz. It is a square of 330 yards size partly carved into the rock of the mountain against which it leans, partly built of stone walls, and it is about 6 yards deep with a small island pavilion in the center. Empty during the winter, it fills with the melting snow from the mountain in spring. Not only is the fertile valley below thus protected from spring floods, but the peasants obtain a regular water supply for their fields from it while the governor of Āẕarbaijān enjoys the cool nights in the pavilion when the city nearby becomes unbearably hot in summer.

Water lifting devices so well known in Egypt, Mesopotamia, Pakistan, and India, such as the *šadūf* and the Roman *noria*, in Pakistan and India to this day called the "Persian wheel," are no longer in use on the Plateau but are to some extent in the plains of Ḫūzistān. Figure 345 shows such a wheel on the bank of the Indus river. They were used in eastern Ḫorāsān in historic times. The files of the ancient irrigation office (*dīvan-e mā*) at Merv[71] describe mule- or camel-driven pot wheels (*sāqiyeh*, *nāᶜūra*) and also river-driven mills (*ᶜarāba*, *dūlāb*, *doulāb*) with water-lifting

[68] G. Le Strange, "Mesopotamia and Persia under the Mongols in the 14th century," p. 131.

[69] J. Fryer, *A New Account of East Indies and Persia*, p. 168.

[70] W. Foster, *Thomas Herbert's Travels*, p. 52.

[71] E. Wiedemann, *op. cit.*, pp. 307 ff.

buckets attached to them. It is interesting to note here that the Persian name *doulāb* spread with the Arabs as far as Spain and Italy where these river-driven mills are still in use.[72]

Agricultural Methods

Most Western observers claim that agricultural methods in Persia are extremely primitive. Yet the writer would not like to join the chorus of those condemning everything traditional and advocating wholesale introduction of Western methods. The reasons for this are twofold. On the one hand any improvement in agricultural method must be preceded by a thorough yet wisely planned reform of land ownership and the abolition of absentee landlordism.[73] On the other hand, every step in the introduction of new techniques must first be tried out locally on a small scale because methods that are proven in moderate climate countries are not necessarily applicable to the conditions in Persia with its hot and dry climate, poor soil, and unusual irrigation systems. Experiments carried out in western Afghanistan under conditions similar to those in Persia indicated that relatively small modifications of traditional plows could already improve yields considerably,[74] while on the other hand the introduction, before World War II, of powerful crawler tractors with disk plows used for deep tillage in sugar beet cultivation in the Marv-e Dašt region in Fārs at first had disappointing results until over a number of years the implements had been adjusted to the local conditions.[75] While admitting that there is a wide scope for improvement it should be realized from the following that the Persian peasant has done remarkably well with the means at his disposal. For the historian of technology it is quite exciting to see methods extant that have in all probability changed little since Neolithic times.

Tillage

Although the animal-drawn plow is generally used in Persia, digging by spade is quite common even in large orchards, in vegetable cultivation, and, in some districts near Iṣfahān, Yazd, and Kermān, for field tillage. The market gardeners around the larger cities claim that the spade provides a better turning over of the soil and burying of the trash. They dig in springtime when nothing else is to be done, and there would not be much work for draft animals for the rest of the year. For the digging by spade of the wheat fields in central Persia there seem to be different reasons. It is true that the soil there does not yield enough to feed men and animals as well. A deeper lying reason seems to be the fact that many of the cultivators there are Zoroastrians for whom the bovine is a sacred rather than a laboring animal. Besides the spade the peasants in this region often use a pointed iron pick (*kolang*) to break up the soil.

There is a surprisingly large variety of spades (*bīl*), apparently developed for the varying conditions. The one from Šīrāz (No. 1, Fig. 346), has a triangular blade (*kaf-e bīl, kap-e bīl*) that easily penetrates the hard soil with its pointed tip (*bīl-nōkī*). It has a forged-over socket (*lūleh-ye bīl, damāģeh*) and is fixed to the handle (*dasteh*) by a pair of wedges (*gōveh*). Pushed over the handle, above the wedges, is a wooden

[72] R. J. Forbes, *op. cit.*, Vol. 2, p. 47.

[73] Mohammed Reza Shah Pahlavi, *op. cit.*, pp. 195–216, and A. K. S. Lambton, *op. cit.*, pp. 391 ff.

[74] G. F. Hauser, "Comparison of the Afghan Plough and Tillage Methods with Modern Implements and Method," p. 75, and P. H. T. Beckett, "Tools and Crafts in South Central Persia," p. 145.

[75] The writer's own observations from 1936 to 1941.

footrest or tread bracket (*čūb-e pā*, *čūẖ-e pā*, *taẖteh-pā*). The spade of Yazd (No. 2, Fig. 346) is very much longer, square-tipped, and has turned-over edges (*bīl-nōkī*) that act as footrests. The Iṣfahān and North-Persian spade (No. 3, Fig. 346) is pointed with curved reinforced sides and turned-over upper edges. The spade of Gīlān and Māzandarān (No. 4, Fig. 346) has a wide round cutting edge well suited to penetrate the soft soil of the Caspian region.

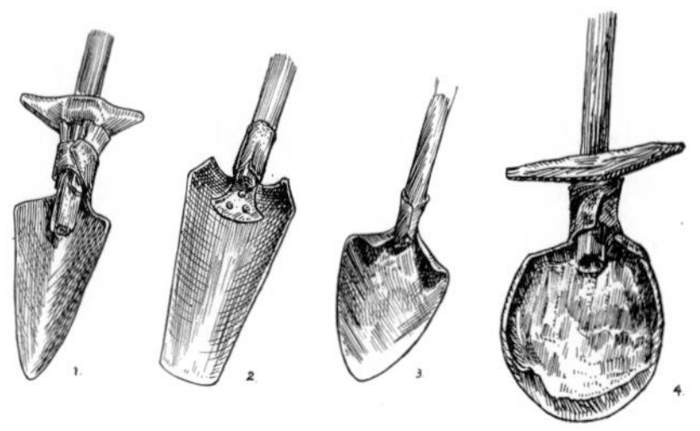

Figure 346 Types of Spades

These are the principal types of digging spade (*bīl-e zamīn-kanī*). The spade used in irrigation work (*bīl-e āb-yārī*), to open and close the supply channels, is broad and short, similar to the one shown last. When digging (*zamīn kandan*, *bīl kašīdan*) in wet clay soil, the peasant (*dehātī*, *kešāvarz*, *rustār*, *zārī*[c]) cleans the blade from time to time with a wedge-shaped wood (*bīl-pākkon*) that he carries behind his waistband. In March and April one can often see cultivators working side by side in groups of three and more, driving their long-handled spades into the soil with a kick, swinging the handle back, and turning the soil over, all in perfect rhythm to the shouting of one of them. To prevent the kicking foot from becoming sore or to protect the soft sole of their cloth shoe, many peasants wear a kind of wooden sandal (*taẖteh-pā*) on the foot with which they kick the spade (Fig. 347). A particularly large hoe (*tīšeh*) is found in the Hamūn depression in Zābolistān. It con-

Figure 347 Digging with a Spade (*note foot protection board*)

sists of a blade (*sar-e tīšeh*) 12 inches wide and 14 inches high that is riveted onto an iron bar (*gulījān*). The center of this bar is forged into a socket (*mohreh*) that holds a wooden handle 3 feet 6 inches long. Sometimes used for tilling on small holdings, this hoe's main purpose is the digging of irrigation channels (*jū-kārī*, Fig. 348).

Figure 348 Working with Hoes in Zābolistān

Mattocks (*kolang, koland, kaland*) are little used except for the clearing of brush roots in the preparation of new land. One with two opposing and crossed edges (*kolang-e dō-sar*) is particularly useful for this kind of work.

Plowing

Nearly all Persian plows are of the chisel or nail type. The soil is just broken up and lifted; no mold-board is provided, nor is there a twisted share to cause a turning-over of the soil. They all have a long, rigid plow beam to which a yoke (*jot, jüt, jed, jūġ, jīgō, kalāf-sar, yō*) is hitched by means of a strong loop (*jīn, hojang, hūyang, halešt, jūġān, balk, ūjambar*) made from donkey hide (*pūst-e olāġ*). This loop runs through a hole (*sūrāḫ, sūrāḫ-e parvāʾī, ulūkeh*) or over a peg (*parang, talk, talkeh, kalk, samar, hameh-kaš*). In the province of ʿArāq the yoke has an iron ring (*ḥalqeh*) that engages in an iron hook (*razā*) attached to the plow beam. This joint (*ḥalqeh-razā*) is more durable than the rope sling. For the plowing with a pair of bullocks (*gāv, varzā-gāv, varzū*) a double yoke is used (Fig. 349) that rests on the shoulders of the animals between neck and hump, held in position by two pairs of yoke pegs (*sīm-čūq, čūb-e semiyān, zālā, šalleh, mardak, jūġlā, yūġān, saim, čūġ-e sīm-e yō, šol-čūb*) and tied around the neck with bands (*band-e semiyān, sīmak, sarōbī, ṭanāb, saimband*). When plowing is done with other animals such as horses, mules, donkeys, or camels the yoke is replaced by an appropriate harness (*ḥāmūt*). For the plow itself we can distinguish five different types: the Caspian, the southeastern, the northwestern, the northern, and the Ḫūzistān.

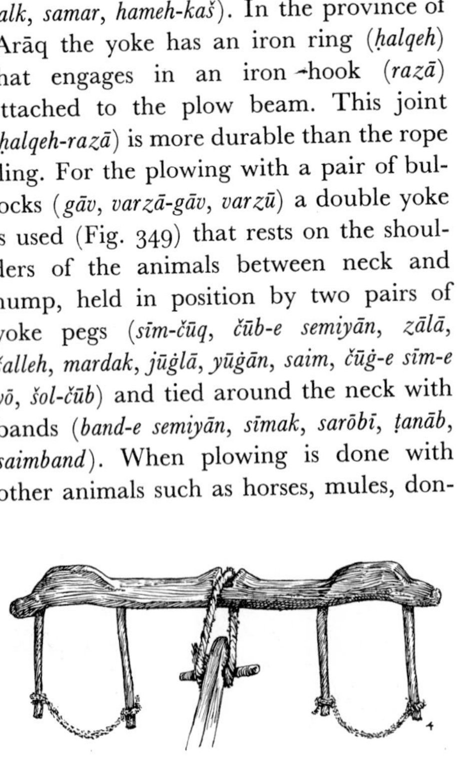

Figure 349 Yoke and Harness

The Caspian plow (*gājemeh*) is the most primitive of them all. It is widely used for rice cultivation in the Caspian provinces, and outside Persia in India and Southeast Asia. It is a suitably trimmed tree fork (Fig. 350). One branch forms the plow beam (*rāst-e dār*), and the tip of the branch hook (*kuluseh*) is protected by a socket-type plowshare (*āhan-rārī*). The share is fixed to the wood by a number of forged nails (*panj-mīḫ*). A plow stilt (*šāneh*) with a handle (*moštegeh*) is morticed into the rear of the plow. The most suitable timbers for the manufacture of this plow are elm wood (*čūb-e āzād*) and mulberry wood (*čūb-e tūt*).

Figure 350 A Caspian Plow

The other plows seem to have developed from the branch hook plow, although they are made from individual parts. The closest resemblance to it is the southeastern plow, which inside Persia is used in the southern provinces of Fārs, Kermān, and the eastern provinces of Zābolistān, Sīstān, and Ḫorāsān. Outside Persia this plow is found throughout southern and eastern Afghanistan as far as the high

Figure 351 A Plow from Fārs

Figure 352 A Plow from Sīstān

valley of Kafiristan in the Hindukush, in Pakistan, and Northwest India. Figure 351 shows this plow (*ḫīš*, *raḫ*, *raḫt-e jūġ*, *raḫt-e jigō*) as used in Fārs. Its main parts are the plow beam (*tīr*, *dār-ḫīš*, *parvāʾī*, *kirčou*, *čūb-e raḫt*) and the plow sole (*pedarsel*, *reḫez*, *kondeh*, *čūb-e miyād*), which carries the iron share (*gouāhan*, *gōhan*, *sar-e āhan*, *sarnak*, *miyād*). The shape of the share on this type of plow is a flat, broad triangle. In the south the share iron is fixed to the sole by means of strong, forged nails (*mīḫ*, Fig. 352). The peasants of Ḫorāsān have two strong nails with large heads (*mīḫ-e goubandī*) driven into the sole, with space left between nail and head and sole surface. The triangular share blade has a long slot (*šekafteh*), and before the peasant begins to plow he slips the blade onto the sole so that the nails fit into the slot. There is no danger of the blade falling off during plowing as the soil pressure keeps it pushed against the nails. All plows of this type have beam and sole tied together by means of a forged iron hoop (*ḫalqeh*, *alġār*). In Fārs and Zābolistān the distance between the two is kept at the required angle by a board (*taḫteh*, *goak*, *gāvak*). In Ḫorāsān, however, an iron wedge (*āhan-gāz*, *gol-gāz*) is driven between beam and sole and a wooden wedge (*pūš-gāz*) between beam and hoop (*gāl-band*, *ḫalqeh*) to allow adjustment of the angle between beam and sole that determines the depth of plowing. Morticed into the beam and held in position by a wedge (*gāz*, *gōveh*) is a plow stilt (*dast-miyān*, *mad-gīr*, *nī-dasteh*) that at the upper end carries a handle (*mošteh*, *moštī*, *mištak*).

The northwestern plow (*gāv-āhan*, *ḫēš*, *gāb-e amrāz*, *amrāz*, Fig. 353) has this in common with the southeastern one: beam (*tīr*, *tīr-e ḫēš*, *oujar*) and sole (*parsīšt*, *pedarsel*, *koreh*) are separate elements. The characteristic differences are in the way they are joined together and in the shape of the share iron. The northwestern plow has two upright columns (*būšeh*, *bāzūneh*, *šamšīrak*, *šūnak*, *qel-e jakt*) to which the handle (*mošteh*, *mošterūn*, *dasteh-šūnak*, *totāḫ*) is attached. All parts are morticed together and are kept in position by wooden wedges (*gōveh*, *šūrak*, *mīḫ*, *tarāḫ*). Figure 354 shows a similar plow but has the handle attached to one column only. Another variety of this plow has the distance between sole and beam

Figure 353 A Plow from Iṣfahān

Figure 354 A Plow from Hamadān

Figure 355 Forged Plowshares for the North-western Plow

controlled by a small board (*būšū, barak*). The share iron (*gōvan, gouhan*) of this plow is long and heavily built. Figure 355 shows a number of them upside down just made by the blacksmith. The two jaws of the iron fit over the tapered end of the sole, an iron hoop (*ḥalqeh*) is slipped over iron and sole, and the soil pressure keeps it on.

The region in which this plow is used is almost identical with the area that the linguists have established as that of former Media, i.e., north of Sumaq in Fārs, the provinces of Iṣfahān, Tehrān, ᶜArāq, Zenjān, and Āẕarbaijān. Outside Persia it extends into Armenia, the Caucasus, East Anatolia, and Bulgaria.

A fourth plow, called by the writer the "bent sole plow" (*āzel, āzāl, āzāl-e jed*), occurs mainly in the Alburz mountains and their extensions toward the Caucasus as well as in Central Anatolia;[76] in the south it occurs in Balūčistān, Pakistan, and Northwest India.[77] Its characteristic is a bent piece of wood, called *ben-gāb, bānēgā* (Fig. 356), that is plow sole and stilt at the same time. The plow beam (*tīr, tīrak*) is morticed into the stilt part of the wooden piece. A wooden stay (*šāneh, šānak*), morticed into the sole part of it and through the plow beam, carries a peg (*sībak*) above the beam. The required plowing angle is adjustable by means of a wooden wedge (*rīšbīnī*) driven between beam and peg. The plowshare (*varzā-āhan, gāb-āhan*) is similar to the one of the north-west plow and is likewise held in position with an iron hoop (*gālband*).

The Ḫūzistān plow[78] has beam and sole

[76] *Turk Etnografya Dergisi*, No. 1 (1956), Pl. 2.

[77] A. A. Memon, *Indigenous Agricultural Implements in Bombay State*, p. 16.

[78] No Persian terms have been recorded, as the peasants of Ḫūzistān speak Arabic.

Figure 356 A Northern Plow

Figure 357 A Ḫūzistān Plow

in two pieces (Fig. 357) like the southeastern and the northwestern plows. The sole is loosely morticed into the beam and held in position by a long peg. The angle between beam and sole is controlled by a stay that is either an iron bar with a threaded end or a piece of wood morticed into the sole and through the beam and set in position with a wedge (Fig. 358). The peculiar feature of this plow is that it has spreading stilts that begin near the plowshare. They are held in position by a peg joining sole and beam and are linked at the top by a wide, horizontal handlebar. A rope wound into a tourniquet keeps them together in the middle. The plow shown in Figure 357 has a triangular share inserted into a slot of the sole, whereas the share of the plow shown in Fig. 358 is forged into a rectangular socket pushed onto the sole. Apart from Ḫūzistān this plow is used throughout Iraq.

An Assyrian seal of 722 B.C. (Fig. 359) shows a plow that closely resembles the

Figure 358 A Ḫūzistān Plow (*front view*)

Figure 359 A Seed Plow on an Assyrian Seal, 722 B.C.

Figure 360 A Seed Plow from Balūčistān

Ḫūzistān plow. But it has a seed tube attachment. Travelers who visited the region at the beginning of this century[79] report that sowing of wheat was commonly done by dropping the seed grains into a funnel at the back of one of the stilts from where it dropped through a bamboo tube into the furrow just made by the plow. European agricultural experts working in Ḫūzistān assured the writer that some seed plows are still in use there. The only other region in Persia where seed plows are still in use is Balūčistān. Figure 360 shows a plow of the "bent sole" type with a seed tube attached to it. Outside Persia seed plows are widely used in Pakistan and Northwest India.[80]

Wherever a change from the traditional

[79] T. Mann, *Der Islam, einst und jetzt*, p. 62, Fig. 69.

[80] A. A. Memon, *op. cit.*, pp. 31 ff.

plow to a Western style mold-board plow took place it was coupled with a change from animal traction to motor traction. An exception was that in the provinces of Gorgān and Māzandarān an iron, horse-drawn mold-board plow was introduced about 100 years ago under Russian influence. Now it is manufactured by the local blacksmiths. It is called *šoḫm-e dōdastī* on account of its double-handled stilt. It has a flat sole (*baġal-band*) carrying the share (*tīġ*). A wooden mold-board (*ḫāk-bargardāneš*) is screwed to the frame and a setting device (*darajeh*) allows adjustment of the plowing depth. The soil of the Caspian provinces seems to be suitable for mold-board plowing, while experiments with this plowing technique on the Plateau often had disappointing results. For this reason modern tractor-drawn implements are either of the disk plow or chisel plow type. The latter is in fact the nearest to the traditional plow, thus proving that the peasant was using the best implement for his soil for animal traction.

Seed Bed Preparation

Immediately after plowing the rather coarse soil clods (*kolūḫ*) are broken up. In areas where spades are used for tillage the breaking up is done with large wooden mallets (*kolon-kūb*, *kolūḫ-kūb*, Fig. 361) followed by raking. When the field has been irrigated the same mallet is used again to break up the hard crust caused by the drying of the soil. Market gardeners, e.g., those of Iṣfahān, Ahvāz, and Dizful, often till their fields with an oxen-drawn plow but break the clods up with mallets. In most parts of the country, however, an animal-drawn harrow (*māleh*, *vaz*, *garrā*, *bezān*, *mislafeh*, *pīškabūl*, *māleh-čīlak*) is used. In its simplest form, e.g., in southern Fārs, it is just a board (*taḫteh-mālā*) about 6 feet long and 8 inches wide that is hitched to a

Figure 361 Beating the Clods

Figure 362 Riding on a Spiked Harrow

Figure 363 A Harrow Beam Attached to a Plow (*Hamadān*)

yoke by a pair of chains (*zanjīr*) over steel eyebolts (*rīz*) and rings (*ḥalqeh*). The cultivator stands on the board, giving it a slight tilt with his feet, and while it slides over the clods it breaks them up (Fig. 362). He keeps his balance by holding on to a rope (*band*) that is attached to the yoke too. Often the board is weighted down by a number of heavy stones. In Ḫorāsān the board is connected to the yoke by means of a harness beam (*māleh-kaš*) consisting of a forked piece of wood. The forked ends carry steel rings (*ḥalqeh*). The harrowing board has two forged hitching hooks (*zulfī*, *zulfīn*) that are connected to the fork end rings by a pair of S-hooks (*čaperāseh*, *čaperāsteh*). The peasants of the Hamadān region use their plow for clod crushing. They take the plowshare off the sole and slip a wooden beam, 4 feet long and 3 × 3 inches in section with a rectangular hole in the center, over the sole tip (Fig. 363).

Tined harrows are also found in many parts of the country. For example, the peasants of Fārs and Iṣfahān use a board that is studded with several rows of iron or wooden tines (*dandeh*, Fig. 364). A particularly heavy harrow is used in Kurdistān, where a square beam about 10 feet long carries strong wooden tines 10 to 12 inches long. It is drawn by two pairs of bullocks, the cultivator standing on the beam (Fig. 365). A more elaborate harrow has been observed in the provinces of ʿArāq and Āẕarbaijān, where the tined board is permanently fixed to a draw beam with stilt and handle like a plow. For the first run the cultivator stands on the board, leaning against the stilt, while he walks behind it for the finer harrowing (*māleh kašīdan*, *ṣāf kardan*), applying the right pressure through the handle of the stilt. The harrow used in the rice fields around Fasā and Jahrum in southern Fārs is different again. It consists of a single square beam about 6 feet long to which a row of sharp wooden tines is attached

Figure 364 A Spiked Harrow (*Iṣfahān*)

Figure 365 A Spiked Harrow (*Kurdistān*)

Figure 366 A Handled Harrow (*Jahrum*)

(Fig. 366) and a tall square frame provides a comfortable handle to guide the harrow, which is drawn by a pair of chains attached to the yoke. Both this harrow and the spiked-board one are shown in exactly the same form on woodcut illustrations in a twelfth-century Chinese handbook on agricultural techniques.[81] A nineteenth-century author, describing agricultural implements then used in China, notes the surprising similarity of Chinese and Near East implements.[82]

If the crop is to be irrigated the raised borders (*tamand*, *marz*, *marz-band*, *kūleh-marz*, *dīvār*, *bast*) surrounding each field are prepared while the soil is still friable. Depending on the amount of water supplied during an irrigation turn, the height of these borders varies between 10 and 15 inches. The border raising (*zamīn bastan*) is done with a long-handled iron scoop (*karreh*, *katar*, *panjeh*). Figure 367 shows the scoop blade with eyelets (*zulfī*), rings (*ḥalqeh*), and the socket (*angošteh*, *maik*). It is guided by one man and drawn, over a pair of chains (*zanjīr*) or ropes (*ṭanāb*) joining in a wooden handle (*dasteh-kaš*, *moštegeh*, *mošteh*, *dast-e dār*), by another man (Fig. 368). The soil for the borders is taken

Figure 368 Raising Borders with a Scoop

Figure 369 An Irrigated Field for Vegetable Cultivation

Figure 367 An Iron Scoop

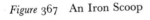

Figure 370 A Wooden Scoop

[81] O. Franke, *Keng Tschi T'u—Ackerbau und Seidengewinnung in China*, Plates 15–18.
[82] *Chinese Repository*, pp. 485 ff.

Figure 371 Terraced Irrigation in Ḫorāsān

from the edge of the plowed field (*korzeh*). The slight depression thus caused acts as an inlet channel (*baigāh, faṣl-kaš*) leading the water around the field at the beginning of the flooding. The same iron scoop is used to provide deep furrows and high ridges so characteristic of vegetable cultivation, e.g., melons, cucumbers, and so forth (Fig. 369). The bigger branch channels between main canal and field are scooped out (*panjeh kašīdan*) with a larger bullock-drawn wooden scoop (Fig. 370). It consists of a large hoop bent from the green wood of the jujube tree (*čūb-e senjed*) to which a number of boards are nailed, the lowest one being reinforced by an iron edge. Chains connect the scoop to the yoke. At the beginning of each cycle the operator presses the scoop into the soil with its handle, and the bullocks draw it toward the channel edge where it is tilted and the soil deposited on the channel bank. The same type of scoop is used for cleaning the channels of silt and water plants. When new fields are made, this scoop serves for leveling each field after the first flooding when irregularities of the surface become apparent. Figure 371 shows wheat fields in Ḫorāsān, ready for irrigation. The terracing, the raised borders, the leveled fields, the water storage basins, the canals —all this work has been done with the two types of scoops just described, the man-drawn and the oxen-drawn.

Manuring

While it is true that large wheat fields receive very little manure, especially in the north where dung is used for fuel, this does not hold for fruit and vegetable growing. Since orchards and market gardens are always near villages and towns, sufficient animal dung and human feces are available. As the latter are collected in cesspits near the houses and are regularly strewn with quicklime and wood ashes, calcium and potassium too are contained in the manure. Towers (*borj-e kaftar*) to obtain pigeon manure (*čelġūr*) are a peculiar feature of an area of about 100 miles around Iṣfahān, but are also found near Kabul in Afghanistan. Small pigeon towers are attached to the houses; the larger ones in the fields are either circular mud brick buildings (Fig. 372) 30 to 50 feet high and 15 to 30 feet in diameter, or, as near Gulpāʾīgān, northwest of Iṣfahān, they are square and of similar dimensions. There are many holes on the top for the birds to enter, and inside along the walls and niches there are thousands of perching stones (Fig. 373) where the birds rest during the night and leave their droppings. About a thousand pigeons live and breed in an average size tower, and the yield of such a tower is about 6,000 pounds of dung (*zelā*) per year. Used at the rate of about 1,500 pounds per acre for most crops and 2 pounds per fruit tree, the peasants claim an increase in yield of at least 50 per cent. This benefit, however, could be a dubious one as the pigeons fly to the surrounding wheat fields where they feed on the grain and probably do more damage to the crop than the benefit to the gardeners is worth. This might be the reason for the steady decrease in the number of these towers from about 3,000 in the Iṣfahān district during the time of Sir John Chardin[83] to a fraction of that today.

Figure 372 A Pigeon Tower near Iṣfahān

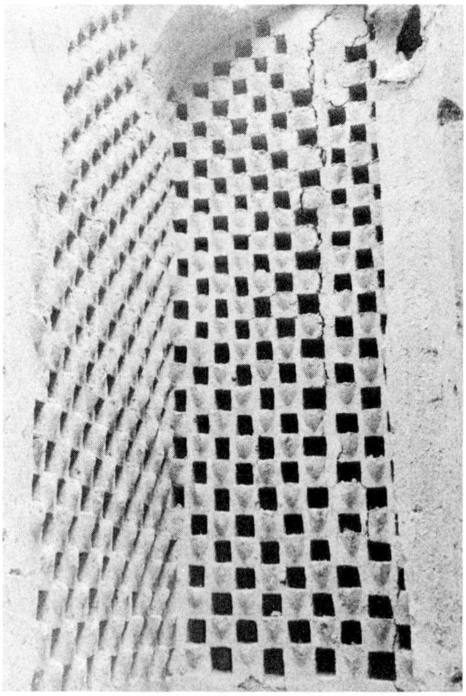

Figure 373 Perching Stones inside a Pigeon Tower

Sowing and Crop Growing

Without going into too much detail on all the crops grown in Persia[84] it may be

[83] Sir J. Chardin, *Travels in Persia*, p. 177.

[84] For detailed descriptions see A. K. S. Lambton, *op. cit.*, and P. H. T. Beckett, "Agriculture in Central Persia."

said here that crops are divided into winter crops (*šatvī*) and summer crops (*ṣaifī*). Wheat, mainly sown (*kāštan, pāšīdan*) as a winter crop between the end of October and the third week of November, is irrigated twice before the winter rains and twice in spring if on land under irrigation (*ābī, ābyārī*). In dry farming (*daim, dāmī, ḫodā-dādeh, baḫsī*) it depends entirely on rain. Summer wheat is sown from the end of February on and harvested in September with about four irrigations. There are two varieties of barley, spring or sweet barley (*jou-ye šīrīn*), which is sown toward the end of February, irrigated three to four times, and harvested by the end of June, and sour barley (*jou-ye torš*), sown early in August, likewise irrigated, and harvested by the end of October. The same variety is also grown as a winter crop, sown in November, and harvested by the end of May or early June. Both wheat and barley are sown by broadcasting at the rate of about 100 to 150 pounds per acre[85] except where a seeding plow is employed.

Rice (*šaltūk*) is generally grown by transplanting (*nešā kardan*) from seed beds (*tombeh-jā*) into flooded fields, work mainly performed by women, but in Ḫūzistān and in some parts of Fārs, rice is sown by broadcasting about the time of the spring equinox. Most vegetable crops are grown, as previously mentioned, on high ridges with deep furrows in between for weekly irrigation (Fig. 369). In districts where the groundwater level is not too low, trenches 3 to 6 feet deep are dug that allow the roots of some plants to search for the groundwater that may be supplemented by spring rains collecting in the trenches, and by additional irrigation. Grapevines are grown in this way in many parts of the country. In Āzarbaijān the vines rest on the ridges, whereas in Fārs, Kermān, and the central districts wooden bars resting on mud brick pillars support the vines.[86] The vine dressers (*angūrčīn, angūrzan, razbān*) are quite skilled in grafting (*paivand zadan, jūš zadan*), which they do either by drilling (*mateh'ī, qalamī*) and inserting the cutting (*jūš*) into the hole or by inserting it into a cut in the bark (*paivand-e pūst, jūš-e pūst*). Pruning (*par kardan*) is done in winter either with seccateurs (*qaičī*), a pruning knife (*kard, dāsġāleh*), or a small saw (*arreh*). Deep trench cultivation is also used for date-palm (*deraḫt-e ḫormā*) growing. Al-Balḫī (about 1105 A.D.)[87] mentioned palm groves in South Fārs with trenches as deep as 6 feet that were filled with water in spring and retained the moisture a long time before they needed irrigation again.

Throughout the entire growing season the peasant has to do some weeding. For this he uses a small weeding spade (*bīlak, pāš-gūn, ḫasūm-e pāšgūnī*). Figure 374 shows a weeder in a squatting position using the crook-handled weeding spade.

Figure 374 A Weeding Spade

Harvesting

Most cereals are reaped (*derou kardan, čīdan*) with a sickle after the grain is fully

[85] P. H. T. Beckett, "Agriculture in Central Persia," p. 20.

[86] P. H. T. Beckett, "Tools and Crafts in South Central Persia," p. 146, and E. Gauba, "Botanische Reisen in der persischen Dattelregion," Part 1, p. 2.

[87] G. Le Strange, *Description of the Province of Fars*, p. 48; Sir J. Chardin, *op. cit.*, p. 257; and E. Gauba, *op. cit.*, Part 1, p. 2.

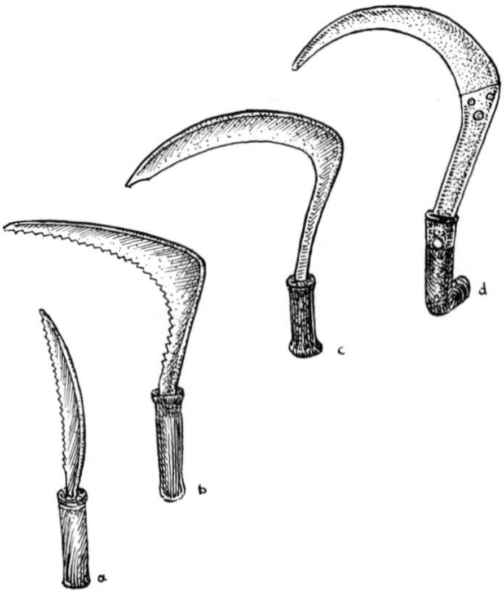

Figure 375 Types of Sickle

Figure 376 Harvesting with a Sickle

Figure 377 Binding Rice into Sheaves

Figure 378 A Bullock Cart from Āẕarbaijān

matured, except barley, which is pulled out by the roots. Two types of sickle (*dās, dāreh, dast-qalā*) are found, hooked grain-cutting sickles (*dās-e derou*, Fig. 375 *b*, *c* and *d*) and a much smaller, almost straight one that is actually a grass-cutting sickle (*dās-e* ᶜ*alef-bor*, Fig. 375 *a*) but is sometimes also used for smaller plots of grain. In some districts it is customary to have tooth-edged sickles, and the teeth are kept sharp with a triangular file. In other parts the edge is straight, surface-hardened with horn meal and kept sharp with a whetstone or a steel (*fūlād*). The reaping is done from a squatting position (Fig. 376). To protect the forefinger the reapers of Gīlān wear a horn protector, made of the tip of a cow's horn. The stalks are tied into sheaves (Fig. 377) and often carried on donkey back to the threshing ground (*ẖarman, ẖarman-gāh*), a centrally situated level place some 30 to 40 feet in diameter where the surface has been hardened by soaking a layer of earth in water, mixing it thoroughly with chaff, and subsequently rolling it with a stone roller until it becomes dry without cracks. Usually a pole 5 feet high is erected in the center of the threshing ground. In the north the sheaves are carried to the threshing ground by large bullock carts (Fig. 378). After the reaping the poor of the village are allowed to walk over the field to glean (*ḫūšeh-čīn*) lost ears. At the threshing ground sheaves are piled (*āšām kašīdan*) into a circular heap (*ḫarman-kūh*) about three feet in height and 20 to 30 feet in diameter. The threshing (*ḫarman kūbīdan*) is done in four different ways:

Figure 379 Threshing Peas with a Flail

1. By beating (*tāleh kūbīdan*) with wooden flails (*čūb-e guzel-kūbī*, Fig. 379) or the heavy ribs of palm leaves (*gorz-e ḫormā*). This method, as far as cereals are concerned, is confined to areas where draft animals are not commonly used and to peasants with small holdings. Pulse crops are generally threshed from their pods by beating.

2. Threshing by driving teams of draft animals over the threshing ground is not very efficient but can still be seen, especially in combination with one of the following methods when the walking animals are used to break the straw and flatten the heap (Fig. 380).

3. Use of a threshing wheel, or wain (*čarḫ*, *čar*, *čān*, *čūm*, *borreh*, *ḫarman-kūb*,

Figure 380 Threshing with a Wain and a Team of Animals

Figure 381 A Wain with Wooden Beaters

Figure 382 A Wain with Iron Beaters

čarḫ-e ḫarman-kūbī, čarḫ-e ḫarman-kūʾī, čangal, jangal). It consists of a pair of skids (*langar, ārdāl, aldār, yōn, rāneh*) that are held together by two cross-beams (*qamčī, pāḫūnī, pā-gozāšteh*) tightened to the skids by wedges (*čūb-e qāšūneh, mīḫ-e āsūnī*). Placed between the skids and rolling in holes in them are two threshing rollers (*mīzān, mīl, mīl-e borreh, girk, gīlīleh*) that carry the beaters (*dandān, dandeh-borreh, parreh-borreh, dēš*). In their simplest form these beaters are wooden pegs (*dandāneh-ye čūbī*) wedged to the surface of the rollers, a form often found in Northwest Persia (Fig. 381). In Fārs the beaters are sharp-edged iron blades (Fig. 382) fixed to the front roller with their edges parallel to the axis while on the rear roller the edges are at right angles to the axis. These beaters are forged and have a long tang going through the roller that is bent over on the outer side. In the districts of Iṣfahān, Varāmīn, and Tehrān each roller is fitted with 6 to 8 sharp-edged iron disks (*tāveh, tōveh-čūm*, Fig. 383). The rollers run on iron axles (*mīl, mīleh, mīl-e čūm*) while the ends of the rollers are reinforced with iron bandages (*ṭouq*). The driver of the wain sits on a seat board (*kursī, taḫt, taḫt-e savārī, košk*) supported by four posts (*pāyeh, hala-čūb, dō ġečak*); he rests his feet on a footboard (*zīr-e pā*).

4. Equally efficient is the threshing

Figure 383 A Wain with Iron Disks

board (*vāl*), which is drawn over the grain heap by draft animals. It is a solid, heavy board about 2 inches thick measuring 2 feet 6 inches by 6 feet and studded with sharp flint stones (*čaḫmāḫ-dašī*, Fig. 384). Slightly bent up on the front end, the threshing board is attached to a yoke with a chain so that it slides over the stalks between the drawing bullocks, the peasant standing on it to give it more weight. In Persia this board is mainly used in Āẕarbaijān and parts of Ḫūzistān. The flint stones are mined and shaped to size near Yām, northwest of Tabrīz. A set of these flint stones costs $5 to $8. Both the wain and the threshing board were already known in antiquity. The Roman name for

Figure 384 A Threshing Board *(cutting-side up)*

the threshing board was *plaustrum triturans*. It was still used in Syria, Turkey, Bulgaria, Greece, Sicily, Spain, Portugal, and North Africa at the turn of this century, and the writer observed it still in use in Turkey and Greece in 1963. The wain was known to the Romans as *plostellum poenicum*, a name indicating Asian origin; indeed the Prophet Isaiah mentions it too.[88]

For the threshing (*čūm kardan, čūm kašīdan, borreh kašīdan*), the board or wain is drawn over the heap of sheaves in circles. The implements are hitched to either a yoke (*jū*), or a harness (*qūl, āšormeh*) if horses are used, by a beam (*tīr-čūm, čān-kaš, čaġejak*) or by a chain (*zanjīr*) or a pair of belts (*dūvāl*) over an eyebolt (*par-e dūvāl*) and a ring (*ḥalqeh*). A rein (*dast-e jelou*) from a halter (*osar*) gives the driver control over the animals. In Fārs a rope links the draft animals to the center pole of the threshing ground, whereas in the north the distance from the center pole is maintained by a beam (Fig. 380).

The threshing goes on day and night, drivers and animals working in shifts. Normally the animals are allowed to feed on the materials to be threshed, but when threshing millet (*arzan*), a muzzle (*pūz-band*) is tied to the mouth to prevent overeating. For greater efficiency, combinations of several methods are common. Apart from the combination of wain and team of animals as in Fig. 380 it is the practice in Āẕarbaijān to start threshing with the wain and finish with the board. A combination of traditional and modern implements for threshing has been observed in the provinces of ᶜArāq and South Āẕarbaijān. Many villages there own tractors; the peasants hitch a disk plow or a disk harrow on and run it over the heap on the threshing ground for two hours, which is sufficient to break the straw so that a wain or a board can take over. A boy with two oxen does the finishing operation in 20 working hours. Using traditional implements only it would have taken two boys and four oxen 100 working hours to thresh the same amount of grain. During the threshing one or two of the peasants walk around the heap with forks (*ābsī, hočūm, hōčīn, āsī, qolāb*) or rakes (*panjeh*) to move straw, chaff, and grains back into the course of the implement and to turn them over.

When the straw is broken up sufficiently and the husks have separated from the grain, winnowing (*bād dādan, dast-e bād dādan, bojārī kardan*) can begin (Fig. 385). There is usually a fair wind in the early morning and especially in late afternoon.

Figure 385 Winnowing

[88] Isaiah 41:15: "... for I have made thee a new threshing wain with teeth like a saw."

Figure 386 A Winnowing Fork

Figure 387 A Device for Bending Fork Prongs

Then the peasants throw the threshed material about 6 feet high into the air with winnowing forks (*čāk, šāneh, hōčīn, āsīn*, Fig. 386) so that the wind carries the chaff and husks away (*bād kāhrā bordan*) while the grains drop straight down (*gandom oftādan*). These forks are made from the tough wood of the mountain ash (*čūb-e ār-e kūhī*). Branches from these trees are bent by the local carpenter in special bending devices (*kaj-gīr*, Fig. 387). The sharpened bent prongs are attached to a handle with laces of gazelle hide (*pūst-e āhū*). In Āẕarbaijān winnowing is also done with wooden shovels (*parū*). The chaff is valuable fodder for the animals and is carried to the village for storage in coarse nets (*tūr, ġerār*) of goat hair (*mū*), usually on donkey back (Fig. 388). In Āẕarbaijān the chaff is also carried in canvas bags on ox carts (Fig. 389). A final

Figure 388 Bringing the Chaff into the Barn

Figure 389 A Bullock Cart for the Transport of Chaff

cleaning of the grain is done by sifting (*ġarbāl kardan, sarang kardan*), first with a coarse sieve (*kām*) to separate the grain from remaining straw and ears and then with a finer one (*ġarbāl, halbīl*) for the removal of stalk knots and gravel.

Division of the crop between landlord and peasant is done on the field by weighing, usually with a pair of scales with wooden boxes about 12 inches square and 9 inches deep, suspended from a lever. Sometimes the grain is put into woven goat hair bags and weighed with a steelyard suspended from a tripod.[89]

Donkeys or packhorses carry the grain from the field either straight to the mill or into storage rooms in the village. An unusual storage method is reported from Rūdār in Southeast Persia,[90] where the grain is placed into deep trenches dug into the ground, lined with straw, and covered with chaff and earth. It is kept there until milling facilities become available.

Flour Milling

The mill (*āsiyā, āsiyāb*) for the actual grinding (*āsiyā kardan*) of wheat (*gandom*), barley (*jou*), and a number of other foodstuffs such as millet (*arzan*), maize (*ẕorrat*), pulse (*noḫōd*), and spices such as turmeric (*zard-čūbeh*) and saffron (*zaʿfrān*) is essentially the same whether it is hand-operated, animal-driven, or activated by a power source, such as water or wind. In each case the mechanism is a rotary one with a fixed bed stone (*āsak-e zīrī, sang-e zīr*) and a revolving upper stone or runner (*āsak-e rūʾī*). The more primitive grinding implements, like the saddle quern and the grain rubber, which have been in use throughout the prehistoric Middle East,[91] were quite common in Republican Rome[92] and have survived in the Far East to this day, are today in use in Persia only in the province of Ḫūzistān for small household tasks. It appears from archaeological evidence that the rotary mill developed during the second millennium B.C. Pairs of millstones with matching pivots have been found, by Selling at Tel ʾAnnek, by Schumacher at Tel El-Mutesellim, and by McAlister at Gezer, all three in Palestine.[93] It is not quite clear how these early mills were operated, but a pair of millstones belonging to the ninth century B.C. has been found at Tel Halaf in Syria, and its runner has provision for a handle.[94]

The rotary mill appeared in Greece during the fourth century B.C. We have an illustration on a Boeotian clay beaker from this era.[95] It seems to have been brought to Italy by the Etruscans, since Pliny[96] credits them with its invention. Rotary mills are mentioned for the first time by Marcus Partius Cato (234–149 B.C.) in his book *De Re Rustica*. This type of mill spread to Northern Europe with the Celtic people of the La Tène civilization and reached England during the first century B.C.[97]

In its simplest form as a hand quern the rotary mill is widely used in Persian households, in the camps of the nomads, and by the potter for grinding glazes. Figure 390 shows a woman of the Qašqāʾī tribe doing her daily flour milling on such a hand quern (*āsiyā dastī*). The stones are about 18 to 20 inches in diameter, the lower one carrying a wooden axle peg, tightly wedged-in, around which the runner

[89] For more detail on this question see A. K. S. Lambton, *op. cit.*, p. 306.

[90] A. Gabriel, *Im weltfernen Orient*, p. 166.

[91] H. Gleisberg, "Herkunft und Verbreitung der Windmühlen," p. 16.

[92] R. J. Forbes in C. Singer, *A History of Technology*, Vol. 2, p. 106.

[93] H. Gleisberg, *op. cit.*, p. 16.

[94] R. J. Forbes in C. Singer, *op. cit.*, Vol. 2, p. 108.

[95] H. Gleisberg, *op. cit.*, p. 18.

[96] R. J. Forbes in C. Singer, *op. cit.*, Vol. 2, p. 108.

[97] Pliny, *Historia Naturalis*, xxxvi.135.

Figure 390 A Hand Quern

revolves, the latter carrying a wooden handle near the edge. The hole in the center of the runner leaves sufficient clearance to pour the grain into the center so that it can enter the face between the two stones. There is no provision in this type of mill for adjusting the distance between the stones to prevent their mutual rubbing. Grain is fed in all the time, and the grist leaves the mill on the circumference of the stone, where it drops onto a mat. Since it is only used for rough grinding (*lapeh kardan*) the lack of provision for adjustment matters little.

A more advanced form is the hand mill known in medieval England as the pot quern (Fig. 391), a type still widely used in Persian households where a servant grinds fresh flour every day and bakes the bread shortly before every meal. As an important technical improvement the pot quern shows provision for the adjustment of the distance between the stones. For this purpose a vertical, stationary steel axle is provided that passes through the bed stone (*sang-e pā'īn, sang-e zīr, sang-e buzurg, sang-e mādeh*) and rests on a pair of wedges (*gōveh*). At its top the axle has a turned-on shoulder on which a steel bar or "rind" (*tabar, tavar, beleškeh, espāreh*) revolves as a support for the runner (*sang-e bālā, sang-e rū, sang-e kūčak, sang-e nar*), spanning the latter's aperture. Adjustment is achieved by lowering or lifting the axle by shifting the wedges. Small pot querns have an ordinary wooden handle fixed in a hole in the runner at an appropriate distance from the center, whereas larger querns have a long handlebar (*nājī*) that is attached to the runner over a link and runs through a bearing block (*āsporeh*) in a ceiling rafter.

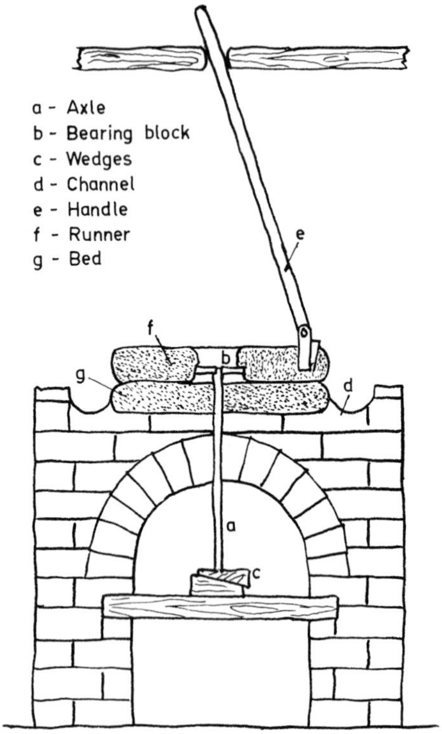

Figure 391 A Pot Quern

For water mills the rotating shaft passes through the bed stone carrying at its upper end the rind, which is inserted into a groove (*borīdegī*) cut into the runner (see Fig. 394, p. 280). The windmills of eastern Persia have the runner suspended from the lower end of the wind wheel shaft (see Fig. 402, p. 286). All power mills are fed from a hopper (*dūl, galū-ye āsiyā, kateh gandomī, sar-e nō, čādūnī*) from where the grain runs over a wooden feeder channel (*nāvdān, noudān, nāv, nō*) into the center hole of the runner, which measures about four inches in diameter. The feeder channel is kept oscillating by an eccentric pin (*zīnak, šaiṭānak, čūb-e sar-e čak, čūb-e rājeh*ᶜ) that is attached to the rind on the millstone about 2 inches off center (Fig. 392); the flow of grain is controlled by a shutter board (*taḫteh, sok*) at the mouth of the hopper. To keep the ground flour together and lead it into the lower hopper (*čāldūnī, čālehdān, kalandeh, nō-kar*), the stones are often surrounded by wooden hoops (*taḫteh-barsang, taḫteh ḫalbūn*, Fig. 393). The millstones are made from a special coarse sandstone. In Fārs these stones are quarried near Ḫollār, 40 miles northwest of Šīrāz, from where they have been sent to all mills in the province since medieval times.[98] The millstones for the Iṣfahān and Kāšān regions come from the Kargez mountains and are hewn in Natanz. The average diameter of millstones driven by water wheels is about 4 feet 3 inches. In order to make use of smaller stones too these are cut to a diameter of about 3 feet and used as fixed bed stones. The remainder required to make them the same size as the runners is made up of 4 to 6 pieces of stone, laid around the smaller bed stone and set into a mortar bed. Depending on the power source available the speed varies between 60 and 120 r.p.m. Some of the faster running stones are protected from breaking by an iron band (*ṭouq*) around their circumference. The stones have hewn-in spiral flutes, and when the miller notices a heating up (*pūs kardan*) of the flour they have to be redressed (*āsiyā tīz kardan, zebr kardan, čarḫ kardan*) with an iron pick (*kolang, āsiyā-āžan, čalūj, kener*), work which is either done by the miller (*āsiyāban*) himself or, in valleys with many mills, by a millwright (*āsiyāgar, āsiyāzan*). The stones have an initial height of about 9 inches. The runner lasts about 3 years; after that it is too thin to be used without danger of breaking. The bed stone lasts about four years because it is firmly embedded and would cause no harm when breaking.

No conditioning of the grain takes place prior to grinding, and afterwards only the bran (*sapūs, sabūs, sās, sūs*) is sifted off from the whole meal (*ārd*) with a fine sieve (*alak*).

The transition from hand to power milling was marked by the use of animals as a source of power. Ibn Ḥauqal mentioned that in his time they employed asses and horses in the mills at Sarḫes near Nīšāpūr.[99]

Figure 392 Mill Stones, Feeder, and Hopper

Figure 393 A Flour Mill with Retaining Hoop and Lower Hopper

[98] G. Le Strange, *op. cit.*, p. 127.

[99] Ibn Ḥauqal, *The Oriental Geography of Ebn Haukal*, p. 222.

Water Mills

The most common type of power for milling today is water. Three types of water mills can be distinguished, the Norse mill, the Vitruvian mill, and the floating mill. The so-called Norse mill has a vertical shaft and a number of scooped blades and is said to be a Greek invention[100] although the first one ever mentioned was erected, according to Strabo, by the Parthian king Mithridates in 65 B.C. for his palace in Asia Minor. This type of mill reached China during the third or fourth century A.D.; whether through Persian middlemen or from the Greeks in Bactria is still a matter of conjecture, as China at that time had close contacts with both these civilizations.[101] The other water mill still widely used in Persia is the Vitruvian mill with a horizontal shaft to the water wheel and a gear drive to transmit motion to the vertical shaft of the mill stones. Its invention is attributed to the Roman engineers of the first century B.C.[102] It spread through the Roman empire, was in use in Athens, Gaul, and Byzantium during the fourth century A.D.,[103] and a Persian named Metrodorus is credited with its introduction into India early in the fourth century A.D.[104]

Mills of the third type, the so-called floating mill, must have been quite numerous in the tenth century A.D. according to the historian Muqaddasī,[105] who was very impressed by "these wonderful mills" that were anchored in the great rivers of Mesopotamia, Ḫūzistān, and Ḫorāsān and driven by large paddle wheels. According to Procopius they were invented by the Roman general Belisarius during the siege of Rome in 537 A.D., when the Goths had cut off the water supply from the aquaducts, thus immobilizing the flour milling industry.[106] Floating mills are no longer used in Persia. In accordance with their basic characteristics we find the Norse mill in the mountain valleys with relatively small water volume in their streams but a high head, and the Vitruvian mill near the larger rivers offering more water at a lower head.

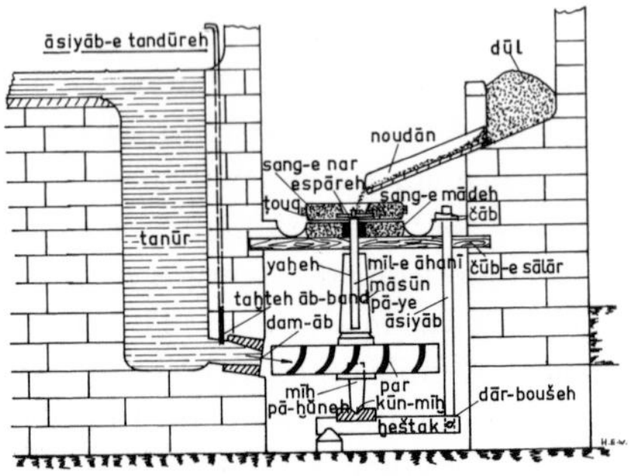

Figure 394 A Norse Type Water Mill

Figure 394 shows a sectional view of a Norse type of water mill (*āsiyāb-e parī*, *āsiyāb-e tandūreh*). The stone-built penstock (*tanūr*, *tanūreh*, *nō-e āb*) for the water varies between 20 and 30 feet in height so that the water discharges at the interchangeable jet at a high speed against the scooped blades (*par*), thus causing the wheel (*čarḫ*, *čarḫ-e āsiyāb*, *čāleh-par*) to turn. In order to maintain the water head in the penstock, the jet can be exchanged. For the maximum water supply a Sīrāz miller uses a wooden jet with a bore 4.5 inches in diameter, and with 25-foot water head the mill runs at 164 revolutions per minute, producing about 10 h.p. and a grain throughput of 5.5 bushels per hour. In

[100] R. J. Forbes, *Studies in Ancient Technology*, Vol. 2, p. 89.
[101] J. Needham, *The History of Science and Civilisation in China*, p. 232.
[102] R. J. Forbes, *Studies in Ancient Technology*, Vol. 2, p. 88.
[103] *Ibid.*, p. 89.
[104] *Ibid.*, p. 93.
[105] E. Wiedemann, "Zur Technik und Naturwissenschaft bei den Arabern," p. 322.
[106] R. J. Forbes, *Studies in Ancient Technology*, Vol. 2, p. 102.

drier seasons, with less water available, jets with bores 4.0, 3.5, or 3.0 inches in diameter may be inserted. The reduced power output is then 8.5, 6.1, or 4.5 h.p., respectively, the speed drops to 160, 155, or 151 r.p.m., respectively, and the grain throughput to 4.7, 3.4, or 2.5 bushels per hour, respectively. A shutter (*taḫteh-āb-band, kalvezān*) between penstock and jet allows the control of the water flow. As the shutter is not completely watertight, a rope (*čulūk*) connecting a peg on the runner with a ring in the wall near it makes sure that the wheel does not turn when the mill is not used. Figure 395 shows the shaft (*mīl*) of a Norse wheel whose main part is a wooden trunk (*māsūn*) having at its lower end inclined slots (*kān*) for the insertion of the blades (*par*). The upper part of the trunk has a vertical slot (*yaḫeh*) into which the steel part of the shaft (*mīl-e āhanī*) is inserted. This steel part (bottom, Fig. 396) is forged into a flat section that fits into the vertical slot. Above the slot it is round and smooth and acts as a bearing journal. The bearing itself consists of two semicircular wooden blocks having a hole in the center when put together. They are placed into the hole in the middle of the bed stone. The top end of the steel shaft above the round section is forged into another flat (*zabāneh-ye afzār*) that fits into an oblong hole (*afzār, ouzār*) in the rind (center, Fig. 396). A steel pivot pin (*mīḫ, kūn-mīḫ*, top, Fig. 396) fits with its square end into the lower end of the wooden trunk. A steel reinforcement (*ḥaddād*) across the foot of the trunk centers the pivot pin properly and prevents the trunk from splitting. The conical point of the pivot pin rests in the tapered hole (*kūn*) of a thrust bearing block (*taḫteh, pā-ḫūneh, pā-ḫāneh*) that is placed on a steel bar (*ḫeštak*). It is part of a millstone setting device (*pārs-dār, dār-boušeh*) that works in this way: One end of the steel bar below the thrust bearing is

Figure 395 The Shaft of a Norse Mill

resting on the floor, whereas the other end is suspended slightly above floor level and linked to a vertical pole (*pā-ye āsiyāb*) that passes through a hole in one of the heavy floor beams (*čūb-e sālār*). At its upper end this pole is slotted and a wedge (*čāb*) passes through it and rests on the floor beam. When this wedge is driven in with

Figure 396 The Steel Parts of a Norse Mill Shaft

a hammer the pole rises, lifting at the same time the mill shaft, rind, and runner. The slender taper of the wedge and the lever ratio of the floor bar allow very fine adjustments in order to obtain the required flour grade in the milling process (*gandom ḫord kardan*).

Figure 397 A Group of Norse Mills with Wooden Penstocks

In Āẕarbaijān it is customary to lead the water from the mill race (*čārū*, *čūġ*, *čūġ-e šāh*) into a hollowed tree trunk (*nāv*) that is closed again with boards and acts as a penstock (Fig. 397). This variety of the Norse mill is known as *āsiyāb-e noudāneh*. In long mountain valleys there is often a whole series of mills, the water serving one mill after the other as it descends. The historian and geographer Ḥamdullāh Mustoufī[107] mentions a valley in Ḫorāsān where 40 mills operated along the same stream whose waters were so swift that it took no longer to grind one ass load of grain (about 160 pounds) than to sew the heads of two flour bags. It should be mentioned here that a great number of mills are built underground where they operate in conjunction with the *qanāt* system.

The Vitruvian mill has wheel and shaft horizontal; it is the type of wheel first described by Vitruvius, the Roman historian of technology of the first century B.C. Figure 398 shows such a mill (*āsiyāb-e čarḫī*), which is operated with a breast-shot arrangement, the water entering at axis height through a narrow space (*kāseh-āsiyāb*) between wheel and stonework (Fig. 399). The water is branched off, perhaps half a mile upstream, from the river by a dam that at the same time serves for irrigation purposes. The water arrives at the mill in a mill race (*čūġ-šāh*) and shortly before it reaches the spill (*čāh-rāh*) behind the water wheel there is a sluice door (*harz-āb*, *harz-ābī*) where it can be diverted (*ābrā harz kardan*, *harz dādan*) to bypass the wheel if the mill is not operating.

This wheel (*čarḫ-e āsiyāb*, *par*) requires a water head of about 5 feet. It is built around a heavy wooden pole (*mīzān*, *mīl*) that is keyed to a steel main shaft (*sar-e*

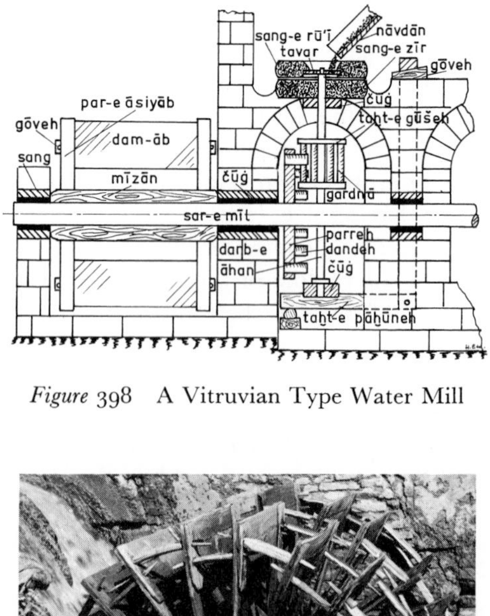

Figure 398 A Vitruvian Type Water Mill

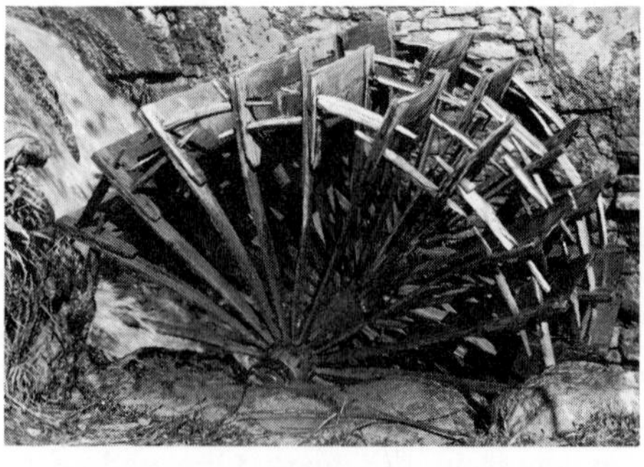

Figure 399 A Breast Shot Mill Wheel

[107] G. Le Strange, *Mesopotamia and Persia under the Mongols in the 14th Century*, p. 147.

mīl). The shaft runs in wooden bearing blocks (*bālešmeh, čūġ, čūb*) that are supported by specially hewn stones (*sarbandān, sang*) built into the mud brick walls of the mill. In other constructions a wooden main shaft (*mīzān, mīl*) carries the water wheel and extends under the mill house, having at its ends short steel axles (*tīġ-e āhan*) that run in bearings as described above. About twenty pairs of spokes (*par, par-e āsiyāb*) radiate from the axle. Wooden blades (*dam-āb*) are attached to these spokes by means of wedges (*gōveh*). On the outer circumference all blades are held by tangential links (*tang*) to equalize the impact of the water on the blades. The main shaft enters the basement wall of the mill house over a bearing block, and inside the first vault we find a large gear wheel (*čārangeleh, parreh*) with four spokes and 35 elliptical pivot gear teeth (*dandeh*) made from the tough wood of the apricot tree (*čūb-e zardālū*). Equally suitable for the making of these teeth is the dense and hard wood known as *čūb-e vašm*, which is probably dogwood (*Cornus mascula*). This all-wooden gear wheel meshes into a cage pinion (*gardnā*) whose vertical steel axis (*darb-e āhan, navordān*) just bypasses the main shaft, resting in a thrust bearing block (*gareh, gereh, pā-ḫūneh*) that in turn is supported by a solid board (*taḫteh-ḫūneh, taḫteh-pāḫūneh*). The pinion (Fig. 400) has six elliptical gear teeth (*lang*) of kokan wood (*čūb-e kōkan*). The six teeth are set into two circular disks (*taḫt-e gūšeh*) made of plane wood (*čūb-e čenār*) and surrounded by iron tires (*tāqeh*). The journal of the pinion shaft is supported at floor level by a split bearing (*gereh*) of medlar wood (*čūb-e kavījeh*). The lower end of the pinion shaft runs in a wooden thrust bearing that is inserted into a horizontal bearing board (Fig. 400). This board is loosely morticed into slots of two short vertical posts (*dārmeh*). A pair of wedges under each end of the board allows the setting of the gap between the mill stones. In some mills of this type the pinion bearing board is suspended at one end from a vertical pole, similar to the adjusting pole on the Norse mill, with a setting wedge at floor level in the milling room. Depending on the size of the water wheel, the water head, and the amount of water available, several sets of gear wheels and mill stones are sometimes attached to the extension of one horizontal main shaft, usually three to five.

Figure 400 The Pinion of a Vitruvian Mill with Thrust Bearing, Journal, and Rind

A historian describing the development of the water wheel[108] claims that the efficiency of the Norse mill was so low that the inventive spirit of the Romans led to the development of the more efficient Vitruvian mill. The writer does not agree with this claim, since efficiency can only mean the ratio between the power input, viz., the product of water volume and head, and the power output delivered to the millstones. As the size of these stones is the same in both types of mill and the Vitruvian mill is so geared that its speed is basically the same as that of the Norse mill, their flour output should be the same. This is in fact true; as already mentioned, a greater water volume of the Vitruvian mill at a lower head is balanced by a smaller water volume at a considerably higher head in the case of the Norse mill.

108 R. J. Forbes, *Studies in Ancient Technology*, Vol. 2, p. 86.

Windmills

Windmills (*āsiyāb-e bādī, šāteqī*) are extensively used in the eastern parts of Persia, viz., Ḫorāsān and Sīstān, where during the summer months the "wind of the 120 days" (*bād-e ṣad-ō-bīst rūz*) blows unabated from the Qizil-Qum steppes of Turkestan. All the way from between Mašhad and Herat to the Indian border the traveler finds these unusual windmills with the vertical axes. Most modern authors on the history of technology agree on the Persian origin of the windmill. It should be of interest to quote earlier references to this power that point to Indian and Central Asian applications.

The earliest known mention of a windmill is in an ancient Hindu book, the Arthasastra of Kantilya (about 400 B.C.), containing a reference to lifting water.[109] Although windmills as a source of power were not known in the Greek and Roman world, it was Heron of Alexandria (260 B.C.) who described a small wind motor (*anaemourion*), a mere toy to provide air pressure for an organ.[110] There is no proof that it was ever built. The next we hear about wind motors are the prayer wheels of the Buddhists in Central Asia described by Chinese travelers about 400 A.D.[111] From early Islamic times on, the evidence becomes more specific and refers to genuine windmills, viz., a power source for grain grinding and water lifting. In quoting Ṭabarī (834–922 A.D.), Al-Masᶜūdī (about 956 A.D.) writes a story about a Persian slave, Abū Lulua, whom the caliph ᶜOmar (634–644 A.D.) asked: "I have been told that you boasted to be able to build a mill which is driven by the wind," to which the Persian replied: "By God, I will build this mill of which the world will talk."[112] The same Al-Masᶜūdī says more about the country of the windmills: "Segistan (Sīstān) is the land of winds and sand. There the wind drives mills and raises water from the streams, whereby gardens are irrigated. There is in the world, and God alone knows it, no place where more frequent use is made of the winds."[113] One of his contemporaries, the historian and geographer Istaḫrī (about 951 A.D.) confirms this: "There strong winds prevail, so that, because of them, mills were built, rotated by the wind." These windmills still impressed a later geographer, Al-Qazvīnī (d. 1283 A.D.). When writing about Sīstān he says: "There the wind is never still, so in reliance on it mills are erected; they do all their corn grinding with these mills. It is a hot land and has mills which depend on the utilization of the wind."[114] We are fortunate in having an early description of the construction of a Sīstān windmill, together with a drawing (Fig. 401) by the Syrian cosmographer Al-Dimašqī (1256–1326 A.D.) who has this to say:

When building mills that rotate by the wind, they (in Sīstān) proceed as follows: They erect a high building, like a minaret, or they take the top of a high mountain or hill or a tower of a castle. They build one building on top of another. The upper structure contains the mill [*raḥa*] that turns and grinds; the lower one contains a wheel [*doulāb*, meaning "scooped water wheel"] rotated by the enclosed wind. When the lower wheel turns, the upper mill stone turns too. Whatever wind may blow, the mills rotate, though only one stone moves. After they have completed the two structures, as shown in the drawing, they make four slits or embrasures [*marmā*, meaning "loophole of a fortress"] like those in walls, only they are reversed, for the wider part opens outward and the narrow slit

[109] Narenda Nath in F. Freese, *Windmills and Mill Wrighting*, p. 1.

[110] H. T. Horwitz, "Über das Aufkommen, die erste Entwicklung und die Verbreitung von Windrädern," p. 94.

[111] R. J. Forbes in C. Singer, *op. cit.*, Vol. 2, p. 615.

[112] H. T. Horwitz, *op. cit.*, p. 96.

[113] F. Klemm, *A History of Western Technology*, p. 77.

[114] *Ibid.*

Figure 401 Drawing of a Windmill (*from Al-Dimašqī's Cosmography*)

is inside, a channel for the air in such a way that the wind penetrates the interior with force like in the case of the goldsmith's bellows. The wider end is at the entrance, and the narrower end on the inside so that it is more suitable for the entry of the wind, which penetrates the mill house from whatever direction the wind may blow (hence the four openings in the structure). If the wind has entered this house through the entrance prepared for it, it finds in its way a reel [*sarīs*] like that on which the weavers find one thread over another. This machine has twelve ribs [*dil*ᶜ], one could diminish them to six. On these, fabric [*čām*, meaning "rough unbleached linen"] has been nailed, like the covering of a lantern, only in this case the fabric is divided over the different ribs, so that each single one is covered. The fabric has a hump which the air fills and by which they are pushed forward. Then the air fills the next one and pushes it on, then it fills the third. The reel then turns, and its rotation moves the mill stone and grinds the corn. Such mills are wanted on high castles and in regions which have no water but a lively movement of the air.[115]

Windmills of this type were still operating in Afghanistan in 1952.[116]

The windmill with the vertical axis and the sails on a frame apparently reached China during the time when the Mongols ruled there as well as in Persia (thirteenth century A.D.). The mill retained its characteristic form, though without the housing, according to a description by the sixteenth century Dutch traveler Johann Nieuwhof. Some were still in use for irrigation purposes and pumping salt brine late in the nineteenth century.[117]

The vertical axis windmill spread rapidly through the Moslem world; it became an important power source in Egypt for the crushing of sugar cane,[118] and thence it spread to the West Indies during the sixteenth century where Arab experts helped the Spaniards to establish a cane sugar industry. During the eleventh century the windmill had already reached the Aegean Islands, Spain, and Portugal, still having sails to catch the wind. However, the axis was no longer vertical but inclined about 30° to the horizontal.[119] Some authors regard this change in the direction of the axis as sufficient proof for an independent invention of the windmill in Europe. This seems unlikely, since at that time many inventions reached Europe through intense contacts with the Arab world. It is rather more probable that the European miller, through his knowledge of the Vitruvian water mill, applied the gear drive of this mill to the windmill to place the wind wheel in a new position, which at the same time gave him better

115 R. J. Forbes, *Studies in Ancient Technology*, Vol. 2, p. 111.

116 *Ibid.*

117 H. T. Horwitz, *op. cit.*, p. 101, Fig. 10.

118 R. J. Forbes, *Studies in Ancient Technology*, Vol. 2, p. 116.

119 *Ibid.*, p. 117.

bearing conditions for the shaft and a higher speed of the millstone through the gear ratio.

The first mention of a windmill (*molindina ad ventum*) for northern Europe is a French charter of 1105 A.D.; the statute of Arles in France imposed a 5 per cent tax on windmill turnover, while the apparently less efficient water mill had only 3 per cent to pay. In 1180 A.D. a windmill is mentioned in Normandy, and the so-called windmill psalter, written in Canterbury in 1270 A.D., shows the first illustrations of European windmills.[120] It is interesting that the Venetian Faustus Veranzio, in 1616 A.D., suggests a number of windmill constructions that do not follow the European form with an almost horizontal axis but show clearly the old oriental arrangement with a vertical axis.[121]

This type is still very much alive in Persia today. The modern geographer Sven Hedin says of the town of Neh in Sīstān that it has 400 houses and 75 windmills.[122] Their construction is shown in Figs. 402 and 403. The mill house (*ḫāneh*) forms the lower part of the structure. It is about 20 feet wide, 20 feet deep and 12 feet high. The two opposing side walls of it (*dīvār, dīvār-par*) extend to an additional height of 20 feet, and a wing wall (*pakorak*) of the same height but only 10 feet wide leaves an orifice (*dar-bād*) that faces north, the main wind direction, and leads the wind against one-half of the vertical wind wheel (*bālāpī*).

The wind wheel itself has an effective height of about 18 feet. Its main shaft (*tīr, tīreh*) is made of plane wood (*čūb-e čenār*). The shaft is led through a hole in the center of the arched roof of the mill house. It has a strong steel bandage (*kamān, bast*) at its lower end where it measures 17 inches in diameter. Inserted into this end is a steel thrust pin (*mīḫ*) that is forged square where it fits inside the wooden shaft and round at the lower end, having a diameter of 3 inches. Its semispherical thrust end (*sar-e tah-tīr*) rests in a wooden thrust block (*tah-tīr, čūb-e koloft*). The cavity in this block that accommodates the thrust pin is lined with a tallow-soaked lubrication pad (*kohneh*) made of many

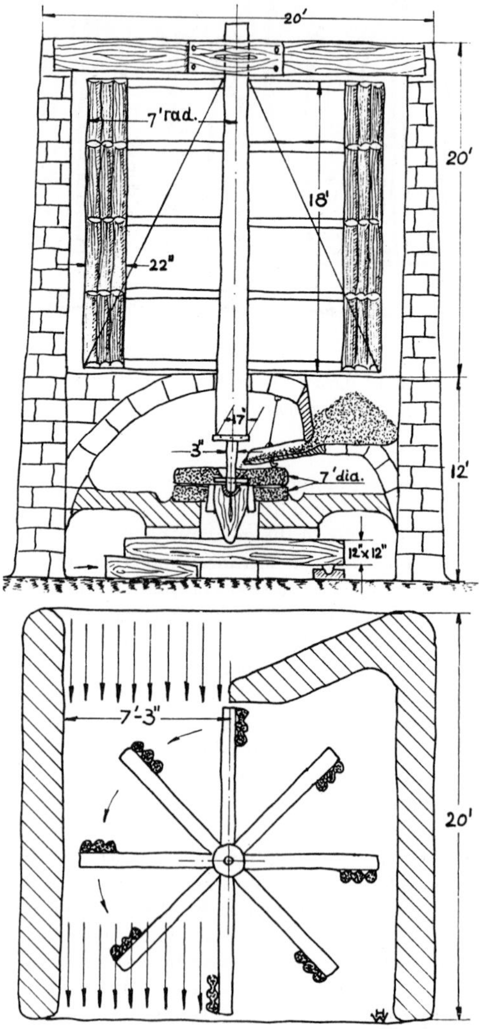

Figure 402 A Sīstān Windmill (*section*)

[120] R. Wailes, "A Note on Windmills," in C. Singer, *op. cit.*, p. 623.

[121] Faustus Veranzio, *Machinae Novae*, Plates 11–13.

[122] S. Hedin, *Eine Routenaufnahme durch Ostpersien*, Vol. 2, p. 141.

Figure 403 A Sīstān Windmill

Figure 404 The Wind Wheel of the Sīstān Mill

layers of strong cotton cloth (*karbās*). The thrust block is about 18 inches in diameter and is made from the wood of the jujube tree (*čūb-e ʿanāb*).

At its upper end the shaft runs in a wooden bearing (*kalleh-tīr*) whose halves are fixed to a heavy horizontal cross beam (*sar-gāzak*, *sarām*, *čūb-e sarām*) by means of strong wooden pegs (*mīḫ*, *mīḫ-e sar-gāzak*) and secured with ropes (*gīs*, Fig. 404). Five tiers of spokes (*bāzī*, *pošdīvō*) with eight spokes in each tier are inserted into housings (*ḫāneh*) of the shaft and held in position by wedges (*gāz*). Three or four bundles of reed (*nai*), each 18 feet high, the row of them together 22 inches wide and 6 inches thick, are pressed against the ends of the spokes by wooden tie bars (*rūband*), the latter secured to the spokes with pegs (*gāz*) and ropes. In two places between every two tiers of spokes the reed bundles are held together with further ropes (*gīs*). These eight bundles with a total area of about 280 square feet form the blades (*taḫteh*) of the wind wheel. Diagonal stay ropes (*par-kaš*) running from the top of the shaft to the outside of the lowest tier of spokes prevent sagging of the spokes under the heavy weight of the reed bundles. All eight spokes in each tier are linked on the circumference with horizontal rope stays (*rīsmān*), their tightening being achieved by twisting short stay tourniquets (*partō*).

Returning to the mill house we will remember that the shaft ended in a steel thrust pin, resting in a wooden thrust block. The upper end of this block fits into the center hole of the bed stone (*tahtāh*). The bed stone itself rests on a brick structure (Fig. 405), and the space between thrust block and bed stone is filled all the way round with wooden wedges to prevent grain and flour from falling through. The runner (*rūtāh*) rests on a strong steel rind (*tabareh*) that passes through a slot in the thrust pin underneath the feeder throat (*golū-ye sang*) of the runner. The rind fits into a groove (*borīdeh*) cut into the underside of the runner.

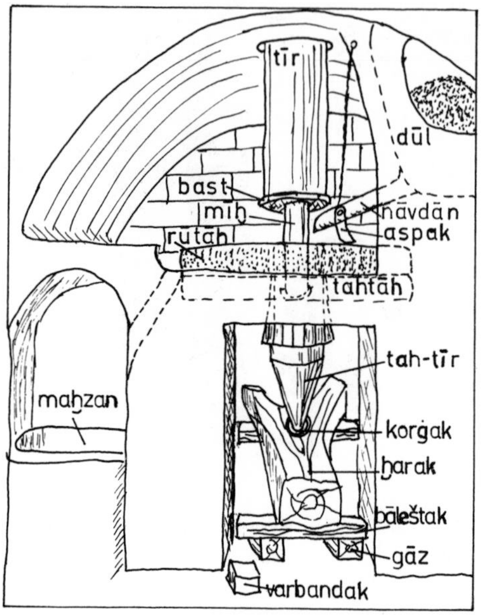

Figure 405 The Mill House of a Sīstān Windmill

At its lower end, the thrust block is shaped to a point that fits into a cup-shaped cavity (*korġak*) of a heavy horizontal foot beam (*ḫarak*), made of the particularly strong turpentine wood (*čub-e baneh*, *čūb-e ḫanjak*) with a cross section measuring 12 by 12 inches. This foot beam is part of a mill-adjusting mechanism. Its far end, resting on a short sturdy beam on the floor, forms a fulcrum, whereas the other end rests on a similar beam (*bāleštak*) that is supported by two adjusting wedges (*gāz*). By placing a short fulcrum block (*varbandak*) near the short front beam, inserting a long lever pole (*dahmak*) between the two, and pressing it down, the miller lifts thrust block, runner, and wind wheel up, although only by hundredths of an inch. Before he releases the lever, he pushes the wedges forward with his foot. He repeats the lifting and pushing until the gap between the millstones is set to the required distance. By the same token the mill becomes ready to operate.

The grain is fed into the throat of the runner from the grain hopper (*golī*, *dūl*) through a feeder channel (*nāvdān*) that is suspended from the roof of the vault by thin ropes (*dō-bōtak*) of such a length that two wooden pegs (*aspak*) attached to the sides of the feeder channel just slide on the surface of the moving runner, thus keeping the feeder vibrating and the grain flowing. The ground meal is collected in a meal hopper (*kanduk*, *maḫzan*) at the side below the bedstone.

Both millstones, like those of the other mill types, have to be trimmed (*tīz kardan*) at the end of each milling season. The new flutes are cut in by the miller with a trimming hoe (*kutnak*). The millstones of Sīstān are quarried near Ḫūnīk and have a diameter of about 7 feet compared with 4 to 4½ feet of the water millstones. The amount of grain milled in each of these windmills during 24 hours averages 1 ton, which means 120 tons in a milling season. This means that the 50 mills that were still operating in Neh when the writer saw them in 1963 (Fig. 406) had a seasonal throughput of 6,000 tons of wheat, a significant amount for a small town on the fringe of the desert.

Historians of technology may wonder what the power of this machine may be. Based on Gabriel's[123] measurement of the wind velocity at Neh in the middle of the "wind of the 120 days" of $v = 32$ *m*/second, the observed speed of $n = 120$ r.p.m., the conservative assumption that only 1.5 blades are exposed to the wind at any time, and a mill efficiency of only 50 per cent, the mill would have a power output of

[123] A. Gabriel, *op. cit.*, pp. 144–145.

about 75 HP. A modern grain mill recently installed in Neh to work outside the wind season was said to have only half the output of the windmill, i.e., half a ton in 24 hours. It was driven by a diesel engine of 40 HP, a figure confirming the above estimate.

A comparison of the description of the Sīstān windmill by Al-Dimašqī (Fig. 401) with the mills still working today shows an essential difference, viz., that the old mill had the millstones above the wind wheel, whereas the present-day mill house is below the wind wheel. The old construction seems to indicate that the windmill in that form had developed from the Norse mill where the runner had to be placed above the prime mover. The reversing of the arrangement was certainly an important development; first it brought the mill house back into the far more convenient position for its operation, and second, by having the wind wheel higher up it became more exposed to the wind and thus gave more power. To make this possible, the problem of securing the heavy runner around the lower end of the thrust pin had to be overcome, which in itself was quite an achievement.

Rice Husking

Although wheat is the most important staple food in Persia, rice (*berenj*) is also grown in considerable quantity and is of excellent long-grained quality.

In order to get the rice sheaves off the ground as soon as possible after harvesting, the farmers in the main rice-growing areas of Gīlān and Māzandārān stack the harvest unthreshed on ricks (Fig. 407) that rest on four or more strong pillars (*langeh*). These are connected by horizontal beams (*nar*). Round wooden disks (*kolāh*) near the tops of the pillars underneath the beams prevent the rats from getting at the rice.

Figure 406 A Row of Windmills

Figure 407 A Rice Rick in Māzandarān

The harvest is left on the ricks until the farmer is ready for threshing it with a wain.

Before rice is ready for cooking it has to be husked (*pūst kandan, safīd kardan*). In its simplest form this is done in the bronze household mortar (*hāvan*). Peasants who deliver polished rice to the market use a large wooden or stone mortar (*jouġan*) into which the rice pounder places 6 to 10 pounds of unhusked rice (*jou, šaltūk, čaltūk*) and pounds it with a double-ended wooden pestle (*dasteh-jouġan*). Rice huskers (*berenj-kūb*) who do this work for a living have still larger stone mortars and a kind of seesaw lever (*dang-e berenj-kūb, pātang*), with the pestle attached to one end just above the mortar. The pounder, by jumping on the other end, lifts the lever end. When he lets it go the pestle drops heavily into the mortar. He adds a small quantity of the mineral meerschaum (*kaf-e daryā*) to the grain in the mortar, which acts as a polishing agent.

In the Caspian provinces, where more rice is grown than wheat, the husking is done in water mills (*andang, āb-dang*). The husking mills in the coastal plains are driven by large undershot wheels. Such a wheel has a heavy wooden shaft (*tīr*) that runs through the full length of the mill and carries a series of cams (*kūtīnā, čobelāq*) that are inserted into slots (*čūneh*) in the shaft and held in position by wedges (*čūb-e pārs*). Of the previously mentioned seesaw levers (*pol*) 12 to 15 are arranged along the main shaft, each one pivoted to wooden uprights by means of strong wooden pegs (*marzeh*). As the shaft turns the cams lift the levers in succession and let the pestle (*sāreh*) at the end of each lever (Fig. 408) drop into a mortar (*čāleh*) from a height of about 18 inches. The pestle is studded with roughened (*borīdeh*) iron spikes (*dandāneh-*

Figure 408 The Pestle of a Rice-Husking Mill

āhan) that are held together with a forged iron band (*dalband*). If the husker wants to empty and refill a mortar he suspends the lever for a while by a rope hanging down from the ceiling.

In the Alburz mountains, where higher water heads are available, the water for the husking mills is led through a hollowed tree trunk (*nāv, nāb*) to drive a kind of Pelton wheel consisting of a horizontal shaft into which 16 scooped blades (*par, parreh*), each 3 feet long, have been inserted. The shaft has a single cam that operates a single pestle lever (Fig. 409). Usually a series of these husking mills follow one another as the water descends. Many of these mills are now used for millet (*arzan*) cleaning, since more and more rice is treated in modern motorized husking plants.

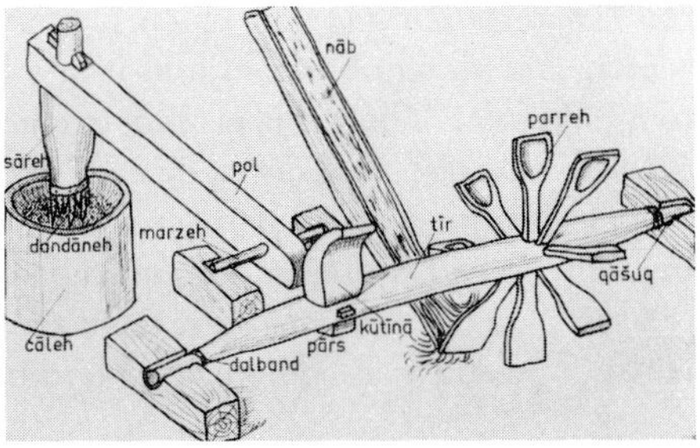

Figure 409 A Rice Mill in Māzandarān

Bread Baking

Most of the bread (*nān, nūn*) eaten in Persia is wheaten flat bread. Only in some rice-growing districts, e.g., the Caspian provinces, was a rice bread customary[124] which has lately been largely replaced by bread from wheat flour from the Plateau.

The more common bread varieties are:

1. *Nān-e sāj*, an unleavened bread (*nān-e faṭīrī*) baked by the nomads in the open, about $\frac{1}{8}$-inch thick.

2. *Nān-e tābūn*, a bread similar to this, also baked by the nomads, but in a primitive underground oven.

3. *Lavāš*, a thin, crisp bread, about $\frac{1}{8}$-inch thick, unleavened or mildly leavened. This bread is also known as *nān-e tanūrī, nān-e tāftūn*. A bread made from the same dough, but stretched out particularly thinly is known as *nān-e ḫūnegī*. After baking it is almost as thin as paper.

4. *Sangak* is a bread particularly popular in large cities. It is softer than the *lavāš* and about $\frac{3}{8}$-inch thick and leavened. It is also called *nān-e ḫamīrī*.

5. *Nān-e barbarī* is a bread of medium hardness, about $\frac{3}{4}$-inch thick and leavened like the *sangak*. It has its name from a community of Berbers which one of the Qajār *šāhs* settled south of Tehrān during the last century.

6. *Nān-e rouġanī* or *nān-e ḫošk, ḫoškeh* is made from an unleavened dough but contains fat in the form of melted sheep's butter (*rouġan-e gūsfand*). After baking it becomes dry and brittle like biscuits. It is available unsweetened or "ordinary" (*ma'mulī*), often sprinkled with sesame seed (*konjed*), and in a sweet variety (*šīrīn*) for which grape syrup (*šīreh*) or sugar (*šakar*) is added to the dough.

7. *Nān-e šīrmāl, nān-e daštarī* is a fine bread, more like a cake, eaten on feast days.

8. *Ġolāj* is similar to *nān-e barbarī*, but baked to a thickness of about $1\frac{1}{2}$ inches. It is a popular bread in Māzandarān and Gorgān.

The most primitive form of bread baking is found among the nomadic tribes all over the country. Chardin, who traveled for the king of France in Persia between 1665 and 1668, gave a description that would not be much different today:[125]

[124] Ibn Ḥauqal, *op. cit.*, p. 179, and *Travels of Venetians*, p. 83.

[125] Sir J. Chardin, translated from E. Diez, *Iranische Kunst*, p. 211.

The baking is done daily and begins shortly before the meal starts. Whole meal and water are poured into a wooden mixing bowl and kneaded thoroughly. Then a fire is kindled between two stones, and a copper or steel plate is placed in position [Fig. 410]. The dough [*ḫamīr*] is molded into a flat cake, placed on to the hot plate and baked for about three minutes. In the meantime the next cake is prepared, and a person can bake the need for a family of twelve in one hour. Sometimes poppy seed is sprinkled over the dough after it has been placed onto the hot plate, or the bread is rubbed with Asa foetida [*ahing*] the gum of a desert plant [*Ferula foetida*] which gives the bread a peculiar taste. This bread [*nān-e sāj*] would have a diameter of 12 to 15 inches.

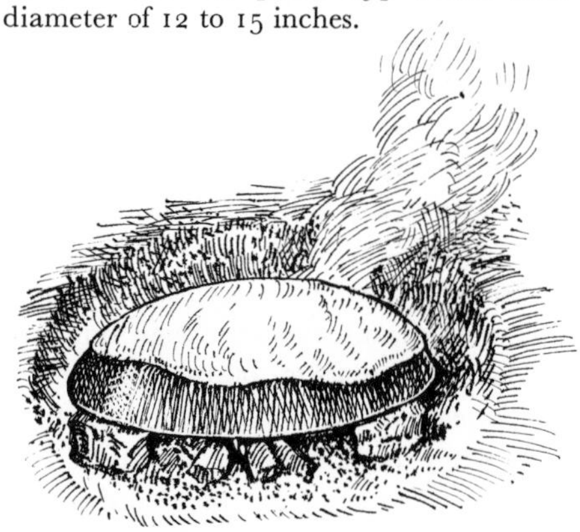

Figure 410 Baking on the Sāj

Another type of oven, known as *tābūn*, is used by the nomads of the north and the northwest. A fire is kept for a while in a clay-lined hole in the ground. When its walls are sufficiently hot the embers are taken out with an iron shovel, the flattened cake of dough is placed on the bottom of the hole, a steel plate or an earthenware dish is placed over it, and the whole is covered with the hot embers. After three to five minutes the bread is baked. An improvement on this oven is used by other nomads, e.g., those of Ḫorāsān and Balūčistān. Near their camp they dig a hole in the ground, place the excavated earth around its edge, and also dig an air duct (*bādkaš*, Fig. 411) leading to its bottom. The surface of this oven is smeared over

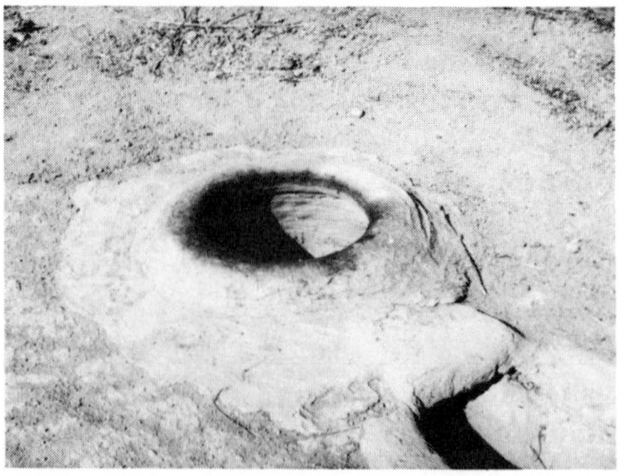

Figure 411 A Primitive Bread-Baking Oven

with a mixture of loam and water, and after drying a fire is lighted at the bottom, and when the walls are sufficiently hot the flattened dough is placed against them and baked.

This method is in fact the transition to the most common oven, viz., the drum oven (*tanūr*, *tāftūn*, *taftūn*), which is found in town and village bakeries and in many private homes. The core of this oven is formed by a huge earthenware vessel with an open bottom and a narrower top (Fig. 412). This vessel is placed over a fireplace (*āteš-ḫāneh*) in the ground where a charcoal fire (or nowadays an oil burner) obtains

Figure 412 Bread Baking in the Tanūr (*partly sectioned*)

its air through a channel that ends where the baker stands so that he can control the fire with a shutter operated by his foot. Since most baking has to be done shortly before the three meals of the day, breakfast (*ṣobḥāneh*), lunch (*nāhār*), and dinner (*šām*), there is usually a rush at the bakeries (*nān-pazī*) at these times, and most bakers work in teams to satisfy their customers' demand for oven-fresh bread. The first to start work, about two hours before baking begins, is the mixer (*ḫamīr-gīr*). Standing in front of a large trough (*taštak, tougal, ṭaġār*), he mixes (*āmīḫtan*) one part of wheat meal and six parts of water, adds salt, and, when required, the leaven (*āb-e torš*). The latter is made from left-over dough from the day before, dissolved in water and kept in a warm spot near the oven. After thorough kneading (*varzīdan*) by hand the dough is left for fermentation.

Shortly before baking time the dough former (*čūneh-gīr*) takes dough from the trough and shapes it into lumps (*čūneh, mošt,* background, Fig. 413). Although the law today requires weighing the dough lumps on a pair of scales the experienced baker usually forms them to the required size without weighing them. These lumps are taken over by the next man in the team, the dough flattener (*nān-pahn-kon*), who places one lump after the other on a marble block (*sang-e marmar*) and rolls (*vardāneh kardan*) each lump into a flat piece (*pahn*) about $\frac{3}{8}$-inch thick, using a wooden rolling pin (*vardāneh, ḫūneh, čūb-e nān-paz*). This finished, he throws the flat piece of dough across the bench to the dough stretcher (*vāvar, šātir*), who places it on a cotton-stuffed cushion (*nān-banā, navan, navand*) of 15 to 20 inches diameter and stretches (*čap kardan*) the dough right over the cushion (right side, Fig. 413), grips the underside of the cushion by a handle, inserts it into the hot oven, and

Figure 413 Baking of Lavāš

throws (*gozaštan*) it against the inside wall so that it sticks to it. His forearms are bandaged to protect him from the radiating heat inside the oven. He takes the cushion back to the bench, puts the next piece of flattened dough on it, etc. The youngest in the team, the baker's boy (*pādō*), does all the odd jobs such as getting water and meal to the trough, fuel to the oven, and so forth. The bread bakes partly through the heat accumulated in the oven walls and partly by direct radiating heat from the fire underneath. During the baking the bread develops bubbles (left foreground, Fig. 413). As soon as it is baked it begins to peel from the oven wall, and the oven man (*vardas*) picks it up with an iron skewer (*sīḫ*, *nān-čīn*) on a long wooden handle (right foreground, Fig. 413) just before it would drop into the fire. This bread (*nān-e tanūrī*, *nān-e taftān*, *lavāš*) is of good taste (and so are all the other bread types available in Persia), and while fresh it is crisp and resembles the Scandinavian Knäkke bread.

The same oven is used for baking the bread known as *nān-e rouġanī* or *ḫoškeh*. If a baker specializes in making this bread he is called *ḫoškeh-paz*.

Bakeries in the populous cities of Tehrān, Iṣfahān, and other provincial capitals could not manage to provide the amount of fresh bread that is needed at every mealtime by baking all this bread in drum ovens. A cheaper bread popular in these places is baked in huge ovens fired with wood (*hīzum*), dry desert shrubs (*ḫār*) or, lately, crude oil (*māzūt*). The oven (*tanūr-e sangakī*, *kūreh*, Fig. 414) contains an inclined, brick-built bank (*sang-kūh*) that is covered with clean river pebbles (*sangak*). In front of this bank there is a fireplace with an iron grill (*sehpāyeh*); fuel and combustion air enter through a hole in one side wall (*sūrāḫ-e zambūrak*, *sūlāḫ-e zambūrak*). The oven is covered with a vaulted cupola (*ṭāq*) made from sun-dried

Figure 414 Baking the Sangak Bread (*partly sectioned*)

bricks. It has one or two smoke holes (*dūd-kaš*). Two hours before baking begins the pebbles are leveled with a shovel (*sang-kūb*), and the firing begins. When the pebbles are hot enough, the fire is either switched over to another oven by means of an iron shutter, or the heat is reduced to maintain the baking temperature. The dough is prepared in the same way as the dough for the drum oven bread, but with the addition of yoghurt (*māst*) instead of leaven. The baker stands between the dough trough and a long-handled wooden shovel (*pārū*) with a blade about 18 inches square and slightly convex. The end of the blade rests on a ledge in front of the oven while the end of the long handle rests in a wooden fork. The baker wets the shovel blade with water (*āb-e ḫamīr*), takes a certain quantity of dough from the trough, and by beating it with his hands stretches it over the shovel blade (Fig. 415). He then takes the shovel by its handle, inserts the blade into the oven, and by turning it over, places the dough square on the hot pebbles. While he prepares the next charge his assistant observes the baking, which takes about two minutes. When baked the assistant takes the bread from the oven with a two-pronged fork (*dō-šāḫeh*). This bread, weighing about 1½ pounds, is soft and shows the imprints of the pebbles, hence its name "pebble bread" (*nān-e sangak(ī)*). Some customers like this bread with coriander seed (*siyāh-dāneh*), which is sprinkled over the dough before it is placed into the oven.

For the baking of the *barbarī* bread the baker rolls a slightly drier dough into thin coils and arranges them on the shovel side by side, with one coil surrounding them. The shovel with the dough coils is transferred to an oven similar to the pebble oven, but with a horizontal bottom and without pebbles.

All the bread described so far is wholesome but coarse bread (*nān-e ārd-ḫošk*). At certain times of the year special kinds of fine bread (*nān-e daštarī*) are baked. For the dough of this bread (*nān-e šīrmāl*),

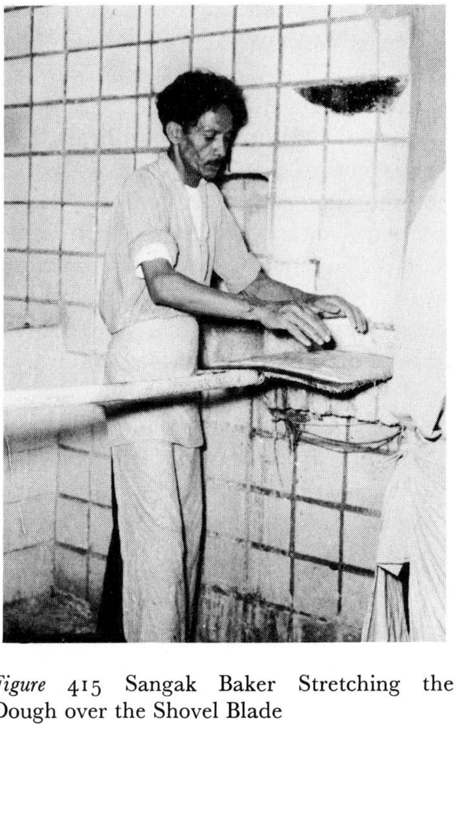

Figure 415 Sangak Baker Stretching the Dough over the Shovel Blade

Figure 416 Fine Bread

sugar (*šakar*), honey (*ᶜasal*), eggs (*toḫm-e morġ*), milk (*šīr*) and yoghurt (*māst*) are mixed with white flour (*ārd-e daštarī*), meal from which the coarser particles have been sifted off. After rolling and stretching on the cushion many slots are cut into the surface of the dough, and it is baked in the drum oven where the cuts open up, looking like lattice work (Fig. 416). Often poppy seed (*ḫašḫāš*), sesame (*konjed*), cardamom (*hēl*), or the grated roots of the nard plant (*sombol-e hindī, nārdīn, Nigella sativa*) are sprinkled over the dough before baking. People present one another with these breads, for instance, at the New Year celebrations, and for days the houses are filled with their sweet scent, contributing to the festive atmosphere.

Oil Milling

The fat needed in the diet of the Persian people comes from several sources. A certain amount is meat fat, especially the fat from the heavy tail (*dombeh*) of the oriental sheep, carefully kept by the housewife for cooking purposes. The most important one is melted butter (*rouġan-e kareh, rouġan-e gūsfand*), produced from sheep's and goat's butter and supplied by the nomadic tribesmen in sewn-up skins. Another substantial part of the edible fat is derived from oil seed growing in the country in reasonably large quantities, such as linseed (*bazr*), poppy seed (*ḫašḫāš*), cottonseed (*pambeh-dāneh*), rape (*mendāb, kakuj*), mustard seed (*kāpšeh*), and sesame (*konjed*). Certain oils are used for technical purposes, e.g., in tanning and painting. For the latter, linseed oil (*rouġan-e bazrak*) is widely used for the preparation of oil paints (*rang-e bazrak*). A certain mixture of cottonseed oil (*rouġan-e pambeh*) and castor oil (*rouġan-e bīdanjīr, rouġan-e karčak, rouġan-e berengīl*) was used as lamp oil (*rouġan-e čerāġ*), but oil lamps have been widely replaced by more modern lighting methods.

The edible oils from these seeds have different tastes and are valued accordingly. Much appreciated for cooking is sesame oil (*rouġan-e konjed, rouġan-e ḫwoš*); less valuable are cottonseed oil, poppy seed oil (*rouġan-e ḫašḫāš*), and an inexpensive mixture of rape oil (*rouġan-e mendāb, rouġan-e kakuj*) and mustard seed oil (*rouġan-e kāpšeh*), referred to as "bitter oil" (*rouġan-e talḫ*).

The Oil Mill

All these seeds are treated in the oil mill (*ᶜaṣṣārī, ᶜaṣṣār-ḫāneh, bazr-ḫāneh, rouġan-kadeh*) in the same way, viz., crushed (*sābīdan, narm kardan*) on an edge runner (*sang-e narm*) and the oil separated in a beam press (*kārmāleh*). Figure 417 shows a section through an oil mill at Iṣfahān with the edge runner in the center and the oil press extending from one side of the vaulted room to the other.

In comparing the Persian method of oil extraction with the one described in much detail by Cato the Elder (234–149 B.C.) and Vitruvius (about 16 B.C.),[126] it has been found that the pressing of the crushed material was done in ancient Italy and North Africa in essentially the same way as in Persia today. Only the ancient seed-crushing mechanism was different from the edge runner used in present day Persia. The Roman oil miller used as runners a pair of semispherical stones that rotated inside a large, hollow stone bed, shaped more like an oversized mortar, whereas the Persian runner has a single stone that is only mildly curved on its working edge. J. Needham credits the Chinese with the invention of the edge runner.[127] As nothing is known about the ancient methods of crushing oil seeds in Persia, it must be assumed that the edge runner they use now is of Chinese origin.

The edge runner (*sang-e narm, astarḫān*) works on a circular, brick-built platform (*lūbī, ḫeštak, tah-gāh*) that has a circular bed stone (*zīreh, sang-e tahgāh*) in the middle. A wooden center post (*mīzān, tīr-e zīrak, māskūh*) passes through a hole in the bed stone and is firmly embedded in the ground. A horizontal axle beam (*tīrak, tīr-e sang-e narm, lakeh*) runs in an iron pivot (*mīl-e mīzān, mīleh*) at the top of the center post. A lubricated hardwood block (*bālešmak*) between axle beam and center-post reduces friction, while the iron pivot pin runs inside a bearing block (*šāneh*) that is inserted into the horizontal beam. The shorter end of this axle beam is inserted into the edge-runner stone, which in its center has an iron or bronze bush (*ḫaštak, ḫīšteh, ḫištak*) to reduce friction, while a strong wedge (*ḫift*) on the outside keeps the stone on the beam. The runner is about 6 feet in diameter, 2 feet wide, and weighs over 4 tons. Both bed stone and runner are of a fine granite that the Iṣfahān oil millers (*ᶜaṣṣār*) obtain from a quarry at Lāsō near Kāšān.

A camel (*šotor*) with a draw harness (*sar-šāneh, teġeleh*) in front of its hump is hitched to the longer end of the axle beam

[126] T. Beck, *Beiträge zur Geschischte des Maschinenbaus*, pp. 38 and 68 ff. and A. Neuburger, *Die Technik des Altertums*, pp. 113 ff.

[127] J. Needham, *op. cit.*, Vol. 1, p. 240. In the opinion of the writer the difference between the Chinese edge runner and Cato's oil mill is only one of design, not of principle.

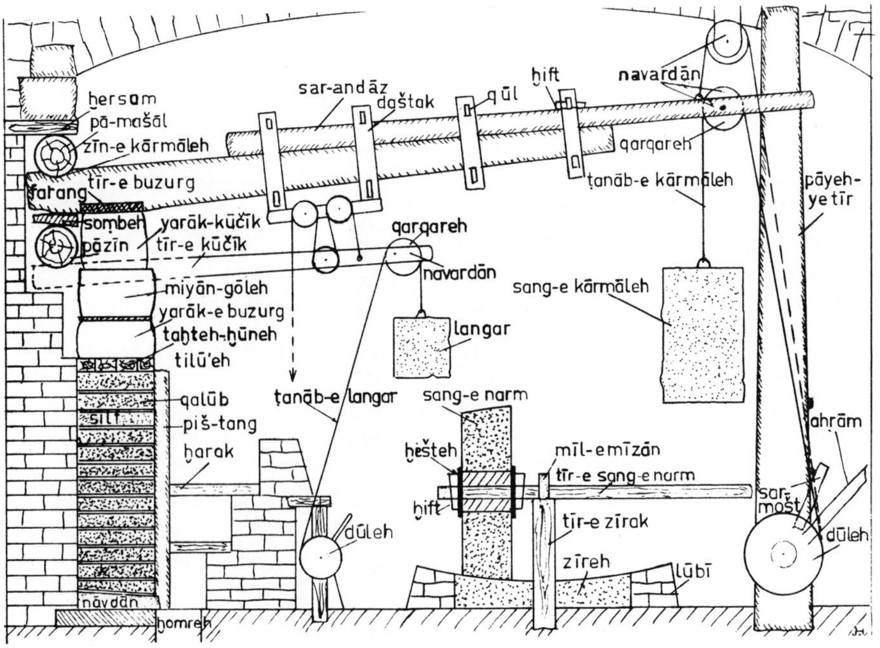

Figure 417 An Oil Mill (*section*)

while a light bar or leather belt (*sar-kaš*) ties the camel to the center post so that it can only walk on a circular path around the platform. Blinkers (*čašm-bandeh*) prevent the animal from becoming dizzy.

About 30 to 35 *man* (200–230 pounds) of oil seed are ground at a time. The grinding of this quantity takes about three hours, during which time the oil miller brings the crushed material (*gōleh*, *ḫamīr*) back into the path of the runner with a wooden shovel (*pārū*). Toward the end of the milling time the crushed seeds are moistened with water, and about 20 pounds of rice chaff (*kāh-berenj*) or, if this is not available, wheat chaff (*kāh-safīd*) or crushed wheat straw (*kāh-gandom*) are added. The addition of this dry material prevents the crushed seeds from becoming too pasty for the subsequent pressing process. The chaff also makes the oil cakes remaining after the pressing less rich and better digestible as fodder. When the chaff is well mixed in, about a dozen trays (*qālūb*, *qābī*), braided from strong rushes (*haṣīr*) or reeds (*ḫong*) and having a diameter of about 30 inches are placed in a circle around the mill bed. After a layer of clean straw (*kāh*) has been laid on each tray the miller shovels the crushed oil seeds onto the trays (Fig. 418), each of them taking about 20 pounds.

Figure 418 Placing the Ground Oil Seeds onto Trays

The filled trays are placed into a press pit (*tilouʾeh*) that takes about 36 of these trays representing the result of about three cycles of crushing on the edge runner. The press pit is a vertical brick-lined shaft about 12 feet deep and 32 inches in diameter with a narrow slot (*tang*) facing a work pit (Fig. 419). When the press pit has been filled with trays this slot is closed with a heavy beam (*pīš-tang*, right in Fig. 419) held in position by horizontal supporting beams (*ẖarak*). A particularly strong reed mat (*sar-māleh*) is placed on top of the last tray and then covered by four strong boards (*taẖteh-ẖūneh, ẖūneh-kār*) that together correspond to the size of the tray. In preparation for the preliminary pressing, the oil miller places a large wooden block (*yarāk-e buzurg*) on top of these boards and a medium-sized one (*miyān-gōleh*) over it, with a rush mat (*jol*) between them to prevent slipping. The blocks are pushed into the right position with a heavy wooden mallet (*gerdekū*).

Before the pit is loaded, the main beam (*tīr-e buzurg*) and the short beam (*tīr-e kūčik*) suspended from it are lifted with the big winch (*dūleh*) operated by capstan levers (*ahrām*, Fig. 420). After each quarter turn a locking peg (*sar-mošt(ī)*, *sar-mošteh*) is inserted into the winch drum to prevent it from running back.

The main beam has a particularly strong bearing (Fig. 417) that consists of two heavy cross beams built into the wall, a lower one (*pā-zīn*) to take the weight of the press beam and an upper one (*pā-mašāl*) to take the reaction forces during the actual pressing. The upper bearing is forced against a heavy wooden board (*ẖersom*) likewise built into the wall above it. The bearing end of the main pressing

Figure 419 A Press Pit Filled with Trays

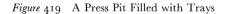

Figure 420 A Large Winch and a Counter Weight

beam has a saddle-like depression (*zīn-e kārmāleh*) on its upper side that prevents it from slipping out of its bearing. Where the press beam's underside comes into contact with the pressing blocks, a steel plate (*farang*) protects it from undue wear. A wedge (*soṃbeh*) beneath the beam keeps it in contact with the bearing. In its middle section, where it is most severely stressed, the main beam is strengthened by a reinforcing beam (*sar-andāz*) clamped on with a number of vertical wooden bars (*dastak*), held together by horizontal bars (*qūl*) and secured by wooden wedges (*ḥift*).

During the preliminary pressing stage, which is carried out with the short beam, the main beam is kept up by a vertical support (*ḥammāl-e tīr-e buzurg*), placed under its free end between two heavy upright posts (*pāyeh-ye tīr*) that carry the shaft of the big winch between their lower ends. The short beam is let down on two blocks, thus compressing the pile of trays with the crushed seeds on them. Pressure is exerted in the following way: A rope (*ṭanāb-e langar*) runs from a small winch over a tackle block (*navardān*) with a sheaf pulley (*qarqareh*) attached to the free end of the short beam to a stone weight (*langar, sang-e buneh*). This stone is gradually raised by operating the small winch (*dūleh*), and as it descends it lowers the beam, thus compressing the trays in the pit. When the stone has reached the ground it is detached from the rope, the beam is lifted and swayed sideways, the two wooden blocks, the reed mat, and the boards covering the trays are removed, and the press pit is filled up with more trays. Then everything is placed in position again; this time an extra large wooden block (*šāgerdeh*) is placed next to the trays, and the two former ones are put on top of it.

Now the main pressing beam is lowered onto the blocks, and for about half an hour the weight of this heavy beam is sufficient to press a considerable amount of oil from the seeds on the trays. The oil runs down to the bottom of the pit, which is formed by a stone with a gutter (*nāvdān*) on one side. This leads the oil into a brick-lined sump (*ḥomreh*). When the beam no longer moves under its own weight, the oil miller and his assistants attach a heavy stone (*sang-e kārmāleh*), weighing about 2.8 tons, to it. This stone operates in a similar way to the one described above for the short press beam. It is lifted with the main capstan to a height of 10 to 12 feet. The capstan levers are 13 feet long. The miller inserts a lever into one of the capstan holes so that it is almost vertical, climbs up the lever, and when he reaches the end of it, holding on with his hands he swings his body away from the lever, thus setting the winch drum in motion. As soon as he lands on the ground he holds the lever there while his assistant places another lever into the next hole, climbs up, and swings out. At this moment the miller withdraws his lever, making room for the assistant to land on the ground, himself being free to insert his lever into a further capstan hole, and so on. During the subsequent 48 hours the stone has to be lifted again in this way from time to time until no more lowering of the press beam can be observed and no more oil issues from the trays.

By that time the 110 *man* (720 pounds) of the total filling of the trays have yielded about 33 *man* (216 pounds) of poppy seed oil or castor oil, or, in the case of linseed or rape, 22 *man* (145 pounds). After the completion of the pressing the beams are lifted, the wooden blocks removed, and the dry trays separated with a wooden bar (*kūpīkan*) and lifted out of the press pit. The oil cakes (*silf*) are taken from the trays, broken into lumps (*berz*), and stored in basket-like shallow containers (*ġarbār, ġalbāl*). Oil cakes from linseed, rape, poppy seed and cottonseed are used as supplementary fodder for camels, donkeys, and cattle, whereas the castor oil cakes can only be used as manure. The oil is scooped out of the sump and poured into glazed earthenware jars (*rouġan-dūreh*) in which it is sold in the bazaar.

Other Uses of the Edge Runner

The edge runner of the oil mill is fully occupied to crush all the oil seeds for the subsequent oil pressing. In the larger bazaars there are, however, edge runners operating for a variety of raw materials. These edge mill shops (*ḫān-e sābā*) charge their clients on the basis of weight of the commodities crushed and ground. The latter include rock salt (*namak*), potash (*qaliyāb, keliyāb*) and whiting (*sang-e safīdāb*). There is a great demand for whiting as a massaging agent in the bath (*ḥammām*) and for industrial uses. The edge miller usually performs all the relevant operations, like crushing the raw minerals under the edge runner (*kūbīdan zīr-e sang*), washing (*šostan*) the crushed whiting in a vat (*taġār, ṭaġār bār-šūrī*), filtering off the fine mineral (*loᶜāb*) from the coarse, and returning the latter to the edge-runner. Organic matter treated under the edge runner includes the rind of the pomegranate (*pūst-e anār*) and the gall nut (*māzū*), both for tanning, henna leaves (*ḥanā*), used for hair washing and dyeing, the spice turmeric (*zard-čūbeh*), and the medicinal herb soapwort (*pošveh, čūbak*).

Making of Syrup and Sweets

Most Persians are very fond of sweets. Many sweet dishes are prepared with grape syrup (*šīreh-angūr, dūšāb*). Grape syrup is made in regions too far away from the markets for the sale of fresh grapes, or in the sultana and currant regions from any surplus grapes not converted into dried fruit. The juice is separated from the grapes by pressing (*tang kardan*). This is either done in screw presses (*tang*) or in the following way: The grapes are placed in a large bag (*kīseh*) made from strong hand-woven cotton (*karbās*). A rope, forming a loop (*ḥalqeh*) under the middle of the bag, has been sewn along its sides. The closed bag is hung from a horizontal beam (*tīr*) that rests on two upright posts (*pāyeh*). A copper dish about 4 feet in diameter and one foot deep (*dīg*) underneath receives the juice. A twisting pole is placed through the loop under the bag, and two persons walk around the dish with its ends, thus twisting the bag and forcing the juice out. Toward the end of the pressing a pair of animals, usually donkeys or mules, take over. When this juice is boiled into a thick syrup it becomes a commodity that can easily be stored in earthenware jars, where it lasts almost indefinitely. Pomegranate juice is similarly treated; the resulting syrup (*robb-e anār*) is almost black and an indispensable ingredient for a number of sweet and sour meat dishes.

For sweetening their tea, the national drink, the Persians like very hard and sweet sugar lumps and therefore prefer candy (*qand, nabāt*) and loaf sugar (*qand-e kalleh*) to the finely crystallized, less sweet refinery sugar. The latter is today produced in modern sugar mills throughout the country. Its conversion into candy and sugar loaves (*kalleh-qand*) is done in the bazaar by the confectioner (*qannād*). For making sugar loaves he dissolves refinery sugar (*šakar*) in a large copper boiler (*pātīl*), and brings it to the boil (*puḫtan*) under constant stirring with a wooden paddle (*kamānčeh*). When sufficient water has evaporated he pours the solution into cast iron molds (*qāleb*) and leaves them to crystallize into sugar loaves. For the production of candy crystals, sticks are placed across the boiler from which cotton threads are suspended. The solution is left to cool, and the more time this cooling is given and the less the solution is disturbed the larger the crystals become which form around the strings. The remaining solution (*āb-e nabāt*), from which no more crystals can be produced, is the raw material for a hard, boiled sweet called *āb-nabāt*. By further boiling to evaporate more water the sugar is caramelized and then left to cool sufficiently so that it can be worked by hand. The confectioner takes a lump of this boiled sugar mass (*bār gereftan*) from the boiler (Fig. 421), draws it into a strand (*sar kašīdan*), and cuts pieces off (*čīdan*) with a knife (*kārd*) or a pair of scissors (*qaičī*). All this is done while the mass is still warm. The soft sugar lumps drop down on a large tray where the confectioner's assistants flatten them (*pahn kardan*) with iron pestles (*mošteh*) before they harden (Fig. 422).

Figure 421 Drawing the Boiled Sugar into Strands

A sweet much celebrated over the centuries in fairy tales and poetry is *ḥalvāᶜ*, which is made by a specialist confectioner, the *ḥalvāᶜ-paz*. The raw materials are raisins, sugar, and sesame. Raisins (*kašmeš*) are soaked in water in large vats. The resulting juice is boiled into raisin syrup (*šīreh-kašmeš*) in a semispherical copper pan (*pātī*) about 4 feet in diameter, inclined about 45° and built into a brick fireplace. Glazed tiles surround the rim of the copper pan. Sugar is added to the syrup, and the whole is thickened (*seft*

Figure 422 Sugar Boilers and a Pressing Tray

kardan, ḫošk kardan) while the confectioner constantly stirs it with a wooden paddle (*kamānčeh*), the working end of which is shaped like a shovel. He throws the mixture up and against the back extension of the pan from where it runs back, losing much of its water with every throw. Meanwhile sesame (*konjed*) has been sifted (*bīḫtan*) to remove impurities, washed (*šostan*) in water, and dried (*būm kardan, ḫošk kardan*) on a separate platform heated by an oil fire from underneath. When dry and still warm the seeds are transferred to a small edge runner (*āsiyāb-e konjed, sang-e vardeh*) that is driven by a donkey. It crushes the seeds into an oily paste (*ārdeh*).

For the making of hard *ḥalvāᶜ*, sesame paste corresponding to half the amount of boiling syrup is added to the latter, thoroughly stirred in and boiled for a short time. Then the mass is ladled out onto flat trays, sprinkled with crushed pistachio kernels and left to harden. After hardening the *ḥalvāᶜ* is broken into pieces and is then ready for sale. Some confectioners pour the mass onto trays, and after sufficient cooling form it into small cakes about 4 inches in diameter and ⅛-inch thick.

For the softer variety of *ḥalvāᶜ*, equal amounts of boiling syrup and sesame paste are mixed, and after another short boiling left to cool to a temperature that enables the confectioner to handle the mass. He takes a large lump, draws it into a long strand, folds it up, draws it out again, and repeats this many times, and all the time some of the sesame oil comes to the surface and forms a film that prevents the coils from sticking together. After he has continued this process for about half an hour the sweet consists of hair-thin threads, each surrounded by a thin film of sesame oil. This mass is pressed onto a large tray (Fig. 423) and after complete cooling is cut into blocks, ready to be sold.

Figure 423 A Confectioner Spreading Ḥalvāᶜ onto a Tray

Another sweet, tasting more like nougat, is made from a white substance called *gaz* or *gaz-angebīn*. This substance is often referred to as manna. It is produced between June and August by a plant louse living on the leaves of the manna tamarisk (*Tamarix mannifera, gaz*), certain willows (*bīd*), and the shrub *šīrḫešk* (*Cotoneaster nummularia*). The manna exuded by the insects dries on the leaves and peels off. It is collected by women and children. It can be used for the sizing of warp threads, but the greater part of it is bought by the confectioners. The confectioner beats it up with eggs and sugar, flavors the mix with rose water, and mixes crushed pistachio kernels in. Finally he forms the mass into cakes about 1 inch in diameter and ½-inch thick, and packs it into boxes together with wheat meal. This prevents softening of the highly hygroscopic sweet during transport and storage. Before eating the sweet the wheat meal is just shaken off. Today the small cakes are individually wrapped in plastic.

OUTLOOK

From late Ṣafavid times on, increasing poverty has unfortunately gone hand in hand with continuous decay in the standards of many craftsmen's work. Poverty reached an all-time low when after the end of World War I the last Qājār ruler had taken his country's crown jewels with him to Paris, and taxes and revenues were pawned as securities for loans advanced by the Western powers. It is to the credit of the late Reżā Šāh that he brought Persia on the road toward economic health and prosperity again by a program of vigorous industrialization in which both private enterprise and state-controlled industries played equally important parts. This is true in spite of errors in planning and hardships to individuals.

His program of establishing industries had a two-fold drive: to produce goods for home consumption and to yield a surplus for currency-earning exports. One of the first steps in this direction was in the field of metallurgy, namely, the reopening and modernization of the ancient mines in the Anārak district for the production of copper, lead, zinc, and antimony. Since 1935 a modern electrolytic plant near Tehrān does the refining of some of these metals. The systematic prospecting for minerals since about 1930 has resulted in the discovery of important deposits of high-grade iron, and the construction of blast furnaces and steel works is planned for the near future.

Cement works in several provinces are an outward sign that the country is changing from sun-dried mud bricks to reinforced concrete structures for many of its buildings. A modern ceramic industry provides articles for the sanitation programs of many municipalities, while several glass works produce for the needs of the builder and provide containers for the food industry. This country that for centuries has been poor in timber supplies, and still is, now makes more economical use of its resources in the form of plywood produced in a number of mills, mainly in the forest districts of the Caspian provinces. The use of timber for fuel has almost completely ceased, and only wood that would otherwise be useless is still converted into charcoal. The greater amount of fuel for industrial and domestic uses today comes from modern hard coal mines and oil refineries. Several factories manufacture efficient stoves and bath and room heaters to be operated with these fuels, and some even produce thermostatically controlled units.

One of the most striking transitions has taken place in the textile industry. Many textile mills have been built between the two world wars where wool, cotton, and silk are spun into yarns of good quality and woven into cloths on modern machines. The center of the wool and cotton industry is Iṣfahān, the city with the great tradition in this field, but most of the other provincial capitals have textile factories too. The modern silk industry is located around Šāhī and Ašraf in Māzandarān.

Most of the hides from the pastoral industry are now treated in modern tanning works that produce all the leather needed by the state-owned shoe factories and by the numerous bazaar shoemakers.

A similar, although slower, transition toward modern methods is taking place in the most conservative of all industries, agriculture. Tractor-drawn multiple-disk plows, seeder drills, and self-propelled combines are no longer a novelty, at least not in the richer provinces of Ḫūzistān, Āẕarbaijān, and Māzandarān, or the fertile plains around Tehrān. An increasing number of Diesel-driven motor pumps supplement the *qanāt* to obtain water for irrigation. Once the problems arising from the traditional relationship between landlord and peasant are solved, a wider use of mechanical agricultural equipment in rural cooperatives will be possible. The increased use of fertilizers and the combating of pests are responsible for higher returns, and a country-wide system of wheat silos has considerably reduced grain losses.

This is not the place to argue in favor of the retention of often highly interesting traditional crafts or to plead for modern economical methods for the benefit and welfare of the greatest number of the country's citizens. The decisions had to be made in favor of the latter. Political wisdom, finding a strong desire for a higher standard of living in all these brave and hard-working people, was left no alternative. In this process of industrialization, one fact seems to be indisputable, namely that the country's age-old tradition in industrial arts, always adaptable to new conditions, has been and will be of great help in this most significant change.

BIBLIOGRAPHY

Ackerman, P. "Persian Textiles," *Ciba Review*, No. 98 (June 1953), pp. 3506–3535.

"Agricultural and Industrial Activity and Manpower in Iran," *International Labour Review* (Geneva), Vol. 59 (May 1949), pp. 550–562.

Al-Balkhi. *Description of the Province of Fars*. Translated by G. Le Strange. London, 1912.

Al-Dimashqī, Mohammad ibn ᶜAlī Tālib. *Manuel de la Cosmographie du Moyen Age*. Translated by Mehren. Paris, 1874.

Al-Hamdānī. *Sources of Gold and Silver*. See Dunlop, D. M.

Al-Ḫāzīnī. *Al kitāb mīzān al ḥikma* (*The Book of the Balance of Wisdom*). Translated by N. Khanikoff. *Journal of the American Oriental Society*, Vol. 6, No. 1 (1860).

Al-Masᶜūdī, ᶜAli ibn Ḥusain. *El Masᶜūdī's Historical Encyclopedia, entitled Meadows of Gold and Mines of Gems*. Translated from the Arabic by A. Sprenger. London, 1841.

Amman, Jost. *Eygentliche Beschreibung aller Stände* (*The Book of Trades*). Frankfurt, 1568.

Anossoff, P. A. "On the Bulat," in *Gorny Journal*, Petersburg, 1841 (Russian); in *Annuaire du Journal des Mines en Russie 1843* (French); in *Archiv für wissenschaftliche Kunde von Russland*, Vol. 9, p. 510 (German). See Belaiew, N., "On the Bulat."

Apollonius of Rhodes. *Opera*. Translated by W. Preston. 1810–1813.

Arberry, A. J. *The Legacy of Persia*. Oxford, 1953.

Aristophanes. *Opera*. Text edited by Bergk. 2 vols. Teubner, 1867.

Arnold, Sir. T. W. *The Legacy of Islam*. Oxford, 1931.

Avesta. See *The Zend Avesta*.

Bagchi, P. C. *India and China, 1,000 Years of Sino-Indian Cultural Relations*. Bombay, 1944.

Barbaro, J., and Contarini, A. *Travels to Tana and Persia*. Hakluyt Society Edition, Ser. 1, Vol. 49 (1873).

Beal, S. (translator). *Si-Yu-Ki, Buddhist Records of the Western World*. 2 vols. London, 1884–1906.

Beck, L. *Die Geschichte des Eisens in technischer und kulturgeschichtlicher Beziehung*. Braunschweig, 1884–1903.

Beck, T. *Beiträge zur Geschichte des Maschinenbaus*. Berlin, 1899.

Beckett, P. H. T. "The Soils of Kerman, South Persia," *Journal of Soil Science*, March 1958, pp. 20–32.

Beckett, P. H. T. "Agriculture in Central Persia," *Tropical Agriculture*, Vol. 34 (1957), pp. 9–28.

———. "Tools and Crafts in South Central Persia," *Man*, Vol. 57 (Oct. 1957), pp. 145–148.

———. "Qanats Around Kerman," *Royal Central Asian Journal*, Vol. 40 (1953), pp. 47–57.

———. "Waters of Persia," *Geographical Magazine*, Vol. 24 (1951), p. 230.

———. "Qanats in Persia," *Journal of the Iranian Society* (London), Vol. 1, p. 125.

Beckett, P. H. T., and Gordon, E. "The Climate of South Persia," *Quarterly Journal of the Royal Meteorological Society*, Vol. 82 (1956), pp. 503–514.

Beckmann, J. *A History of Discoveries, Inventions and Origins*. Translated from the German. London, 1846.

———. *Paradoxographoi or Scriptores Rerum Mirabilium*. Göttingen, 1786, and London, Westermann, 1839.

Belaiew, N. "Damascene Steel," *The Journal of the Iron and Steel Institute*, Vol. 97 (1918), pp. 417 ff.

———. "On the Bulat" (Russian, *O Bulatah*), Petersburg, 1906, and "Über Damast," *Metallurgie*, 1911.

Bellinger, L. "Textile Analysis, Early Techniques in Egypt and the Near East," *Workshop Notes*, Parts 2, 3, 6, Textile Museum, Washington, 1952.

Bent, J. T. "Village Life in Persia," *New Review*, October 1891.

Bernison, E. W. *Ground Water*. St. Paul, Minnesota, 1947.

Beveridge, H. "The Papermills of Samarkand," *Asiatic Quarterly Review*, 1910, pp. 160–164.

Biringuccio, V. *Pirotechnia*. 1st edition, Venice, 1540.

Biringuccio's *Pirotechnia*. Edited by O. Johannsen (German translation). Braunschweig, 1925.

Biringuccio, Vannoccio. *The Pirotechnia*. Translated with introduction and notes by Cyril Stanley Smith and Martha Teach Gnudi. Published in 1942 by the American Institute of Mining and Metallurgical Engineers, and reissued in 1959 by Basic Books, Inc., New York. M.I.T. Press Paperback Edition published in March 1966.

Blümner, H. *Die gewerbliche Tätigkeit der Völker des klassischen Altertums*. Leipzig, 1869.

———. *Technologie und Terminologie der Künste und Gewerbe bei den Griechen und Römern*. 4 vols. Leipzig, 1887.

Böhne, E. "Die Eisenindustrie Masenderans," *Stahl und Eisen*, Vol. 48 (1928), p. 1577.

———. "Überlick über die Erzlagerstätten Persiens und den derzeitigen Stand von Gewinnung und Verhüttung," *Metall und Erz*, Vol. 26 (1929), pp. 57–61.

Bosch, K. G. "Islamic Bookbinding: 12th–17th Centuries." Unpublished Ph.D. dissertation, University of Chicago, 1922.

Bossert, H. T. *Geschichte des Kunstgewerbes aller Zeiten und Völker*. 6 vols. 1928.

Braun, E. W. "Das Kunstgewerbe im Kulturgebiet des Islam." In Lehnert, G. *Illustrierte Geschichte des Kunstgewerbes*, Vol. 2 (Berlin, 1909), pp. 627–717.

Braun-Ronsdorf, M. "Gold and Silver Fabrics from Mediaeval to Modern Times," *Ciba Review*, 1961–1963, pp. 2–16.

———. "Silk Damasks" and "Linen Damasks," *Ciba Review*, No. 110 (June 1955), pp. 3983–4002.

Bréant, J. R. "Description d'un procédé à l'aide duquel on obtient une espèce d'acier fondu semblable à celui des lames damassées orientales," *Bulletin de la Société d'Encouragement pour l'Industrie Nationale*, Vol. 22 (1823) pp. 222–227.

Bretschneider, E. *Mediaeval Researches from Eastern Sources*. 2 vols. London, 1888.

———. *History of European Botanic Discoveries in China*. 1898.

———. *Botanicon Sinicum*. 3 vols. London, 1882.

Brown, H. B. *Cotton*. New York and London, 1938.

Brown, T. B. *Excavations in Azarbaijan, 1948*. London, 1951.

———. "Iron Objects from Azarbaijan" (Second Report of Ancient Mining and Metallurgy Committee), *Man*, January 1950, pp. 7–9.

Brugsch, H. C. *Die Reise der königlich preussischen Gesandtschaft nach Persien 1860–61*. 2 vols. Leipzig, 1862.

Butler, M. A. "Irrigation in Persia by Kanats," *Civil Engineering* (American), Vol. 3, No. 2 (1933), pp. 69–73.

Cameron, G. G. *History of Early Iran*. Chicago, 1936.

Candolle, A. de. See De Candolle.

Case, P. E. "I Became a Bakhtiari," *The National Geographic*, Vol. 91 (March 1947), pp. 325–358.

Chardin, Sir J. *Travels in Persia.* (A reprint of a 1720–1724 English edition.) London, 1927.

Childe, G. V. *What Happened in History?* Penguin Books, 1942.

———. "India and the West before Darius," *Antiquity,* Vol. 13 (1939), p. 5.

Chinese Repository, Vol. 5 (1837), p. 485. Description of the agricultural implements used by the Chinese.

Christensen, A. *L'Iran sous les Sassanides.* Copenhagen, 1936.

Chronicles of the Carmelites in Persia and the Papal Mission of the Seventeenth Century. 2 vols. London, 1939.

Claudianus, C. *Carmina.* Berlin, 1892.

Clément-Hallet, J. J. "Sur les noms des céréales chez les anciens," *Journal Asiatique,* Sixième Série, Vols. 5–6 (1865), p. 185.

Coghlan, H. H. "Native Copper in Relation to Prehistory," *Man,* 1951, pp. 90 ff.

———. *Notes on Prehistoric and Early Iron in the Old World.* Oxford, 1956.

———. "Some Fresh Aspects of the Prehistoric Metallurgy of Copper," *Antiquaries Journal,* Vol. 22 (1942), pp. 22 ff.

———. *Notes on the Prehistoric History of Copper and Bronze in the Old World.* Oxford, 1951.

———. "The Evolution of the Axe from Prehistoric to Roman Times," *Journal of the Royal Anthropological Institute,* Vol. 73 (1943), pp. 27–56.

Contenau, G., and Ghirshman, R. *Fouilles de Tépé Giyan.* Paris, 1935.

Coomaraswamy, A. K. *The Treatise of Al-Jazarī on Automata.* Boston, 1924.

Costa, A., and Lockhart, L. *Persia.* Thames and Hudson, Ltd., London, 1957.

Covarrubias, M. *The Island of Bali.* New York, 1937.

Creswell, K. A. C. *A Bibliography of Arms and Armour in Islam.* London, 1956.

———. *Early Muslim Architecture.* 2 vols. 1932–1940.

———. *A Short Account of Early Muslim Architecture.* London, Penguin edition, 1958.

Curzon, Lord G. N. *Persia and the Persian Question.* London, 1892.

Darmstädter, L. *Handbuch zur Geschichte der Naturwissenschaften und der Technik.* Berlin, 1908.

De Candolle, A. *Origin of Cultivated Plants.* London, 1886.

Deerr, N. *The History of Sugar.* 2 vols. London, 1949.

Della Valle, P. *Fameux Voyages de Pietro della Valle.* 4 vols. Paris, 1669.

De Morgan, J. J. M. *Délégation en Perse.* 4 vols. Paris, 1900–1902.

———. *Mission scientifique en Perse.* Paris, 1894–1904.

Dewar, M. L. "Pigeon Towers and Pigeon Guano in Iran," *World Crops,* Vol. 7 (1957), p. 102.

Dickmann, H. "Chinesischer Eisenguss," *Stahl und Eisen,* Vol. 57 (1937), p. 528.

Didérot, D. (with d'Alembert, J.) *Encyclopédie ou Dictionnaire Raisonné des Sciences et des Arts et Métiers.* (17 vols. text, 11 vols. plates). Paris, 1763.

Diez, E. *Chorassanische Baudenkmäler.* Berlin, 1918.

———. *Iranische Kunst.* Vienna, 1944.

Dodwell, C. R. *Theophilus, The Various Arts* (Latin-English edition). London, 1961.

Dono, T. S. "The Chemical Investigation of the Ancient Metallic Cultures in the Orient," *Journal of the Faculty of Science of the Imperial University of Tokyo,* Sect. I, Vol. III, Part 6 (1937), pp. 287–325.

Dörpfeld, W. *Troja und Ilion.* Athens, 1902.

Drouville, G. *Voyage en Perse.* 2 vols. Petersburg, 1819.

Du Mans, R. See Raphaël, le père.

Dunlop, D. M. "Sources of Gold and Silver in Islam According to Al Hamdānī" [tenth century A.D.], *Studia Islamica,* Fascicule 8 (1957).

Eberhard, W. *Early Chinese Culture and Its Development.* London, 1950.

Eras, V. J. M. *Locks and Keys Through the Ages.* Dordrecht, 1957.

Erdmann, K. *Der orientalische Knüpfteppich.* Wasmuth Verlag, Tübingen, 1960.

Falke, O. See Von Falke.

Farman, H. F. *Iran, a Selected and Annotated Bibliography.* Washington, 1951.

Feldhaus, F. M. *Die Technik der Antike und des Mittelalters.* 1st ed. Potsdam, 1931; 2nd ed. Cologne, 1953.

Ferrand, G. *Relations de voyages et textes géographes arabes, persans et turcs relatifs à l'Extrême-Orient.* Paris, 1913.

Fisher, B. "Irrigation Systems of Persia," *Geographical Review* (1928) (New York), Vol. 18, pp. 302–306.

Forbes, R. J. *Metallurgy in Antiquity.* Leiden, 1950.

———. *Man the Maker, A History of Technology and Engineering.* London, 1950.

———. *Studies in Ancient Technology.* 6 vols. Leiden, 1955–1958.

Forster, G. *A Journey from Bengal to England*. 2 vols. London, 1798.

Foster, W. *Thomas Herbert's Travels*. London, 1928.

Fox-Pitt-Rivers, Lt. Col. *On the Development and Distribution of Primitive Locks and Keys*. London, 1883.

Franke, O. *Keng Tschi T'u—Ackerbau und Seidengewinnung in China, Ein kaiserliches Lehr und Mahnbuch*. Hamburg, 1913.

Frankel, J. P. "The Origin of Indonesian Pamor," *Technology and Culture*, Winter 1963, pp. 14–21.

Frankfort, H. *The Arts and Architecture of the Ancient Orient*. Harmondsworth, 1954.

Freese, F. *Windmills and Mill Wrighting*. Cambridge, 1957.

Fryer, J. *A New Account of East Indies and Persia (Nine Years Travel 1672–1681)*. London, 1915.

Furnival, W. J. *Leadless Decorative Tiles, Faience and Mosaic*. Staffordshire, 1904.

Gabriel, A. *Im weltfernen Orient*. Munich, 1929.

———. *Durch Persiens Wüsten*. Stuttgart, 1935.

———. *Aus den Einsamkeiten Irans*. Stuttgart, 1939.

———. *Die Erforschung Persiens*. Vienna, 1952.

Gadd, C. J., and Campbell-Thompson, R. "A Middle Babylonian Chemical Text," *Iraq*, Vol. 3 (1936), 87–96.

Gauba, E. "Botanische Reisen in der persischen Dattelregion," *Annalen des Naturhistorischen Museums in Wien*, 1949–1953.

———. *Arbres et Arbustes des forêts caspiennes de l'Iran*. Publication of the Ministry of Agriculture, Tehran, 1317 A.H. 1938.

———. "Ein Besuch der kaspischen Wälder Nordpersiens," *Annalen des Naturhistorischen Museums in Wien*, Vol. 60 (1954–55, Dec. 1955), pp. 60–76.

Gershevitch, I. "Sissoo at Susa," *Bulletin of the School of Oriental and African Studies*, Vol. 19, No. 2 (1957), pp. 316–320.

Ghirshman, R. *Iran*. London, 1954.

———. *Fouilles de Sialk*. Vol. 1, Paris, 1938; Vol. 2, Paris, 1939.

———. "The Ziggurat at Tchoga Zanbil," *Scientific American*, Vol. 204, No. 1 (Jan. 1961), pp. 68–81.

———. "Tchoga Zanbil près de Suse," Rapport préliminaire de la 6e campagne, *AAS*, 1957, 4.

Gleisberg, H. "Herkunft und Verbreitung der Windmühlen," extract from *Technikgeschichte der Getreidemühle*, by the same author. Düsseldorf, 1956.

Goblot, H. "Le rôle de l'Iran dans les techniques de l'eau," *Techniques et sciences municipales*. Paris, Feb., 1961.

Gompertz, G. *The Master Craftsmen*. London, 1933.

Goodrich, L. Carrington. "Cotton in China," *Isis*, Vol. 34 (1942–43), pp. 409–411.

———. "China's Earliest Contacts with other Parts of Asia," The G. E. Morrison Lecture, 1961. Australian National University, Canberra, 1962.

Goris, R. "The Position of the Blacksmiths," *Bali, Studies in Life, Thought and Ritual*, Vol. 5 of *Selected Studies on Indonesia*, 1960, pp. 291–297.

Grumm-Grjmailo. "History of the Introduction of the Grape Vine to China," *Archives d'histoire de la technologie* (USSR), Vol. 5, No. 15 (1935).

Gupta, R. N. *Iran, an Economic Survey*. Published by Indian Institute of International Affairs, New Delhi, 1947.

Haas, W. *Iran*. New York, 1946.

Haim, S. *New Persian-English Dictionary*. 2 vols. Tehran, 1962.

———. *The Larger English-Persian Dictionary*. 2 vols. Tehran, 1959.

Hakluyt, R. *The Principal Navigations, Voyages and Discourses of the English Nation*. Vol. 2. London-New York, 1926.

Ḥamdullāh Mustawfī-ye Qazvīnī. *The Taʾrīḫ-e Guzīdeh*. Reproduction in facsimile and abridged translation by Edward G. Browne. Leiden, 1910–1913.

———. *The Geographical Parts of the Nuzhat-e qulūb*. Edited by G. Le Strange. Gibb Memorial Series. London-Leiden, 1915–1919.

———. *The Zoological Section of the Nuzhat-e qulūb* (Persian and English). Edited and translated by J. Stephenson. London, 1928.

———. *Nuzhat al-Ḳulūb*. Translated by M. C. Huart. Paris, 1905.

Hammer-Purgstall, J. "Sur les lames des orientaux," *Journal Asiatique*, Vols. 3–4 (1854), p. 66.

Hannak, G. "Japanischer Damaststahl," *Beiträge zur Geschichte der Technik und Industrie* Vol. 20 (1930), pp. 87–90.

Harnecker, K. "Beitrag zur Frage des Damaststahls," *Stahl und Eisen*, Vol. 44 (1924), pp. 1409 ff.

Hausbuch der Mendelschen Zwölfbrüderstiftung zu Nürnberg. Printed edition by Wilhelm Treue *et al*. Munich, 1966.

Hauser, G. F. "Comparison of the Afghan Plough and Tillage Methods with Modern Implements and Method," *Empire Journal of Experimental Agriculture* (London), Vol. 23 (1955), p. 75.

Hawley, W. A. *Oriental Rugs.* (London), New York, 1927.

Hawthorne, John G., and Smith, Cyril S. *On Divers Arts.* The treatise of Theophilus, translated with introduction and notes. Chicago, 1963.

Hedin, S. *Eine Routenaufnahme durch Ostpersien.* Stockholm, 1906 and 1908. 2nd ed., 1926.

———. *Zu Land nach Indien durch Persien, Seistan und Belutschistan.* Leipzig, 1910–1920.

———. *Overland to India.* London, 1910.

Heinecke, A. "Persia, a Land of Medieval Farming," *Science Monthly* (New York), Vol. 40 (1935), pp. 116–121.

Herodotus. *The Histories.* Translated and edited by A. de Selincourt. London, 1954.

Herzfeld, E. E. *Archaeological History of Iran.* London, 1935.

———. *Iran in the Ancient East.* Oxford, 1941.

Herzfeld, E. E., and Keith, A. "Iran as a Prehistoric Centre," in Pope, A. U. and Ackerman, Ph., *A Survey of Persian Art,* Vol. 1. London, 1938.

Hetherington, A. L. *Chinese Ceramic Glazes.* Pasadena, 1922.

Hinz, W. *Irans Aufstieg zum Nationalstaat im fünfzehnten Jahrhundert.* Berlin, 1936.

———. *Iran (Politik und Kultur von Kyros bis Reza Schah).* Leipzig, 1938.

———. *Islamische Masse und Gewichte umgerechnet auf das metrische System.* Leiden, 1955.

Hirth, F. *China and the Roman Orient.* Leipzig and Munich, 1885.

Hobson, R. L. *A Guide to Islamic Pottery of the Near East.* London, 1932.

Hoernle, R. "Who Was the Inventor of Rag Paper?" *Journal of the Royal Asiatic Society,* 1903, pp. 663–684.

Holmyard, E. J. *Alchemy.* London, Penguin Books, 1957.

Homer. *The Odyssey.* Translated by E. W. Rieu. London, Penguin Books, 1946.

Hommel, R. P. *China at Work.* New York, 1937.

Honey, W. B. *The Ceramic Art of China and other Countries of the Far East.* London, 1945.

Hooper, D., and Field, H. "Useful Plants and Drugs of Iran and Iraq," *Field Museum of Natural History,* Botanical Ser., Vol. 9, No. 3, pp. 73–241.

Hora, S. L. "The History of Science and Technology in India and South East Asia," *Nature,* Vol. 168 (1951), pp. 1047–48.

Horwitz, H. T. "Über das Aufkommen, die erste Entwicklung und die Verbreitung von Windrädern," *Beiträge zur Geschichte der Technik und Industrie,* Vol. 22 (1933).

Houtom-Schindler, A. "A Note on the Kur River in Fars, Its Sources and Dams and the District It Irrigates," *Proceedings of the Royal Geographical Society,* Vol. 13 (1891), pp. 287–291.

Huart, C. *Ancient Persia and Iranian Civilisation. London,* 1927.

Hunting, H. B. *Hebrew Life and Times.* New York, 1939.

Hūšangpūr, Karīm. *Fašondak, An Investigation of the Material Culture of an Alburz Village.* Tehran, 1341 A.H., 1962.

Ibn al-Balkhi. See Al-Balkhi.

Ibn Bādīs. *ᶜumdat al-kuttāb.* See Bosch, K. G. and Levy, Martin.

Ibn Ḥauqal. *The Oriental Geography of Ebn Haukal.* Translated by Sir William Ouselley. London, 1800.

Ibn Qutayba. *The ᶜuyūn al Akhbār.* (The Natural History section from a ninth-century *Book of Useful Knowledge.*) Translated by L. Kopf. 1949.

Jacquin, A. "Chemical Observations on the Sagh," *Asiatic Journal and Monthly Register,* Vol. 5 (1818).

Jenkinson, A. See Morgan, E. D., and Coote, C. H.

Johannsen, O. *Geschichte des Eisens.* Düsseldorf, 1925.

———. "Alter chinesischer Eisenguss," *Stahl und Eisen,* Vol. 62 (1942), p. 783.

———. "Die Erfindung der Eisengusstechnik," *Stahl und Eisen,* Vol. 39 (1919), pp. 1457 and 1625, and Vol. 49/2 (1929), p. 1496.

———. "Eine Anleitung zum Eisenguss vom Jahre 1454," *Stahl und Eisen,* Vol. 30 (1910), p. 1373.

Joret, C. *Les Plantes dans l'antiquité.* 2 vols. Paris, 1897.

Kaempfer, E. *Amoenitatum exoticarum politico-physico-medicarum fasciculi V.* Lemgo, 1712.

———. *Am Hofe des Persischen Grosskönigs (1684–85).* Edited by W. Hinz, Leipzig, 1940.

Kahle, P. "Bergkristalle, Glas und Glasflüsse nach dem Steinbuch des Al-Biruni," *Zeitschrift der Deutschen Morgenländischen Gesellschaft,* Vol. 90 (1936), pp. 322–356.

Karabacek, J. von. "Das arabische Papier," *Mitteilungen aus der Sammlung der Papyrus Erzherzog Rainer*, 5 vols. (1886–1892), Vol. 2, pp. 87–178.

———. "Zur orientalischen Altertumskunde: IV Muhamm. Kunststudien," *Sitzungsberichte der philosophisch-historischen Classe der Königlichen Akademie der Wissenschaften*, Vol. 172, Abh. 1, pp. 33–60.

Keen, B. A. *The Agricultural Development of the Middle East.* Her Majesty's Stationery Office, 1946.

Keng Tschi T'u. Ackerbau und Seidengewinnung in China. See Franke, O.

Khanikoff, N. "Al Kitāb mīzan al-ḥikma (The Book of the Balance of Wisdom) by Al Khāzinī," *Journal of the American Oriental Society*, Vol. 6 (1860), No. 1.

King, F. H. *Farmers for Forty Centuries, or Permanent Agriculture in China, Korea and Japan.* Madison, Wisconsin, 1911–1912.

Klemm, F. *A History of Western Technology.* London, 1959. Reprinted by the M.I.T. Press in 1964.

Krenkow, F. "The Construction of Subterranean Water Supplies during the Abbaside Caliphate," *Transactions of the Glasgow University Oriental Society*, Vol. 13 (1951), pp. 23–32.

Kühn, H. *Der Aufstieg der Menschheit.* Frankfurt M., 1955.

———. *Die Entfaltung der Menschheit.* Frankfurt M., 1958.

———. "Frühformen der Keramik," *Berichte der deutschen keramischen Gesellschaft*, Heft 4 (1958).

Lacam, J. "La céramique musulmane des époques Omeyyade et Abbaside, VII au X siècle," *Cahiers de la céramique du verre et des arts du feu*, No. 20, Sèvres, 1960.

Lambton, A. K. S. *Landlord and Peasant in Persia.* Oxford, 1953.

Lamm, C. J. *Das Glas von Samarra. Forschungen zur islamischen Kunst*, Vol. 4. Berlin, 1925.

———. *Glass from Iran.* Published by the National Museum, Stockholm. Stockholm, 1935.

Lane, A. *Early Islamic Pottery, Mesopotamia, Egypt, Persia.* London, 1947.

———. *Later Islamic Pottery.* London, 1957.

Latour, A. "Velvet," *Ciba Review*, No. 96 (Feb. 1953), pp. 3445–3467.

Laufer, B. *Sino-Iranica.* Field Museum of Natural History, Publication No. 26, Chicago, 1919.

———. "The Beginning of Porcelain in China," *Field Museum of Natural History*, Publication No. 192, Anthropological Series, Vol. 15, No. 2. Chicago, 1917.

Leach, B. *A Potter's Book.* London, 1940.

Ledebur, A. "Ein altchinesisches Handbuch der Gewerbekunde," *Glasers Annalen für Gewerbe und Bauwesen*, Vol. 16 (1885), pp. 192 ff.

Le Strange, G. "The Cities of Kirman in the time of Hamd-Allah Mustowfi and Marco Polo," *Journal of the Royal Asiatic Society*, April 1901, pp. 281–290.

———. *Description of the Province of Fars.* (A translation of Ibn al-Balkhi.) London, 1912.

———. *Mesopotamia and Persia under the Mongols in the 14th Century.* London, 1903.

Levy, Martin. "Mediaeval Arabic Bookbinding and Its Relation to Early Chemistry and Pharmacology," in *Transactions of the American Philosophical Society*, New Series, Vol. 52, Part 4 (1962), pp. 1–79.

Lucas, A. *Ancient Egyptian Materials and Industries.* 2nd ed., London, 1934; 3rd ed., revised, 1948.

MacCown, D. E. "The Material Culture of Early Iran," *Journal of Near Eastern Studies*, Vol. I (1942), pp. 424 ff.

Mackay, E. *The Indus Civilization.* London, 1935.

Maczek, M. "Der Erzbergbau im Iran," *Montan Rundschau* (Vienna), Heft 7 (July 1956).

Maczek, M., Preuschen, E., and Pittioni, R. "Beiträge zum Problem des Usprungs der Kupfererzverwertung in der Alten Welt," 1st Part. *Archaeologica Austriaca* (Vienna), Vol. 10 (1952).

Mann, T. *Der Islam, einst und jetzt.* Leipzig, 1914.

Marco Polo. *The Travels of Marco Polo.* Translated by R. Latham. Penguin Books, London, 1958.

Martin, F. R. *A History of Oriental Carpets before 1800.* 2 vols. Vienna, 1908.

Massalski, "Préparation de l'acier damassé en Perse," *Annuaire du Journal des Mines de Russie 1841*, pp. 297–308.

Meissner, B. *Babylonien und Assyrien.* 2 vols. Heidelberg, 1925.

Memon, A. A. *Indigenous Agricultural Implements in Bombay State.* Government Press, Baroda, 1955.

Mendelsches Stiftungsbuch. See *Hausbuch der Mendelschen Zwölfbrüderstiftung.*

Mohammed Reza Shah Pahlavi. *Mission for My Country*. London, 1961.

Morgan, E. D., and Coote, C. H. "Early Voyages and Travels in Russia and Persia by Anthony Jenkinson and other Englishmen," *Publications of the Hakluyt Society*, Vols. 72–73, Series I (1885–1886).

Morier, J. J. *Journey through Persia, Armenia and Asia Minor 1808–09*. London, 1812.

———. *A Second Journey through Persia, Armenia and Asia Minor, to Constantinople*. London, 1818.

Moule, A. C. and Pelliot, P. *Marco Polo, The Description of the World*. London, 1938.

Mūsa ibn Banū Shākir. *The Book of Artifices*. Edited by F. Hauser, *Abhandlungen zur Geschichte der Naturwissenschaften und der Medizin*, 1922.

Needham, J. *The History of Science and Civilisation in China*. Cambridge, 1954.

———. *The Development of Iron and Steel Technology in China*. Published by the Newcomen Society, 1958.

Neuburger, A. *Die Technik des Altertums*. 2nd ed. Leipzig, 1921.

Neumann, B. "Römischer Damaststahl," *Archiv für Eisenhüttenwesen*, Vol. 1 No. 3 (1927), pp. 241–244.

Noel, E. "Qanats," *Royal Central Asian Journal*, Vol. 31 (1944), pp. 191–202.

Nothing, F. W. "Antimongewinnung in Anarek," *Metall und Erz*, Vol. 37 (1940), pp. 106 and 130.

Oberhofer, P. "Über das Gefüge des Damaszenerstahls," *Stahl und Eisen*, Vol. 35 (1915), p. 140.

Olearius, A. *Voyages très curieux et très renommés faits en Moscovie, Tartarie et Perse*. Amsterdam, 1719.

Olmer, L. J. "L'Industrie Persane, Rapport sur une Mission Scientifique," *Nouvelles Archives Scientifiques*, Vol. 16, fasc. 4, Paris, 1908.

Orth, F. "Der Werdegang wichtiger Erfindungen auf dem Gebiete der Spinnerei und Weberei," *Verein Deutscher Ingenieure Beiträge zur Geschichte der Technik*, No. 17 (1927), pp. 89–105.

Oxford Regional Economic Atlas, The Middle East and North Africa. Oxford University Press, 1960.

Parker, E. H. "Chinese Knowledge of Early Persia," *Imp. and Asiatic Quarterly Review*, Vol. 15 (1903), pp. 144–169.

Pearson, G. "Experiments and Observations on a Kind of Steel called Wootz," *Transactions of the Royal Society*, Vol. 85 (1795), pp. 322–346.

Pelliot, P. *Notes on Marco Polo*. Paris, 1959.

Persian Embroideries (*A Brief Guide*). Published by the Victoria and Albert Museum, London, 1950.

Picolpasso, C. *Le tre libre dell 'Arte del Vasaio*. 1548.

———. *The Three Books of the Potter's Art*. Translated and introduced by Bernard Rackham. London, 1934.

Piggott, S. "Dating the Hissar Sequence—the Indian Evidence," *Antiquity*, Vol. 17 (1943), pp. 169–182.

———. *Prehistoric India to 1000 B.C.* Penguin Books, Harmondsworth, 1950.

Pliny "the Elder." *Historia Naturalis*. 6 vols. Edited by L. Janus. Leipzig, 1854.

Polak, J. E. *Persien, das Land und seine Bewohner*. 2 vols. Leipzig Brockhaus, 1865.

Polybius. *The Histories*. Edited by E. S. Shuckburgh. London, 1889.

Pope, A. U., and Ackerman, P., eds. *A Survey of Persian Art*. 6 vols. London, 1938.

Pope, A. U. *Masterpieces of Persian Art*. New York, 1945.

Procopius. *De Bello Gothico*. Edited by Dindorf. 1833–1838.

Qāḍī Aḥmad, Son of Mīr Munshī, Calligraphers and Painters. Translated by V. Minorsky. Washington, 1959.

Qalqašandī, A. *Ṣubḥ al*c*aša*. See Bosch, K. G.

Qazwini, Zakarīya ibn Muḥammad ibn Maḥmūd al-. *Kosmographie*. Edited by F. Wüstenfeld. Göttingen, 1848.

Quintus Curtius, *Opera*.

Rabino, H. L. "A Journey in Mazanderan," *Geographical Journal*, 1913, pp. 435–454.

———. "Mazanderan and Astarabad," *Gibb Memorial Series* (New), Vol. 7 (London, 1928).

———. "Silk Culture in Persia," *Board of Trade Journal*, June 6, 1907, pp. 455–459.

Raphaël (le père) du Mans. *Estat de la Perse en 1660*. Ch. Schefer, Paris, 1890.

Read, T. T. "Chinese Iron a Puzzle," *Harvard Journal of Asiatic Studies*, Vol. 2 (1937), pp. 398–457.

———. "The Early Casting of Iron," *Geographical Review*, Vol. 24 (1934), p. 544.

Rieth, A. "Anfänge und Entwicklung der Tauschierkunst," *Eurasia*, Vol. 10 (1936), pp. 186 ff.

———. *Die Eisentechnik der Hallstattzeit*. Leipzig, 1942.

Ritter, H., Ruska, J., Sarre, F., and Winderlich, R. "Orientalische Steinbücher und persische Fayencetechnik," *Istanbuler Mitteilungen des Archäologischen Instituts des Deutschen Reiches*, Heft 3 (1935), pp. 16–48.

Robertson, J. "An Account of the Iron Mines of Caradagh," *The Practical Mechanic*, December, 1843, pp. 84–86.

Rosenberg, M. *Niello bis zum Jahre 1000 n. Chr.* Frankfurt/M., 1910.

———. *Niello seit dem Jahre 1000 n. Chr.* Frankfurt/M., 1910.

Ruska, J. *Das Steinbuch des Aristoteles.* Heidelberg, 1922.

Rütimeyer, L. *Urethnographie der Schweiz.* Basel, 1924.

Sarre, F. *Die Kunst des alten Persien.* Berlin, 1923.

———. *Die Keramik von Samarra* (Vol. 2, *Forschungen zur islamischen Kunst*). Berlin, 1925.

———. "Eine keramische Werkstatt aus Kaschan im 13.-14. Jahrhundert," *Istanbuler Mitteilungen des Archäologischen Instituts des Deutschen Reiches*, Heft 3 (1935), pp. 57–70.

Sarre, F. and Herzfeld, E. E. *Iranische Felsreliefs.* Wasmuth Verlag, Berlin, 1910.

Sarre, F., and Trenkwald, H. *Old Oriental Carpets.* Translated from German by A. J. Kendrick. 2 vols. Vienna, 1926–1929.

Savage, G. *Pottery through the Ages.* Penguin Books, London, 1959.

Savickaja, M. A. *Ukazatel' Literatury po irrigacii i melioratii Stredne-Aziatskich republik i Kazakstana.* Leningrad, 1928.

Schaefer, G. "Der Anbau und die Veredelung der Krappwurzel," *Ciba-Rundschau*, Vol. 47 (Dec. 1940), p. 1715.

———. "Die frühesten Zeugdrucke," *Ciba Rundschau*, Vol. 24 (April 1938), pp. 854–861.

Schäfer, H. *Ägyptische Goldschmiedearbeiten.* Berlin, 1910.

Schliemann, H. *Ilios.* Leipzig, 1881.

———. *Mykene.* Leipzig, 1878.

Schmidt, E. F. *Excavations at Tepe Hissar. Philadelphia*, 1937.

———. *The Treasury of Persepolis.* University of Chicago Press, Chicago, 1939.

———. *Persepolis.* 2 vols. Chicago Oriental Institute Publication. Vol. 68, 1951–1957.

———. *Flights over Ancient Cities of Iran.* Chicago, 1940.

Schmitz, F. "Orientalischer Damaststahl," *Verein Deutscher Ingenieure Beiträge zur Geschichte der Technik, 1930*, pp. 81–86.

Schranz, H. Report to the Department of Mines, Tehran, 1937 (unpublished).

Schumann, T. "Oberflächenverzierungen in der antiken Töpferkunst," *Berichte der deutschen keramischen Gesellschaft*, Vol. 23 (1942), pp. 408–426.

———. "Terra Sigillata und Schwarz-Rot Malerei der Griechen," *Forschungen und Fortschritte deutscher Wissenschaft und Technik*, Vol. 19 (1943), pp. 356–358.

Schwarz, Chevalier de. "Sur l'industrie du fer et de l'acier dans les Indes Orientales," *Stahl und Eisen*, 1921, pp. 209–277.

Schwarz, P. *Iran im Mittelalter nach den arabischen Geographen.* 9 vols. Leipzig, 1926–1936.

Seligman, C. G., and Beck, H. C. "Far Eastern Glass: Some Western Origins," *The Bulletin of the Museums of Far Eastern Antiquities*, No. 10 (Stockholm, 1938).

Singer, C. *A History of Technology.* 4 vols. Edited by Singer, C., Holmyard, E. J., and Hall, A. R. Oxford, 1954–1958.

Si-Yu-Ki. See Beal, S.

Smith, A. *Blind White Fish in Persia.* George Allen & Unwin Ltd., London, 1953.

Smith, C. S. "Four Outstanding Researches in Metallurgical History," published by the American Society for Testing and Materials, 1963.

Spies, H. "Der derzeitige Stand des Erzbergbaus in Iran," *Metall und Erz*, Vol. 35 (1938), pp. 170 ff.

Springer, A. *Handbuch der Kunstgeschichte.* Leipzig, E. A. Seemann, 1901.

Spuler, B. *Die Mongolen in Iran. Politik, Verwaltung und Kultur der Ilchanzeit, 1120–1350.* Leipzig, 1939.

———. *Iran in früh-islamischer Zeit. Politik, Kultur, Verwaltung und öffentliches Leben zwischen der arabischen und der seldschukischen Eroberung, 633–1055.* Wiesbaden, 1952.

Stahl, A. F. "Persien," *Handbuch der regionalen Geologie*, Vol. 6 (Heidelberg, 1911).

———. "Zur Geologie von Persien," *Petermann Mitteilungen*, Ergänzungsheft No. 122 (Gotha, 1897), pp. 1–75.

Stein, M. A. *Archaeological Reconnaisance of N.W. India and S.E. Iran.* London, 1937.

Steingass, F. *A Comprehensive Persian–English Dictionary.* 2nd ed. London, 1930.

Stodart, J. "A Brief Account of Wootz or Indian Steel," *Asiatic Journal and Monthly Register*, Vol. 5 (1818), p. 570.

Strabo. *Geography.* Ed. Bunbury, *Ancient Geography*, 1878.

Stratil Sauer, G. "Iran, eine länderkundliche Skizze," Institut für Auslandsbeziehungen, No. 3/4 (1961), pp. 179–186.

Sufyānī. *Ṣināʿat tasfīr al-kutub* (*The Technique of Bookbinding*). See Bosch, K. G.

Sustmann. "Felt," *Ciba Review*, No. 129 (Nov. 1958), pp. 2–25.

Sykes, P. M. *A History of Persia*. 2 vols. London, 1922.

———. *Ten Thousand Miles in Persia*. London, 1902.

Symonds, M., and Preece, L. *Needlework Through the Ages*. London, 1928.

Tavernier, J. B. *Les six voyages de M. J. B. Tavernier en Turquie, en Perse et aux Indes*. 2 vols. Paris, 1679.

Theobald, W. *Technik des Kunsthandwerks im zehnten Jahrhundert*. Berlin, 1933.

Theophanes of Byzantium. *Photios Myrabilion*.

Theophilus Presbyter. *Diversarum Artium Schedula*. Edited by W. Theobald. Berlin, 1933.

———. *On Divers Arts, The Treatise of Theophilus*. Translated and annotated by J. G. Hawthorne and C. S. Smith. Chicago, 1963.

———. *The Various Arts*. Translated by C. R. Dodwell. London, 1961.

Thompson, R. C. *A Dictionary of Assyrian Geology and Chemistry*. Oxford, 1936.

Thomson, W. G. *A History of Tapestry*. London, 1906–1930.

Travels of Venetians in Persia. Published by the Hakluyt Society, 1873. See also J. Barbaro.

Thorndyke, L. *A History of Magic and Experimental Sciences*, 2 vols. London, 1929.

Türk Etnoğrafya Dergisi (*Turkish Review of Ethnography*), Vols. for 1956, 1957.

Unterhössel, F. "Die wichtigeren Erzvorkommen des persischen Karadag-Gebirges," *Metall und Erz*, Vol. 31 (1934), p. 237.

Veranzio, Faustus. *Machinae Novae*. Venice, 1615–1616.

Vitruvius, Pollio. *De Architectura*. Ed. Gwilt, 1860.

Von der Osten, H. H. *Die Welt der Perser*. Stuttgart, 1956.

Von Falke, O. *Kunstgeschichte der Seidenweberei*. Vols. I and II. Berlin, 1913.

Von Karabacek. See Karabacek, J. von.

Von Lecoq, A. *Buried Treasures of Chinese Turkestan*. London, 1928. (English translation.)

Vowels, H. P. "Inquiry into the Origin of the Windmill," *Transactions of the Newcomen Society*, Vol. (1930–1931), pp. 1–14.

Wailes, R. "A Note on Windmills," in C. Singer, *A History of Technology*, Vol. 2, pp. 623–628.

Weigel, C. *Abbildung der Gemein-Nützlichen Haupt-Stände*. Regenspurg, 1698.

Weissbach, F. H. "Zur keilschriftlichen Gewichtskunde," *Zeitschrift der Deutschen Morgenländischen Gesellschaft*, Vol. 65 (1911), pp. 625–696.

Wiedemann, E. "Zur Mechanik und Technik bei den Arabern," *Sitzungsberichte der Physikalisch Medizinischen Sozietät* (Erlangen), Vol. 38, No. 1 (1906).

———. "Zur Technik und Naturwissenschaft bei den Arabern," *Sitzungsberichte der Physikalisch Medizinischen Sozietät* (Erlangen), Vol. 38, No. 1 (1906).

———. Über Eisen und Stahl bei den muslemischen Völkern," *Beiträge zur Geschichte der Naturwissenschaften* (Erlangen), Vols. 24 and 25, (1911), pp. 114–131.

Wiedemann, E., and Hauser, F. "Über die Uhren im Bereiche der islamischen Kultur," *Abhandlungen der Kaiserl. Leopoldinischen Carolingischen Deutschen Akademie der Naturforscher*, Vol. 100, pp. 1–272.

Wiesner, J. "Zur Archaeologie Sibiriens," *Atlantis*, January 1959.

———. *Mikroskopische Untersuchungen alter ostturkestanischer Papiere*. Vienna, 1902.

Wiet, G. *Histoire de l'Egypte*. Cairo, 1933.

Wilkinson, C. K. "The Kilns of Nishapur," *Bulletin*, Metropolitan Museum of Art, May 1959, p. 235.

———. "Fashion and Technique in Persian Pottery," *Bulletin*, Metropolitan Museum of Art, November 1947, pp. 99–104.

Wilson, Sir A. T. *A Bibliography of Persia*. Oxford, 1930.

———. *Persia*. London, 1932.

Winter, H. J. J. "Science in Medieval Persia," *Journal of the Iran Society*. London, January 1951, pp. 55–70.

———. "Muslim Mechanics and Mechanical Appliances," *Endeavour*, Vol. 15, No. 57, pp. 25–28.

———. "Formative Influences in Islamic Science," *Archives Internationales d'histoire des Sciences*, No. 23–24 (1953), pp. 171–192.

———. "The Optical Researches of Ibn al-Haitham," *Centaurs*, Vol. 3 (1954), pp. 190–210.

———. "Notes on al-Kitab Suwar al-Kawakib of al-Sufi," *Archives Internationales d'histoire des Sciences*, Paris, April–June 1955.

Winter, H. J. J., and Arafat, W. *A Discourse on the Concave Spherical Mirror by Ibn al-Haitham* (translated from Arabic), *Journal of the Royal Asiatic Society of Bengal*. Science. Vol. 16, No. 1 (1950).

Witter, W. *Die älteste Erzgewinnung im nordisch-germanischen Lebenskreis*. Leipzig, 1938.

Xenophon. *Anabasis* (*The Persian Expedition*). Translated by Rex Warner. Penguin Books, London, 1954.

Yates, J. *Textrinum Antiquorum. An Account of the Art of Weaving among the Ancients*. 2 vols. London, 1843.

Zend Avesta, The. Translated by James Darmesteter, Paris, 1892.

REVIEW OF RELEVANT LITERATURE

Bibliographies on Persia

A Bibliography of Persia by A. Wilson lists a wide range of books on almost every aspect of Persia. It is well annotated and not only covers the large number of books written in English but does equal justice to those in other languages.

Iran, a Selected and Annotated Bibliography by the Persian scholar Hafez F. Farman contains a substantial list of books on his country, but only those from the Library of Congress at Washington. It is up-to-date, even giving information on the United Nations Organization and foreign aid missions reports up to 1951, all with good annotations.

Alphons Gabriel's study *Die Erforschung Persiens* is an account of Western writers on the geography of Persia. The author takes geography in the widest possible sense, and the book is therefore a most valuable guide to more detailed reading. It ranges from the early Greeks to the time of World War II, brings many quotations of the authors reviewed, and is well illustrated with maps and etchings.

Geography and General History of Persia

The same author has written three books: *Im Weltfernen Orient, Durch Persiens Wüsten,* and *Aus den Einsamkeiten Irans,* all on expeditions that led him through rarely crossed deserts of Central and South Persia as a desert morphologist. The books yield much information on the civilization of the humble people living on the fringes of these deserts.

Two books of the Swedish explorer Sven Hedin, *Eine Routenaufnahme durch Ostpersien* and *Zu Land nach Indien durch Persien,*

Seistan und Belutschistan, contain many references to the way of living in those remote areas, including descriptions of vertical windmills used for corn milling as well as for irrigation.

The botanist Erwin Gauba has seen many parts of the country, in his search for Persia's flora, that the ordinary traveler would not normally see. His book *Arbres et Arbustes des Forêts caspiennes de l'Iran* gives valuable information on climate and vegetation and the Caspian region's timber in particular.

Details on various aspects of industrial arts are contained in his two articles "Botanische Reisen in der persischen Dattelregion" and "Ein Besuch der kaspischen Wälder Nordpersiens."

A. F. Stahl, a former Postmaster General of Persia, who called himself an amateur geologist, has produced an important account of the country's geology under the title: "Persien." This article is still regarded as the most comprehensive general survey. It is well illustrated and contains many references to metallurgical deposits. In his monograph "Zur Geologie von Persien" the same author describes geological observations during his travels in North and Central Persia, illustrated by very good colored geological maps that are based on military maps of the Imperial Russian General Staff.

Iran, by Walther Hinz, is a good introduction to Persia's general history from Achaemenian to modern times.

Iran, Past and Present, by Donald Wilber, deals essentially with the more recent history and economic conditions. Most revealing is a chapter on patterns of culture and society, and equally interesting is one on the people and their customs.

An excellent analysis of the religious, cultural, and economic situation of the modern country with due reference to its history is *Iran* by William Haas.

Two books that specialize in the tremendous influence the Islamic world had on Western Europe, especially during the Middle Ages, are: *The Legacy of Islam* by Sir Thomas Arnold, and *The Legacy of Persia* by A. J. Arberry. Both books give due credit to the many influences on science and technology.

Archaeology, Prehistory, and Ancient History of the Middle East

In his books *Der Aufstieg der Menschheit* and *Die Entfaltung der Menschheit*, Herbert Kühn makes many references to Persia's place and its contributions to material culture in its early stages.

J. J. M. de Morgan, one of the many archaeologists who worked in Persia during the second half of the last century, collected much evidence in his systematic searches for early civilizations. His main book, *Mission scientifique en Perse*, shows that the author was not satisfied with merely unearthing the past, for he recorded many instances where forms and techniques have survived until modern times.

G. G. Cameron, *History of Early Iran*, and C. Huart, *Ancient Persian and Iranian Civilization*, are good introductions to these early periods. The most revealing book in this group has been written by the archaeologist R. Ghirshman, *Iran*. It is the story of Persia from earliest times until its transformation by the Islamic conquest. The same author reports on his own expeditions in *Fouilles de Sialk*, Vols. 1 and 2, and together with G. Contenau, in *Fouilles de Tépé Giyan*. All three books contain much detail on early building techniques, tools, ceramics, and metallurgy. Details on early glazes, glass, tiles, and brickwork of the thirteenth century B.C. are given in R. Ghirshman's articles "The Ziggurat at Tchoga Zanbil" and "Tchoga Zanbil près de Suse."

Another archaeologist who worked in the field for almost 30 years was E. E.

Herzfeld. In three of his numerous publications, *Archaeological History of Iran*, *Iran in the Ancient East*, and "Iran as a Prehistoric Centre," he clearly defines Persia's place in the early civilizations with particular reference to material evidence.

E. F. Schmidt, who had already worked at the site of Ray, the Rhages of the ancients, for several excavation seasons, succeeded Herzfeld as head of the excavation team at Persepolis. In his books *Excavations at Tepe Hissar*, *The Treasury of Persepolis*, and *Persepolis*, Schmidt presents his findings in carefully stratified detail, showing much of the material wealth of the Achaemenians. In *Flights over Ancient Cities of Iran* he describes the new method of aerial survey in archaeology that he had pioneered in Persia. The book is richly illustrated with magnificent aerial photographs.

Much light has been thrown on early metallurgy by the investigations of H. H. Coghlan: "Native Copper in Relation to Prehistory," "Some Fresh Aspects of the Prehistoric Metallurgy of Copper," and "Notes on the Prehistoric History of Copper and Bronze in the Old World." The author also touches on early furnaces and mining tools.

Detailed chemical analyses of metal objects found on a number of excavation sites in Western Asia are given in two reports by T. B. Brown: *Excavations in Azarbaijan* and "*Iron Objects from Azarbaijan.*"

Two cuneiform texts dealing with Mesopotamian ceramic and glass techniques have been translated and interpreted, one by B. Meissner, *Babylonien und Assyrien* and C. J. Gadd with R. Campbell-Thompson, "A Middle Babylonian Chemical Text." Both are important sources for our knowledge of the development of ceramic techniques.

S. Piggott, a specialist on the early Indus Valley culture, in "Dating the Hissar Sequence—the Indian Evidence," deals with Sumerian-Indian contacts and the contemporary civilization at Tepe Ḥisār on the Iranian Plateau. In *Prehistoric India to 1000 B.C.* he shows many links between early Persian and Indian civilizations, especially in Balūčistān.

More concerned with Egypt, but interesting for comparison is the book by A. Lucas *Ancient Egyptian Materials and Industries*. Lucas was an analytical chemist in the Museum of Antiquities in Cairo, and his attempts to reconstruct ancient processes have contributed to our understanding of ancient working techniques.

The period of ancient Persia, i.e., from the Achaemenians to the Islamic conquest, is well covered in the books by F. Sarre, *Die Kunst des alten Persien* and F. Sarre and E. E. Herzfeld: *Iranische Felsreliefs*.

A profound study of the Sasanian period has been made by the Danish Iranist A. Christensen in *L'Iran sous les Sassanides*. If it is considered that their time was marked by growing international relations with subsequent sharply increased industrial activities, the importance of this book cannot be overestimated.

Relations with the Greco-Roman World

The first of the Greek writers, so far as we know, who traveled widely in Persia was Herodotus (484–429 B.C.). In *The Histories* are many references to the civilization of the Achaemenian empire.

Apollonius of Rhodes (245–186 B.C.) is another of the Greek writers who in his *Opera* gives us interesting details on the history of steelmaking. He is the first to mention the so-called smithing tribes.

The historian Polybius (204–122 B.C.) is the first to report, in *The Histories*, on the subterranean water channels, a unique feature of Persia's irrigation system.

A wide range of information on industrial arts in the Middle East is contained in the *Historia Naturalis* by Pliny "the Elder" (23–79 A.D.).

Many other Greek and Roman accounts on the origin of crafts and techniques point to Asia Minor and Persia. Good sources from which the Western scholar may trace these claims can be found in a number of books on the general history of technology that will be reviewed in the following section. One of them, by H. Blümner, specializes in the technology of all the peoples of the ancient world. His two principal works, *Die gewerbliche Tätigkeit der Völker des klassischen Altertums* and *Technologie und Terminologie der Künste und Gewerbe bei den Griechen und Römern* can be regarded as standard works for this kind of investigation.

Aristotle's writings on mineralogy have strongly influenced medieval Persian ceramists and alchemists. J. Ruska has made a new translation under the name *Das Steinbuch des Aristoteles* for a better understanding of the book's significance.

Arabian and Persian Sources

When it is remembered that the conquering Moslems of the seventh century inherited Greek and Sasanian tradition in the search for knowledge, it is not surprising to find many Arabs and Persians writing on technological and scientific subjects in the early centuries of the caliphate. Of special interest as sources for material on the industrial arts are the so-called cosmographers who give detailed descriptions, in our case of Persia, including history, geography, industries, and customs. The most outstanding ones are the Taʾrīḫ-e Guzīdeh by Ḥamdullāh Mustawfī-ye Qazvīnī and the Nuzhat-Qulūb by the same author. Both works contain numerous references to local industries, mining, timber, and other resources. Extracts of both books concerning the province of Kermān have been edited by G. Le Strange.

Al-Hamdānī (tenth century A.D.) gave an account of the origin of gold and silver used in his days. His book has been translated by D. M. Dunlop under the title Sources of Gold and Silver in Islam.

Al-Ḫāzinī of Merv in a long treatise, *The Book of the Balance of Wisdom* expounded the theory of the balance, its design and practical application.

A description of 100 machines and mechanical devices has been given in Mūsā ibn Banū Shākir's *The Book of Artifices*.

The Indian historian of science, A. K. Coomaraswamy, has translated *The Treatise of Al-Jażārī on Automata*, a book showing many applications of mechanical principles.

Abul Qasim's treatise of 1301 A.D. on the potter's materials and techniques is of direct interest to the historian of pottery. It has been edited and commented on by Ritter *et al.* in "Orientalische Steinbücher und persische Fayencetechnik."

Another group in this section consists of books by modern scholars based on oriental sources. A comprehensive history of Persia during the Middle Ages with much reference to aspects of civilization is *Iran im Mittelalter nach den arabischen Geographen*, 9 Vols., by P. Schwarz. A remarkable source of information on minerals is the medieval encyclopedist Al-Bīrūnī. Paul Kahle presents us with details on quartz, glass and glazes taken from this source in: "Bergkristalle, Glas und Glasflüsse nach dem Steinbuch des Al-Biruni." Two articles by E. Wiedemann, "Zur Mechanik und Technik bei den Arabern" and "Zur Technik und Naturwissenschaft bei den Arabern" are highly relevant to the topic of this study.

Investigations by the English historian of Moslem science, H. J. J. Winter, reveal much detail on the design and manufacture of scientific apparatus in the Middle

Ages in "Muslim Mechanics and Mechanical Appliances," "Science in Medieval Persia," "Formative Influences in Islamic Science," "The Optical Researches of Ibn-al-Haitham" and "Notes on al-Kitab Suwar Al-Kawakib of al-Sufi." In conjunction with W. Arafat he edited Ibn-al-Haitham's *A Discourse on the Concave Spherical Mirror*. The work contains interesting details on a lathe used to produce true spherical and parabolical mirrors by using a templet.

The recently founded Institute of Social Studies at the University of Tehrān initiated a series of projects for the study of various aspects of community life. Under this scheme K. Hūšangpūr wrote about the material culture of Fašondak, a remote mountain village.

Medieval European Sources

One of the most fascinating works in many respects is the Diversarum Artium Schedula by Theophilus Presbyter. Although English, French, and German translations already existed in the eighteenth century, the book did not arouse much interest among historians of technology until W. Theobald, a professional engineer and Latin scholar, prepared a Latin–German edition of it together with extensive technical interpretations and commentaries. Theophilus' work is now regarded as the major source for our knowledge of medieval technology, and it has much bearing on eastern technology too. A Latin–English edition has recently been prepared by C. R. Dodwell. It has no technological commentaries but contains the full text of Theophilus' treatise. The recently published English edition by J. G. Hawthorne and C. S. Smith is not only a scholarly translation of this important source but at the same time is precise in technical detail and is amply supported by notes and illustrations.

Medieval descriptions of professions and trades form another group. The oldest of these is the *Mendelsches Stiftungsbuch* of about 1400 A.D. Particularly well illustrated with a woodcut for each vocation is Jost Amman's *Eygentliche Beschreibung aller Stände* (1568 A.D.). An English translation is available under the title *The Book of Trades.* Similar in style and range, although written about one hundred years later, is Christoff Weigel's *Abbildung der Gemein-Nützlichen Haupt-Stände.* Many of the illustrations in these books show technical features that could still be found in Persia in 1963.

A manual of the industrial technology of his time, also well illustrated, is the *Pirotechnica* of Vanuccio Biringuccio, first printed in 1540.

European Historians, Travelers, Ambassadors, and Missionaries

B. Spuler's *Iran in frühislamischer Zeit* deals with early Islamic times, while his *Die Mongolen in Iran* is important for the relations between Persia and China during the thirteenth century, when cultural exchanges were particularly strong between those two countries. Persia's national renaissance under the Ṣafavids, a period of equally strong contacts, this time with China and Europe, has been treated in detail by W. Hinz in his *Irans Aufstieg zum Nationalstaat im fünfzehnten Jahrhundert.*

The most famous of the early travelers, who came through Persia on his way to China, was Marco Polo, and he had a good deal to say about the country's industries. A most scholarly translation of his *The Description of the World* is the one by A. C. Moule and P. Pelliot, particularly useful through an abundance of notes.

Four other Venetians, Barbaro, Contarini, Zeno, and d'Alessandri, who traveled to the Šāh's court between 1471 and 1520, had, like the Polos, political motives, i.e., the establishment of military alliances. They too found time for lively descriptions of the country and its people, revealing much information for this book's purpose. The Hakluyt Society has arranged a well annotated English edition under the title *Travels of Venetians in Persia.*

An interesting parallel to it is *Chronicles of the Carmelites in Persia,* by an anonymous modern author. The book covers mainly the time of the Ṣafavids and shows that they not only had a surprisingly tolerant attitude toward Christian missions, but were also outspokenly eager to settle skilled Christian craftsmen around the capital, Iṣfahān, for the development of local industries.

Raphaël du Mans' book *Estat de la Perse en 1660* is an excellent account of the life at the Ṣafavid court of Iṣfahān. It devotes one chapter each to the craftsmen, the merchants, and the scientists.

Equally informative is the book by the sixteenth-century adventurer Pietro della Valle, *Fameux Voyages,* which mentions many technical details in passing.

An authority on the Persia of the seventeenth century was the French gem merchant, J. B. Tavernier. In his *Les six voyages en Turquie, en Perse et aux Indes* he is full of praise for the high standard of the crafts and industries, of which he describes many in detail.

Another Frenchman, also a gem dealer, John Chardin, made two journeys to Persia between 1665 and 1675, staying in the country for a total of six years. His *Travels in Persia* is by far the most comprehensive of all the descriptions of the country under the Ṣafavids, giving much detail about custom, civilization, and industries. Chardin in his writings reveals a quality which very few European travelers show, a deep understanding of the country's culture and mentality.

More concerned with an all-round description of the country and its civilization is A. Olearius, who was attached to a diplomatic and trade mission sent by the Duke of Holstein in 1635. His report, *Voyages très curieux et très renommés faits en Moscovie, Tartarie et Perse* is illustrated by many etchings.

A man who has largely contributed to our scientific knowledge about Persia was the German E. Kaempfer, physician attached to the embassy of King Karl XI of Sweden. He was in Persia between 1683 and 1688. In *Amoenitates exoticae* he described a good deal of the Persian flora, illustrated by many of his beautiful drawings. He also gave many accounts of local industries and details on harvesting and processing of certain gums. He later traveled to Japan and became famous as an explorer of that country. A German translation of that part of Kaempfer's book dealing with Persia has been edited by W. Hinz under the title *Am Hofe des Persischen Grosskönigs.* This edition contains reproductions of many of Kaempfer's engravings.

British interest in Persia began before the establishment of a land route to India. Already in 1561 Queen Elizabeth had sent Anthony Jenkinson to the Persian court via Russia. Although the aim of this mission, to open trade, did not succeed, Jenkinson's journals are quite informative. They have been edited by E. D. Morgan and C. H. Coote under the title *Early Voyages and Travels in Russia and Persia by Anthony Jenkinson and other Englishmen.*

With the growing importance of India we find an increasing number of Englishmen exploring the land route. We owe the finest description of the Persia of that time to Thomas Herbert, who accompanied an English mission to the court of Šāh ᶜAbbās in 1628 that aimed at the establishment of an English monopoly of Persia's silk export. W. Foster edited the Herbert diaries under the title *Thomas Herbert's*

Travels. The book contains many references to industrial activities.

G. Forster, an eighteenth-century traveler, has left a good description of the vertical windmills of East Persia in his book *A Journey from Bengal to England.*

A French colonel in Russian services, G. Drouville, has given a vivid picture of the country and its people at the turn of the eighteenth century. Customs, industries, and institutions are well described in his book *Voyage en Perse.*

There are many travelers of the early nineteenth century whose writings possess small relevance to the purpose of this study. But there is an exception, the diary of H. C. Brugsch, *Die Reise der königlich preussischen Gesandtschaft nach Persien 1860–61.* The author, who accompanied the only Prussian diplomatic mission ever sent to Persia, was a trained orientalist and included many items on local crafts in his book, a good number of them illustrated by fine drawings.

A prolific writer with substantial contributions to the geography and geology of the country was A. Houtom-Schindler, who served as a general in the Šāh's army between 1875 and 1880. He included many details about Persia's ancient storage dams and irrigation systems in his geographical articles, all well illustrated by carefully drawn maps and sketches. Most of his articles were published in journals of learned societies.

A British consular agent, H. C. Rabino, who was stationed in northern Persia, published several monographs on the Caspian provinces. In "A Journey in Mazanderan" and "Mazanderan and Astarabad" he recorded much detail on local industries, such as silk production, timber-getting, house construction, and mining. A monograph going into much detail, especially on production figures and export routes, is his "Silk Culture in Persia."

One of the well-known modern experts on Persia is P. M. Sykes. He traveled extensively in the country between 1893 and 1921, first as British Consul, later as a general commanding the South Persian Rifles. His books, *Ten Thousand Miles in Persia* and *A History of Persia,* are great contributions to many aspects of the country's civilization.

Lord G. N. Curzon, a former Viceroy of India, has written an interesting book on the political situation in Persia at his time, with many sidelights on the country's history and civilization, under the title *Persia and the Persian Question.*

L. J. Olmer was a science teacher at the Ecole Polytechnique at Tehrān at the beginning of this century. In "L'Industrie Persane, Rapport sur une Mission scientifique" he gives much detail on industrial practices in local manufacture, mainly under the chemical and raw material aspects of production.

Relations to China and India

China and the Roman Orient by F. Hirth mainly deals with Chinese-Syrian relations. Since the trade and with it the traveling of techniques between this easternmost Roman colony and the Far East went via Persia, the book has a direct bearing on the subject of the present study. Large sections of Hirth's book are devoted to such items as silk, brocade weaving, dyeing, glass, gems, metals, damascene steel, asbestos, and paper.

The part that Bactria and Iranian Central Asia played as links to China in Hellenistic times is well expounded by A. von Lecoq in the reports on his discoveries in the cave temples at Turfan. The summary of these in English has been published under the title *Buried Treasures of Chinese Turkestan.*

A carefully collected and well annotated

account of a large number of reports by travelers to the Far East during Islamic times has been edited by G. Ferrand under the title *Relations de voyages et textes géographes arabes, persans et turcs relatifs à l'Extrême-Orient.*

By far the most important work on East-West relations is J. Needham's *Science and Civilisation in China.* Four of the planned seven volumes are already available. Needham does not rely solely on Chinese historical sources but considers equally well the findings of archaeologists in China, a field that was taken up in that country relatively late. In comparing all these findings with the observations of many Western writers, Needham, more than any author before him, stresses the importance of the continuous exchange of ideas and techniques in the development of civilizations, especially the exchange that has taken place between China and Persia.

Another Western scholar who saw the wide range of give and take between the two countries in their material culture was Berthold Laufer. In his *Sino-Iranica* he gives an account of what the Chinese owe to Persia and vice-versa. It deals extensively with the transmission of fruit plants, fiber plants, dyestuffs, textile techniques, minerals, and metals. Similarly important is *The Beginning of Porcelain in China* by the same author, a book stressing the role that glazes, developed in the Middle East, played in the development of Chinese ceramics.

Writing along similar lines, although often less convincing, is E. Bretschneider in *The History of European Botanic Discoveries in China, Medieval Researches from Eastern Sources,* and *Botanicon Sinicum.*

E. H. Parker's *Chinese Knowledge of Early Persia* is a valuable interpretation of Chinese sources on pre-Islamic Persia.

Another European author who often emphasizes the diffusion of ideas across Asia is W. Eberhard in his book *Early Chinese Culture and Its Development.*

The results of an expedition to China to record Chinese traditional industries have been laid down in the well illustrated book by R. P. Hommel, *China at Work.* It gives a full account of Chinese tools and working methods at the time of the expedition (1921).

Western authors writing on specific technical topics are O. Johannsen ("Alter chinesischer Eisenguss"), H. Dickmann ("Chinesischer Eisenguss"), and B. Leach (*A Potter's Book*). In the latter the author mentions a number of East-West relations in the field of ceramics.

F. H. King, writing on farming techniques in the Far East in *Farmers for Forty Centuries,* gives many details regarding tillage, silk production, cotton growing, and fiber treatment that are of interest for comparison with the respective Persian methods.

A purely Chinese source is the *Keng Tschi T'u,* a well illustrated medieval handbook on agriculture, silk production, and weaving. It is important for a comparative study of weaving techniques.

Early relations between India and Persia are illustrated in M. A. Stein's book *Archaeological Reconnaissance of N.W. India and S.E. Iran.* A continuation of this topic back to the beginning of history is G. V. Childe's "India and the West before Darius."

Important references are contained in S. L. Hora's "The History of Science and Technology in India and South East Asia." P. C. Bagchi's *India and China* is a scholarly study of relations in culture and civilization between the two countries. Although it contributes only a few references to Persia, these show by contrast that the Sino-Indian relations have been much more intense through a religious link, i.e., Buddhism, whereas the influence of Islam on Sino-Persian relations has been less pronounced.

Histories of Art, Science, and Technology; Encyclopedias

The six volumes of *A Survey of Persian Art*, edited by A. U. Pope and P. Ackerman, are by far the best in this group. The various articles of this magnificently illustrated work are written by specialists in their respective fields, many of them dealing with the technology of the arts under consideration. A. U. Pope's *Masterpieces of Persian Art* also contains some references to the industrial side.

A much smaller book specializing in the industrial arts of the Islamic world is E. W. Braun's "Das Kunstgewerbe im Kulturbereich des Islam."

H. T. Bossert's *Geschichte des Kunstgewerbes aller Zeiten und Völker*, in six volumes, contains many references to the industrial arts of Persia. Its bibliography is of particular value for specialized reading.

Iranische Kunst, by E. Diez, although a book on art, includes *inter alia* technical details regarding metals, ceramics, building techniques, and textiles.

Histories of technology are another group of sources on industrial techniques. One recently published is *A History of Technology*, edited by C. Singer, E. J. Holmyard, and A. R. Hall. It gives due credit to Persia's part in the development and diffusion of techniques. Lists for further reading at the end of its chapters enhance its value.

The Master Craftsmen by G. Gompertz is a history of the evolution of tools and implements in their early stages. It provides excellent reading in the chapters on ancient times of the Middle East, but is less interesting in the description of the development of ancient Greece and Rome and in the discussion of the Middle Ages.

A. Neuberger's *Die Technik des Altertums* and F. M. Feldhaus' *Die Technik der Antike und des Mittelalters* suffer from an overemphasis on Greece and Rome, yet contain many references to Persia's contributions.

F. Klemm's *A History of Western Technology* contains a chapter in which the impact of Islamic technology on Europe during the Middle Ages is well treated.

J. Beckmann, a pioneer in the recognition of technology as an academic discipline, has written *A History of Discoveries, Inventions and Origins* that has been a valuable source of information for the purpose of this study.

A similar work is L. Darmstädter's *Handbuch zur Geschichte der Naturwissenschaften und der Technik.* It has been arranged in chronological order of discoveries, year by year, and is particularly useful in the establishment of priorities.

The *Studies in Ancient Technology* by R. J. Forbes have been of special value. Each of the six volumes of this work contains one or two monographs on particular aspects, such as textiles, glass, furnaces, water supply, irrigation, and so forth. Forbes has taken full account of up-to-date knowledge on Middle East and Classical technology. The books therefore have been most revealing in showing the extent of diffusion.

E. J. Holmyard's *Alchemy*, in showing the development of the predecessor of modern chemistry by the Greeks, the Arabs, and the Persians, refers to many tools and processes which are still used by today's craftsmen in the Middle East.

The ʿuyūn al Akhbār from the *Book of Useful Knowledge* by Ibn Qutayba, written in the ninth century A.D., includes mechanical science in its section on Natural Science, translated into English by L. Kopf. Its Chinese counterpart is the *Thien Kung Kai Wu* (cf. A. Ledebur, "Ein altchinesisches Handbuch der Gewerbekunde"). It contains much detail on blast furnaces, refining of steel, and casting of iron and bronze.

When toward the end of the eighteenth

century a number of encyclopedias were written, many articles on technological processes were included that have proved to be of special interest for this study. In its 28 volumes the *Encyclopédie ou Dictionnaire Raisonné des Sciences et des Arts et Métiers* by Didérot and d'Alambert contains a great number of copper plates illustrating the industrial arts of their time.

Individual Industries

When reading the review on individual branches of industry it will be noticed that they are not equally well represented. There is an abundance of books and articles on the metalworking industries, but not a single one on the wood crafts, a remarkable amount on building techniques, many again on ceramics, little on textiles, but much on agriculture and food. This is probably not a reflection on the relative importance of these industries or an indication of the interest paid by the various observers but seems to have been caused by the fact that wood and textiles are perishable materials.

Metallurgy and Metal Industries

A comprehensive study of prehistoric ore mining is contained in the two volumes of W. Witter's *Die älteste Erzgewinnung im nordisch-germanischen Lebenskreis*. In the second volume, *Die Kenntnis von Kupfer und Bronze in der Alten Welt* due credit is given to the earliest developments in the Middle East.

R. J. Forbes' *Metallurgy in Antiquity* has likewise been extremely useful for this study, as it shows early metallurgy in western Asia and its diffusion into Europe and the Far East in its true perspective.

A report by J. Robertson under the title "An Account of the Iron Mines of Caradagh" has led to the rediscovery of ancient mines in Āẕarbaijān. In the 1930's European experts investigated old and new ore deposits as well as mining and smelting techniques. The following is a selection of publications resulting from their findings: E. Böhne, "Überblick über die Erzlagerstätten Persiens;" F. Unterhössel, "Die wichtigeren Erzvorkommen des persischen Karadagh-Gebirges;" H. Spies, "Der derzeitige Stand des Erzbergbaus in Iran;" and M. Maczek, "Der Erzbergbau im Iran." Maczek, Preuschen, and Pittioni—the former a mining engineer for the Persian Department of Mines, the latter metallurgists of Vienna University—have investigated the origin of copper used in prehistoric implements. They applied the method of spectroscopic analysis and were able to identify the mines from which the copper had come. They reported on their findings in "Beiträge zum Problem des Ursprungs der Kupfererzverwertung in der Alten Welt."

F. W. Nothing, also a mining engineer working in Persia, wrote on the production of antimony in "Antimongewinnung in Anarek." E. Böhne's "Die Eisenindustrie Masenderans" is a well illustrated article on the old mines and blast furnaces of Māzandarān.

Three books on the history of iron often refer to Persia's part in the development: L. Beck, *Die Geschichte des Eisens*; O. Johannsen, *Geschichte des Eisens*; and A. Rieth, *Die Eisentechnik der Hallstattzeit.*

The Chinese had cast iron before they had steel. If it is kept in mind that the casting technique gradually spread to the West it is interesting to follow its path through Persia. Two informative articles on this subject are "The Early Casting of Iron" and "Chinese Iron a Puzzle," both by T. T. Read.

J. Needham's monograph, *The Development of Iron and Steel Technology in China* is based on archaeological evidence as well as on historical records.

O. Johannsen traces the arrival of the

iron casting technique in Europe in "Eine Anleitung zum Eisenguss vom Jahre 1454" and "Die Erfindung der Eisengusstechnik."

E. Wiedemann's article "Über Eisen und Stahl bei den muslemischen Völkern" is based on Arabian and Persian sources. There is no single field in metallurgy which interests historians and scientists more than damascene steel. C. Schwarz traced its Indian origin in "Sur l'industrie du fer et de l'acier dans les Indes Orientales." G. Pearson, "Experiments and Observations on a Kind of Steel called Wootz," and J. Stodart, "A Brief Account of Wootz or Indian Steel" are contributions to this theme by eighteenth-century English scientists.

J. R. Bréant's "Description d'un procédé à l'aide duquel on obtient une espèce d'acier fondu semblable à celui des lames damassées orientales" was stimulated by the experiments of Stodart and Faraday with damascene. In this article he not only reveals for the first time the true nature of this steel but marks a breakthrough toward modern steelmaking.

We have learned from Roman history that Rome obtained some of its damascene steel from India. B. Neumann has published an analysis of Roman steel objects in "Römischer Damaststahl."

Persian and Arabian texts indicate that damascening spread to the Middle East from India. J. Hammer-Purgstall has translated some of these texts in "Sur les lames orientaux." L. Thorndyke quotes medieval European reports on damascene steel in *The History of Magic and Experimental Sciences*. The spread of the damascening technique across Asia to Japan has been treated by G. Hannak in "Japanischer Damaststahl."

The use of meteorite nickel-iron in combination with ordinary iron for the production of the Indonesian damascene steel, "pamor," by the Bali blacksmiths has been described by M. Covarrubias in *The Island of Bali*. The book also gives interesting details on the special social position of the *pandé*, the blacksmithing caste of Indonesia.

In "The Origins of Indonesian Pamor," J. P. Frankel wrote on his investigations regarding the Indonesian type of damascene steel. The article gives important details on metallurgical aspects of the steel. It mentions Persia and India as possible countries of origin of the technique. The part of vitriol in the etching of this steel to bring out the watery lines has been described by A. Jacquin in "Chemical Observations on the Sagh."

Russian contributions are P. A. Anossoff, *On the Bulat*, and Cpt. Massalski, "Preparation de l'Acier damassé en Perse." Later, two Russian metallurgists analyzed these steels, and N. Belaiew wrote about their findings in two articles, "Damascene Steel" and "On the Bulat." Further scientific investigations have been carried out in Solingen, as reported by K. Harnecker in "Beiträge zur Frage des Damaststahls;" P. Oberhofer, "Über das Gefüge des Damaszenerstahls;" and F. Schmitz, "Orientalischer Damaststahl."

Metal inlay work has been traced back to prehistoric times by A. Rieth in "Anfänge und Entwicklung der Tauschierkunst." M. Rosenberg in the monographs *Niello bis zum Jahre 1000 n. Chr.* and *Niello seit dem Jahre 1000 n. Chr.* devoted one chapter in each volume to the influence of the Middle East on the development of the niello technique. Persia's role in the development of mail armor is stressed in K. A. C. Creswell's book *A Bibliography of Arms and Armour in Islam.*

Many references to locks and keys in the Near East are contained in two richly illustrated studies, one by Fox-Pitt-Rivers, *On the Development and Distribution of Primitive Locks and Keys*, and the other by V. J. M. Eras, *Locks and Keys Through the*

Ages. The great skill of the medieval Islamic instrument maker becomes apparent in E. Wiedemann and F. Hauser's study on clocks, "Über die Uhren im Bereiche der islamischen Kultur." A useful aid in the conversion of oriental weights and measures into metric units is the book by W. Hinz *Islamische Masse und Gewichte*.

Building Crafts and Ceramics

Four thousand years of building from the Sumerians to the beginning of Islam, are covered in H. Frankfort's study *The Arts and Architecture of the Ancient Orient*. Good introductions to later styles and techniques are the two works by K. A. C. Creswell, *A Short Account of Early Muslim Architecture* and *Early Muslim Architecture*. E. Diez, in *Iranische Kunst*, has a well illustrated chapter on Persian architecture with emphasis on the Sasanian cupola and vaulting technique, whereas *Chorassanische Baudenkmäler* by the same author specializes in developments in East Persia.

The *yakā* wood used in the construction of the palaces of the Achaemenians has been identified by I. Gershevitch in "Sissoo at Susa."

An introduction to early ceramics in general, with proper reference to Persia's place, is H. Kühn's article "Frühformen der Keramik." Similarly, G. Savage's book *Pottery through the Ages* outlines the whole history of pottery, emphasizing Persia's central position. The early contact of Islamic pottery with the Chinese craft is well described and richly illustrated by F. Sarre in *Die Keramik von Samarra*. A. Lane's studies *Early Islamic Pottery* and *Later Islamic Pottery*, although covering the ceramic industry of the whole Islamic world, devote much space to the Persian contribution and include much technical detail.

More concerned with the artistic side of ceramics is *A Guide to Islamic Pottery of the Near East* by R. L. Hobson. An article by Jean Lacam, "La céramique musulmane des époques omeyyade et Abbaside, VIIe au Xe siècle," is richly illustrated with colored plates. Lacam attempts to reconstruct a series of Islamic kilns. Molding techniques and kilns in East Persian potteries are well described by C. K. Wilkinson in "The Kilns of Nishapur" and "Fashion and Technique in Persian Pottery." Wilkinson was a member of an excavating team from the Metropolitan Museum of Art, New York; he has illustrated his articles with many photographs of mold fragments and kiln wasters.

Early developments of glazes in Egypt and Babylonia have been dealt with in W. J. Furnival's book *Leadless Decorative Tiles, Faience and Mosaic*. A. L. Hetherington's highly specialized book *Chinese Ceramic Glazes* mentions the introduction of Parthian glazes into China. A possible source for the tracing of diffusion of pottery techniques is the Renaissance work *Le tre libre dell' Arte del Vasaio* by Cipriano Picolpasso.

A good study on early glass and transmission of techniques from the Mediterranean via Persia into the Far East is "Far Eastern Glass: Some Western Origins" by C. G. Seligman and H. C. Beck. Glass and glass techniques during early Islamic times are treated in: *Das Glas von Samarra* by C. J. Lamm, whereas *Glass from Iran*, by the same author, confines itself to Iran but covers a range of 1,000 years from pre-Islamic to Ṣafavid times.

In "Oberflächenverzierungen in der antiken Töpferkunst," T. Schumann shows that the Greeks never used true glazes but did all their ceramic decorations with specially treated clay slips.

Textile Crafts

Volume IV of R. J. Forbes' work, already mentioned, *Studies in Ancient Technology* deals exclusively with textiles in antiquity and devotes much space to the development of fibers and dyeing and weaving techniques in the Middle East. An unusual book printed in 1843 with much useful information is the *Textrinum Antiquorum* by J. Yates, an account of the art of weaving among the ancients.

An informative chapter on the history of cotton growing and its early spread from India is contained in *Cotton* by H. B. Brown. The relatively late arrival of the cotton plant in China and Persia's part in it is described in "Cotton in China" by L. Carrington Goodrich.

The history of silk cultivation and its introduction into the Middle East is treated in the magnificently illustrated book *Kunstgeschichte der Seidenweberei* by O. von Falke. The main part of the book deals with silk weaving, outlining the important part of the Sasanians in the development of figural pattern weaving. W. G. Thomson's *A History of Tapestry* also acknowledges Persia's leading role in the development of this craft. Mention should be made here of the many publications on special branches of the textile industry in the periodical *Ciba Review*, published by the dyestuff manufacturers Ciba Ltd. of Basle. Many of these articles deal with the history of the textile crafts in Persia and the Middle East.

From the abundance of books on Persian carpets only those will be mentioned here that yield substantial information on the technical side.

A beautifully illustrated book is *A History of Oriental Carpets before 1800* by F. R. Martin. It deals with the development of the industry from early Islamic times and mentions many instances of influence from Central Asia and China. *Old Oriental Carpets* by F. Sarre and H. Trenkwald has a short introduction to the technical terms and describes carpets from Ṣafavid times on. A recently published and well illustrated book is *Der Orientalische Knüpfteppich* by K. Erdmann. It takes due account of recent findings of ancient carpets in Central Asia.

Persian needlework and its high standard are mentioned in *Needlework Through the Ages* by M. Symonds and L. Preece. It is a well illustrated history of this craft.

Details on early paper [illegible]on in Samarkand are given in [illegible] Karabacek's profound study of [illegible]per of early Islamic manuscripts, "[illegible]bische Papier." His claims regar[illegible] fibers used are supported by J[illegible]er in *Mikroskopische Untersuchung[illegible] ostturkestanischer Papiere*. Investi[illegible]arding the work of the early pa[illegible]ave also been made by R. H[illegible]ho Was the Inventor of Rag [illegible] and H. Beveridge "The Paperm[illegible]narkand."

The technique of bookbinding has been treated by K. G. Bosch in her dissertation, "Islamic Bookbinding: 12th to 17th Centuries." Her investigations are based on the original description of the craft by Ibn Bādīs in *ᶜUmdat al-kuttāb*, by the master bookbinder Sufyānī in *Ṣināᶜat tasfīr al-kutub* and in A. Qalqašandī's *Ṣubḥ al-ᶜašā*. A full translation of the work of Ibn Bādīs has been made by Martin Levy and published under the title *Mediaeval Arabic Bookbinding and Its Relation to Early Chemistry and Pharmacology*. A well-selected bibliography and an Arabic-English technical glossary make this book particularly valuable.

In "Zur Orientalischen Altertumskunde" J. von Karabacek investigates the origins of Persian and Arabian bookbinding methods. His observations are based on an analysis of bindings of a great number of manuscripts in the state archives in Vienna.

Agriculture and Food-Treating Crafts

The most comprehensive book on Persian agriculture is *Landlord and Peasant in Persia* by A. K. S. Lambton. In the first part the author shows the development of the peasant's position in the community from the Arab Conquest to the nineteenth century. In the second part the present-day situation has been dealt with. The chapters on irrigation, agricultural methods, and crops have been particularly important for the purpose of this study.

A study of life in a Persian village has been compiled by three Oxford students who spent three months with peasants in a small place near Kermān. *Blind White Fish in Persia* by A. Smith, one of the team, is not meant to be a scholarly book, but it is full of first-hand observations on soil, agricultural methods, irrigation, and village crafts.

"Village Life in Persia" by J. T. Bent brings among other things a detailed description of the harvesting of manna, the gum so much used in Persian confectionery.

P. H. T. Beckett and E. Gordon, both members of the previously mentioned Oxford team, published their meteorological observations under the title "The Climate of South Persia." P. H. T. Beckett also wrote three interesting articles, "The Soils of Kerman," "Agriculture in Central Persia," and "Tools and Crafts in South Central Persia." A. Heinecke makes good observations on present-day farming methods in "Persia, a Land of Medieval Farming."

In an article, "Comparison of the Afghan Plough and Tillage Methods with Modern Implements and Methods" G. F. Hauser reports on draft experiments he made as a member of a technical assistance mission. Since the Afghan plow is similar to one of the Persian plow types, these observations have a direct bearing on the subject of the present study.

M. L. Dewar's description of the pigeon towers around Iṣfahān, "Pigeon Towers and Pigeon Guano in Iran," is well illustrated.

Many references to cereals grown in Persia are made in an article by J. J. Clément-Hallet, "Sur les noms des céréales chez les anciens." A comprehensive list of plants grown in the area is contained in the study by D. Hooper and H. Field, "Useful Plants and Drugs of Iran and Iraq." A short description of the nature and use of each plant is given, together with its popular name, the equivalent in English, and the botanical name in Latin.

A comprehensive study of all the systems of irrigation employed in Persia is given by B. Fisher in "Irrigation Systems of Persia." Sir A. Wilson's *Persia* contains references to the Kārūn river diversion scheme, the qanāt, and windmills for lifting water. The Kārūn scheme is also described by a civil engineer, P. E. Case, in "I Became a Bakhtiari."

A scholarly investigation into the history of the qanāt system is the study by F. Krenkow, "The Construction of Subterranean Water Supplies during the Abbaside Caliphate."

P. H. T. Beckett has written three articles on the qanāt system, "Qanats Around Kerman," "Qanats in Persia," and "Waters of Persia." Further details on this topic are contained in the following articles: M. A. Butler, "Irrigation in Persia by Kanats," E. Noel, "Qanats," and G. Stratil-Sauer, "Kanate, Persiens Künstliche Bewässerlungsanlagen."

The development of power sources for the milling of grain is well treated in the second volume of R. J. Forbes *Studies in Ancient Technology*. It gives much detail on the various types of water mills and quotes ample evidence on the development of the windmill in East Persia. A well illustrated monograph on the latter source of power is H. T. Horwitz, "Über das Aufkommen, die erste Entwicklung und die Verbreitung von Windrädern." It gives an outline of the development of wind power and its transmission to northern Europe via the Aegean Islands, Greece, and Italy. A paper by H. P. Vowels, "Inquiry into the Origin of the Windmill," traces its history and proposes a theory of diffusion to the North through Russia to Holland.

UNO and Government Documentation

A comprehensive survey for the International Labour Organisation (ILO), "Agricultural and Industrial Activity and Manpower in Iran," makes many references to crafts and industrial arts. A study under the title *Iran, an Economic Survey*, often mentioning home industries and crafts, has been compiled by R. N. Gupta and was published by the Indian Institute of International Affairs.

B. A. Keen reports the findings of a British-American scientific advisory team to the Middle East in *The Agricultural Development of the Middle East*. It contains an excellent analysis of the existing conditions and makes many realistic suggestions for technical improvements.

GLOSSARY OF TECHNICAL TERMS

āb, water, irrigation water, 254
ᶜabā, cloth and cloak made of goat hair*
āb-aṃbār, water reservoir, 117, 258
āb-bān, water bailiff, 255
āb-bareh, water fountain, basin, 132
āb-bargardān, water bailiff, 255
ᶜabbāsī, equivalent of one farthing, 65
ābčāk, brick bond (Šīrāz), 112
āb dādan, to harden by quenching*, to wet, 108, to rinse, 194
ābdang, rice-husking mill, 290
ābdār, hardened steel, 52
āb-deh, aquifer, water-bearing stratum, 249, 252
āb-e āhak, bleaching solution, 93
āb-e ᶜaraq-e zamīn, underground water of a temporary nature, 252
āb-e ḫamīr, water to wet dough, 294
āb-e ḫarī, ground water on an impermeable bed, 252
āb-e jūš, boiling water, 224
āb-e ṣābūn, soap water for fulling, 223
āb-e tond dādan, to harden steel by rapid quenching, 59
āb-e torš, leaven, 293
ābgar, water bailiff, 255
āb gereftan, to anneal steel*, to wet clay*
ābgīneh, frit, 160, glaze*, glass*

---

* Denotes words that have been recorded with the crafts but do not appear in the text.

† Denotes words that are not so much used by the craftsmen but by the technicians trained in technical colleges.

A strict alphabetical order has been maintained, regardless of the fact that words with the same base could have been grouped together. Diacritical points and signs such as ᶜ, ˇ, and ˯ do not affect the alphabetical order.

āb-ḫẉordeh, rinsed, 194
ābī, pale blue, 162, 192, blue in textile print, 225, irrigated land, 271
ābī-meškī, cobalt-colored, cobalt blue, 147
ābī-sangar, a blue-green color, 191
āb kardan, to melt, 20, to place hemp in water, 182
āb-kaš, *āb-keš*, water drawer, 256, rice strainer, 28
āb-kašī, draw well, 256
āb-māl, water bailiff, 255
āb-miyān, extra share of water, allocated in between two normal allocations*
āb-nabāt, boiled sweets, 301
ābnūs, ebony (*Diospyros ebenum*), 75, 93
āb-pāš, spraying can, 30
āb pāšīdan, to water bamboo for softening, 219
ābrā harz kardan, to open sluice door, 282
abrī, half case book cover, 238
abrīšam, silk, 183, silk thread, 46
abrīšam-dūzī, silk embroidery, 233
abrīšam-tāb, silkwinder, silkspinner, 183
āb rūš rīḫtan, to pour water on, to soak, 165, to wet clay*
ābsāb, see *āsiyāb-e ābsāb*, 151
ābsī, fork (Šīrāz), 275
āb var dāštan, to pour water off*
ābyār, water bailiff (Sīstān)*
ābyārī, agriculture with irrigation, irrigation, water supply, 245, 271
abzār, tool, turning tool; cf. *afzār*, 91
abzār-e bangī, a certain molding profile, 84
abzār-e qāleb-borī, pen box cutting-tool, 239
āčār, spanner, wrench, 61
āčār-e boks, box spanner, 61
āčār-e čakošī, monkey wrench, 61
āčār-e faranseh, shifting spanner, 61

āčār-e haftsarī, multiheaded spanner, 61
āčār-e inglīsī, shifting spanner, 61
āčār-e lūleh-gīr, pipe wrench, 61
āčār-e pīč-gūštī, screwdriver, 61
āčār-e pīč-kašī, screwdriver†
āčār-e polomb, lead seal pliers, 61
āčār-e sehtofangeh, multiheaded spanner, 61
āčār-e zanjīrī, chain wrench, chain vice, 60
ᶜadl, bundle of bamboo or rushes, 219
adviyejāt, chemicals for the still, 163
affaz, gall apple, oak apple (Tehrān), 189
afrā, āfrā, maple tree (*Acer insigne*) (Caspian Provinces), 75, 97
āftāb dādan, to dry in the sun (textiles), 194
āftābeh, water can, ewer, 28
āftābeh-ō-lagan, set ewer and handwashing pan, 28
āftābeh-naftdān, kerosene can, 30
āftāb ḫwordan, to dry in the sun, 194
afzār, tool, device†, oblong hole in mill rind, 281
afzār-gīr, pin vice†
āhak, lime, powdered lime, 108, 112, 113, quicklime, 231, limestone, 161
āhak-e siyāh, waterproofed mortar, 113
āhak-paz, lime burner*
āhak-pazī, lime works, 126
āhan, wrought iron, 52, mild steel, 7, iron scraper for treating chamois leather, 233
āhan-ᶜaqab-e otāq, cross beam on coach body, 90
āhan-e čap-ō-rāst-kon, saw-setting tool, 82
āhan-e čūb-e korūk, joints connecting hoops, 90
āhan-e dastgāh, carpenter's bench iron†
āhan-e dūl, iron hoop of bucket, 234
āhan-e laḥīm, soldering iron, 31
āhan-e nar, hardenable steel, tool steel*
āhan-e narm, wrought iron, mild steel*
āhan-e safīd, galvanized iron, 30
āhan-e tīr, journal peg of axle, 155
āhangar, blacksmith, ironworker, 50
āhangar-ḫāneh, ironworks*
āhangarī, smithcraft, smithy*, fees paid in kind to the blacksmith for services*
āhan-gāz, iron plow wedge, 263
āhanī, āhanīn, made of iron*
āhanī-dūš, made of steel, 63
āhanīn-kursī, anvil*
āhanjad, windlass, capstan*
āhanjeh, weaver's comb, 52
āhan-rārī, plowshare, 262
āhan-rubā, magnet*
āhār, warp size, starch, 196
āḫereh, manger at end of oxen runway (Šīrāz), 257
ahing, the condiment *asa foetida*, 292
āḫor, manger at end of runway, 257
ahram, ahrām, lever to rotate breast beam, 210, 216, capstan lever, 297, 298
āhrū, coach beam support, 90
aivān, verandah, portico, 106
ᶜaiyār, metal, 17, raw glass, 169
āj, cut of file, 239, maple tree (*Acer laetum*) (Caspian provinces), 75
ᶜāj, ivory, 92
ᶜajamī, mild-colored turquoise, 39
āj-e bālā, second cut of file†
āj-e dorošt, coarse cut of file, 58
ᶜāj-e fīl, ivory, 92
āj-e narm, bastard cut of file, 58
āj-e pāᵓīn, main cut of file†
āj-e pardāḫt, āj-e rīz, fine cut of file, 58
āj-e ṣaiqal, extra smooth cut of file, 58
āj-e zabr, coarse cut of file, 58
ājīdan, to sharpen a file*
āj-kon, file cutter, 57
ᶜāj-tarāš, ivory turner, 92
ājur, burnt brick, 109, 112, 122
ājur čīdan, to lay bricks, 112
ājur-čīnī, brick bond*
ājur-e dandāneh, toothed cornice brick, 122
ājur-e morabāᶜ, whole brick, 122
ājur-ḫāneh, brickworks, 115
ājur-paz, brickmaker, 115
ājur-pazī, brickworks, brickmaking, 116
ājur puḫtan, to fire bricks, burn bricks*
ājur-tarāš, ornamental brickworker, brick cutter, 121
ājur tarašīdan, to cut bricks, 122
āj-zan, file cutter*
ᶜalaf-e būdār, herb used for silkworm raising, 182
ᶜalaf-e farangī, linen, 219
ᶜalaf-e katān, flax, 178
alak, flour sieve, fine sieve, 18, 236, 279
alak kardan, to pass through a fine sieve*
ᶜalāmat-e sang-tarāš, stonemason's mark, 128
ālam-e poštband-e šelīt, beam supporting draw harness*
ālaš, ālāš, beech tree (*Fagus silvatica, F. orientalis*) (Caspian provinces), 75
ālat, ceiling batten, 87, crossbar of window frame, 86, reed blade, 195
ālāt (pl. of *ālat*), tools, utensils, vessels, 153
ālat-e bālā, top rope, 257
ālat-e zīr, guide rope, 257
ālat-sāz, door and window joiner, 81
aldār-kaš, frame of threshing wain, 274, skid*
ᶜalef-e būdār, see *ᶜalaf-e būdār*, 182
ᶜalef-e katān, see *ᶜalaf-e katān*, 178
āleh, half log (Iṣfahān), 79
alġar, alġār, plow stay (Ḫorāsān), 263
aliāž, alloy (fr. *alliage*)†

alvār, plank 4 to 6 inches thick, 79
ambār, storehouse, barn*
ambārbū, a rice variety (Māzandarān), 242
ambār-e gel, potter's clay store, 152
ambār-e żarfdānī, drying chamber, 155
ambīq, still head, alembic, 163
ambor, drawing pliers, 43
ambor-dast, pliers, tongs, 26, 60
ambor-dast-e ʿāyeq, electrician's pliers, 60
ambor-dast-e dambārīk, flat-mouthed pliers, 60
ambor-dast-e damgerd, round-nosed pliers, 52, 60
ambor-dast-e dampahn, flat-mouthed pliers, 52, 60
ambor-dast-e lūlehgīr, pipe wrench, 60
ambor-dast-e jūl, tongs with a lap (Nihāvand), see *ambor-e jūl*, 52
ambor-dast-e movāzī, parallel-jawed pliers, 60
ambor-e āteškārī, fire tongs, 52
ambor-e bōteh, crucible tongs, 19
ambor-e damgerd, round-nosed tongs, 52
ambor-e dampahn, flat-nosed tongs, 52
ambor-e fanarī, spring-loaded pliers†
ambor-e jūl, tongs with laps, tongs to hold round bars (Nihāvand), 52
ambor-e kaj, tongs with bent tips, crucible tongs, 22, 52
ambor-e kūreh, fire tongs, 52
ambor-e lūleh, tongs to hold round bars, 52
ambor-e manganeh, punch pliers for leather, 60
ambor-e mīḫparč, rivet-heating tongs, 52
ambor-e qalam-gīr, tongs to hold a chisel, 52
ambor-e safīdgarī, tinner's tongs, 31
ambor-e tōġ, crucible tongs, 19
ambor-ḥalqeh, tongs with hollow mouth, 26
ambū, Sebestens tree (*Cordia myxa*, *C. crenata*), 75
āmīḫtan, to mix, 293
amrās, *amrāz*, plow, plow column (Ahar), 263
ʿanāb, French jujube tree (*Ziziphus vulgaris*), 75, 93, 287
anār, pomegranate, 232, 245
anār-e jangalī, wild pomegranate, 233
andām kardan, to turn the outside (Rašt), 92
andang, husking mill (Alburz), 290
andāzeh, measure, yard, quantity, 61, marking gauge block, 80
andāzehgīr-e dāḫelī, inside calipers, 61
andāzehgīr-e ḫārejī, outside calipers, 61
andāzehgīr-e pīč, screw pitch gauge, 61
andāzeh-gīrī, marking off, measuring†
andāzeh-maidān, standard brick size, 110
angāreh, shaped but unfinished stone block, 131
angereh, wool pad, 222
angoštāneh, *anguštāneh*, thimble, finger protection, 99, 228
angoštar, finger ring, 32, thimble, 228
angošteh, socket on scoop blade, 268
angūrčīn, vinedresser, 271
angūrdān, wine press*
angūrzan, vinedresser, 271
anjīlī, Transcaspian iron wood (*Parrotia persica*) (Caspian provinces), 75
anjīr, fig (*Ficus caria*), 245
aqāqī, *aqāqiyā*, acacia tree (*Acacia spp.*), 75
aqāqī-ye jangalī, a forest variety of acacia, 75
āqčeh-aġāč, elm tree (*Zelkova crenata*) (Turcoman steppe), 75
āqčeh-qaiyīn, maple tree (*Acer mouspesassulanum*) (Caspian provinces), 75
ʿaqrabak, fork on spinning head, 46
āqṭī, elder tree (*Sambucus niger*), 75
ār, ash tree (*Fraxinus excelsior*, *Fraxinus oxyphylla*) (Šīrāz), 75
ʿarāba, ship mill, 259
arābeh, four-wheeled truck, 89
ʿaraq-gīr, saddle cloth, 218
ʿaraq kardan, to vaporize, 163
ārčī, hand mill, quern (Iṣfahān) dialect for *ārdčī*, 232
ārd, flour, meal, 279
ārdāl, skid or cross beam of threshing wain (Iṣfahān), 274
ārd-bīz, flour sieve*
ārd-e daštarī, fine meal, 295
ārd-e dūreh, flour jar, 157
ārd-e gandom, wheat meal, 196
ārdeh, ground sesame seed, 302
ārd-e ḫošk, whole meal, 196
ārd-e jou, barley meal for tanning, 231, 233
ārd-e jou-ḫwordeh, swelled (hides), 231
ārd-e jou kardan, to swell (hides), 231
ārd-e šāḫ, horn meal for steel hardening, 59
ardī, heavy ceiling joist (Šīrāz), 79
ārd-ō-namak, tanning mixture, 233
arġavān, Judas tree (*Cercis siliquastrum*); see *arjavān*, 75
arjan, wild bitter almond tree (*Amygdalus spp.*), 75
arjavān, Judas tree (*Cercis siliquastrum*); see *arġavān*, *arjevān*, 75
arreč, weaver's temple, broad holder, 205
arreh, saw, 79, pruning saw, 271
arreh-āhanbor, hacksaw, 60
arreh-baġal-šīšbor, inlay work saw, 93
arreh-borešt, tenon saw, 82
arreh-čakeh, *arreh-čakī*, a small bow saw, 82
arreh-dandeh-dorošt, coarse saw, 99
arreh-dandeh-rīzeh, fine saw, 99
arreh-dastī, hand saw, 82
arreh-dehandeh, sawyer on top of jack leading the saw, 80
arreh-dom rūbāh, hand saw, 82
arreh-dō-sar, two-handed saw, 79

arreh-felezzbor, metal cutting saw†
arreh-kalāfī, bushman's saw, 82
arreh-kamāneh, hacksaw, bow saw, 60
arreh-kamānī, hacksaw, bow saw, 60, bushman's saw, 82
arreh-kamānī-dastī, hacksaw†
arreh kardan, to apply saw cut for bookbinding, 237
arreh-kaš, sawyer of a team who pulls the saw, 79, 80
arreh kašīdan, to saw, 79
arreh-koneškāf-bor, arris-cutting saw†
arreh-laṭīf, small hand saw, 82
arreh-mārī, hole saw, 82
arreh-māšū, bow saw, 80, 82
arreh-mošābak, fretsaw, 60
arreh-mūhī, fretsaw, 82, 98
arreh-mūʾī, fretsaw†
arreh namūdan, to saw†
arreh-navārī, band saw†
arreh-nōkī, hole saw, 82
arreh pošt-dār, tenon saw†
arreh-qabāreh, *arreh-qavāreh*, bow saw, 80, 82
arreh-qatᶜkon, cross-cut saw, 82
arreh-rūkaš-bor, veneer-cutting saw†
arreh-sareš-qatᶜkon, inlay saw*
arreh-ṭarḥ-e farang, tenon saw, 82
arreh-ṭarḥ-e farang-bor, arris-cutting saw†
arreh-tīzbor, hole saw†
arreh-ye zīr-zan, *arreh-zīr-zan*, saw cutting to root of tooth, 99
arreh-zabāneh-bor, dovetail-cutting saw†
arreh-zargarī, jeweler's fretsaw, 34
arreh-ẓarīf, small hand saw, 82, fine-cutting saw†
arūčak, bearing for spinning head pulley, 46
ᶜarūsak, loom pulley, 204
arzan, millet, 242, 275, 277, 291
arzīz, lead, 161
āš, mixture of salt and barley meal, 233
āsak, glaze mill, frit mill, 151
āsak-e āb-sāb, wet quern, 151
āsak-e rūʾī, upper millstone (runner), 277
āsak-e zīrī, lower millstone (bed), 277
ᶜasal, honey, 295
āšām kašīdan, to spread sheaves on threshing floor, 273
asbarg, a yellow dye from *Delphinium zalil*, see *asparg*, 191
āṣer, backing boards for gluing inlay slices, 96
asīd, soldering flux, 61
āsī(n), fork (Šīrāz), 275, 276
āsiyā, mill, hand mill, quern, 131, 277
āsiyā-āžan, dressing pick for millstone, 279
āsiyāb, mill, quern, 151, 277
āsiyā-bād, windmill (Ḫorāsān), 284
āsiyābān, miller, 279
āsiyāb-e ābsāb, wet grinding mill, 151
āsiyāb-e bādī, windmill, 284
āsiyāb-e čarḫī, water mill, mill driven by water wheel, 282
āsiyāb-e ḫoškehsāb, dry grinding mill, 151
āsiyāb-e konjed, sesame mill, 302
āsiyāb-e noudāneh, mill with wooden penstock, 282
āsiyāb-e parī, mill driven by water wheel, 280
āsiyāb-e tandūreh, free jet water mill, 280
āsiyā-dastī, hand quern, 277
āsiyāgar, millwright, 279
āsiyā kardan, to grind, to mill, 277
āsiyā tīz kardan, to dress a millstone, 279
āsiyā-zan, millwright, 279
askarī, a grape variety, 244
āsmān-negāh, underground water channel depending on rain for supply, 254
āšormeh, shoulder belt of harness (Iṣfahān), 275
aspak, peg riding on millstone, 288
aspareh, mill rind (Jahrum)*, millstone couplings, 52
asparg, a yellow dye, 191
aspist, lucerne, alfalfa (*Medicago sativa*), 243
āsporeh, bearing block (Šīrāz), 278
ᶜaṣṣār, oil miller, 296
ᶜaṣṣār-ḫāneh, oil mill, 296
ᶜaṣṣārī, oil mill, 296
āstāneh, doorsill, threshold, 86
āstar, lining of shoe upper, 230, fancy paper (book), 237
astarḫān, edge roller mill (Kāšān), 296
aṣṭurlāb-e ḫaṭṭī, *asturlāb-e ḫaṭṭī*, linear astrolabe, 21
aṣṭurlāb-e kūrī, *asturlāb-e kūrī*, spherical astrolabe, 21
āsūneh, doorsill, 86
asvarg, yellow dye from *Delphinium zalil* (cf. *asbarg*), 191
āteš dādan, to fire (ceramic ware), 166
āteš-gāh, fire hole in kiln, 116, 126
āteš-ḫāneh, fireplace of baking oven, 292, of brick kiln, 116, 159
āteš-kār, *āteš-kārī*, forging, 56
ᶜatīq, the antique steel, 55
ᶜatīqeh-sāz, stone paste potter, 151, 165
ᶜatīqeh-sāzī, making of stone paste ware, 151
aṭrāf, edge, 158
aṭrāf sāvīdan, to clean the edges, 158
āvers, Cypress tree (*Cupressus sempervirens*) (Caspian provinces), 75
āvīz, suspended stirrup of balance, 63
āvīzān, pivot point of balance, 63
āyineh, mirror, 88
āyineh-dardār, mirror with doors, 88

āzād-borī, setting of saw-teeth†
āzāl, plow (Kalārdašt), 264
āzāl-e jed, plow (Kalārdašt), 264
āzād, elm tree (*Zelkova crenata*), 75, 77, 262
āzangū, hoop on file cutter's bench, 58
azār, cedar tree (*Cedrus spp.*), 75
azdār, elm tree (*Zelkova crenata*) (Caspian provinces); cf. *āzād*, *azār*, 75
āzel, plow (Alburz), 264
azgīl, medlar tree (*Mespilus spp.*), 75, 77, 92

bā āb sāf kardan, to smooth over with water, 153
bābak, vertical arm of reed batten, 204
bačeh-fanar, smallest leaf in laminated spring, 90
bačeh-gord, shed rod (Šīrāz), 200, 214
bādām, almond, almond tree (*Amygdalus communis*), 75, 245
bādām-bun, almond tree (*Amygdalus communis*)*
bādām-e aržan, sweet almond (*Amygdalus orientalis*), 75
bādām-e boḫūrak, sweet almond (*Amygdalus orientalis*), 75
bādām-e kāġẕī, sweet almond (*Amygdalus fragilis*), 75
bādām-e kūhī, mountain almond (*Amygdalus scoparia*), 75
bādām-e šīrīn, sweet almond (*Amygdalus dulcis*), 75
bādām-e talḫ, bitter almond (*Amygdalus amara*), 75
bādāmī, chisel with almond-shaped face, 36, 37
bād dādan, to winnow grain, 275
bad-dum, unsafe roof of underground water channel, 253
bād-e ṣad-ō-bīst rūz, "Wind of the 120 days," a seasonal wind, 284
bād-gīr, ventilation shaft, wind catcher, 15
bād kāhrā bordan, to let the wind carry the chaff away, 276
bād kardan, to blow glass, 170
bād-kaš, surgeon's cupping glass*, air duct, 292
bādrank, lemon tree (*Citrus medica*), 75
badreqeh, fancy paper (book), 237
bādū, mine ventilation shaft, 15
badūmak, end batten of reed, 195
bāfandeh, weaver, 203
bāft, fabric*, weaver's cross, 184, lease, 204
bāftan, to weave, to plait, 219
bāftan-e qālī, to knot a carpet, 215
baġal, edging of cloth shoe, 230
baġal-band, sole of plowshare, 266
baġal borīdan, to cut sides of comb, 99
baġal-bur, division in course of underground water channel, 253
baġal-e dōrāheh, sash plane, 84, a certain molding profile, 84
baġal-šīš, triangular inlay bead, 94, 95
baġal-šīš-e sabz, green inlay bead*
baġal-šīš-sāvī, filing block for triangular beads, 94
bāham kardan, to align quires for bookbinding, 237
bahār-āb, underground water of temporary nature, 254
bahreh, wooden spade*
baḫs, dry land farming (Dārāb)*
baḫsī, dry land farming, 271
bāhū, door frame, 86
bāhū-pāšneh, outer stile of door frame, 86
bāhū-pīšneh, inner stile of door frame, 86
baigāh, opening for water in raised border, 269
bailak, maple tree (*Acer insigne*) (Gīlān), 75
bairam, crowbar, 130
baj, dry land farming (Tangestān)*
bāj-dār, floor bearer (Šīrāz), 107
bājīr, fallow land*
bā-laᶜāb, glazed*
bālā gereftan, to throw clay, 155
bālank, lemon tree (*Citrus medica*), 75
bālāpī, wheel of the vertical windmill (Sīstān), 286
bālā qabżeh gereftan, to draw clay up during throwing, 155
bālā raftan, to come forward (thread in chain stitch) (Rašt), 218
baᶜlāveh-sir, ash tree (*Fraxinus excelsior*) (Caspian provinces), 75
bālā-ye čakoš, hammer peen†
bāleh, spade (Varāmīn)*
bālešak, pincushion, 227
bālešmak, bearing in cotton gin (Kāšān), 180, rubbing block on edge runner pole, 296
bālešmak-dān, wooden bearing block in cotton gin (Kāšān), 180
bālešmeh, wooden bearing, 283
bāleštak, bearing of rolling mill, 33, pincushion, 228, supporting pole, 288
bālišmeh = *bālešmeh*, 283
bālištak = *bāleštak*, 33
balk, loop connecting yoke to plow beam (Varāmīn), 262
ballūṭ, oak tree (*Quercus castaneifolia*, *Q. iberica*, *Q. atropatena*, *Q. persica*), 75, oak wood*
baltak, *bāltak*, iron part of wheel axle, 155
bām, mud roof, 114, horizontal bar of windlass, 258
ban, hard wood for tool handles (Šīrāz) (*Pistacia acuminata*), 75
bān, myrobalan tree (*Prunus cerasifera*); cf. *vān*, 75
banabšāl, *banafšāl*, wedge in carpenter's plane (Iṣfahān), 82

band, bucket handle, 15, transmission cord, 44, 46, 47, brick joint, 113, dam, 246, joint in pottery, 165, rope belt, 221, yoke rope, 256, 267, a pair of bullocks, plowland*
bandak, potter's cutting wire or thread, 155, cotton cleansed of its seed*
band-e āb, water storage dam, 246
band-e āb-kaš, rope of water well, 258
band-e čarḫ, rope of windlass, 109, 258, transmission cord of twisting wheel (Kāšān), 196
band-e gāv, a yoke of oxen (Nairīz, Kermān)*
band-e gord, heddle, heald (Šīrāz), 215
band-e ḫongī, rope made of rushes, 156
band-e kār, lathe adjustment, 91
band-e kenāreh, reinforced carpet edge, selvage, 217
band-e mīl, lathe adjustment, 91
band-e parīčeh, rope made from palm fiber, 156
band-e semiyān, tie between yoke and plow beam, 262
band-e tōmūn, tablet weaving*
band-kašī, joint in face-brick work, 113
bandok, plant used for potash production, 161
bānēgā, bent beam forming plow sole and stilt (Kalārdašt), 264
baneh, Persian turpentine tree (*Pistacia acuminata*, P. Khinjuk), 75
bāneh, rim of cloth shoe, 229
bānkeh, fruit-preserving jars (Šīrāz), 170
*bannā*ʾ, builder, bricklayer, 108
bannīy, stand to hold silk winding eyelet (Yazd), 183
baqaleh, *bāqelā*, broad beans, 245
baqam, *baqem*, logwood (*Haemotoxylon campechianum*); 75, 93
baqāreh, reel holding round wire in flattening rollers (Šīrāz), 45
baqem-e benafš, logwood (*Haematoxylon campechianum*), 75
baqem-e qermez, sapan wood (*Caesalpinia sapan*), 75
baql, vegetable, 245
baqlat, *baqleh*, beans, leguminous plant, 245
baqūl, *baqūlāt*, vegetables, 245
bār, nonprecious content in gold and silver alloys, 33, manure (Būjnurd)*
barak, board between plow sole and beam (Iṣfahān), 264
bar-ʿaks, face-down, reverse, 123
bārāndār, water bailiff (Ḫorāsān), 255
bar-andāz, peg locking breastbeam of loom (Yazd), 204
bā rang maḫlūt kardan, to mix oxides into frit, 164
barāstī, ruler, straight-edge (Šīrāz), 81
barbarī, thick flat bread (Tehrān), 295
bardū, threshing wain (Ḫorāsān)*
bargardāndan, *bargardānīdan*, to rewind, reverse, 45, to turn upside down, 156
barg-e mou, leaf of the grapevine, a dyestuff, 191
barg-e qīṭarān, leaves of *Chrizophora tinctoria*, a dyestuff, 192
bār gereftan, to take a lump of boiled sugar, 301
barg-e tūt, mulberry leaf, 183
barīz, frit kiln, 158, 161
barjesteh, relief work, repoussé work, 35, 36, 166
barjesteh-kār, relief work, repoussé work, 35
barjesteh kardan, to chase (metal), to do repoussé work, 36
barjīn, threshing wain (Fasā, Dārāh)*
bār kardan, to stretch yarn from wall to wall (Kāšān), 196
barm, sluice gate in irrigation channel (Fasā)*
bar miḥakk zadan, to essay, to test on a touchstone, 33
barōšāl, wedge of carpenter's plane (Šīrāz), 82
bārrīz, manured land (Būjnurd)*
bār-šūrī, to wash crushed whiting in a vat, 300
bārūt, gunpowder, 59, 127, 131
bārūt-dān, powder horn, 59
bārūt-e bīdūd, smokeless gunpowder, 59
bārūt-sanj, powder measure, 59
bārūt-sāz, gunpowder maker, 59
baš, weaving comb, 220
baṣrī, blades of Basra steel and forged there, 55
bast, a row of molds tied together, 19, hinge, hasp, 70, metal decorations on trunk, 88, overlap joint of mat, 220, measure for the flow of water, 255, raised border in irrigated fields, 268, steel tire, 286, 288
bastan, to spin silk cocoons, 183
bastan be gīr, to tighten a workpiece in the vice†
basteh, bundle of bamboo, rushes, 219
bast-e pīčī, a G-clamp†
bast-e pīčī movāzeh, parallel clamp, toolmaker's clamp†
bātāl, clay–lime mixture used for house foundation (Šīrāz), 108, mortar, 113
baṭūneh, putty, lining of window panes, 86
bāʾū, door frame, 86
bāʾū-daftīn, vertical batten of reed frame (Yazd), 204
bāz čīdan, to open up a felt cap, 223
bazdarak, small yoke for single oxen, small harness (Behbehān), 257
bāzī, windmill spoke (Sīstān), 287
bāz kardan, to stretch, 24
bazr, *bazr*, seed, linseed, 296
bazr-ḫāneh, oil mill, 296
bāzū-band, amulet container, armlet, 32
bāzūleh, threshing wain (Varāmīn, Semnān)*

bāzūneh, plow column (Iṣfahān), 263
bāzū-ye arreh, upright part of a bow saw†
bāzū-ye daftīn, vertical batten of reed frame (Iṣfahān), 204
be dīvār naṣb kardan, to attach mosaic panel to wall, 123
behānij, foreign steel blades with coarse grain, 55
beleskeh, mill rind*
benabš, benafš, violet colored*
ben-gāb, plow sole (Alburz), 264
be qāleb zadan, to place in a mold, 157
bērak, bottom roller, guide roller (Behbehān), 257
berenj, brass, 13, 18, 94, rice, 242, 289
berenjīl, castor bean*
berenj-kūb, rice pounder, husker, 290
berenj safīd kardan, to husk rice, 290
berz, broken-up oil cakes, lumps of oil cakes, 299
bezān, harrow, 266
bīd, willow (*Salix micaus*, S. fragilis), 75, 160, 302
bīdanjīr, castor bean, 296
bīd-anjūbīn, willow (*Salix fragilis*)*
bīd-e jūdān, bīd-e jūdānak, bīd-jūdān, a willow variety (*Salix zygostemon*), 75
bīd-e majnūn, weeping willow (*Salix babylonica*), 75
bīd-e muᶜallaq, weeping willow (*Salix babylonica*), 75
bīd-e siyāh, a willow variety (*Salix sp.*), 75
bīd-e ḫeštī, bīd-ḫeštī, a willow yielding willow honey (*Salix fragilis*), 75
bīd-e zard, a willow variety (*Salix acmophylla*), 75
bīd-mašk, musk willow (*Salix aegyptiaca*), 75
biḫtan, to sift, to strain, 151, 302
bīl, spade, shovel, 52, 109, 260
bīlak, weeding spade, 271
bīl-dasteh, heddle of *zīlū*-loom, 210
bīl-e ābyārī, irrigation spade, 261
bīl-e kār, well-sinker's short-handled spade, 252
bīl-e zamīn-kanī, digging spade, 261
bīl kašīdan, to dig with a spade, 261
billūr, crystal, rock crystal, glaze; cf. *bullūr*, 151
bīl-nōkī, spade with turned-over edge, 261, pointed spade, 260
bīl-pākkon, wood for cleaning spade, 261
binā᾽ kardan, to build, to erect a building, 108
birkeh, cistern, reservoir; cf. *burkeh*, 258
birmāhīnī, the "female iron"; viz., wrought iron, 55
bīrūn kardan, to place dyed yarn in the open for drying, 194
bōġčeh, bōġeh, bundle of bamboo or rushes, 219
boḫārī, oven, room heater, boiler, 30
boḫārī-sāz, oven maker, 30
boḫār-kaš, steam outlet of samovar, 29
bojārī kardan, to winnow (Iṣfahān), 275
bōkū, bōkūb, ramming iron, 18
boland kardan, to put bricks upright, 116
bolqū, reamer (Šīrāz), 60
bolūr, see *bulūr*, 160
bon, lap or rim on vessel, 24
bondoq, nicker tree (*Caesalpina bonducella*), 75, 161
borādeh, filings, scrapings, 60
bōrak, borax, 61
boreh, threshing wain (Fārs)*
boreš, notch in adjusting board, 203, notch in harness device, 204
boreš dādan, to trim, 238
boreš kardan, to shear*
borīdan, to cut plaster ornament, 135, to cut, to tailor, 233, to cut velvet pile, 209, to rip timber with rip saw†
borīdan bā arreh, to saw fretwork, 73
borīdan darajeh, to cut off the riser, 18
borīdegī, groove for mill rind, 278
borīdeh, roughened, 288, 290
borj-e kaftar, pigeon tower, 270
borm, light ceiling joist (Šīrāz), 79
boronz, bronze, 18
boros, brush, 166
boros-e souhān, file-cleaning brush†
borqū, reamer (Šīrāz, Iṣfahān); cf. *bolqū*, 60
borqū-lūleh, tapered pipe reamer (Šīrāz), 60
borqū-motaḥarrek, adjustable reamer (Šīrāz), 60
borreh, threshing wain (Šīrāz), 273
borreh kašīdan, to thresh (Šīrāz), 273, 275
bōteh, crucible, 19, a certain embroidery design, 219
botō, clay-lime paste used for foundations (Šīrāz), 108
boučāl, bobbin winder*
boujār, sifter, winnower*
boz, goat, 177
bulat, steel, 9
buleh, small hoe (Gīlān)*
bulūr, glass, frit, glaze, rock crystal, 160
būm, background of an ornament, 37, warp, 209, main warp of velvet loom, 209, quilt field, 227
būm dādan, to spread on the ground*
būm-e kār, rear beam of loom, 209
būmgerd, round-edged plaster molding knife, 135
būm-ḫwor, plasterer's molding knife with concave edge, 135
būmkan, subterranean dwelling (Sīvand)*
būmkand, subterranean dwelling, 102
būm kardan, to dry, 302
būm-konī, plasterer's deep cutting knife, 135
buneh, agricultural implements (Varāmīn)*

būra, būrāk, būrak, būrāq, būraq, būreh, borax, 52, 61, 147
burīš, see *boreš*, 204
būriyā, reed mat, plaited mat, 219
būriyā-bāf, mat braider, 219
būriyā bāftan, to plait mats, 219
būriyeh, reed mat, 219
*burkeh, burqā*ᶜ, cistern, reservoir; cf. *birkeh*, 258
būšeh, plow column (Surmaq), 263
būsū, board between plow sole and beam (Varāmīn), 264
būteh, crucible; cf. *bōteh*, 19, 33
buzbarak, buzbarg, maple tree (*Acer laetum*) (Caspian provinces), 76
buzġanj, pistachio tree (*Pistacia khinjuk Stocks*)*
buzvālak, maple tree (*Acer laetum*) (Caspian provinces); cf. *buzbarak*, 76

čā, shaft in primitive lime-burner's kiln, 126
čāb, lifting wedge (Šīrāz), 281
čādār, rye, 242
čādor-bāf, cloth weaver, 205
čādor-šab, piece of cloth worn around waist (Māzandarān), 204
čādūnī, grain hopper (Iṣfahān); cf. *čāldūnī*, 278
čaġejak, pole of threshing wain (Hamadān), 275
čāh, well, vertical shaft of *qanāt*, 246, 252, 256
čāh-āb, čāh-ābī, animal-operated well, water well, 256
čahār-čūb, frame of gem cutter's bench, 39, door frame, 86, frame of bow saw, 82, trestle, 112
čahār-gūš kardan, to forge square*
čahār-lā, four-ply thread, 197
čahār-pāreh, deer shot, 59
čahār-pāyeh, stand of rolling mill*, frame of gold thread spinning device, 47, frame of wire drawing bench, 43, frame of roper's reel, 221
čahār-qolāb, spinning head, 221
čahār-šāḫ, winnowing fork*
čahār-sellī, a brick profile (Šīrāz), 123
čahār-tanḫūš, wild pistachio (*Pistacia* spp.)*
čahār-yak, quarter brick, 112
čāh-āteš-ḫāneh, fire place, 160
čāh-e dastī, hand-operated well, 258
čāḫ-e kelīd, key notch, 66
čāh-ḫū, well-sinker, *qanāt*-builder, 251
čāh-kan, well-sinker, 256
caḫmā, čaḫmāḫ, flint, firing lock of gun flint, 160
čaḫmāḫ-dašī, flint stones on threshing board (Āẕarbaijān), 274
čaḫmāq, flint, quartz; cf. *caḫmāḫ, caqmāq*, 160
čāh-rāh, spill of water mill, 282
čāhrak, water basin (Behbehān), 257
čak, cotton dresser's mallet, 180, 181
čāk, winnowing fork, 276
čāk-e ḥalqeh, notch in padlock shackle, 69
čakeh kardan, to condense, 163
čakoš, hammer, 15, 38, 51, 60
čakoš-e čahār-sūk, square-faced hammer, 24
čakoš-e cārsū, flat hammer, square-faced hammer (Šīrāz), 22, 26
čakoš-e čūbī, mallet, 26, 84, 127
čakoš-e dam-bārīk, narrow peen hammer, 26
čakoš-e dam-gerd, round-faced hammer, 26
čakoš-e dōbahrī, edging hammer, 26
čakoš-e kaf, stretching hammer, 22, 26
čakoš-e maṭbaqeh, carpenter's hammer, 84
čakoš-e maṭvaqeh, carpenter's hammer (Šīrāz), 84
čakoš-e mīḫ-kaš, claw hammer, 60
čakoš-e mīḫparč, čakoš-e miṭraqeh, riveting hammer, 26, 60
*čakoš-e na*ᶜ*lbandī*, farrier's hammer, 54
*čakoš-e na*ᶜ*lčīn*, heavy hammer for upsetting edge of horse shoe, 54
čakoš-e parčkon, riveting hammer, 26
čakoš-e qalamzanī, hammer for metal chasing work, 36
čakoš-e sīnehdār, ball hammer, 26
čakoš-e ṭelā-kūbī, gold-inlayer's hammer, 41, 42
čakoš-ḫwor, malleable, 23
čakoš ḫwordan, to bend the rim, 24
čakoš-kārī, beating of metal, hammer work, 22, 24
čakoš zadan, to beat out an ingot, to hammer, 22
čāl, pit, 109, 161, pit to receive molten metal, 16, clay-soaking pit*, glass-melting pan, 169, pit to receive molten frit*, furnace hearth, 159, 161, dynamiting hole, 130
čalak, hook to keep weaver's shed open, 208
čāldūnī, grain hopper, lower hopper; cf. *čādūnī*, 278, 279
čāl-e čūb-borī, čāleh-čūb-borī, saw pit, 79
čāleh, groove for cleaning, 31, mortar basin, 290
čālehdān, lower hopper, 279
čāleh-par, water wheel (Alburz), 280
čalōr, stone pot half finished (Mašhad), 131
čaltūk, unhusked rice, paddy, 271, 290
čalūj, pick for dressing millstone, 279
čām, canvas, coarse linen used for windmill sails, 285
čaṃbal, circular hoop; cf. *čaṃbar*, 252, 257
čaṃbar, guard on gem cutter's wheel, 39, circular hoop, 252
čaṃbareh, armrest cushion, 181
čampeh, a rice variety (Šīrāz), 242
čamseh, fabric used for upholstery, 90
čān, threshing wain (Hamadān), 273
čandal, Persian name for Arabic *ṣandal*, *q.v.*, 76
*čand lā*ᵓ*ī kardan*, to make veneer†

čāneh, see *čūneh*, 152
čang, hooked link at balance beam, 63
čangal, *čangāl*, fork, 29, threshing wain, 274
čangām, peg holding mat loom (Māzandarān), 220
čangāz, hook on twisting wheel (Kāšān), 196
čangeh, iron spiked harrow, 52
čān-kaš, draw harness of threshing wain (Hamadān), 275
čapāndan, to ram, to compact molding sand*
čapčapī, red dogwood (*Cornus sanguinea*), 76
čapeh, scale of balance, 63
čaperāseh, *čaperāsteh*, S-shaped hook (Ḫorāsān), 267
čap kardan, to stretch out (dough), 293
čap-ō-rāst, S-shaped hook on balance, 63, set of a saw, 82, warp cross, 184, 204, 215
čaqmāq, flint, flint lock; cf. *čaḫmāḫ*, *čaḫmāq*, 160
čāqū, pocket knife, 56, wood carver's chisel, 98, plaiter's knife, 221
čāqū-sāz, cutler, knifesmith, 55
čāqū-tīzkon, cutlery grinder, 57
čar, weaving shed (Iṣfahān), 204, threshing wain (Damāvand), 273
čār, brushwood used for fuel, 116, 159
čārak, quarter *man* weight, 62, 65, quarter brick, 112, 122
čarak-kār, *čārak-kār*, weaving shed, 204
čārak kardan, to arrange bricks to an ornamental form, 123
čārangeleh, spokes of large gear wheel, 283, frame of groove-milling device, 87
čārčūbeh-ye dastgāh, lathe frame, 132
čardevār, scoop (Āẕarbaijān)*
čarḫ, winch, windlass, 109, 251, rollers, rolling mill, 33, 40, grinding wheel, 39, gear wheel, 43, 184, cart wheel, 90, grinding bench, 57, potter's wheel, 154, cotton gin, 180, heddle pulley, 205, wheel driving roper's reel, 221, windlass pulley, 256, threshing wain, 273, water wheel, 280
čarḫ-e ālatsāz, groove-milling device, 87
čarḫ-e āsiyāb, mill wheel, water wheel, 280, 282
čarḫ-e bačeh, reeling wheel (Kāšān)*
čarḫ-e bīd, willow wood disk, 40
čarḫ-e čāh, winch, pulley above well, 109, 258
čarḫ-e čarmī, leather-covered disk, 40
čarḫ-e čehel tābī, rotary warp winding frame, 185
čarḫ-e dūvāl, copper-polishing lathe, 26
čarḫ-e golābatūnsāz, gold thread spinning machine, 46
čarḫ-e ḥakkāk, *čarḫ-e ḥakkākī*, gem cutter's polishing machine, cutting wheel, 37, 39
čarḫ-e ḥalabīsāz, beading rollers*
čarḫ-e ḫarman-kūbī, *čarḫ-e ḫarman-kūʾī*, threshing wain, 274
čarḫ-e jelā, intermediate smoothing wheel, 40
čarḫ-e kalāfeh, spool winder, 183
čarḫ-e kamāneh, bow-operated lathe, 34
čarḫ-e kūzehgarī, potter's wheel, 154
čarḫ-e lōhanān, cotton gin, 180
čarḫ-e maftūl-kašī, coarse wire drawing wheel, 43
čarḫ-e māsūreh, winding wheel, 183, 189
čarḫ-e mateh, fiddle drill, 167
čarḫ-e naḫ-kūbī, wire-flattening rollers, 45
čarḫ-e naḫ-rīsī, spinning wheel, 185
čarḫ-e naḫ-tābī, gold thread spinning bench, 46
čarḫ-e pā, treadle disk, 154
čarḫ-e pardāḫt, polishing block of gem cutter, 37
čarḫ-e rīsandehgī, spinning wheel (Nāʾīn), 185
čarḫ-e rīseh, spinning wheel*
čarḫ-e rīsmān-tāb, cord-making reel, 221
čarḫ-e sangtarāš, grinding wheel, 57
čarḫ-e sīmpīčī, gold thread spinning wheel, 46
čarḫ-e sombādeh, grinding wheel, emery wheel†
čarḫ-e tābī, twining wheel, 184
čarḫ-e ṭanāb-tāb, ropemaker's reel, 221
čarḫ-e vartābī, twisting wheel (Kāšān), 196
čarḫ-e vaškanī, cotton gin (Kāšān); cf. *vaš kardan*, 180
čarḫ-e zarī, gold thread spinning machine, 46
čarḫ gardāndan, to roll metal, 33
čarḫ kardan, to cut a groove*, to wind onto bobbins*, to dress a millstone, 279
čarḫ-pīč, stay rope on windlass*
čarḫ-zan, wheelwright, 89
čarī, bobbin, spool, 183
čarī-ḫāneh, bobbin stand (Yazd), 184
čarm, leather for bellows, 101, leather hide, 230, leather for coach hood, 90, leather lining wheel bearing*, leather rim edge, 229
čarm-e būmī, local skin, 231
čarm-e dūl, leather for bucket*
čarm-e gāv, cow hide, leather bag used by well-sinker, 252
čarm-e zāqī, tawed leather; cf. *zāq*, 231
čarm-e zīr-e zeh, leather protecting bow string, 180
čarm-gar, *čarm-sāz*, leather trimmer, 232
čārpāyeh, loom frame; cf. *čahārpāyeh*, 204
čārū, waterproof mortar, 113, mill race, 282
časb, glue, adhesive paste, 39
časbāndan, to glue, 238
časbāndeh, cemented, 132
časb-e kandeh, adhesive to glue turquoises to grinding stick, 39
časb-e šakar, sugar syrup used for pottery ornamenting, 166
časbīdan, to glue, to paste, 166, 238
časb kardan, to join, to cement, 166
čašm-bandeh, blinkers, 297
čašmeh-bulbul, a certain embroidery design, 219

čašnī, percussion cap, 59
čavdār, rye, 242
čeft, hasp, 88, door chain, latch catch, 52
čefteh, wall foundation, 108
čelangar, tinker, iron worker*
čelġūr, animal manure, especially pigeon manure, 270
čelīt, cross harness (Kāšān), 206
čelleh, warp (Iṣfahān), 184, 203, 214, string of cotton bow, 180, main warp of velvet loom, 209, warp ball (Yazd), 185
čelleh dādanī, warping frame (Yazd), 184
čelleh davān, warp winder (Kāšān), 214
čelleh davānī, warping frame (Kāšān), 203
čelleh dāvīdan, to wind a warp (Kāšān), 214
čelleh-kāš, warp winder, 215
čelleh kašīdan, to wind a warp, 214
čelleh-pīč, warp-winding peg, 185
čelleh-rūʾī, upper warp, 206
čelleh-tūn, warping frame, 184, 203
čelleh-zamīneh, lower warp, 206
čelō, boiled rice*
čeltūk, unhusked rice, paddy; see _čaltūk_, 271, 280
čelūn, warp, 203
čenār, plane tree (_Platanus orientalis_), 76, 81
čerāġ, miner's lamp, 15
čerāġ-e alkolī, spirit lamp for soldering†
čerāġ-e laḥīm-kārī, blowtorch for soldering†
čerāġ-e pā, pedestal lamp, 18
čerāġ-e rouġanī, oil lamp, 254
češmeh-band, blinkers (Iṣfahān); see _čašm-bandeh_, 297
čīd, maple wood (_Acer laetum_), 76
čīdan, to upset edge of horseshoe, 54, to trim a carpet, 216, to mow, to reap, 271, to cut boiled sugar, 301
čīdan (_pašm-e gūsfand_), to shear a sheep, 177
čīdan tū kūreh, to place in a kiln, 159
čīd-sāz, see _čīt-sāz_, 98
čīneh, mud brick block, 108, lump of earth, 116, course of bricks, 157, house foundation, 106
čīneh-kaš, builder of _pisé_ wall, 108
čir, spinning wheel (Māzandarān), 185
čīt, printed textile, 224
čīt-sāz, textile printer, 98, 225
čīt-sāzī, textile printing, 225
čobelāq, cam on mill shaft, trip cam (Alburz), 290
čodan, cast iron, 18
čodan-e qaičī, malleable cast iron, 18
čoġāleh, light-colored turquoise (Mašhad), 39
čoġondar, beet root (Beta vulgaris), 242
čōl, rod of hand spindle (Alburz); cf. _čoul_, 185
čōl-e gīreh, spindle hook (Alburz), 185
čorūk-angūr-kūbī, grape-mashing vat, 153
čoudār, rye, 242
čoul, rod of hand spindle, 185
čūb, bench top*, wood, log, tree, 283, frame of spinning wheel, 186, stirring stick, 194, mat weaver's warp beam, 220, timber, 79, builder's straight-edge, 110
čūbak, soapwort (_Saponaria officinalis_), 300
čūb-bandī, _čūb-bast_, scaffold, 111
čūb-bastī, mine tunnel support, 16
čūbbor, sawyer, 79, 80
čūb-e ālūbālū, cherry wood (_Cerasus spp._), 76
čūb-e āmak, shaft of potter's wheel, 155
čūb-e anār, pomegranate wood (_Punica granatum_), 76
čūb-e anār-e surḫ, red pomegranate wood (_Punica granatum_), 97
čūb-e anār-e zard, yellow pomegranate wood (_Punica granatum_), 97
čūb-e ār-e kūhī, wood of the mountain ash, 276
čūb-e āzād, elm wood, 262
čūb-e baneh, turpentine (_Pistacia acuminata_, _P. khinjuk_), 288
čūb-e bīd, poplar wood (_Salix micaus_, _S. fragilis_), 180
čūb-e bīl-dastī, hard wood used for tool handles, also known as _vašm_ (Kāšān), 283
čūb-e čahār-zeh, bowstring tightener, 181
čūb-e čenār, plane tree (_Platanus orientalis_), 283, 286
čūb-e čopok, wild cherry wood (_Cerasus orientalis_), 76
čūb-e dam, skin bellow slats, 29, 101
čūb-e dang, rice-pounding pestle, 190
čūb-e dast, wooden handle*
čūb-e dasteh, wedge to fix milling handle, 152
čūb-e dastūr, wood supporting draw harness, 206
čūb-e dōšak-ṣāf-kon, cushion-beating stick, 227
čūb-e dūl, foot for drinking water bucket, 234
čūb-e dūlčeh, foot of leather bucket, 234
čūb-e fanar, wooden block below spring, 90
čūb-e funduq, hazel wood (_Corylus avelana_), 76
čūb-e gerdū, walnut wood (_Juglans regia_), 76, 97
čūb-e golāb, _čūb-e golābī_, pearwood (_Pyrus communis_), 76, 97, 98, 99
čūb-e gormeh, hardwood for chisel handles*
čūb-e gōveh, wedge for tightening vice, 38, 180
čūb-e guzel-kūbī, flail, threshing stick, 273
čūbeh, hatter's felt burnisher, 224
čūb-e ḫanjak, turpentine wood (_Pistacia acuminata_, _Pistacia khinjuk_), 76, 288
čūb-e ḫarak, main beam of sawyer's jack, 80
čūb-e ḫormālū, persimmon tree (_Diospyrus sp._), 76
čūb-e jangalī, forest timber, especially all beech wood, 76
čūb-e kabūdeh, poplar wood, 180
čūb-e kamarī, stay of bow saw, 82

čūb-e kavījeh, medlar wood, 283
čūb-e kōkan, wood used for gear teeth, 283
čūb-e koloft, bearing block on windmill beam, 286
čūb-e korūk, hoop inside hood, 90
čūb-e limūn, lemon wood (*Citrus limonum*), 76
čūb-e miyād, plow sole (Zābol), 263
čūb-e mou, grapevine wood, 76
čūb-e nān-paz, baker's rolling pin, 293
čūb-e nāranj, orangewood (*Citrus spp.*), 76, 93
čūb-e nō; see *čūnō*, 88
čūb-e pā, tread bracket on spade, 260
čūb-e pardāẖt, polishing block*
čūb-e pārs, wedge to hold pestle, 290
čūb-e pol, beam supporting heddle, 204
čūb-e poštband, warp beam of mat loom, 220, straightening wood, 230
čūb-e qaliyān-sāzī, centering tool for pipe cobs, 155
čūb-e qāšūneh, wedge on threshing wain (Iṣfahān), 274
čūb-e raẖt, plow beam (Zābol), 263
*čūb-e rājeh*ᶜ, oscillating pin on millstone, 279
čūb-e sālār, beam carrying mill floor, 281
*čūb-e šam*ᶜ*ak*, shaft of potter's wheel*
čūb-e šamšād, boxwood (*Buxus sempervirens*), 99
čūb-e sarām, top beam of windmill (Ḫorāsān), 287
čūb-e sar-e čak, oscillating pin, 279
čūb-e sarẖak, upright post above well (Behbehān), 256
čūb-e semiyān, yoke peg, 262
čūb-e senjed, jujube wood (*Ziziphus vulgaris*), 269
čūb-e sīb, apple wood (*Pyrus malus*), 76
čūb-e tang, tightening toggle, 221
čūb-e ṭavaq, coppersmith's mandril, 26
čūb-e tūt, mulberry wood (*Morus alba*, *Morus nigra*), 76, 98, 262
čūb-e vašm, a hard wood used for tools and gear teeth (Iṣfahān), 283
čūb-e vezg, elm wood (*Ulmus campestris*), 90
čūb-e zabān-gonješk, ash wood (*Fraxinus excelsior*), 51, 181
čūb-e zardālū, apricot wood (*Prunus persica*, *Prunus armeniaca*), 76, 283
čūb-e zīr-e fūlād, *čūb-e zīr-e pā*, *čūb-e zīr-e pūlād*, tool-supporting bar, 91
čūbsā, wood rasp (Šīrāz), 56
čūbsāb, *cūbsāʾī*, wood rasp, 84
čūġ, wooden fork (Lūristān), 25, bearing block for mill axle, 283, mill race (Iṣfahān for *jūy*, *q.v.*), 282
čūġ-e dam, bellow slats (Lūristān), 29
čūġ-e šāh, upper mill race (Iṣfahān for *jūy*, *q.v.*), 282
čūġ-e sīm-e yō, neck sticks on yoke (Iṣfahān for *čūb*), 262
čūẖ-e semiyān, yoke peg, neck stick (Fārs for *čūb*), 262
čūẖ-pā, tread bracket on spade (Fārs), 260
čūleh, hard stem of hemp plant, 182
čulleh, distaff, 181
čulleh pīčīdan, to wind wool on distaff, 181
čulūk, rope to stop millstone from turning (Alburz), 281
čūm, threshing wain (Iṣfahān), 52, 273
čūm kardan, *čūm kašīdan*, to thresh (Iṣfahān), 273, 275
čūn = *cūm*
čūneh, lump, lump of clay, 116, 152, 154, 157, slot in water wheel axle, 290, lump of dough, 293
čūneh-gīr, man who forms dough lumps, 293
čūneh-ye gel, big lump of clay, 152
čūnō, wooden mold to make metal strips (*nō*) (Burūjerd), 88
čūpāndan, to ram, to compact molding sand*

dabbāġ, tanner, 231
dabġ kardan, to tan, 231
dādan be tāb, to dry yarn in the sun (Kāšān), 194
daftar, copy book, 236
daftī, *daftīn*, loom batten, 204, beater comb (Iṣfahān), 216
daftīn-e sorb, lead-weighted reed frame (Kāšān), 209
dāġdaġān, nettle tree (*Celtis australis*); cf. *diġdiġān*, *dāġdārān*, 76
dāġdārān, nettle tree (*Celtis caucasia*), 76
dahān-e aždarī, a certain shape of pen box, 239
dahāneh, charging hole of glass kiln, 169, weaving shed, 204
dahāneh-jazval, mouth of underground water channel*
*dahān-e ma*ᶜ*dan*, mine entrance, 15, ore outcrop, 15
dah-lā, ten-ply (Kāšān), 197
dahmak, lifting lever (Sīstān), 288
dailam, quarryman's crowbar, 127, warp-winding bar, 204
daim, *daimī*, unirrigated, dry farming, dry farming land, 271
dāiyāq-e farš, support for coach footboard, 90
dāl-ābī, water jar, 155
dalband, iron band on mill shaft, 290
dālborʾ dālbort, a zig-zag hem in embroidery, scallop festoon, 219
dālbor-e dōbarī, double zig-zag hem, 219
dāleh, leather bucket, 234
dālī, large water bucket, 234
dalv, leather bucket, 258
dalv-e āb-kašī, leather bag for drawing water, 257

dam, bellows, 19, 50, 51, vapor in underground water channel, 254, heddle support*
dam-āb, blades of water wheel, 283, jet of water mill, 280
damāġeh, filing block, 34, lathe center, 91, socket of spade or mattock, 260, leather on toecap, 229
dambārīk, narrow-mouthed pliers, 34
dambor, plaster-molding knife with pointed edge, 135
dam-e būrī, hand bellows, 101
dam-e čarḫ, shavings from copper lathe, 94
dam-e dasteh, dam-e dastī, skin bellows, 16, 31, 101
dam-e dō dam, dam-e dō dastī, dam-e dō lūleh'ī, double-acting bellows, 19, 51, 101
dam-e dūlī, skin bellows, 29, 50
dam-e fānūsī, concertina bellows, 17, 29, 51, 101
dam-e maftūl, round-nosed pliers, 34
dam-e miqrāz, edge of scissors, 56
dam-e pūst-e boz, goatskin bellows, 50
dam-e qāšoqī, hollow chisel, 129
dam-e qolāb, dam-e tīġ, sharp edge of carpet knife, 215
dam-e tīšeh, cutting edge of adze, 79
dam-e ṭorafeh, double bellows, 19
damgāh, pegs to produce cross in warp, 184
dam-gerd, round-nosed tongs, 52
dāmī, dry farming, depending on rain (Arāq); cf. *daimī*, 271
damīr-aġājī, ironwood tree (*Parrotia persica*) (Caspian provinces), 76
damirdeh, board with handle for smoothing tilled earth* (Gīlān)
dam-nāzok kardan, to sharpen edge, 99
dam-ō dāšt, kiln, 58
dam-pahn, flat-mouthed pliers, 34, 52
dam-sāz, maker of bellows, 101
dandān, saw tooth, 79, threshing beater, 79, 274
dandāneh, lock ward*, teeth on a door bolt, 66, teeth of pick*, reed blades, 195, gear tooth, 290
dandāneh-āhan, iron spike, 290
dandāneh čīdan, to cut teeth for joint, 24
dandāneh kardan, to dovetail metal joints, 24
dandāneh-ye arreh, saw-tooth†
dandāneh-ye čūbī, wooden thresher beater, 274
dandān-mūšī, tooth-profiled brick, 113
dandeh, tooth of wool comb (Kalārdašt), 182, hook at end of spindle (Kalārdašt), 185, 187, tooth on threshing roller, 274, harrow spike, 267, gear tooth, 283
dandeh-borreh, threshing spike (Šīrāz), 274
dandeh-dorošt, coarse cut of saw, 99, coarse comb teeth, 99
dandeh-rīzeh, fine cut of saw, 99, fine comb teeth, 99
dāneh, spout, 18, name of first-grade silk (Kāšān), 183
dāneh-dāneh, granulate, 161
dang, rice-husking mortar, 190
dāng, time unit for water allocation, 255
dang-e berenj-kūbī, rice-husking mortar, 190
dāpū, block on which glass blower rests blow pipe, 170
daqīq, granulate, 151
daqq, to pound in a mortar*
dar, door, 86, trunk lid, 88
dārā, sickle (Varāmīn)*; cf. *dāreh*, 272
darajeh, molding box, 18, riser of casting, 18, plow setting device, 266, foresight of gun, 60
darajeh borīdan, to cut off the risers, 20
dar-andāz, peg to lock loom breastbeam (Iṣfahān), 204
dar-arreh, frame of bow saw, 82
darband, strap to tie bucket, 15
darb-e āhan, iron pinion shaft, 283
darb-e āteš, firing hole in kiln, 159
darb-e havā, air hole in kiln, 160
darb-e kūreh, charging door in kiln, 159
dār-bouševeh, setting device for millstone (Šīrāz), 281
dardār, elm tree (*Ulmus campestris*), 76
dār-e arreh, frame of bow saw, 82
dar-e āyineh, mirror door (Qazvīn), 88
dar-e bād, wind inlet, 286
dar-e dūlčeh, wooden stopper of drinking water container, 234
dāreh, sickle (Gīlān); cf. *dārā*, 272
dāreh-berenj-borī, sickle for rice harvesting (Gīlān), 272
dār-e qālī, carpet loom, 214
dar-e šāhgāh, dar-e šahgāh, fire hole of kiln, 160
dār-ḫīš, plow beam (Surmaq), 263
darī, mold top, 157
darkand, mouth of underground water channel (Kermān), 252
darmaneh, wormwood (*Artemisia santonica*), a fuel used for kilns, 116, 159
dārmeh, upright post supporting mill gear (Iṣfahān), 283
darou, darū, harvesting scythe*
darouš, awl, 229
dar-sāz, joiner, carpenter specializing in making doors, 81
dar-vājeh, inlet valve of bellows (Iṣfahān), 101
dārvan, elm tree (*Ulmus campestris*), 76
darvāzeh, housing for spinning head, 46, suspension shackle of balance, 63, housing for rolling mill, 33
darvāzeh-bār, shackle on steelyard to suspend load, 65

darz, joint of two boards, 85, joint in masonry, 113, splice of two strings*, joint of pen box*
darz dandāneh kardan, to make teeth for joint, 24
darz-e dandāneh, toothed seam, dovetailed joint, 24
darz-e mīḫ-čūbī, doweled joint, 85
darz-e qelift, feather key, 85
darz-e sang, joint in stone masonry, 113
darz kardan, to join timber†
dās, sickle, 52, 272, brush-cutting knife, 79, 107, rush-cutting knife, 219, tanner's fleshing knife, 231
dāš, potter's kiln (Kāšān), 158, useless mineral, gangue, 15
dasāb, water basin for quenching steel, 59
dās-e ᶜalafbor, dās-e ᶜalefbor, grass-cutting sickle, 272
dās-e derou, dās-e darou, grain-reaping sickle, 272
dāsġāleh, small sickle, pruning knife, 271
dašt, field, division of land*
dāšt, potter's kiln; cf. *dāš*, 158
dast afšār, annealed, 23
dastak, roof batten, 114, traverse on windlass, 109, weaving comb, 200, windlass handle bar, 109, 258, dividing stone of weir, 255, vertical clamping bar, 297, 298
dastās, hand mill, quern, 232
dašt-bān, field guard*
dastband, bracelet, 32
dastdān-e āb, water dish for moistening clay, 155
dast-e bād dādan, to winnow (Šīrāz), 275
dast-e dār, scoop, scoop stilt (Gīlān), 268
dasteh, handle of tin snips, 26, crank handle, 43, 47, 180, reel handle, 186, plane handle, 82, hoe handle, 122, frit mill handle, 151, spade handle, mattock handle, 260, driving handle on spinning wheel, 186, handle, 18, 33, 43, 51, 154, 155
dasteh-āčār, a set of spanners, 61
dasteh-āčār-e tofang, tool kit for gun maintenance, 60
dasteh-āftābeh, ewer handle, 29
dasteh-arreh, saw handle, 79
dasteh-ās, hand mill, quern, 131
dasteh borīdan, to cut handle on printing block, 98
dasteh-čarḫ, handle of spinning wheel (Ardistān), 186
dasteh-dar, door knocker, 18
dasteh-gūniyāh, base of marking square†
dasteh-jelō, rein (Iṣfahān), 275
dasteh-jouġān, rice-pounding pestle, 290
dasteh-kaš, draw handle of scoop, 268
dasteh-samōvar, handle of samovar, 29
dasteh-šūnak, plow handle (Alburz), 263
dasteh-ye āftābeh, ewer handle, 29
dasteh-ye čakoš, hammer handle, 51
dasteh-ye dar, door knocker, 18
dasteh-ye dūl, bucket handle, 234
dasteh-ye hāvan, mortar pestle, 18
dasteh-ye penjeh-korūk, bolt joining hoops, 90
dast-e jelou, see *dasteh-jelō*, 275
dast-e qalāvīz, tap wrench, 60
dastgāh, working bench, 154, blow pipe, 170, loom, 203, bookbinding frame, 237
dastgāh-e čarḫ, polishing lathe*,
dastgāh-e ḥakkākī, gem cutter's bench, 39
dastgāh-e ḫarrāṭī, turner's lathe, 91
dastgāh-e ḥaṣīr-bāfī, mat-weaving loom, 220
dastgāh-e jājim-bāfī, band loom, 201
dastgāh-e maḫmal-bāfī, velvet loom, 209
dastgāh-e naḫ-kūbī, wire-flattening bench, 45
dastgāh-e najjārī, carpenter's bench, 81
dastgāh-e naqšbandī, dastgāh-e naqšeh-bandī, draw loom, 206
dastgāh-e qālī-bāfī, carpet loom, 214
dastgāh-e randeh, carpenter's bench, 81
dastgāh-e sang-tarāš, stonecutter's lathe, 132
dastgāh-e tōn-bāfī, tent fabric loom, 199
dastgāh-e zarī-bāfī, draw loom, brocade loom, 206
dastgāh-e zar-kašī, fine wire drawing bench, 43
dastgāh-e zīlū-bāfī, *zīlū*-loom, 210
dastgīreh-ye dar, door knocker, 18
dastgīr-e pardar, main beam on coach body, 90
dast-kaš, lever operating cloth beam (Māzandarān), 205
dast-miyān, plow stilt (Ḫorāsān), 263
dast-pambeh, cotton pad, 31
dast-qalā, sickle (Gīlān), 272
dastūn, loom draw-harness (Iṣfahān), 206
dastūr, drawstring in loom harness (Tehrān), 206
davā (pl. *advieh*), substance, chemical, condiment, 163
davāt, writing set, 28
davātgar, davātsāz, inkpot maker, brassworker, 28, 29
dāyāq-e farš, rear support for footboard, 90
dāyereh zadan, to place in a circle, 152
dehātī, peasant, cultivator, 261
dehqān, landowner, cultivator*
deleh-kūčī, Caucasian wing nut (*Pterocarya caucasia*) (Gīlān), 76
delgerān, bobbin for mat weaving, 221
delgerān pāᵓīn kašīdan, to lower bobbin, 221
derabš, awl (Iṣfahān); cf. *darouš*, 60
derafš, awl, 60, scriber, 81, cobbler's awl, 229; cf. *derabš*, *darouš*
derafš-e šīveh, awl for piercing cloth shoe soles (Ābādeh), 229

deraht-e ambeh, mango tree, 75, 76
deraht-e hormā, date palm (*Phoenix dactilifera*), 76, 245, 271
deraht-e mou, grapevine (*Vitis vinifera*), 244
derahtī, chisel with oval face, 36, 37
derāz kašīdan, to pull rope strands*
derou, awl, 60 (Šīrāz); cf. *derabš*, *derafš*, *darouš*, 229
derou kardan, to reap, 271
dēš, threshing beater (Hamadān), 274
dīg, boiler, kettle, 28, 300
diġdiġān, nettle tree (*Celtis australis*); cf. *daġdaġān*, 76
dīg-e mesīn, copper boiler, copper kettle, 28
*dil*ᶜ, rib of windmill, 285
ding, *dingī*, rice-husking mortar; cf. *dang*, 190
dīrak, windlass axle, 258
dīvak, rye, 242
dīvār, wall, main wall, 110, 114, partition in irrigated field, 268, windmill wall, 286
dīvār-e vasat, partition wall, 114
dīvārī, vertical carpet loom, 214
dīvār-par, windmill wall (Horāsān), 286
dīzī, stone cooking pot (Mašhad), 131, 133, earthenware pot*
dō-āteš, twice-fired glazed pottery ware, 165
dō-bōtak, support for feeder channel (Sīstān), 288
dō-faslī, pottery made in two pieces, 165
dō-ġečak, seat supporting column (Hamadān), 274
dō-gereh, Ghiördes knot, 215
dō-jā, double flap on hat (Šīrāz), 224
dokmeh, nose of roof tile (Gīlān), 113
dō-lā, two-ply thread, 196
dō-lā kardan, to arrange in pairs*
dō-lap kardan, to halve a log*
dolqū, bush inside wheel hub (Šīrāz), 90
dombāl-e rageh raftan, to follow the ore vein, 15
dombeh, fat tail of sheep, 295
dombī, tail support of sawyer's jack, 80
dombī-ābyārī, water bailiff's assistant (Varāmīn)*
dom-e asp, shackle of horse-shaped lock*
dom-e čelčeleh, dovetail joint, 86
dom-e mahrūtī, tapered shank of drill, 60
dom-e souhān, tang of file*
dom-gerd, cylindrical shank of drill, 60
dom-mahrūtī, see *dom-e mahrūtī*, 60
dō-pā, chaplet, 18, live center bearing of lathe, 27, bearing, 26
dō-rāheh, *dō-rāj*, rabbet joint, 85
dorōš, awl, lancet; cf. *darou*, *derabš*, *derafš*, 229
doroškeh, horse cab, 89
dorūdgar, *dorūdkār*, carpenter, cabinetmaker, 81
dos, ring to line underground water channel, 154
dō-šāheh, fork to operate baking oven, 295, wooden hook to lift draw harness*
dōšak, upholstered seat, 90
dos-sāz, maker of lining rings, 154
dōt, printing block for blue, 226
dō-tū, chisel marking double circles, 36, 37
doulāb, water wheel of ship mill, 260, 284
doureh, rim of cloth shoe, 229
dour-e kūreh, drying chamber above kiln (Šāhreżā), 159
dour-e qāleb, around the mold, 154
dous, treading on the ground, threshing wain (Fārs)*
dovāzdeh-anguštar, size of brick*
dozdī, covered dovetail joint, 86
dūd-kāš, chimney, flue, 19, 50, smoke hole in kiln, 159, 160, smoke hole of baking oven, 294
dūġ, dried yoghurt, 190
dūġāb, lime-clay mortar used for masonry, 113, 128, sloppy plaster mix, 123
dūġāb rīhtan, to pour plaster of Paris mix, 123
dūġī, deep red madder dye, 190
dūhtan, to sew, 237
dūhtan-e lehāf, to quilt, 227
dūk, hand spindle, 92, 185, spinning head, 46, twisting spindle, 196, spindle of spinning wheel, 186, warp spool, 184
dūk-dān, spindle box of twisting wheel (Kāšān), 196
dūk-e jalak, spindle (Kermān), 185
dūk-hāneh, spool holder, 184
dūk-rīs, spinner using hand spindle, 185
dūk-sareh, spin whorl, 185
dūk-sāz, spindle maker, 92
dūl, leather bucket, leather bag, 234, 252, 258, hopper of flour mill, 278, 288
dūlā, leather bucket*
dūlāb, water wheel, 259
dūl-ābī, leather bag of water well, 257, earthenware jar, 155
dūl-ābkašī, leather bag of water well, 257
dūlčeh, leather bucket, 234
dūlčeh-ye ābhworī, drinking water container, 234
dūl-dūz, leather bucket maker, 234
dūl-e čarmī, miner's leather bag, 15
dūleh, winch to lift oil press beam, 297, 298, 299
dūl-sāz, leather bucket maker, 234
dum, hard stratum in underground water channel digging, 253
dūšāb, syrup of grapes, 164, 300
dūvāl, belt to drive grinding wheel, 57, hide lace, 229, draw belt of threshing wheel (Isfahān), 275, leather belt of polishing lathe, 27

edāreh-tohm-e nōğān, silkworm-treating office, 182
edāreh-ye abrīšam, silk monopoly agency, 182
ehtelāt, alloy, 18
ertefāʿ-e dandeh, depth of saw-tooth†
ešdī, lease or crossing of warp threads (Iṣfahān), 184, 204
esfandān, maple tree (*Acer laetum*), 76
esfīdār, white poplar (*Populus alba*), 76
esgeneh, heavy wood chisel (Iṣfahān), 84
eškanjeh, sash clamp (Iṣfahān), 86
eskenā, heavy wood chisel (Zābolistān), 84; cf. *eskeneh*, *eškeneh*, *eskenak*
eskenak, *eskeneh*, flat turning chisel (Rašt), 92
eškezeh, coping wood on walls (Šīrāz), 109
eškīneh, heavy wood chisel (Šīrāz), 84
espāreh, rind (Šīrāz), 278
esperek, a yellow dye (Iṣfahān); cf. *isparag*, *asparg*, 191
espīdār, white poplar (*Populus alba*), 76
etteṣāl, joint in woodwork, 85
etteṣāl-e farangī, arris fillet joint†
etteṣāl-e mīh-čūbī, doweled joint, 85
etteṣāl-e zabāneh-ye domčelčeleh, dovetailed joint†
etteṣāl kardan, to join, 85

fahhār, brick maker or potter, 115, 151
fahhārat, earthenware*
fahmīdan, to gin cotton, 180
fain, time unit for water allocation, 255
fakk-e gīreh, vice jaw, 60
falaqeh, *falakeh*, circular firing chamber, 159
falaqeh kardan, *falakeh kardan*, to roast copper ore, 16, to sinter ore dust†
fanar, spring, 90, spring to open tin snips*, spring inside lock, 69, 70
fāneh, tongue of balance, 63, pin tumbler to secure lock, 68
fāq, groove, mortise, 85
fāqīrūn, Indian steel, 55
fāq-ō-zabān, mortise-and-tenon joint, 85
farang, cover strip, 86, steel reinforcing on oil press, 297, 299
farangī-sāz, cabinetmaker, 81
fārsī, beveled edge, 40, miter joint, 86, bevel-edged brick, 122
farsī-bāf, Sehna knot, Persian knot, 215
faṣl, piece, section, 165
faṣl-kaš, water outlet, 269
fatā, hewn stone in water distributor (Semnān)*
fatīleh, fuse, wick, 127, 131, clay coil, 152
felezz, metal tuyère, 3
ferčeh, jeweler's brush, 34
ferčeh-kār, metal polisher, 29
fešang, cartridge, 60
fešang-e hālī, blank cartridge, 60
fešang-e jangī, military cartridge, 60
fešang-e šekārī, shotgun cartridge, 60
fešang-kaš, cartridge ejector, 60
fešār, bookbinder's press, 237
fešār dādan, to press, 239
fešārī, pressing clamp, 19, standard size whole brick, 112
fīlervāf, feeler gauge (corrupt English), 61
finjān, dish, time unit for water allocation, 255
finkāl, flow measure, 255
fīq, heavy short pillar supporting floor beams, 106
firind, name for damascened steel, 8, 55
firū gereftan, to beat an edge, a flange
fīrūzeh, turquoise, 38, turquoise-colored, 162, 167
fīrūzehʾī, turquoise-colored*
fīrūzeh-tarāš, turquoise cutter, 39
firzeh, share in irrigation water, 254
fiżżī, made of silver*
fōq, spin whorl, 185
forū kardan, to pierce through cloth, 218
forū raftan, to recede (metalwork), 36
fūfal, *fūfel*, palisander wood, rosewood (*Dalbergia spp.*), 76, 93, 97
fūlād, steel, especially carbon steel, 7, 8, 55, chisel, 15, drawing die, 43, tool steel, 52, whet steel, 272
fūlād-e ābdār, hardened steel, 52
fūlād-e hošk, hardened steel, 36, 52
fūlādī, made of steel, 52
fūlāẓ, a high-quality steel*
fūlmīnāt, priming charge in detonator, 60
fuqarā, *fuqarat*, underground water channel, 249
furn, kiln, furnace, oven, 158
fūt kardan, to blow glass, 170
fuzaqareh, wing-nut tree (*Pterocarya fraxinifolia*), 76

gāb, cow, ox (Alburz), 262
gāb-āhan, plowshare (Alburz), 264
gāb-e amrāz, plow (Gīlān), 263
gač, gypsum, 134, 161, plaster, chalk, 36, 108
gač bīhtan, to sift plaster, 134
gač-bīz, plaster sifter, 134
gač-bor, plasterer, stucco maker, 134
gač-borī, plaster work, 134
gāčeh, oxen-operated well (Behbehān); cf. *gāv-čāh*, 256
gač-e kušteh, set or spoiled plaster of Paris, 134
gač-e seft, a thick plaster of Paris mix, 123
gačgar, *gač-kār*, plasterer, 134
gačkeneh, a certain rug design, 211
gač mālīdan, to render plaster onto wall, 134
gač-paz, gypsum burner, 126
gač-pazī, gypsum burning, 126

gač rūš rīḫtan, to pour plaster over back of mosaic, 123
ġaibeh, blade at end of cloth beam, 205
ġair-e muwallad, foreign steel blades, 55
gājemeh, plow (Gīlān), 262
ġalambeh, warp ball, 209
galangeh-dān, cocking lever, breech block, 59
ġalbāl, container to store oil cake (Iṣfahān), 299
gāl-band, iron ring on plowshare (Kalārdašt), 263, 264
galbīl, fine sieve (Āẕarbaijān), 277
gal-e ḫus, floor joist, 107
gālī, rushes, thatching (Māzandarān), 107, 220
gālingor, embossed bookbinder's cloth (Šīrāz), 238
galiyās, a certain brick form (Šīrāz)*
ġalleh, grain crop, cereals, 242
galōʾī, turning gouge, 92, draw harness for animals, 257; cf. *gelōʾī*
ġaltak, *ġalṭak*, pulley*
ġaltak-e ḥurūfī, lettered rings on keyless lock, 72
ġaltīdan, to roll*
galūband, necklace, 32
galūʾī, gouging chisel, 84, 92
galū-ye āsiyā, mill hopper, 278
gamāneh, trial shaft for underground water channel*
gamej, boiling pot (Gīlān), 159
gandal, a yellow dyestuff, 191
gandalāš, a herb; cf. *gandal*, 191, maple tree (*Acer insigne*) (Gīlān), 76
gandom, wheat, 241, 277, a measure of weight, 62
gandom ḫord kardan, to grind wheat, 282
gandom oftādan, to drop the grains to the ground, 276
ġār, laurel tree (*Lauris nobilis*), 76
gārān, plowman*
ġarbāl, sieve, 151, 235, 277
ġarbāl-bāf, *ġarbāl-band*, sieve maker, 234
ġarbāl-e dorošt, coarse sieve, 235
ġarbāl-e gač-bīzī, plaster sieve, 235
ġarbāl-e rīz, fine sieve, 235
ġarbāl-e šen-bīzī, sand sieve (Šīrāz), 235
ġarbāl-e sīmī, wire sieve, 236
ġarbāl kardan, to sift, 277
ġarbār, container to store oil cake; cf. *ġalbāl*, 299
garbāz, digging spade (Gīlān)*
ġarbīl, *ġarbīr*, sieve*; cf. *ġarbāl*, 235
gardāndan, to bring warp forward, 216
gardāndan dar ḫomreh, to turn yarn over in vat, 194
gardan-e kūzeh, neck of jar, 155
gardeh-šāḫ, horn meal for file hardening, 59
gardnā, pinion of mill gear, 283
gareh, thrust bearing for mill pinion, 283
ġarġareh, pulley, warp guide, warp rollers, 204, 209
ġarġġar, pulley, 204
garḫat-e eṣmet, Caucasian elm tree (*Ulmus pedunculata*) (Gīlān), 76
gārī, a horse-drawn cart, 89
gārī-sāz, wheelwright, 89
garjīn, threshing wain (Nairīz)*
garmḫāneh, cooling furnace in glassworks, 170
garmsīr, hot region, lowlands, 241
ġarq-e āb, ingress of water in subterranean channel, 254
garrā, harrow, 266
garūn-sangī, tropical almond tree (*Terminalia catappa*), 76
gauz, walnut wood, wild almond wood, 160
gāv, bullock, 262
gāvāhan, plow (Šīrāz), 263
gāvāhan-e dō-dasteh, Western-type plow, 52
gāvak, board between plow beam and sole, 263
gavang, brushwood, 109
gāv-čāh, animal-operated well, 256
gāvdom, pulley driving warp spool, 184
gāv-dūšī, jars for curdled milk (Alburz), 155
gāv-rāh, runway for animal at well, 257
gāz, clamping wedge, 19, tin snips, shears, 26, pincers, 54, 60, carpenter's pliers*, shoemaker's pliers, 229, tie peg, 287, wedge, 39, 263, 288
gaz, tamarisk tree (*Tamarix mannifera*), 76, manna issued from certain trees, 302
gaz-alafī, tamarisk tree (*Tamarix gallica*)*
gāz-ambor, cutting pliers, 26
gaz-angebīn, *gaz-anjabīn*, tamarisk tree (*Tamarix gallica*)*, manna issued from tamarisk tree, 302
ġażār, pure, greenish clay, 151
ġażāreh, pottery, earthenware, 151
gāz-e čap-ō-rāst-kon, saw-setting device, 82
gaz-e ḫānsār, manna tamarisk (*Tamarix mannifera*), 76, the gall tamarisk (*Tamarix gallica*), 76
gāz-e kūh-kan, miner's heavy crowbar, 15
gaz-e māzej, manna tamarisk (*Tamarix pentandra*), 76
gaz-e siyāh, tamarisk tree (*Tamarix articulata*)*
gaz-ḫānsār = *gaz-e ḫānsār*, 76
gaz-mazej = *gaz-e mazej*, 76
gaz-šakar, tamarisk tree (*Tamarix gallica*)*
gazuk, warp-winding cross, 195
gāzūr, fuller, bleacher, launderer, 222
gel, sand, 18, loam-straw mixture, 108, mud, 109, clay, 115, any ceramic body, 165, spoil excavated during underground water channel construction, 252

gel-čāl, see *gel-e čāl*, 109
gelčī, clay-soaking pit (Hamadān), 151
gel-e armanī, ruddle, red chalk, 123, yellow chalk, 80, red ocher, 40
gel-e bōteh, very fine clay, bentonite, 165
gel-e bōteh va sang-e čaḫmāq, clay body for stone paste ware, 165
gel-e Čāh-Rīseh, fine clay from a certain locality, 165
gel-e čāl, soaked clay, 109
gel-e lājvard-e Kāšān, cobalt oxide, 163
gel-e lū'īdār, clay and rush seed mixture, 163
gel-e māšī, ruddle, red chalk, 80, 123, iron oxide powder, 30
gel-e melāṭ, mud mortar for mud bricks, 111
gel-e oḫrā, red chalk, yellow chalk, ruddle, 80
gel-e ros, clay, 17, potter's clay, 151
gel-e safīd, fine clay, 165
gel-e varz, a leather dyestuff, 232
gel gereftan, to draw clay into a handle, 155
gelgīr, mudguard, 90
gelīm, tapestry, a mat woven in tapestry, 199, 200
ġeliyūn, elder tree (*Sambucus ebulus*) (Tūneh-kabūn), 76
gel kašīdan, to throw clay on the wheel, 155
gel mālīdan, to knead clay, 108, 152
gel-moč, stand for yarn reel, 188
gelō'ī, spindle nut of ironworker's vice†, breast harness, 257
gel pā zadan, to knead clay with foot, 152
gel rūš kašīdan, to render with mud mortar, 112
gel šostan, to soak clay, 115
gel tūš pūk kardan, to hole a lump of clay for throwing, 155
gelū, hub of water draw pulley, 256
gelūband, necklace, 32
gelū'ī, mouth of carpenter's plane, 82, turning gouge, 92; cf. *galū'ī*
gel varz kardan bā pā, to knead clay with foot, 152
ġerār, net made of goat hair to carry straw, 276
gerdeh, round sheet of copper, 23, 24
gerd-e ḫālī, water-lifting pole, 256
gerdekū, *gerdekūb*, large wooden mallet, 298
gerd kardan, to bend round, to forge round, 52, to round edges, 101
gerdū, walnut (*Juglans regia*), 76, 97
gereftan, to take, to grab*
gereh, knot in timber*, carpet knot, 2, measure used in carpet weaving, 213, bearing block, 283
gereh-sāzī, wooden lattice work, 87, 98
gereh zadan, to knot into fringes, 217
gerezm, a variety of elm wood, 76
gerīdeh, embroiderer's clamp, 218
ġez'elfī, Kurdistān oak (*Quercus valonea*), 76
gīlīleh, threshing roller, 274
gīlō'ī, turning gouge, 92, a certain molding profile, 84, hollow chisel, 98, window sill, 113; cf. *galō'ī*, *gelū'ī*
gīr dādan, to hold firmly in place, 35
gīr-e čūbī, a wooden filing vice, 34, 38
gīr-e dast, hand vice, 38
gīr-e dastī, carpenter's clamp, 86, hand vice*
gīreh, cranked handle end of tongs, 19, vice, 60, beam supporting harness, 200, book-binder's trimming press, 238
gīreh-dast, hand vice, 60
gīreh-dastehdār, hand vice†
gīreh-gāz-ambōrī, blacksmith's vice†
gīreh-kaj, beveling vice, 60
gīreh-komakī, hand vice†
gīreh-lūleh-gīr, pipe vice†
gīreh-movāzī, vice with parallel jaws†
gīreh-pīčī-movāzeh, parallel clamp, 60
gīreh-ye āteškārī, forge vice, 52
gīreh-ye dast, filing vice, hand vice, 38
gīreh-ye lūleh-gīr, pipe vice, 60
gīreh-ye movāzī, vice with parallel jaws (Šīrāz), 60
gīr-e pā, filing vice, 56
girk, threshing rollers (Hamadān), 274
gīr-pā, gripping vice, 38
gīs, band tying rushes together, 287, rope tying bearing beam, 287
gīveh, cloth shoes, 228, 229
gīveh-bāf, *gīveh-dūz*, *gīveh-kaš*, cloth shoe, maker of cloth shoes, 228, 229
giyūneh, block of melted glass, 169
goak, board between beam and sole of plow, 263
godāḫtan, to melt, to liquefy, to refine, 19
godāz, metal-oxidizing furnace, 161
godāzān, melter, gold refiner, 22
godāzandeh, melter, foundryman, 22
godāzandeh-ye mesgarī, copper sheet maker, 22
godāzišgar, melter, foundryman*
godāz kardan, *godāz šodan*, to melt, 161, 162
gōhan, plowshare (Surmaq), 52, 263
gol, compound inlay rod, 95, 96, skin forming on molten metal, 161, ornament, 224
golāb, chain-stitch, 219, embroiderer's needle, 218, crochet hook, 218, iron hook, 252
golāb-dūz, embroiderer, 218
golābdūzī, book-trimming band, headband, 238, chain-stitch embroidery, 219
golābetūn, gold thread, braids, 208, embroidery, 217, gold lace, 46
golābetūn-dūz, a maker of braids, 208

golābetūn pīčīdan, to spin metal around a thread, 46
golābetūn-sāz, gold wire drawer, 46
gol-abrišim, julibrissin tree (*Albizzia julibrissin*), 76
golābtān, embroidery, 217
ġolāj, a bread variety, 291
gol-barjesteh, ornamental relief work, 166
goldān, flower vase, 29, 32
goldāntoq, flower vase, 170
goldūz, fillet embroidery, 219, embroiderer, 218
goldūzī, embroidery, 218
gōleh, ground oil seed, 297
gol-e kilīšeh, book-tooling brass, 238
gol-e nō, cornice brick, sill brick, coping stone, 122
gol-gāz, wedge between plow sole and beam (Ḫorāsān), 263
gol-gūm, glass insert for skylight, 170
golī, grain hopper (Sīstān), 288
gol-mīḫ, ornamental door nails*
golnēkā, ball of spun wool (Lāhijān), 188
golnēkā pīčīdan, to wind wool to a ball, 188
golrang, *gol-e rang*, safflower, 191
golū-ye sang, opening in mill runner, 288
gombad, dome, vault, 110
gom-e čāh, see *gum-e čāh*, 153
ġond, carpet knot (Šīrāz), 215
gondal, *gondaleh*, bowed cotton rolled into a large ball (Kāšān), 181
gondal pīčīdan, to roll bowed cotton into a ball (Kāšān), 181
gondeleh, ball of clay and ore dust, 17
gong, clay pipe, 15
gorāzgā, flue, chimney, 19
gord, heddle rod cord, 210, heddle rod (Šīrāz), 200, 214
gorsavād, chisel marking crossed line, 36, 37
gorūk, *gorük*, ball of carpet wool (Šīrāz), 215, thread of pile wool, 215
gorz-e ḫormā, rib of palm leaf used as flail, 273
gostardan, to stretch in forging (Tehrān)†
gouāhan, *gāvāhan*, plowshare, 52, 263
goučāh, animal-operated well, 256
goučū, runway of animal-operated well (Jahrum), 257
goudāl, pond, 249
goudāl-e pīš-e kār, pit in front of potter's wheel, 155
goud-e čūb, tanning pit, 231
goud šodan, to become hollow, 24
gouhak, plow stilt (Neh)*
gouhan, *gouhen*, plowshare (Varāmīn); cf. *gōhan*, *gouāhan*, 263, 264
gou-rō, runway near well (Šīrāz), 257
gōvān, plowshare (Iṣfahān); cf. *gouāhan*, etc., 263, 264
gōveh, wedge to adjust spinning head, 46, wedge to fix hammer, 51, wedge to open cutting groove, 80, 127, wedge in carpenter's plane, 82, tongue to tighten bow saw, 82, wedge to adjust millstones, 278, wedge to fix spade handle, 260, wedge on plow, 263, wedge on water wheel, 283, wedge, 96, 151
goẕār, the throwing of bread dough into the oven*
goẕardan, to clean, to refine, to purge*
goẕāštan, to place, 182, to throw dough into oven, 294
gūgerd, sulphur, 36
gūiyak, spindle washer, 39
gūleh, heavy shot for shooting wild pigs, 59, heddle rod, 200
gulījān, iron holding hoe blade (Zābol), 261
gulūleh, bullet, 59
gum, *gūm*, well-lining hoop, 154, lining for underground water channel, 253, covered water course*
gumāneh, trial well for underground water channel, 251
gūm, *gum-e čāh*, *gūm-e čāh*, well-lining ring, 153
gūneh, vice jaw†
gūneh-ye gīreh, vice jaw†
gūneh-ye moḥāfeẓī, protective jaw for vice†
gūneh-ye motaḥarrek, movable jaw of vice†
gūnīʾā, *gūniyā*, square, 61, 122, 125, carpenter's square, 81
gūniyā-bāzšō, variable-angle gauge, protractor, 81
gūniyā-fārsī, bevel gauge, miter square, 61, 81
gūniyā-lab-e dār, back or try square, 61
gūniyā-motaḥarrek, *gūniyā-vāšō*, protractor, bevel gauge, 61, 81
gurt, mail for heddle (Yazd), 198, heddle loop; cf. *gord*, 200
gūrūp, a ball of yarn, 186
gusain, collapse of roof in underground water channel, 253
gūšeh, pot handle, 155, spindle bearing, 186, rim of hat, 223, eyelet, 183
gūšeh bastan, *gūšeh časbāndan*, to attach handle to pot, 155
gūsfand, sheep, 177
gūšī, block between weighting bar and bearing, 45
gūšiyeh, water distribution basin, 255
gūšvāreh, ropes supporting heddles, 210, loop to separate harness strings, 207, drawstrings, 208

gūšvāreh-kas, draw boy, 208
gūšvāreh kašīdan, to draw harness string, 208

ḥabb-ulġār, turpentine pistachio tree (*Pistacia khinjuk*), 76
ḥabūbāt, pulse, 245
ḥaddād, steel reinforcement on mill axle, 281
ḥaddādī, fee paid in kind to village blacksmith*
ḥadīd, iron, steel, 151
ḥadīdeh, thread die, 26, 29, 43, 60
ḫafang, fan light of a window (Mašhad), 86
ḥāfeẓ-e māšeh, trigger guard of gun, 60
ḥafr kardan, to dig a channel, 252
haft-čīn, clover, 244
haft jūš, Kermān silver-bronze, 18
haftrang(ī), polychrome glazing, 121, 147
ḫaizarān, bamboo, 219
ḥajar, stone, mineral*
ḥajjār, stone cutter, stone pot maker, sculptor, 128, 130
ḥajjārī-ye ẓarīfeh, ornamental stone sculpture, 129
ḫāk, dust, earth, loam, clay, 108, 115, 151, spoil excavated during channel construction, 252
ḫak-bar-gardāneš, mold board of plow, 266
ḫāk-e āġor, polishing abrasive, 28
ḫāk-e arreh, sawdust, 80
ḫāk-e lājvard, cobalt oxide, 163
ḫāk-e makeh, Tripoli powder, 34
ḫāk-e ros, red oxide, 34, polishing rouge, 30, clay, 19
ḫāk-e sang, stone dust, 130
ḫāk-e siyāh, gray sand, 115
ḫāk-e sorb, lead ore dust, 17, lead dross, 161
ḫākestar, ashes, cinders, 33, 35
ḫākestar-e ḥammām, wood ashes from the public bath, 113
ḫāk-e zoġāl, charcoal dust, 17, 18, 36, molding dust, 98, 164
ḥakkāk, engraver of gem stones, 37, 38, polisher of gems, jeweler*, turquoise cutter, 39
ḥakkāk-e mohr-naqš, *ḥakkākī*, signet maker, 38
ḥakkākī kardan, to engrave, 38
ḫāk šodan, metal turning to oxide, 162
ḫāk-šūrī, clay-soaking pit, 115
ḫāl, repeat mark, 226
ḥalabī, sheet metal, tin plate, 30, 88
ḥalabī-ḫamkon, beading rollers, swaging machine, 30
ḥalabī-sāz, tinsmith, sheet metal worker, 30
hala-čūb, vertical column of threshing wain (Hamadān), 274
ḫalanj, tree heath, briar wood (*Erica arborea*), 76, 81
halbāl, *halbīl*, fine sieve (Iṣfahān), 277
halešt, yoke sling (Alburz), 262
halīleh-ye zard, tanning agent from *Terminalia citrina*, 193
ḫalīlī, a grape variety, 244
ḥallāj, cotton ginner, bower, 180
ḥallāj kardan, *ḥallāj zadan*, to bow fibers (Kāšān), 180
ḥalq-aṃbor, tinner's special tongs, 31
ḥalqeh, ring to suspend scales*, ring at the end of fiddle belt, 85, round opening in kiln, 159, draw ring on threshing wain, 275, iron hook, ring, 257, 262, 264, 267, 268, hoop between plow and yoke, 263, shackle, 69, eyelet, 183
ḥalqeh-qūl, ring on plow harness (Iṣfahān)*
ḥalqeh-razā, joint between yoke and beam, 262
ḥalqeh-ṭanāb, neck rope ring, loop, 300
ḥalqeh-ye qofl, padlock shackle, 69
ḥalvāʾ, a certain sweetmeat, 301, 302
ḥalvāʾ-paz, confectioner, 301
ḫām, stone rubble, 128, raw leather, hide, 231
hambūneh, skin bellows*
ḫāmeh, unspun fibers, raw wool, 185
hameh-kaš, yoke peg, 262
ḥāmel-e taḫteh, board carrier, 180
ḫamgīr, straightening wood, 92
ḫamīr, dough, 292, mashed oil seed, 297, papier maché mass, 238
ḫamīr-e kāġaẕ, *ḫamīr-e moqavvā*, papier maché, 238
ḫamīr-gīr, man who mixes dough in a bakery, 293
ḫamīr kardan, to plasticize clay*
ham kardan, to join parts, 24, to place together, 224
ḥammāl, a heavy beam, joist, 79, load carrier, laborer, 108
ḥammāl-e tīr-e buzurg, support for reinforcing beam, 299
ḥammām, public bath, 28, 80, 300
ḫām-puḫt, biscuit-fired tiles, 158
ḫām-puḫteh, mud bricks, nonfired bricks, 116
ḫāmrā āb zadan, to soak hides, 231
ḫāmrā dās kardan, to remove superfluous flesh from hides, 231
ḫāmtarāš, a rough-ground gem, 39
ḫām tarāšīdan, to square rubble, 128
ḫamūt, horse collar (Šāhī), 262
ḫān, rifling of gun barrel, 59
ḥanā, henna, 192, 300
ḫānčeh, center board in ceiling, 88, painted tray, 88
ḫandaq, pond, 246
ḫan-dār, rifled gun barrel, 59
ḫāneh, a square on a graph paper, 216, mill house, 286, housing for spokes, 287
ḫān-e sābā, edge mill shop, 300

ḫanjak, turpentine wood (*Pistacia acuminata*), 76, 288
ḥaqq-e āb, right to share irrigation water, 254
ḫār, dry shrub used for fuel, 159, 294, peg for warp plug, 185
ḫarak, file cutter's bench, 58, sawyer's jack, 79, trestle, 112, movable block in heddle device, 198, batten adjusting board, 204, warp deflecting beam, 203, supporting block, 298, support for slot beam, 288
ḫarak-e arreh-kašī, *ḫarak-e čūbborī*, sawyer's jack, 79
ḫarak zadan, to thresh rice (Caspian provinces)*
haranj, short channel near mouth of underground water channel, 253
ḫar-čūġ, easel, trestle, 231
harīr, silk screen, 151
harkārečeh, little container, small vessel (Mašhad), 133
harkāreh, cooking pot, cauldron (Mašhad), 133
harkāreh-dīzī, handled stone pot (Mašhad), 133
ḫarman, threshing floor, reaped sheaves piled up on a stack, 272
ḫarman-gāh, threshing floor, 272
ḫarman gereftan, to thresh grain*
ḫarman-kūb, threshing wain, 273
ḫarman-kūbīdan, to thresh, 273
ḫarman-kūh, a heap of sheaves on the threshing floor, 273
ḫarpā-kūb, roof truss carpenter, 81
ḫarpošt, carpenter's bench, 81
ḫarrāṭ, wood turner, 91
ḫarrāṭī, groove milling device, 87
harreh, brickwork, brick bond*
ḫarvār, a standard weight, 62, 63, 65
harz-āb, mill race shutter gate, 282
harzābī, sluice door, 282
harz dādan, to open gate of mill race, 282
harzeh-gard, eccentric to move guide rollers, 46
ḫašāb, cartridge frame, 60
ḥaṣāt, pebble, 151
ḫašen, rough cut of a file, coarse, 58
ḫašḫāš, poppy seed, 295, 296
haṣīn, curing vat, 93, earthenware dish, 155
haṣīn-e goldān, flower pot, 156
ḥaṣīr, roofing mat, 114, rushes, rush mat, reed mat, 181, 220, 224, 297
ḥaṣīr-bāf, mat braider, mat weaver, 220
ḥaṣīr-bāfī, mat weaving, mat braiding, 220
ḥāšiyeh, splint wood, 80, ornamental margin, 96, margin strips, 96, carpet fringe, 215
ḫaštak, bearing inside edge runner, 296
haštī, name for medium-grade silk (Kāšān), 183
hašt-lā, eight-ply thread (Kāšān), 183, 197
ḥasūm-e pāšgūnī, weeding spade, 271
ḫātam, inlaid work, 97
ḫātam-band, inlay worker, 93
ḫātam-bandī, inlaid work, 92
ḫātam-kār, inlay worker, 93
ḫālam-kārī, inlaid work, 92
ḫātam-sāz, inlay worker, 93
ḫaṭṭ, divisions on steelyard to denote measures, 65
ḫaṭṭ andāḫtan, blind tooling, 238
ḫaṭṭeh, groove on velvet pile wire, 209
ḫaṭṭ gereftan, to mark brick, tile, 122
ḫaṭṭ-gīrī, turning tool with serrated surface, 27
ḫaṭṭ kardan, to mark off, 128
ḫaṭṭ-kaš, straight-edge, marking gauge, 61, 81
ḫaṭṭkaš-e andāzeh-dār, graded ruler†
ḫaṭṭkaš-e pāʾīdār, surface gauge, 60
ḫaṭṭkaš-e tīġdār, carpenter's marking gauge, 81
ḫaṭṭkaš-e tīġehdār, marking gauge†
ḫaṭṭ kašīdan, to mark off, 80, 122
ḫaṭṭkašī kardan, to mark off with a marking gauge†
havā ḫwordan, to air dyed yarn*
havā-kaš, air vent in mold, 18, riser in mold, 18, underground duct of kiln, 160
havā kas̱īf, foul air, 15
hāvan, mortar, 18, 290
hāvan-e gūšt-kūbī, meat-pounding mortar, 132
hāvan-e sangī, stone mortar, 238
hazār-bāf, *hazār-bāfī*, ornamental brickwork, 118, 121
hazāreh, ornamental brickwork, 121, rubble masonry, 113
hazeh-gard, reel, winder (Māzandarān), 187, 188
ḫazīneh, magazine in gun, 60
ḫazīneh kardan, to countersink†
ḫeft, carpet knot, 215
hel, *hēl*, the spice cardamom, 295
ḥennā-ye barg, henna, 192; cf. *ḥanā*
ḫersom, beam inside wall above press beam (oil press), 297, 298
hēš, plow, plowshare, 263
ḫešt, mud brick, 109
ḫeštak, iron adjusting-block, 281, platform of edge runner, 296
ḫešteh, bearing inside edge runner, 297
ḫešt-e loʿābī, glazed tile, 166
ḫešt-e puḫteh, burnt brick*
ḫeštgar, brickmaker, 115
ḫešt-kārī, brickworks, 115
ḫešt-māl, brick molder, 109, 115
ḫešt-paz, brickmaker, 115
ḫešt-tābeh, brick kiln*
ḫešt-zan, brickmaker, 115
ḫift, wedge, 296, 297, 299
hindī, Indian steel, 55
hing, the condiment *asa foetida*, 292

ḥirfeh, trade, craft, skill, guild*
hiš, plow (Natanz)*; cf. *heš*, 263
ḫīš, plow (Fārs), 263, plowshare (Āhar)
ḫīsandan dar ḥouż, to soak hides in pit*
*ḥiṣbā*ᵓ, quartz pebble, 151
ḫīš kardan, to filter, 165
ḫīšteh, *ḫištak*, see *ḫaštak*, 296
hīzum, wood fuel, fuel, 159, 160, 294
hōčīn, *hočūm*, threshing fork (Iṣfahān), 275, 276
ḫodā-dādeh, agriculture depending on rain (Hamadān), 271
hōjang, loop connecting yoke and plow beam (Iṣfahān), 262
ḫomreh, large earthenware jar, wine jar, 153, basin to collect oil, 297, 299
ḫomreh-ye nīlkārī, vat for indigo dyeing, 194
ḫong, reed, rushes, 220, 221, 256, 297
ḫongī, rope made of rushes, 256
ḫonok šodan, to cool down, 127
ḥoqqeh, small bottle with a wide neck, 170
ḫorāsānī, blades of Ḫorāsān steel and forged there, 55
ḫord, crack, glaze crack, 166
ḫord kardan, to cut up
ḫormā, see *deraḫt-e ḫormā*, 76, 244
ḫormālū, persimmon (*Diospyros spp.*), 76, wood for the manufacture of weaving shuttles, 204
ḫorūsak, hacksaw tightener, 60
ḫošeh, chisel for chasing metal from the back (Šīrāz), 36, 37
ḫoškandan dar āftāb, to dry in the sun, 232
ḫoškār, coarse meal, flour*
ḫoškeh, hardened steel, 129, 131, a biscuit-like bread, 291, 294
ḫoškeh kardan, to harden, 56
ḫoškeh-paz, baker of biscuit-like bread, 294
ḫoškeh-sāb, see *āsiyāb-e ḫoškeh-sāb*, 151
ḫošk-e kār, dry stratum in underground water channel, 253
ḫošk kardan, to dry, 302
ḫošk kardan dar sayeh, to dry in the shade, 157
ḫoškīdan, to dry up, 238
ḫošk šodan, to become work-hardened, 36, to dry up, 116, the thickening of syrup, 302
ḫosrouwānī, blades forged in Persia from Ceylon steel, 55
houviyeh, soldering iron, 31, 61
houviyeh barqī, electric soldering iron†
houviyeh-čakošī, hammer-shaped soldering iron†
houviyeh-gāzī, gas-operated soldering iron†
houviyeh-nōk-tīz, pointed soldering iron*
ḥouż, watering pit, 231, water basin, 117, 257, 258, flow-measuring basin, 255
hōviyeh, soldering iron (Šīrāz), 61
ḫūneh, rolling pin, 293
ḫūneh-kār, press board, round block, 298
ḫūn-e siyāvūš, dragon blood, a red gum, 190
ḫūᵓōl, wing nut tree (*Pterocarya caucasia*) (Tūnehkabūn), 76
ḫurd, glaze crack; cf. *ḫord*, 166
ḥurūf, letter punches, 60, type for book tooling, 238
ḥurūfrā andāḫtan, to apply tooling type, 238
ḫūšeh-čīn, people who are allowed to glean, 273
hūyang, yoke loop (Ḫorāsān), 262
ḫūz, sugar cane, 242
ḫūzistān, sugar plantation, 243, sugar factory*
ḫwāb, pile warp, 209
ḫwāb dāštan, to sleep (silkworm) (Gīlān), 183
ḫwordeh-ye šīšeh = *ḫordeh-ye šīšeh*, broken glass for remelting, 169

īlāk dādan, to throw shuttle, 205
*inā*ᵓ, vessel, vase (pl. *avānī*), 153
isfarjānī, alchemist, metallurgist, 163
ismid, antimony ore, 163
isparag, yellow from Delphinium zalil; cf. *esperek*, 191
isrinj, cinnabar, red lead, 161
istaḫr, water reservoir, 258
izār-e ḫāneh, wall tile*

*ja*ᶜ*beh*, box under driver's seat, 90, case containing set of scales, 63, drawer, 86, packing case, 79, silkworm egg box, 182
*ja*ᶜ*beh-āyineh*, mirror frame, 88
jā-čerāġ, lamp holder, 90
jad-mou, grapevine (*Vitis vinifera*), 76
jadval, irrigation channel*
jā-estekān, tea glass holder, 32
jaft, rind, shells and galls of wild pistachio (*Pistacia intergerrima*), 189
jag, *jaġ*, sissoo tree (*Dalbergia sissoo Roxb.*), 74, 76
jahat-e boreš, cutting direction of a saw†
jājīm jājim, a strong woolen band, 201, 202
jā-kūzehgī, jar stand, 153
jā-līvān, tea glass holder, 32
jām-e ḥammām, earthenware frame for skylight, 153, cup-shaped skylight, 153
jamīr, center point on piece to be turned (Fārs), 91
jān-e mateh, drill point, 60
jangal, forest, 79, threshing wain (Arāq); cf. *čangal*, 274
janūb, fig tree (*Ficus carica*) (Fārs, Ḫorāsān), 76
jaras, camel bell*
jarīb, a water measure, 256
jarīdeh, embroiderer's clamp (Rašt); cf. *jerīdeh*, *gerīdeh*, 218

jarr, pulley driving rewinding mechanism, 44
jārū, jārūb, broom, brush, 221, 233
jārū-bāf, broom maker, 221
jarz-e čāh, pillars above well, 256
javāher, javāhir, jewelry, 32
javāher-sāz, jeweler, 32
javāl-dūz, pack needle, 234
javān, splint wood, 80
jā-ye dast, bow holder, 181
jā-ye garm, a warm spot, 182
jā-ye māsūn, bearing for windlass axle, 258
jā-ye šast-e dast va angušt, fingerholes in scissors, 56
jā zadan, to upset in forging, 52, 54
jazval, scratched mark on brick, tile, 122
jed, yoke (Alburz); cf. *jot, jüt*, 262
jelā, luster, polish, 40
jelā kardan, half smoothing of gems, pre-polishing, 40
jelangeh-dān, cocking lever of gun; cf. *galangeh-dān*, 59
jelār, beech tree (*Fagus silvatica, F. orientalis*) (Caspian provinces); see *julār*, 76
jeld, book cover, case, 238
jeld-e maᶜmūlī, half-case book cover, 238
jeld-e qalam-dān, pen box cover, 239
jeldgar, bookbinder, 237
jeleqeh, sleeveless sheepskin vest (Mašhad), 232
jellād, skinner, 231
jeqjeqeh, ratchet drill, 60
jerīdeh, see *gerīdeh*, 218
jī, yoke (Zābol), 275
jīb, bush inside wheel hub, 90, yoke (Fārs)*
jīd, glue to laminate cotton bow, 180
jift, rind, shell, and gall nuts of wild pistachio tree (*Pistacia intergerrima*); cf. *jaft*, 189
jīgō, yoke (Zābol); cf. *joug, jouq, jūġ*, 262
jīn, loop between plow beam and yoke (Surmaq), 262
joft, pair, 215
jōhar, soldering flux, 61
jol, mat used for oil pressing, 298
jot, yoke (Varāmīn); cf. *jed, jüt*, 262
jou, barley, 241, 277, a measure of weight, 62, diamond-shaped bead, 94, unhusked rice, 290
joug, yoke (Nairīz)*; cf. *jīgō, jouq, jūġ*, 262
jouġan, stone mortar for rice husking, 290
jouhar, etching acid, 8, 123, soldering fluid, 61, frit, 160, acid, 163
jouhar-dār, etched damascene steel, 8
jouhar-e gel-e māšī, ruddle ink for marking, 123
jouhar-e golī, a leather dye, 232
jouhar-e gūgerd, sulphuric acid, 34
jouq, yoke (Qāᵓen); cf. *jīgō, joug, jūġ*, 262
jou-ye šīrīn, spring barley, 271
jou-ye torš, summer barley, 271
jouzaq, cotton pod (Kāšān), 179
jozv, bundle of sheets, quire, section of book, 237
jū, yoke; cf. *jī*, 275
jūb, open water supply channel, stream (Fārs), 193, 246
jūġ, wooden cross supporting water bag, 257, yoke (Ḫorāsān); cf. *joug, jouq, jīgō*, 262
jūġān, loop joining plow beam and yoke (Ḫorāsān), 262
jūġlā, neck peg on yoke (Ḫorāsān), 262
jūjeh, sticks forming warp cross, 204, heddle frame, 198, heddle, 204, 209
jū-kārī, channel digging (Zābol), 261
jūl, lap at the tip of tongs, 52; cf. *ambor-e jūl*
julār, beech tree (*Fagus silvatica* or *Fagus orientalis*), in Nūr (Caspian provinces), 76
jūnou-mostarāḥ, toilet pan (Bīdoḫt), 153
jurreh, time unit for water allocation (Yazd), 255
jūš, air bubbles in glaze, 164, carbonate of sodium*, sprig for grafting, 271
jūš dādan, to solder, to braze, 29, to weld, 52
jūš-e āteš, forge welding, 52
jūš-e barq, electric welding†
jūš-e berenj, brass welding, brazing, brass joint in ironwork, 52
jūš-e mes, copper joint in iron work, 52
jūš-e oksīžen, oxyacetylene welding†
jūš-e pūst, grafting under the bark, 271
jūšīdan, to pickle metal in acid, 34, to boil dyestuff (Kāšān), 194
jūš kardan, to weld, 24
just, pair of oxen*
jūš zadan, grafting, 271
jüt, plow (Āhar); cf. *jed, jot*, 262
jūy, open water channel, stream; cf. *jūb*, 246

kabal, earthenware well-lining hoop (Šīrāz, Iṣfahān, Varāmīn); cf. *kabūl, kaval*, 154, 253
kabal-māl, maker of well-lining hoops, 151, 154
kabīzeh, hub cap, 90
kabūdeh, greenpool poplar (*Populus dilatata*), 76
kačf, oriental beech tree (*Carpinus orientalis*) (Gorgān, ᶜAlīābād), common beech tree (*Carpinus betulus*) (Katūl), 76
kadḫodā, village headman, 256
kadval, earth scoop (Dārāb)*
kaf, reverse side of gem, 40, floor, 113
kafan-e kamān, spare string of carder's bow, 181
kafčeh-ye āhanīn, iron ladle, 161
kafdasti, iron palm, 234
kaf-e bīl, blade of spade, 260
kaf-e dandeh, round bottom of saw tooth†

kaf-e dariyā, the mineral *meerschaum*, 290, pumice stone, 88
kafeh, scale of balance, 63
kaf-e karreh, scoop blade; cf. *karreh*, 268
kāf-e kūreh, front opening of kiln, 159; cf. *šekāftan*
kaf-e randeh, sole of carpenter's plane, 82
kaffāš, shoemaker, 234
kafgīr, *kafkgīr*, skimming ladle, colander, sieve, 28
kafgīrak, holder of round wire-reel in flattening rollers, 45
kafgīrak-e langar, press bar with spoon-shaped ends, 45
kafgīr-e langar, bar to carry weighting ropes, 45
kafī, frothy, foamy*, iron palm, 234
kaf-kaš, sole of carpenter's plane, 82
kafš-dūz, shoe repairer, cobbler, 234
kafš-sāz, shoemaker, 234
kaft, winnowing shovel (Nairīz)*
kaf-taḫt, chisel to set metal back, 36, 37
kaftar-e ābḫwori, dove-shaped water container, 156
kāġaẕ, paper, 238
kāġaẕak, breastbeam of loom, 204
kāġaẕ-e sombādeh, emery cloth, 130
kāġaz rūham časbāndan, to glue layers of paper together for pen box making, 238
kāġaẕ-sāz, papermaker, 237
kāh, chaff, straw, 108, 109, 154, 297
kāh-berenj, rice chaff, 297
kāh-e gandom, wheat chaff, 297
kāh-e safīd, wheat chaff, chopped straw, 297
kāh-gel, mud-straw mixture, 107, 108, 110, 111, 112
kāh-gel-mālī, to render a wall, 112
kahkīn, well-sinker (Kermān), 251
kahrī, underground water channel supplied from a deep stratum*
kahrīz, underground water channel, 249
kahū, lettuce, 245
kahūr, mesquite tree (*Prosopis spicigera*) (Persian Gulf region), 76
kāh zadan, to add chaff to soaked clay*
kaikō, *kaikōm*, maple tree (*Acer spp.*) (Kurdistān), 77
kāj, pine tree (*Pinus eldarica*), 76
kaj-gīr, bending device, 276
kakuj, rape seed, 296
kālā, potash (Iṣfahān); cf. *qaliyā*, 160
kaláčeh, a grape variety, 244
kalāf, iron rail around driver's seat, 90, door of fire box, 169, skein, 188, 194, reel, 183; cf. *kelāf*, *kilāf*
kalāf-e gelgīr, hoop to support mudguard, 90
kalāfeh, silk winding spool, 183, coil of combed wool, 182, handle of cotton dresser's bow, 181, cage spool, 183
kalāf-e mīz, frame to support table top, 87
kalāf-e sar, yoke beam (Gīlān), 262
kalāf kardan, to wind onto a spool, 183
kalāf-pīč, silk-winder, reel (Māzandarān), 205
kalak, weaving hook (Iṣfahān), 208
kaland, mattock, pick (Kermān), 252, 262
kalandar, door bar*
kalandeh, mill hopper, 279
kalehgūš, a certain brick form*
kālī, hook to hold draw-loom strings, 211
kalk, *yoke peg* (Ḫorāsān), 262
kall-e dūreh, food jar, 157
kalleh, top end of pen box cover*
kalleh-bor, cross-cut saw, 79
kalleh-borī, cutting of pen box cover, 239
kalleh-qand, sugar loaf, 300
kalleh-tīr, top bearing block, 287
kālū, centering pivot, 132
kaluk, *kalūk*, a small piece of brick, 112, a certain brick shape (Šīrāz)*
kalvezān, water shutter (Alburz), 281
kām, coarse sieve, 18, 235, groove slot, 84, 90; cf. *kūm*
kamān, frame of hacksaw, 60, drill bow, 87, turner's bow, 91, steel tire, 286, bow shaft, 180
kamānčeh, tightening string, 181, stirring rod, 300
kamāneh, fiddle bow, 26, bow to drive lathe, 91, 132, bow to drive gem cutter's wheel, 37, 39, bow-shaped lever, 211, bent wood controlling heddles, 211
kamān-e pambeh-zanī, carder's bow, 180
kamān-gar, bowmaker*
kamānkaš-e arreh, middle bar of a bow saw*
kamān zadan, to bow fibers (Kāšān), 91, 180, 222
kamar, crocheted rim of cloth shoe, 230, leather welt of cloth shoe, 230, edging, 230
kamar-kaš, middle lintel in skylight window, 86
kamar-šekān, breech of a shotgun, 59
kamčeh, crucible carrying bar, 19, ladle*, trowel, 111
kām-e ġarbāl, sieve hoop, 235
kām kardan, to cut a groove, 90, to mortise timber†
kām-ō-zabāneh, mortise-and-tenon joint, 86
kān, a mine*, slot, 281
kanaf, hemp (*Cannabis sativa*), 177, 182, 221, jute, mat weaver's warp, 220
kanaf az čūleh savār kardan, to peel fibers off the hemp stem, 182
kandan, to dig, to excavate, 102, 108, to cut relief work, 166, to pluck, 177

kandar, lote fruit tree (*Ziziphus vulgaris*, *Z. nummularia*), 76
kandeh, gem glued to stick (Mašhad), 40, stepped pulley, 44, 46, 47, subterranean shelter, dugout dwelling*
kandeh sar-e mīl-e čarḫ, pulley at end of main shaft, 46
kanduk, meal hopper (Ḫorāsān), 288
kaneh, notch in padlock shackle, 69
kān-e sang, quarry, 108
kapān, heavy balance, steelyard, 62
kap-e bīl, blade of spade; cf. *kaf-e bīl*, 260
kapeh, scale of balance, 63
kappeh, mortar trough, 108
kāpšeh, mustard seed, 296
kar, a low-grade silk cocoon, 183
karb, maple tree (*Acer campestre*) (Caspian provinces), 76
karbās, rag used as filter, 161, cotton fabric, 178, canvas, 219, 287, 300
karbās-e dast-bāf, hand-woven calico, 226
karbā-se pardeh, cloth lining of mat edge, 221
karčak, castor bean; cf. *rouġan-e karčak*, 296
kārd, knife, 55, 183, 301, plaiter's knife, 221, pruning knife, 271, bookbinder's knife, 238
kār-dahān, weaving shed (Māzandarān), 205
kārdak, carpet-trimming knife, 217
kārd-e būm-konī, plasterer's deep-cutting knife, 135
kārd-e deraḫtčīn, pruning knife, 56
kārd-e gač-borī, plaster-cutting knife, 135
kārd-e ᶜorām, depilation knife, 231
kārd-e qāšoqī, hollow plaster-cutting knife, 135
kārd-e šekār, hunter's knife*
kārd-e tarāš, turning tool, 166
kārd-e ṭelā-kūbī, gold-inlayer's knife, 41
kārdī, window sill brick (Šīrāz), 113
kārd-sāz, cutler, knifesmith, 55
kār-e qalam-gīrī, pure line work on surface, 36
kār-e qorṣum, surface metal work, 36
karf, maple tree (*Acer campestre*) (Caspian provinces), 77
kārfūn, bamboo, 107
kārgāh, file bench, 56, carpet loom (Iṣfahān), 214
kār-gāh-dārī, vertical carpet loom, 214
kār-gāh-e zamīnī, horizontal carpet loom, 214
kārgar, craftsman's assistant*
kār-gār, mat-weaving frame, 221
kārḫāneh-kūzehgarī, potter's workshop, see *kūzehgar*, 151
kārḫāneh-navard, copper-rolling mill, 23
kārḫāneh-ye abrīšam, silk cocoon handling factory, 183
kārḫāneh-ye šīšeh-garī, glassworks, 169
kārḫāneh-ye vartābī, silk-twisting shop, warp-winding shop (Kāšān), 196
kārīz, underground water supply channel; cf. *kahrīz*, 154, 249
karkaf, maple tree (*Acer platanoides*) (Gorgān), 77
karkū, maple tree (*Acer opulifolium*, *A. monspesassulanum*) (Caspian provinces, Ḫorāsān), 77
karkum, turmeric, a yellow dye, 191
kārmāleh, oil press, 296
kār-pīč, warp-winding stick (Kāšān), 197
karreh, scoop, 268
kār-tarāš, potter's turning iron, 156
kār-tīġ, molder's spatula, 18
kār-tīġ-e qāšoqī, spoon-shaped spatula, 18
karvar-čāh, spoil around mouth of well, 252
karzul, common beech tree (*Carpinus betulus*) (Caspian provinces), 76
kās, hollow part of scissor blades, 56
kaš-bīl, fire hook, rake, 126
kāseh, dish, 32
kāseh-āsiyāb, space in which mill wheel turns, 282
kašīdan, to draw wire, 43, to draw out in forging, 52
kāšī-gar, see *kāšī-par*, 151
kāšīgarī, tilemaker's craft*
kašī-kārī, smoothing the skin, 232
kašī-kaš, hoeing*
kašīn, purlin, 107
kāšī-paz, *kāšī-sāz*, tilemaker, potter, 151, 157, 164
kāšī-tarāš, tile cutter, 120, 122, 123
kāšī-tarašīdan, to cut tiles, 123
kaškūl, dish, 39, beggar's bowl, 97
kašmeš, sultanas, raisins, 301
kašō, drawer, 85, straight-edge, 122, molding templet, 135
kaš-ō-gīr kardan, to stretch a skin (Mašhad), 233
kās-rand, concave compass plane (Tehrān), 84
kāštan, to sow, 271
kaš zadan, to hoe*
katal, wooden sandal (Gīlān), 88, thick board supporting floor, 107
katān, linen, flax, 178, 219
katar, earth scoop, 268
katar kašīdan, to operate an earth scoop, prepare furrows, 268
kateh gandomī, grain hopper, bin, 278
katerū, wooden shovel (Alburz)*
katībeh, skylight window, 86
katībī, fanlight of window, 86, fancy work around door (Iṣfahān)*
katīrā, *katīreh*, gum tragacanth (*Astragalus gummifer*), 164, 224, 226, 229
kāᵓūl, bent handle of tile cutter's hoe, 122

ka'ūn-e šotor, camel bone, 209
kaval, earthenware well-lining hoop (Tehrān); cf. *kaval, kabal, kūl*, 154, 253
kaval-māl, maker of earthenware hoops, 151, 154
kavījak, bearing supporting breastbeam, 204
kavījeh, medlar wood (*Mespilus spp.*); cf. *kevīj, kevīz*, 77, 283
kavul, earthenware well-lining hoop (Kermān); cf. *kabal, kaval*, 154, 253
kazveh, mat used by cotton dresser, 181
kedeneh, mallet (Šīrāz), 84
kelāf, iron rail around driver's seat (Šīrāz); cf. *kalāf, kilāf*, 90
kelāf, skein of yarn, spool, reel; cf. *kalāf, kilāf*, 188
kelāf-e gelgīr, hoop to support mudguard, 90
kelī, hook for draw harness (Iṣfahān), 211
kelīd, key, 66, 69
kelīdān, kelīdūn, kelīdāneh, lock, bolt, bar, 66
kelīd-ḫwor, keyhole, key position in bolt, 68
kelīd-sāz, locksmith, 66
kelīdūn-e ḫāneh, door lock, 66
kelīlai-band, protection chimney pot, 254
keliyāb, potash (Kāšān); cf. *qaliyā, kālā*, 160, 300
kemar-šekan, breach of a shotgun, 59
kenāreh, splint wood, 80, quilt border, 227
kenār-e kār, selvage, 220
kener, millstone dressing pick (Šīrāz), 279
kerm, worm, 190
kerm-e abrīšam, silkworm, 182
kerm-pīleh, silkworm, silkworm cocoon, 182
kerō, earth scoop (Šīrāz), 52
kešāfat, burnt metal, waste, oxides*
kešāvarz, peasant, cultivator, 261
kešmešī, a grape variety suitable for sultanas, 244
kešt-kār, farmer, tiller, peasant*
ketāb, book, 237
ketrī, small coffee boiler, 28
kevīj, kevīž, medlar wood (*Mespilus spp.*) (Kermān); cf. *kavījeh*, 77, 92
kīkam, maple tree (*Acer laetum*) (Caspian provinces), 77
kilāf, bobbin, 47
kilāf-e farangī, reel with spun gold thread, 47
kilang, keyhole*
kilīd, key (Šīrāz); cf. *kelīd*, 66, 69
kīmiyāgar, alchemist, metallurgist, 163
kirbās, calico, canvas; cf. *karbās*, 219
kīrčou, plow beam (Ḫorāsān), 263
kīš, boxtree (*Buxus sempervirens*) (Caspian provinces), 77
kīseh, ore bag, 15, bag, 183, 185, 300, warp-weighting bag, 204
kīseh-ye ḫāk-e zoġāl, dusting bag, 36
kīseh-ye ḫwāb, warp weight, 209
kīseh-ye zoġāl, dusting bag, 18
kīv, lime tree (*Tilia rubra*) (Āstārā, Gīlān), 77
koḥl, antimony, colyrium, 163
kohneh, cloth edge on reed, 195, rag to keep warp moist, 235, rag for cloth shoe soles, 229, cloth shoe lining, 230, lubrication pad, 286
kohneh-pī, pincushion, 228
kōjī, heddle rod (Sīstān), 200
kōk, coke; cf. *zoġāl-e kōk**
kolāh, rat trap of rick pillar, 289, hat, 224
kolāhak, Morse bush, 60, fiddle drill knob, 85, door lintel, 86
kolāh-čahārčūb, door lintel, head, 86
kolāh-dūz, hat maker, 224
kolāh-e namadīn, felt cap*
kolāh-māl, hat fuller, 222
koland, lock, key*, pick, 262
kolāneh, crank on spinning wheel (Ardistān), 186
kolang, miner's pick, 15, 131, mattock, hoe, 52, mason's pick, 109, 128, 252, pick for dressing millstone, 279, cultivator's pick, 260, 262
kolang-e dō-sar, double-edged mattock, 262
kolangī, roughed stone block, 131
kolang kardan, to roughen a surface with a pick*
kol-e čāh-āb, well lining, 153
kolīs, sliding gauge (Fr. *coulisse*), 61
kolīs-e sūrāḫ, depth gauge, 61
kolk, velvet pile; cf. *kork*, 209, goat underhair, 222
kolon-kūb, mallet for breaking up clods (Yazd), 266
kolūḫ, clod, lump of earth, unharrowed land (Ābādeh), 266
kolūḫ-kūb, cultivator's mallet, 266
kolūn, door bolt, door lock (Yazd, Iṣfahān), 66, 67
kolūndān, lock with wooden bolt, 66
komājdān, earthenware pot, 156
komak-bast-e čūbī, wooden filing vice*
komak-e sāz, auxiliary bow tightener, 181
kom-e zabāneh, tongue and groove joint†; cf. *kūm-e zabāneh*, 86
kom kandan, to mortise timber†
kondeh, anvil stock, 229, wooden stock, 35, 51, working block, 98, 221, comb-cutting block*, mill axle support, 151, cotton gin base, 180, plow sole (Ḫorāsān), 263
kondeh-čūb, wooden anvil stock, 24
kondeh souhānkārī, filing block*
kondū, beehive, 153
kondulū, heavy block supporting floor beams, 107
koneškāf, rabbet, recess, 84

konjed, sesame, sesame seed (*Sesamum orientale*), 291, 295, 296, 302
kopā, stable*; cf. *kūpā*
kōpeh-serkeh, large glass bottle; cf. *kūpeh-serkeh*, 170
kopeleh, plastering board, wooden float, 134
koreh, plow sole (Varāmīn), 263
kōreh, stonecutter's pick, 131
korġak, excavation in supporting block (Šīstān), 288
kork, under-hair of goat, 177, 222, velvet pile; cf. *kolk*, 209, fine wool, 214
korpī, U-bolt to attach springs, 90
korsī, samovar base, 29; cf. *kursī*
korūk, coach hood, 90
korzeh, cultivated surface of irrigated field, 269
košk, seat board on threshing wain (Hamadān), 274
košreh, rabbet plane (Iṣfahān); cf. *košterā*, 84
kosterā, rabbet plane (Šīrāz), 84
kotolām, rush rope winder, 220
Koulī, gypsy, member of a smithing tribe, 49, 234
kūb, ramming iron, 18
kūbeh-ye dar, door knocker, 52
kūbīdan, to pound, 238, to ram*, to flatten bamboo, 219
kūbīdan-e rūniyās, to powderize madder, 190
kūbīdan zīr-e sang, to crush under the edge roller, 300
kūč, *kūčī*, Caucasian wing nut tree (*Pterocarya fraxinifolia*, *P. caucasia*) (Caspian provinces), 77
kudū-māfak, chisel for hollowing inside (Rašt), 92
kū'eh-kaš, removing of cotton capsules (Kāšān), 179; cf. *kūzeh-pambeh*
kuf, lime tree (*Tilia rubra*) (Caspian provinces); cf. *kīv*, 77
kūftan, to flatten rushes, bamboo, 219
kūh-bor, miner, quarryman, 126, 127, 130
kūk, bow used on wire rollers (Šīrāz), 45
kūl, earthenware hoop (Šīrāz, Varāmīn); cf. *kaval*, 154, 253
kulāh = *kolāh*, 224
kuland, mattock, pick (Šīrāz), see *koland*, 262
kūldar, earth-moving scoop*
kūleh, body of carpenter's plane, 82, bar holding live center, 26
kūleh-marz, raised border in irrigated field, 268
Kūlī = *Koulī*
kūl-māl, see *kabal-māl*, 154
kuls, carded cotton, 181
kuluk, earthenware jar, chafing dish, 155, drainpipe, 153
kuluseh, head stock board of lathe (Rašt), 91, branch hook forming plow sole (Gīlān), 262
kulzebuzeh, instrument to remove cotton capsules; cf. *kū'eh-kaš*, 179
kūm, mortise in hub; cf. *kām*, 84, 90
kūm-e ġarbāl, sieve hoop (Šīrāz), 235
kūm kandan, to mortise, to cut a groove*
kūm-ō-zabāneh, mortise-and-tenon joint, tongue-and-groove joint, 86
kūn, bearing point on mill thrust bearing, 281
kunār, lote fruit tree (*Ziziphus vulgaris*, *Z. nummularia*) (Fārs, Kermān, Bandar-ᶜAbbās), 76, 77
kūndeh, axle of spinning wheel (Māzandarān), 186
kūn-e bīnī, stand for reel (Yazd), 185
kungūrt, diversion tunnel in underground water channel (Kermān), 253
kūn-mīḫ, thrust bearing, pivot pin (Šīrāz), 281
kūpā, stable*; cf. *kopā*
kūpeh-serkeh, large vinegar bottle, 170
kūpī, silk-winding spool (Kāšān), 183, 196
kūpīkan, bar to lift oil cakes (Iṣfahān), 299
kūpī kardan, to wind silk onto spool (Kāšān), 183
kūr, core wood to which veneer is glued†
kūreh, fireplace, furnace, 19, 29, forge, 24, 50, brick-kiln, 116, kiln, 126, 157, 158, loom pit, 204, fireplace under fulling dish*, tunnel, underground water channel, 253, baker's oven, 294
kūreh-āhak-pazī, lime-burning kiln, 126
kūreh čīdan, to charge a kiln, 159
kūreh dīvārī, covered forge, 50
kūreh-falaqeh, roasting furnace, 16
kūreh-gač-pazī, gypsum-burning kiln, 126
kūreh-kārī, to forge, to smith*
kūreh-paz, brick burner*, specialized lime and gypsum burner, 126
kūreh-rang, muffle furnace, 161, glazing kiln (Iṣfahān), 164
kūreh-ye ājur-pazī, brick kiln, 116
kūreh-ye kabal-pazī, kiln for firing well-lining hoops, 159
kūreh-ye kāšī-pazī, tile kiln, 164
kūreh-ye loᶜābī, glazing kiln, 164
kūreh-ye pātīl, fireplace under boiler, 193
kūreh-ye qarᶜambīq, still furnace, 163
kūreh-ye rangpazī, glazing kiln, 164
kūreh-ye šīšeh-garī, glass kiln, 169
kūreh-ye ẕōb-e mes, copper furnace, 17
kūreh-zamīnī, forge dug into the ground, 51
kūreh-ẕoub, melting furnace (Šīrāz), 23
kursī, trestle, 232, seat of threshing wain; cf. *korsī*, 274

kūtīnā, cam on mill shaft, 290
kutnak, trimming hoe, pick (Sīstān), 288
kūzeh, water jar, 155, water-measuring jar, 255, water-lifting jar, 256
kūzehgar, potter, 151
kūzeh-pambeh, cotton pod; cf. *kūʾeh-kaš*, *kulzebuzeh*, 179
kūzeh-ye āb-ḫworī, jar for drinking water, 155
kuzeleh, cotton capsule, 179

lā, thin board, ply, 93
laʿāb, turquoise part in gems with matrix; glaze, cf. *loʿāb*, 39, 160
laʿāb kardan, to glaze; cf. *loʿāb kardan*, 163
lāʿatīq-ō-lā muḥaddas, steel that is neither antique nor modern, 55
lab, reinforced edge of molding box, 18
lāb, printing block for red color, 225
labeh, edge, border, flange, 26, 30
labeh gereftan, to beat a flange, 26, 30
lab-e gīreh sorbī, leaden vice jaw†
lab-e ḥouż, rim of water basin, 255
labeh-ye nōk, cutting edge of chisel†
lab-gardān, the doubled edge, 25
lab gardānīdan, to double the edge, 25
lab gereftan, to join two parts, 223
lab kardan, to do finishing work, 131
lāgad zadan, to tread hides, 232
lagan, pan, 28
lāh, silken fabric (Māzandarān)*
lāh-e gāzkon, warp cross, lease (Māzandarān), 205
laḥīm, solder, 31
laḥīm-e berenj, hard solder, brazing, 61
laḥīm-e dandāneh, zig-zag soldering*
laḥīm-e mes, brazing*
laḥīm-e noqreh, silver solder, hard solder, 24, 33
laḥīm-e noqreh dādan, hard soldering, 29
laḥīm-e qalʿ, soft solder, 28, 30
laḥīm kardan, to solder, to braze, 61
laḥīm-kārī, soldering, brazing†
lājvar(d), lapis lazuli, cobalt, ultramarine, 147, 148, 163
lājvardī, cobalt blue glaze, 147
lājvardīna, a certain glazing technique using blue overglaze*
lāk, resin, 39, shellac, sealing wax, 37, red dyestuff from shellac gum, 191
lāk alcol, *lāk-e alcol*, shellac solution, 238, French polish, 88
lakeh, axle beam of edge runner, 296
lākī, shellac dye, 191
lakkeh, spot on turquoise, 39
lāleh, thatching, 107
lambū, sebestens tree (*Cordia myxam*, *C. crenata*), 75, 77
lamr, sand (Šīrāz) (corrupt for *raml*), 113
lang, tooth in pinion wheel, 283
langar, molding core, 18, brake weight, 45, weight bag, 47, spinning whorl, 185, warp-tightening weight, 209, skid of threshing wain, 274, weight, 297, 299
langar-e vard, draw harness weight, 206
lang-e dar, *langeh-dar*, door leaf, 86
langeh, rick pillar, 289, end of lathe bed, 86
langeh-čahārčūb, door lintel, 86
langeh-motaḥarrek, movable traverse of lathe, 132
langeh-s̱ābet, fixed traverse of lathe, 132
lang-e panjareh, *langeh-panjareh*, window leaf, 86
lapak, plowshare (Šīrāz), 52
lapeh, half log, 79
lapeh kardan, to rough-grind, 278
laqaṭ zadan, to center clay on potter's wheel, 155
lārak, Caucasian wing nut tree (*Pterocarya fraxinifolia*, *P. caucasia*) (Nūr, Gorgān), 77
larḫ, Caucasian wing nut tree (*Pterocarya caucasia*) (Māzandarān), 77
lark, Caucasian wing nut tree (*Pterocarya fraxinifolia*, *P. caucasia*) (Katūl), 77
lā-rōbī, cleaning of an underground water channel (Kermān); cf. *lat-rōbī*, *lāy-rōbī*, 254
lāt, roof shingle (Šīrāz), 113, weir for water division, 255
lāt kardan, to divide irrigation water, 255
lat-rōbī, cleaning of an underground water channel (Kermān), 254
latteh, protecting cloth, 40
latteh-kohneh, cloth pieces, cloth strips, rags, 229
lāvān, supervisor of water allocation (Nairīz), 255
lavāš, a certain flat bread, 291, 294
lā-ye baġal-šīš, thin boards for inlaid work (Iṣfahān), 93
lā-ye berenj, brass strip for inlaid work, 95
lā-ye dōsāyeh, layers of inlaid work sliced from a compound block, 96
lā-ye fanar, leaf of a laminated spring, 90
lāyeh, slip, engobe, 166
lāyeh dādan, *lāyeh var kardan*, to apply slip, 166
lā-ye moṣallaṣ, thin boards for inlaid work, 93
lā-ye vassaṭ, intermediate veneer in plywood†
lā-ye yaklāʾī, mounting board for inlaid work, 93
lāy-rōbī, silt removal from water channel, 254
leḥāf, quilt, 227
leḥāf-dūz, quilt maker, 227
lengeh, end of lathe bed, 91
lengeh-čahārčūb, door post, jamb, 86
lengeh-dar, leaf of door; cf. *langeh-dar*, 86
lengeh-panjareh, leaf of window; cf. *langeh-panjareh*, 86

lī, beech tree (*Ulmus spp.*) (Caspian provinces), 77, rushes for matmaking; cf. *liyān*, 220
līqeh, glaze, 160
līqeh-ye dō-āteš, pigmented glaze, 165
lisān, tongue of balance, 63
līseh, wood scraper, 84, carver's scraper*
līseh kardan, to scrape, to smooth, to polish, 87, 101
līvān, beaker, mug, 156
livar, oriental hornbeam (*Carpinus orientalis*) (Nūr), 77
liyān, rushes used for mat weaving, 220
lizārī, the dyestuff *alizarin*, 190
līzeh, spatula, small trowel, 153
loᶜāb, glaze, frit, 160, bands of turquoise, 39, finely-ground minerals; cf. *laᶜāb*, 300
loᶜāb-dār, glazed*
loᶜāb-e safīdāb, washed mineral, 300
loᶜābī puḫtan, to fire a glaze*
loᶜāb kardan, to apply glaze, 163
loᶜāb pāʾīn mīravad, the fine minerals settle*
loᶜāb sāf šodan, the melting of the glaze, 166
lōhanīn, instrument to separate cotton from its seed, 180
long, rag used as a filter, 161
longāz, turning gouge, 92
loqāṭ, ceiling panel, 87
lōr, cotton bow, 180
loulā, hinge, 52, 86, 88, 101
loulā-sīmī, wire hinge, 88
loun, color, hue*
lour, *lūr*, Indian fig tree (*Ficus altissima*) in Bandar ᶜAbbās, 77
lūbeh, small hole in water measuring dish, 255
lūbī, platform of edge runner, 296
lūbiyā, bean, 245
lūʾī, rush seed, 113
lūleh, tuyères, 19, 51, bush inside reel, 44, barrel, 60, tubular body of padlock, 69, 71, adze socket, 79, bellows outlet, 101, drainpipe, 153, small bowl for time measuring, 255, long iron nozzle, 31
lūleh-bor, pipe cutter, 60
lūleh-gīr, pipe wrench†
lūleh-ḫamkon, pipe-bending device, 60
lūleh-kaš, plumber†, conic earthenware vessel, 153, 194, 231
lūleh-laḥīm-kārī, soldering blowpipe†
lūleh-nāvdān, down pipes, 30
lūleh-rāstkon, pipe straightener, 60
lūleh-ye bīl, spade socket, 260
lūleh-ye boḫārī, stovepipe, 30
lūleh-ye čāh-āb, well-lining hoop, 153
lūleh-ye čubuk, stem of tobacco pipe, 92
lūleh-ye felezz, metal tuyères, 16
lūleh-ye karreh, scoop socket*
lūleh-ye qaliyān, stem of the water pipe, 92
lūrak, lurak, cotton bow; cf. *lōr*, 180

maᶜdan, mine, quarry, 15, 130
maᶜdančī, miner, 15
maᶜdan-e sang, quarry, 108
maᶜdaniyāt, ore, minerals, 15
mādar-čāh, head well of underground water channel, 249, 252
mādar-ō-bačeh, a grape variety, 244
mādeh, catch for door bolt, 66, 68, lower half of molding box, 18
mad-gīr, plow stilt (Ḫorāsān), 263
madhūn, painted, colored*
mādī-sālār, overseer of irrigation channel, 256
maᶜdin = *maᶜdan*, 15, 130
madqūq, pounded, crushed in mortar, 151
mafrāġ, bronze, 18
maftūl, core reinforcement, 18, rim reinforcing wire, 26, hinge*, heavy gauge wire, 43, guide pin, 69, brass wire, 209, velvet pile wire, 209
maftūl-e berenj, brass wire, 94
maftūl kašīdan, coarse drawing of wire, 43
maġākī, pit in front of frit kiln, 161
maġn, *maġnīsā*, *maġnīsiyā*, manganese, manganese oxide, 161, 163
maġz, heartwood, core wood, 80
maġzī, decorative edging, 234
mahā, crystal*
maḥaṭṭ, bookbinder's lining tool, 238
maḫlūṭ, alloy, 18, mixed, 108
maḫlūṭ kardan, to mix, 108
maḫmal-bāf, velvet weaver, 209
maḫmal-e barjesteh, embossed velvet, 210
mahtābī, terrace roof, open terrace*
māhūt, cloth, base for embroidery, 218
maḫzan, meal hopper, 288
maik, scoop socket (Ḫorāsān, Āmol), 268
maj, bundle of drawstrings, 211
maᶜjūn, kneaded, mixed, 152
makabbeh, lid, 156, saggar lid, 164
mākū, weaver's shuttle, 204, 205, a certain brick profile, 123
mākū andāḫtan, to throw the shuttle, 208
mākūk, weaver's shuttle, 204
mākū-kūb, goldbeater, 41
māl, horseshoe (Varāmīn), 53
malaj, elm tree (*Ulmus spp.*) (Caspian provinces), 77
malāṭ, mortar; cf. *melāṭ*, 111, 113
mālband, coach beam, pole, 90
māleh, trowel, 108, 111, 134, 153, profiled modeling tool, 155, harrow, 266
māleh-čahārsū, plastering trowel, float, 112
māleh-čīlak, stand-on harrow (Zābol), 266

māleh-kaš, harrow harness (Ḫorāsān), 267
māleh kašīdan, to harrow, 266, 267
malekī, cloth shoe, 228
malekī-dūz, cloth shoe maker, 229
mālīdan, to mold bricks, 110, to smooth, to polish, to rub, 108, 152, to harden felt, 223, to rub sheepskins, 233
malīkī (Ābādeh) = *malekī*, 228
maṃbeᶜ, small reservoir at well top, 257
mamraz, European hornbeam (*Carpinus betulus*) (Caspian provinces), 77
maᶜmūlī, ordinary bread, 291
man, measure of weight, 62, 299, divisions on steelyard, 65
man-e šāh, man-e saġat, man-e Tabrīz, a measure of weight, 62
manganeh, punch, press vice, roller, 60
mangūleh, strap to hold pair of scales, 64
manḫūl, sifted, screened, 151
manjanīq, warp suspension frame; cf. *manjenīq, manzenīq*, 111, 204, 209
manjar, shaft, 43
manjeh, wire-drawing reel, 43
manjenīq, beam holding warp rollers, 209; cf. *manjanīq, manzenīq*, 204
manqal, charcoal brazier, 28
manqal-e boḫārī, manqal-e farangī, charcoal brazier with grill, 28
manqal-e gelī, earthenware brazier, 153
mantaš, rim of cart wheel, 90
manzenīq, scaffold; cf. *manjenīq*, 111, 209
maqsam, water distribution basin (Kermān), 255
mardak, yoke peg (Zābol), 62, plow stilt (Neh)*
marmā, opening in the structure of the windmill (Sīstān), 285
marmahānī, wrought iron, 8
marmar, marble, 129
mārpā, carving tool, 98
martabān, large bottle with wide neck, 170
marz, raised border, bund, 268
marz-band, border raising, bund making, 268
marzeh, pivot (Alburz), 290
marz-kaš, earth-moving scoop, 52
māš, mat weaver's comb, 220
māseh, molding sand, fine sand*, lime-sand mortar, 113
māšeh, trigger of gun, 60
masḥūq, pulverized, 151
māšīn-e boreš, paper guillotine, 238
mašk, leather bucket, 234
māšk-bīd, musk willow (*Salix aegyptiaca*), 77
mašk-fīk, musk willow (*Salix aegyptiaca*) (Caspian provinces), 77
māskūh, pivot post of edge mill, 296
maṣqal, gold-inlayer's burnisher, 42, sharpening steel for scraper, 84
maṣqal kardan, to burnish, 42
maṣqūl, burnisher, 42
masrī, axle of water drawing pulley, 256
māst, yoghurt, curdled milk, 294
masteh, sandy friable soil (Kermān), 253
mastūreh, yarn eyelet in shuttle, 204, 295
māsūn, māšūn, scaffold carrying pulley, 256, windlass axle, 258, wooden part of mill axle, 281
māšūn, trowel (Iṣfahān), 111
māsūreh, bobbin (Nāᵓīn), 188, 195, cage spool shuttle (Yazd), 183, ball of cotton, 211, yarn eyelet in shuttle, 204, weft ball, 211, shuttle bobbin, 205
māsūreh kardan, māsūreh pīčīdan, to wind onto bobbin (Māzandarān), 188
mateh, drill, auger, drilling bit, 60, 85, 92
mateh-čangalbānī, a kind of center drill†
mateh-gīr, drill chuck, 60
mateh-ḥalazūnī, gimlet, fluted drill†
mateh-ḫazīneh, countersinker†
matehᵓī, grafting by drill, 271
mateh-kamāneh, mateh-kamānī, fiddle drill, 29, 57, 85
mateh-markazī, center drill†
mateh-sangbor, masonry drill, 60
mateh-ye bargī, center drill, 85
mateh-ye dastī, gimlet, 85
mateh-ye gīlōᵓī, shell bit, 85
mateh-ye ḫazāneh, countersink bit, 85
mateh-ye mārpīč, mateh-ye pīč, screw auger, 85
mateh-ye qāšoqī, shell bit, gouge bit, 85
mateh-ye seh-nīš, center bit, 85
mateh-ye sūzanī, nail bit, 85
mateh-ye tūpī, countersink bit, 85
maṭḥūn, ground in a mill, 151
matīt, broad holder, weaver's temple (Iṣfahān), 204
matnī, mātīẕ, coarse grade inlaid work, 97
maẓhar, mouth of underground water channel, 252
māzū, gall nut, gall apple, oak apple, 187, 231, 300
māzū kardan, to tan, 231
māzū-kārī, tanning, 231
māzūt, crude oil used for fuel, 294
medād, graphite, 19, pencil*
mehrī, a grape variety, 244
meḥvar-e souhān, tang of file*
mejrī, jewelry box, casket, 88
mejrī-sāz, jewelry box maker, 88
melāt, mortar, mud clay, mortar joint; cf. *malāṭ*, 111
melīleh, gold or silver tinsel, gold lace, 46

melīleh dūzī, embroidery with silver tinsel, 218
melīleh-kārī, filigree work, 33
meᶜmār, architect, builder, bricklayer, 108
meᶜmār-bašī, master builder, 108
mendāb, rape seed, 296
mes, copper, 16
mes-e čakošī, native copper (Anārak), 16
mes-e moḥarraq, copper oxide, burnt copper, 162
mes-e navard, rolled copper strips (Šīrāz), 23
mesgar, coppersmith, 24
mesjūš, copper weld, brazing with copper, 24
meškī, black-colored, 225
meṣqāl, a measure of weight, 62
mesqalᶜ, brass*
meṣqālī, a grape variety, 244
mešqāz, support for drawing die, 43
metr, ruler, 61
metr-e navārī, tape measure, 61
midaqq, *midaqqeh*, pestle of mortar, 151
mīḫ, nail, 52, dowel pin, 85, hook at end of tin snip handle, 26, bearing pin, 63, snarling iron, 25, point on marking gauge, 81, peg, 287, threading needle, pivot pin, 263, 281, thrust pin, 263, nail in windmill bearing, 286, 288
miḥakk, touchstone, test, 33
miḥakk kardan, to essay, to test, 33
mīḫ bā gereh-ye zeh, plug to hold string, 180
mīḫčeh, peg to position tail stock, 91
mīḫčīn, wire cutter, side cutter, 60
mīḫ-čūbī, dowel, 85
mīḫ-e āsūnī, *mīḫ-e āsānī*, wedge on threshing wain, 274
mīḫ-e bālā, upper wedge on plow (Iṣfahān), 263
mīḫ-e čelleh-tūn, warping peg, 184
mīḫ-e čūbī, dowel, 85
mīḫ-e daftīn, peg holding reed batten, 204
mīḫ-e goubandī, rivet holding plowshare (Ḫorāsān), 263
mīḫ-e ḫarak, iron clamp, 80
mīḫ-e kāġaẕak, shaft of breastbeam, 204
mīḫ-e kār, carpenter's working post, 81, bench post, 93
mīḫ-e naᶜl, horseshoe nail, 54
mīḫ-e pūtī, loom peg, 199
mīḫ-e sar-gāzak, peg of windmill bearing (Sīstān), 287
mīḫ-e sāz, pulley block axle, 204
mīḫ-e sefālīn, *mīḫ-e sifālīn*, clay peg in kiln, 160
mīḫ-e tīr, journal peg of axle, 155
mīḫ-e zīr, lower wedge on plow (Iṣfahān), 263
mīḫ-kār, center of work block, 98
mīḫ-nīmeh, heavy anvil with a flat face, 29
mīḫ-qolvar, round topped anvil (Lūristān), 25; cf. *niqolvar*, 25

miḥrāb, prayer niche, 120, 134, 149
mīḫ-sāz, nailer, nailsmith, 53
mijrafeh, shovel, scraper, ladle, 162
mīl, roller, 33, guide pin, 47, cart axle, 90, shaft, 57, steelyard beam, 65, tongue of balance, 63, windlass shaft, 109, shaft of potter's wheel, 154, thin bar of cotton gin, 180, spindle rod, 185, spindle of spinning wheel, 186, warp winding peg, 195, teeth on weaver's temple, 211, bobbin pin in shuttle, 204, velvet pile wire, 209, threshing wain axle, 274, threshing wain roller, 274, water wheel shaft, 282, 283, bookbinding tape, 237, rivet, 29, crowbar, 30
mīl-e āhanī, steel part of mill shaft, 281
mīl-e āsiyāb, mill shaft, 52
mīl-e borreh, threshing wain shaft, 274, threshing roller, 274
mīl-e čarḫ, main shaft, 45
mīl-e čūbī, wooden peg, 194
mīl-e čūm, threshing wain shaft, 52, 274
mīl-e daftīn, batten shaft, 204
mīl-e darajeh, setting peg, 26
mīleh, axle, shaft, 57, guide pin, 69, vertical shaft of underground water channel, 252, iron axle, 70, 274, pivot pin, 296
mīleh-ye qalam, stem of chisel†
mīl-e jarr, axle for rewinding pulley, 44
mīl-e manjeh, reel axle on wire-drawing bench, 44
mil-e mīzān, pivot of oil mill center post, 296, 297
mīl-e nafaskaš, needle to make air vent, 18
mīl-e pīč, reel axle, 46
mīl-e qanbāz, pivot of coach bogie, 90
mīl-e qofl, serrated shaft of lock, 72
mīl-e rāh-qās, push rod between eccentric and guide roller, 45
mīl-e ṭavaq, axle pin of polishing mandril, 26
mīl-e zīr, axle of frit mill, 151
miṃbar, pulpit, desk, 81
mimraz = *mamraz*, 77
mīnā, enamel glaze, 166, enamel work, 33, 38
mīnai, enamel glaze, 147
minḫal, sieve, 151
miqrāż, scissors, 56
miqrāż-e qalamdān, paper scissors in writing set, 56
miqrāż-e šotor, curved carpet-trimming scissors, 57
mīr-āb, water bailiff, 255
mirs, beech tree (*Fagus silvatica*, *F. orientalis*) (Gadūk, Fīruzkūh), 77
mislafeh, harrow, 266
miṣqal, burnishing steel, 35; cf. *maṣqal*

miṣrī, blades of Egyptian steel and forged there, 55
mištak, plow handle (Zābol); cf. *mošteh*, 263
mītīz, weaver's temple (Yazd), 204
mitqāl, a coarse cotton fabric, 219
miṭraqeh, hammer, rod, 151
miyād, plowshare (Zābol), 263
miyād zadan, to plow (Zābol), 263
miyān-e gōleh, intermediate press block in oil mill, 297, 298
miyān-e qaliyān, center stem of water pipe, 92
mīz, table, 87
mīzān, balance with center pivot, 62, 63, threshing roller, 274, shaft of water wheel, 282, 283, center post of edge runner, 296
mīzān-e āhanī-dūš, iron balance; cf. *āhanī-dūš*, 63
mīzān-sāz, balance maker, 62
mīz-e kār, carpenter's bench, 81
mīz-e kašābī, extension table, 87
mīz-e kašō'ī, extension table, 87
mīz-e tāšō, collapsible table, 87
mo'arak, 125, see *mu'arak*
mobāšir, district overseer, 256
mobl-sāz, cabinetmaker, 81
modaher, chequered ornament for margins, 96
modaqqaq, pounded in mortar, 151
mofattat, crumbled, crushed, 151
mofraz, narrow chisel, 132
moġār, wood chisel, 84, 97
moġār-e gīlō'ī, gouging chisel, 84, 98
moġāreh, reel for gold-wire, 46
moġāreh por kardan, to refill wire reel*
moġār-e kaj, skewed turning chisel, 92
moġār-e kebrītī, narrow wood chisel, 84, narrow carving chisel, 98
moġār-e lūleh, gouging chisel, 84
moġār-e lūleh-kūčak, half-round carving tool, 98
moġār-e nīmbāz, mildly curved chisel, 98
moġār-e nīmgerd, hollow chisel, gouge†
moġār-e nīmrāz, mildly curved carving chisel, 98
mohabbā, pounded, powdered, 151
mohāfez-e dast, hand protector of carpenter's plane†
moharraq, burnt, roasted; cf. *mes-e moharraq*, 162
mohayyar, choice, select, mohair, 177
mohkam šodan, to harden, to bind, 135
mohr, signet, 38
mohr-e esm, seal with personal name, 38
mohreh, screw nut, 90, a course of *pisé* work, 108, ceramic bead, 167, roping mold, 222, burnishing stone, 224, burnisher, 232, 239, socket, 261
mohreh-sāz, bead maker, 151, 167
mohreh-šaṭranj, chessman, 97
mohr-e hurūfī, lettered rings of keyless lock, 72
mohreh-yā'ī, nut on hood lever bolt, 90
mohr-naqš, *mohr-tarāš*, signet engraver, 38
moḫtaliṭ, mixed, 152
mojaddeh, expert in measuring flow of water, 256
mojassameh, statue, sculptured work, 97
mojassam-sāz, sculptor, statue carver*
moka'ab-e pā'īn, fixed end of hacksaw, 60
molāyem kardan, to soften, 233
monabbat, chased metal work, repoussé, embossing, raised work, 35, 97
monabbat-kār, embosser, carver, 35, 97, wood engraver, 98
monabbat-kārī, chased metal work, repoussé, embossed work, 35, 97
monabbat-kārī rū-ye sang, ornamental stone sculpture, 129
monabbat-sāz, wood carver, 97
monaqeš, painter, 164
monaqqaš, painted, stained*
monsūjat, textile, fabric, cloth*
moqarreh, electric insulator*
moqavvā, cardboard cartridge wad, 60, blasting wad, 131, cardboard, 238
moqavvā-bor, wad punch, saddler's punch, 60
morabbā'ī, small fruit-preserving jar, 170
morakkab, tracing ink, chemical compound, 129
morġak, center point of lathe, 26, 91
morġ-bor, inside turning tool for removing center pivot, 133
morġ-e dīzī, centering pivot inside pot, 133
morġeh, center point of lathe, 132
mošabbak, pierced metal work, 36, 37, pierced woodwork, 97
mošabbak-kār, fretwork specialist, 37
mošabbak-qal'eh, incense burner, 37
moṣaddeq, expert in measuring flow of water, 256
mosallas, triangular bead for inlaid work, 94
mosallas-e berenj, triangular brass bead, 94
mosallas-e sabz, green triangular bead*
mosallasī, a certain rug design, 211
mosallas-sāvī, filing block for triangular beads, 94
moṣammat, opaque, 162
mošar-kaš, sanyer (Tabrīz), 79
moṣmat, opaque, 162
mošt, lump of clay, 108, 116, 152, lump of dough, 293
moštārūn, plow stilt (Iṣfahān), 263
moštegeh, plow handle, scoop handle (Gīlān), 262, 268
mošteh, clamping wedge, 58, strap to hold scales, 64, lump of clay, 154, pestle, 229, iron mallet, 234, 301, cotton dressing mallet, 180, 181, drawstrings, 206, plow stilt, 263, plow handle, 263, bookbinder's mallet, 238, scoop handle, 268

mošteh pīčīdan, to knead clay by hand, 152
mošteh šodan, to shrink, 223
mošteh zadan, to place clay on wheel, 155
mošterūn, see *moštārūn*, 263
moštī, plow handle (Ḫorāsān), 263
mošt zadan, to beat printing mold*
moṭallā, gilded, 163
motavasseṭ, medium cut of file, bastard file cut, 58
mou, grapevine, 244
mouj, grain in timber, 80, a certain brick profile, 123, center piece of quilt, 227, wavy velvet pattern, 209
mouj-dahī, velvet-pressing tool, 209
mouj-e sūzanī, a pointed chisel, 129
moujī, round cornered profile brick, 113
mouj-kār, velvet finisher, 209
mouj kardan, to press velvet into a pattern, 209
mū, hair for making harvesting net, 276
muᶜadanī, minerals, ore*
muᶜadaniyāt, mineral substances; cf. *maᶜdaniyāt*, 15
muᶜaddin, miner, quarryman*
muᵓarak, cut-out piece of mosaic, 125
muᵓarak čīdan, to compose mosaic, 125
mubāšir, irrigation district overseer, 256
muḥaddaṯ, modern steel, 55
mūhī, chisel marking rows of fine lines, 36, 37
mujassameh; cf *mojassameh*, 97
mūm, wax, 39
mūm-e ᶜasal, beeswax, 38
mūnegā, a grape variety, 244
muqannī, well-sinker, builder of underground water channels, water diviner, 251, 252, 253, 254
murakkab, composite steel, 55
murdā-sang, dross of lead, 161
mūrī, chimney, 160
mūrī-šoġal-rou, irrigation pipe, 153
muṣaffā, refined steel, 55
mūš-borīdeh, angled round anvil, 29
mūsk, handle knob of fiddle bow, 85
mūtāl, Caucasian wing nut tree (*Pterocarya fraxinifolia*) (Gīlān), 77
muṭallā, gilded, 163; cf. *moṭallā*
muwallad, local steel, 55

nā, snarling iron, 25
nāb, water pipe (Alburz), 291
nabāt, crystallized sugar, candy, 300
nabātī, a grape variety, 244
nafas-kaš, air vent in a mold, 18
naft, fuel oil, 19, 117, 159
naft-e siyāh, crude fuel oil, 117
naḫ, leather apron, 34
naḫ, string, 94, 228, warp threads, 196, tie cord on weaver's reed (Kāšān), 195, transmission cord of spinning wheel (Nāᵓīn), 186, thin thread, 186, 218, branch to an underground water channel, 254
naḫ-andāzī, cross-stitch, 219
nāhār, lunch, 293
naḥās, hammerscale, ore, copper, 162
naḫ az dast-e čap gereftan, to take the thread from the reverse side (Rašt), 218
naḫdūzī, type of embroidery (Tehrān), 217
naḫ-e gūleh, *naḫ-e kōjī*, heddle loop (Sīstān), 200
naḫ-e rūš, overhanging weft threads, 211
naḫī, made of cotton yarn*
naḫ kašīdan, to draw threads in embroidery*
naḫ kūbīdan, to flatten wire, 43
naḫl, sifting, separating, 151
nāḫōngīr, hoof shave, 54, flat narrow chisel, 92
nāḫonī, chisel with curved surface, 26, 37, gouge, 92
naḫ pīč kardan, to sling thread around needle, 218
nai, sticks of bamboo, 204, brushwood, 109, blade on weaver's reed, 195, rush, 219, rushes forming wings of windmill, 287
nai, earthenware hoops, 154, 253, flexible hose, 236
nai-hindī, bamboo, 219
nai-kūb, mallet for bamboo flattening, 219
nailāl, drilling tool on lathe, 92
nai-pīč, maker of flexible hoses for water pipes, 236
nai-šekāf, rush-cutting knife, 219
nai-tejīr, cane used for mat weaving, 221
nājī, long handle of frit mill, 152, long handle of pot quern, 278
najjār, carpenter, cabinetmaker, 81
najjār-e seft-kār, carpenter, 81
nāl, bottom frame of house (Gīlān), 107
naᶜl, horseshoe, hoof, 53
naᶜlakī, plate, tray, 28
naᶜl-band, farrier, shoeing smith, 53
naᶜl-bandī, shoeing an animal, 53
nalbekī, flange on axle to position wheel, 90
naᶜlčī, hoofsmith, farrier, 53
naᶜl-e dargā, door lintel, 113
naᶜlekī, heel of shoe, 229
naᶜlgar, hoofsmith, farrier, 53
namad, felt, 222, felt wad, 28, 60
namad-māl, fuller, 222
namad mālīdan, to full felt, 223
namak, salt, 232, 233, 300
namak-e turkī, saltpeter, 163
namek pāšīdan, to salt hides, 231
namak zadan, to pickle skins*

namdār, lime tree (*Tilia rubra*) (Caspian provinces, Tehrān), 77
nān, bread, 291
nān-banā, bread-baking pad, 293
nān-čīn, baker's skewer, 294
nān-e barbarī, thick flat bread, 291
nān-e daštarī, fine bread, 291, 295
nān-e faṭīrī, unleavened bread, 291
nān-e ḫamīrī, leavened bread, 291
nān-e ḫošk, flat bread baked with fat, 291
nān-e ḫošk-ārd, coarse bread, 295
nān-e ḫūnehgī, small flat bread, 291
nān-e lavāš, a certain flat bread, 291
nān-e rouġanī, flat bread baked with fat, 291, 294
nān-e sāj(ī), bread baked over an iron pan, 291, 292
nān-e sangak, *nān-e sangakī*, bread baked on a pebble floor, 291, 295
nān-e šīrmāl, milk loaf, 291, 295
nān-e tābūn, unleavened bread, 291
nān-e tāftūn, a certain flat bread (Iṣfahān), 291, 294
nān-e tanūrī, bread baked in drum oven, 291, 294
nān-pahn-kon, dough flattener, 293
nān-paz, bread baker, 293
nān-pazī, bake house, 293
nān puḫtan, to bake bread*
nānvā, baker*
naqadī kardan, to wind raw silk into skeins, 183
naqālī, square-edged plaster knife, 135
naqašī kardan, to paint, to apply decorative glaze, 164
naqāṭī, four-legged stand for silk winding, 183
naqdeh, metal on brocade thread, 46
naqdeh-pīč, *naqd-e pīč*, reel holding brocade thread, 46
naqqār, carver, sculptor, 128
naqqārī, sculptor's chisel, 129
naqqārī-ye dandāneh, toothed chisel, scatch comb*
naqqārī-ye sūzanī, fine pointed chisel, 129
naqqāš, textile print designer, 98, designer, 125, painter, 88, 121, 164, 166
naqqāšī kardan, to paint, to design, 238
naqš, incised design on ceramic ware, 166, design of embroidery, 218
naqš-bor, side-cutting chisel, 98
naqšeh, design, 36, 122, 129, 164, 216, 225, cartoon for mosaic design, 122, draw harness, drawstrings, 266, chain-stitch, 219
naqš-e ḥajjārī, tracing for sculpture work, 129
naqšeh bā rang kašīdan, to transfer design to cloth, 218
naqšeh-gereh, a certain rug design, 211
naqšeh-kāš, carpet designer, 216
naqšeh-piyādeh, plan of building marked on site, 108
naqš kardan, to engrave, to design, to trace, 38
naqš kašīdan, to draw a tracing, to trace a design, 166
nar, pegged half of molding box, 18, vertical bolt in lock, 68, main beam of rick structure, 289
nār, earthenware hoop for underground water channel (Kermān), 154, 253
nāranj, orange tree (*Citrus medica*), 77
nāranjī, orange colored*
nardebān, ladder, 111
nardīn, grated roots of nard plant, 295
nar-e šīr, plug of cock*
nārestān, sections of underground water channel where hoops are needed (Kermān); cf. *nār*, 253
narmdār, lime tree (*Tilia rubra*) (Gorgān); cf. *namdār*, 77
narm kardan, to soften, to flatten bamboo, 219, to crush oil seed, 296
narm kardan-e fūlād, to temper steel, to anneal steel, 52
narm šodan, to become soft by annealing, 36
nar-ō-mādeh, tongue-and-groove joint, 85
nar randīdan, to plane along the grain†
nārvan, cultivated elm tree (*Ulmus campestris*, *U. densa*), 77
našāsteh, starch, size to bind paper, 237
nāsij, *nassāj*, weaver, 203
nātāreh, coppersmith's anvil with its support, snarling iron, 25
nāʿūra, water-lifting wheel, 259
nāv, grain feeder channel (Alburz), 279, 282, hollow tree trunk for husking mill, 291
navā-bāf, strap weaver, band weaver*
navan, *navand*, bread-baking cushion (Qazvīn), 293
navār-bāf, strap weaver, band weaver*
navard, loom beam, 201; cf. *nōrd*, *nouhard*, *nebārd*, 204, 214
navardan, to roll up, 214
navardān, beam supporting mill pinion, 297, tackle block, 297, 299
navard-e bālā, warp beam of vertical loom, 210, 214
navard-e būm, rear beam of loom, 209
navard-e čelleh, warp beam, 210
navard-e pāʾīn, cloth beam of vertical loom, 210, 214
navard-e pīš, cloth beam of loom, 209
navard-kārī, rolling section of copper mill, 23
navard šodan, to be rolled out, 23
navār-e arreh, saw band†
navār-e fešang, bandelier, 60

nāvdān, gutter, 297, 299, spout, 30, 114, 153, runner of mold, 18, feeder channel, 278, 288; cf. *noudān*
nāv-kārīz, hoop for lining underground water channel, 154
navordān, steel axis of pinion, 283
nāyeh, leather hose, 17
nāzok-kār, fine ornamental work, ornamental plaster sculptor, 112
nāzok-kār kardan, to render a wall with plaster of Paris, 112
nebārd, upright post of vertical loom (Šīrāz); cf. *navard*, 214
nebārd-nāv, loom beam (Šīrāz), 214
nešādor, sal ammoniac, 31, 61, 94
nešā kardan, to transplant, 271
nī-dasteh, plow stilt (Zābol), 263
nīl, dark blue, indigo, 192, elm tree (*Zelkova crenata*) (Caspian provinces), 77
nīl-kārī, indigo dyeing, 192
nīmbor, line-work chisel, 36, 37, sharp-edged cutting chisel, 36; cf. *qalam-e nīmbor*
nīm-dāyereh, semicircular end, 239
nīmeh, half brick, 112, 122
nīm-fanar, semielliptic spring, 90
nīmgaz, half cubit (size of one course of *pisé* work), 108
nīmgerd-e košterādār, a certain molding profile, 84
nīm-ḫošk, half-dry, leather-hard clay, 155
nīm-ō-nīm, lap joint, 86
nīmrāh, medium-sized anvil (Lūristān), 25
nīm-taneh, short sheepskin coat, vest, 232
nīm-vār, chisel with rounded corners, 36, 37
*nīm-zar*ᶜ, size of one course of *pisé* work, 108
niqolvar, small anvil (Lūristān), 25
nišādor = *nešādor*, 94
nīš-e dastgāh, bench stop, 82
nō, a hollow metal strip (Borūjerd), 88, grain feeder channel (Alburz); cf. *nāv*, 279
nō-e āb, penstock, 280
nōġān, silkworm eggs (Māzandarān), 182
noḫōd, a measure of weight, 62, pea, pulse, 277
nōk, point on marking gauge, 81, 132
nō-kār, flour hopper (Alburz), 279
nōk-e dandeh, cutting point of saw tooth†
nōk-e mīḫ, point of nail, 54
nōk tīz kardan, to sharpen teeth of comb, 101
nomreh, number punch†
nomreh-bandī kardan, to sort according to size, 183
nomreh gereftan, to sort hair for fulling*
nongāz, hollowed chisel (Rašt), 92
noqreh, silver, 31
noqreh-kār, *noqreh-sāz*, silversmith, 31
noqreh-ye ḫāliṣ, *noqreh-ye hazār*, *noqreh-ye hezār*, fine silver, pure silver, 33
noqreh-ye jāmhūr, silver not up to standard*
noqreh-ye qorṣ, fine silver, pure silver, 33
noqreh-ye žībaqī, mercury*
noqteh, dead center of lathe, 27
nōrd, warp beam, cloth beam (Māzandarān), 204; cf. *navard*, *nouhard*, *nebārd*
nōrd-gardān, *nōrd-e gardūn*, warp beam release lever (Māzandarān), 205
noudān, feeder channel (Šīrāz); cf. *nāvdān*, 279
nouġān, see *nōġān*, 182
nouhard, *nouvard*, breastbeam (Yazd); cf. *navard*, *nōrd*, *nebārd*, 204
nufār, storehouse (Gīlān)*
nūn, see *nān*, 291

oḫrā, pure iron oxide from Qešm island, 80; cf. *gel-e oḫrā*
oraḫ, sickle (Tabrīz)*
ᶜ*orām-kārī*, depilation in tanning, 231
osar, halter (Iṣfahān), 275
oškaneh, pointed wood-carving chisel (Iṣfahān); cf. *eškeneh*, 98
ošnān, *ošnū*, *ošnūn*, soda plant (*Solsola spp.*), 161
ostā, upright beam, 210
ostoḫwān, bone for inlaid work, 93
ostoḫwān-e šotor, camel bone for inlaid work, 93
oṭāq, coach boot, 90, living room*
oṭāq-e ḫešt-e kāšī, tile drying chamber, 157
oṭāq-e nešīman, boot with main seats in coach, 90
oujar, plow (Tabrīz), 263, plow beam (Hamadān), 263
oušīn, winnowing fork*
ouzār, oblong hole in mill rind (Šīrāz); cf. *afzār*, 281

pā, leg of wire-drawing bench, 43, foot of chest, 88, post of windlass, 109, harness treadle, 204, 209
pābaqal, ornamental molding profile, 122
pāčāl, pit in front of furnace, 126, loom (Māzandarān), 204
pādār, beam to tighten warp, 220, board supporting warp, 220
pādō, baker's assistant, 294
pā fešār dādan, to change the shed, 205
pā-gāh, footrest, 155
pā-gozāšteh, crossbeam of threshing wain (Hamadān), 274
paḫ, facet of gem stone*, tool edge, 27, window sill brick, 113, chamfer†, bevel†
pā-ḫāneh, see *pā-ḫūneh*, 281
paḫdār, beveled*
pahlū, column of vertical loom, 210, 214

pahlū-kaš, lever for advancing breastbeam, 204
pahn, flat rolled dough, 293
pahnā-kaš, *pahn-band*, *pahneh-band*, weaver's temple, broad holder, 211
pahn kardan, to stretch in forging, to flatten, 52, to spread out, 154, to press boiled candy flat, 301
pahn-kaš, weaver's temple, broad holder, 200
pā-ḫūneh, thrust bearing block, 281, 283
pā-ḫūnī, crossbeam of threshing wain, 274
paḫ zadan, to chamfer an edge†
pai, foundation of building, 108
paimāneh, marking gauge, 80
paivand-e pūst, grafting under the bark, 271
paivand zadan, to graft, 271
pājūb, poplar (*Popolus euphratica*) (Damġān, Qair, Nairīz), 77
pak, maple tree (*Acer laetum*) (Kalārdašt), 77
pāk, clean (skin in chamois treatment), 233
pākār, assistant water bailiff (Yazd), 255
pākīzeh kardan, to smooth plaster surface, 135
pakorak, shielding wall of windmill (Sīstān), 286
pāl, main wheel on spinning wheel (Ardistān), 186
pālād, lime tree (*Tilia rubra*); cf. *pālās*, 77
pālān, pack saddle; cf. *pālān-dūz*, 234
pālān-dūz, *pālāngar*, *pālānī*, pack saddle maker, 234
palās, maple tree (*Acer insigne*) (Kūh-e Darfak); cf. *palat*, 77, tent fabric (Sīstān), 200
pālās, lime tree (*Tilia rubra*) (Manjīl); cf. *pālād*, 77
palat, *palāt*, maple tree (*Acer insigne*) (Lāhījān); cf. *palās*, 77
pālāyeš, large rice strainer, 28
pā-mašāl, fixed bearing for press beam, 297, 298
pambeh, tinner's cotton pad, 31, cotton, 177, 221, 227
pambeh-āb, cotton mop to smooth plaster work, 135
pambeh-dāneh, cottonseed, 296
pambeh-rīsīdan, to spin cotton, 185
pambeh zadan, to tease cotton, to bow cotton, 180
pambeh-zan, cotton bower, 180
panj, a certain brick profile, 123
panjareh, window, 86
panjeh, bellows slats, 29, beater comb, 211, rake, 275, scoop, 268; cf. *penjeh*
panjeh kašīdan, to scoop (Ḫorāsān), 269
panj-mīḫ, nails holding plowshare (Gīlān), 262
par, flat plate to attach axle to spring, 90, water wheel, 280, 282, spoke of water wheel, 283, blade of water wheel, 281, 291
parak-e čarḫ, cross wood of windlass, 109
parandeh-zanī, very fine shot, bird shot, 59
parang, plug on plow beam to attach yoke (Iṣfahān), 262
parč, rivet, 70
parč-bor, nail extractor, 54
pārčeh, ornamental brickwork, mosaic, 121, lining on edge of mat, 221, ink pad, 226, quilt cover fabric*
pārčeh-band, rope controlling heddle, 211
pārčeh šāneh zadan, to compact weft, 205
parčīdan, to strike, to bend, to drive down*
parč kardan, to bend point of nail over, 54, rivet, 54
pardāḫt, finishing, polish, 27, 30
pardāḫtčī, carpet trimmer, finisher, 216
pardāḫt-kār, metal polisher, 29
pardāḫt kardan, to polish, 130, fine cutting on lathe, 91, final trimming of carpet, 217, to smooth felt, 224
pardāz, chisel marking fine lines, 37
pardeh, door curtain, blind, 221
pardeh-bāf, maker of door curtains and blinds, 221
pardū, roof batten, 114
par-e āsiyāb, spoke of water wheel, 283
par-e dūvāl, eyebolt on threshing wain, 275
pāreh-dūz, sole maker, 229
par-e mākū, bobbin brake, 204
pargār, pair of compasses, 36, 61, 81, circle made by compasses*
pargār-e andāzeh, outside calipers, 133
pargāreh, small pair of compasses, 61
parīčeh, fibrous bark of palm tree, 256
park, hide strip around shoe sole, 229
par kardan, to prune, 271
par-kaš, stay rope of windmill blade (Sīstān), 287
parreh (cf. *par*), wheel spoke, 90, triangular bead, 94, 95, spindle, 185, spindle flyer, 184, spoke of wheel pulley, 256, blade of water wheel, 283, 291, toothed gear wheel, 283, main wheel of spinning wheel, 186, main wheel of twisting wheel, 196, door bolt, lock bolt*
parreh-borreh, threshing spike (Šīrāz), 274
parreh-sāvī, filing block for triangular (corner) beads, 95
parreh-ye borreh, *parreh-ye čūm*, threshing peg, 52, 274
parreh-varūᶜ, fine-grade inlaid work, 97
parreh-ye āsiyā, sail of windmill, windmill blade (Sīstān)*
parr-e mākū, spring in shuttle, see *par-e mākū*, 204
pārs, wooden block supporting mill axle, 151, wedge holding blade of water wheel*

pārs-dār, millstone-setting device (Alburz), 281
parsišt, plow sole (Iṣfahān), 263
partō, stay tightener of windmill (Sīstān), 287
parū, winnowing shovel, 276, wooden shovel, 276, baking shovel, 294, shovel to handle oil seeds, 297
parvāʾī, plow beam (Ḫorāsān), 263
parvānak, wings on spinning head, 46
parvāneh, silk moth, 183
pasār, top and bottom rail of door frame, 86
pasāv = *pasār*, 86
paseh, blank for cutting a comb, 99
pas-e kār, cloth beam, 220
pas-e kūreh, ash pit of furnace, 19
pasgod, nonlevel bed of underground water channel, 254
pašgūn, weeding spade (Iṣfahān), 52, 271
pāšīdan, to sow, 271
pāšīneh, door hinge; cf. *pāšneh*, 52
pašm, wool, hair, down, 177, 222, 227
pašm borīdan, *pašm čīdan*, to shear sheep, 177
pašm-e firīz, shorn wool, 179
pašm-e šotor kandan, to pluck camel's hair, 177
pašm gereftan, wool to interlock in felting, 224
pašmīn, woolen*
pašm-rīs, wool spinner, 186
pašm rīsīdan, to spin wool, 185
pašm šostan, to scour wool, 179
pāšneh, door hinge (Iṣfahān), 52, socket hinge, pivot, 86, 127, heel leather, heel of cloth shoe; cf. *pāšīneh*, 229
pāsoḫ, plant used for potash production*
pas-pīš, heel of cloth shoe, 229
pasteh, cultivated pistachio tree, 189
pāšūreh, flow measurement for irrigation, 255, stones forming orifice, 255
pā-taḫteh, treadle disk of potter's wheel, 154
pā-tang, foot-operated rice mortar (Gīlān), 290
pāteh, brushwood fuel, 160
pateh-tūreh, a certain rug design, 211
pātī, *pātīl*, dyer's copper boiler, 193, cast iron cauldron, 301, sugar boiler, 300
pātīleh, boiler, cauldron, 193
pā-ye āsiyāb, vertical pole of mill-setting device, 281
pā-ye čarḫ, branch fork to support windlass, 109, bearings for grinding shaft, 57
pā-ye dūlčeh, foot of leather bucket*
pāyeh, post of grinding wheel, 39, table leg, 87, main stand of spinning wheel, 186, stand of cotton gin, 180, foot of wool comb, 182, vertical loom post, 210, seat post, 274
pāyeh-buzurg, column of spinning wheel (Māzandarān), 186
pāyeh-čarḫ, tripod of twisting wheel (Kāšān), 196
pāyeh-kūčik, spindle stand on spinning wheel (Ardistān), 186
pāyeh-ye tīr, guiding beam, 297, 299, upright posts of grape press, 300
pā-ye kūzeh, foot of jar, jar stand, 155
pā zadan, to knead with foot, 152
pāzīn, bearing blocks for press beam, 297, 298
pedarsel, plowsole (Surmaq), 263
pehen, horse manure, 154
peing, water-measuring dish, 255
pelak-bor, wad punch, saddler's punch, 60
pelleh, tail stock of lathe, 91
penjeh, rake*, frame for beehive, 153; cf. *panjeh*, 275
penjeh-korūk, iron ends to join hoops of coach hood, 90
pestānak, anvil on gun lock to carry percussion cap 59, valve, valve flap, 101, blow torch†
pestānak-e jūš, welding torch†
pestānak-e laḥīm-kārī, soldering torch†
pestāneh-ye dam, valves on bellows, 51
pesteh, *pistachio*, pistachio tree (*Pistacia vera*), 189, see *pasteh*
pī, tallow, 39, see *pīh*
pīč, screw, setting screw for rolling mill, 33, warping in timber, 80, chain-stitch, 219
pīč-āmoreh, rivet, 29
pīč-e dastī, carpenter's clamp (Iṣfahān), 86
pīč-e farangī, overlapping joint, 24
pīč-e ḫorūsak, saw-tightening screw, 60
pīč-e mādeh, interior screw thread, 69
pīč-e markazī, screwed center of auger drill†
pīc-e nar, exterior screw thread, 69, 70
pīč-gūštī-sarkaj, angle screw driver, 61
pīč-ḫorūsak, 60; see *pīč-e ḫorusak*
pīč ḫwordan, to turn up mat edges, 219
pīčīdan, to twist (Kāšān), 181, 208, to wind yarn on stick, 188, 197
pīčīdan be sotūn, to wind around column, 135
pīčīdeh, warped (timber), 80
pīč kardan, to cut a thread, 29
pīč-sar-qāmeh, bolt in spring shackle, 90
pīč tarāšīdan, to cut a thread, 29
pīh, tallow, 101; see *pī*
pīl, spindle (Iṣfahān); cf. *pīlī*, 185
pilāv, a certain rice dish; cf. *polou*, 242
pīleh, *pīleh-abrīšam*, silk cocoon, 182, 183, a certain rug design, 211
pīleh jūš kardan, to heat silk cocoons (Māzandarān)*
pīlī, spindle (Iṣfahān); cf. *pīl*, 185
pīlis, burr (Šīrāz), 36
pīneh, beam inside wall above press beam of oil mill*

pīr, heartwood, 80
pīš, weaving cross (Iṣfahān), 204
pīš-band, belt socket to hold winding spool (Kāšān), 196
pīš-e ḫarak, cross beam of sawyer's jack, 80
pīš-e qalāvor, mudguard in front of driver's seat, 90
pīš-kabūl, harrow (Gīlān); cf. *pīš-kāʾūl*, 266
pīš-kār, craftsman's assistant, 152, upper face of tunnel, 253, shaft beyond trial well*
pīš-kāʾūl, harrow; cf. *pīš-kabūl*, 266
pīš-mateh, drilling guide, 92
pīšō, main rod on weaver's reed (Kāšān), 195
pīš-pā, tool support, 91, 132
pīš-panjeh, toe cap, 230
pīš-tang, beam in front of press slot, 297, 298
pisteh ḥaqīqī, pistachio tree (*Pistacia vera*, *P. mutica*); cf. *pesteh*, 77, 245
piyāleh, dish of pair of scales, 63, glaze-pouring dish, 164, water measuring dish, 255
piyāz, onion, 245
pol, seesaw lever, 290
polou, a certain rice dish; cf. *pilāv*, 242
porz, broken-up silk cocoon (Māzandarān), 205
porz kardan, to break up silk cocoons, 205
pošdīvō, windmill spoke (Ḫorāsān), 287
pošt, reverse side of metal work*, flesh side of hide*
pošt-band, cover strip, 86, wood limiting depth of saw cut, 99, pole to hold harness, 211
pošt-band-e kamāneh, horizontal beam supporting heddles, 211
pošt-baqal, cast brick panel, 123
pōšt-e arreh-borešt, back of tenon saw (Šīrāz), 82
pošt-e bām, mud roof, 114
pošt-e gūleh, shed rod, 200
pošteh, board cut from splint, 80, water drawer's shoulder harness, 257
pošt-e kōjī, shed rod (Sīstān), 200
pošt-e kūh-e sang, at the back of the "Stone Mountain," 130
pošt-e māhī, back of scissor blade, 56
pošt-e tīġ, backing iron of plane, 83
pošt-mīl, fixed bar in cotton gin (Kāšān), 180
pošt zadan, to turn the outside, 132
pošveh, soapwort (*Saponaria officinalis*) (Kāšān), 300
potk, sledge hammer, 51, heavy hammer, 157
potk zadan, to strike with a heavy hammer*
poušāl, treadle (Yazd), 204
pū, a row of knots in a carpet, 216
pūd, weft; cf. *pūt*, 200, 204, 211, 215
pūd-e rū, weaving shed, 200
pūd-e zīr, counter shed, 200
pūdī, name for a coarse-grade silk (Kāšān), 183
puf kardan, to blow glass, 170
puḫtan, to fire a kiln, 159, 161, to fire bricks, pots, 154, to boil dye, 193, to cure a hide, 231, to boil sugar, 300
puḫtan-e rūniyāz, to boil madder*
puḫteh, fired*
pūkeh, cartridge case, 60
pūk kašīdan, to roll felt, 224
pūlād, carbon steel, hardenable steel, 7, 8, 9, 52, turner's tool, 91; cf. *fūlād*
pūlād-e hindī, an Indian sword*
pūlād-e kaj, skewed turning chisel, 92
pūlād-gar, steel worker*
pūlak, metal ornaments, 88, leather block, 181
pūreh, scaffold above water well, 256
pūšāl, shavings, 82
pūšāl-šekan, chip breaker iron of carpenter's plane†
pūš-e čoġondar, sugar beet stalk, 117
pūš-gāz, plow wedge (Ḫorāsān), 263
pūšīdeh, covered dovetail joint, 86
pūs kardan, to heat up, to burn, 279
pūst, hide material for leather buckets, 234, rice husk, grain husk, 292
pūst-e āhū, gazelle hide for sieve and fork making, 276
pūst-e anār, pomegranate rind, 191, 226, 233, 300
pūst-e ballūṭ, acorn skins, 192
pūst-e boz, goatskin, 101
pūst-e deraḫt, tree bark*
pūst-e gerdū, outer walnut shell, 192
pūst-e gūsfand, sheepskin, 101, 232
pusteh, section in underground water channel, 249, 253
pūst-e kuzeleh, cotton capsule (Kāšān), 179
pūst-e olāġ, donkey hide, 262
pūstīn, sheepskin garment, 232
pūstīn-dūz, furrier, maker of sheepskin garments, 232
pūstīn-e nīm taneh, sheepskin vest, 232
pūstīn-forūš, dealer in sheepskin garments, 232
pūst kandan, to husk rice, 290
pūt = *pūd*, 200
pūtān-e pubīleh, tapestry weave (Šīrāz), 215
pūz-band, muzzle, 275
pūzeh, toe, 229
pūzeh-bārīk, narrow toecap, 230
pūzeh-pahn, broad toecap, 230

qābī, tray for oil pressing (Iṣfahān), 297
qāb-kūb, ceiling maker, 81, 87
qāb-lameh, window sill, 113
qāb-sāz, maker of paneled ceilings, 81, 87
qabżeh, bow tightener, 91
qāčī zadan, to roughen wood with plane†
qadaḥ, water dish on polishing bench, 155, glaze vat, 164, dyeing vat, 193, salting

qadaḥ—contd.
vat, 231, water dish on textile printer's bench, 226
qadaḥčī, earthenware household vessel, 155
qadd, straight-edge, marking ruler, 122
qaffāl, locksmith, 66
qahrī, underground water channel, 254
qahveh-ḫāneh, tea house, 28
qahvehʾī, brown, 192
qahveh-jūš, *qahveh-rīzī*, small samovar, 28
qaičī, shears, 177, scissors, 56, 301, tin snips, 26, 60, seccateurs, 271
qaičī-āhanbor, heavy shears†
qaičī-ahromī, levered shears, 60
qaičī-dastī, tin snips†
qaičī-mīḫčīn, wire cutter, 60
qaičī-pādār, stock shears†
qaičī-qālī-bāfī, carpet-trimming scissors, 216
qaičī-sāz, scissor maker, 56
qaičī-sīmbor, wire cutters†
qaičī-tīzkon, scissor grinder, 57
qaičī-ye qalamdān, scissors belonging to a writing set*
qaid, tie bar, 43, bar in coach bogie, 90, carpenter's clamp, 86, frame supporting table top, 87, trimming press, 238
qaidčeh, middle rail of door frame, 86
qairā aġāj, Caucasian elm tree (*Ulmus pedunculata*), 77
qaiš, peg on draw harness, 90, leather strip for bellows, 101
qalᶜ, tin, 31, 60, 162
qalāġ, eye to guide wire, 45
qalāᶜī, steel from an unknown locality, 55
qalam, chisel, 34, 38, 58, 60, 129, punch, stylus, 123, dusting brush, 18, 166, turning tool, 91, marking scriber*, mason's chisel, 127, 128, 131
qalaṃbak, warp ball; cf. *qalaṃbeh*, 204, 209
qalam-bā-zūr, hand-operated chisel, 38
qalaṃbeh, warp ball; cf. *qalaṃbak*, 204, 209
qalambok, bar holding harness strings (Tehrān), 206
qalam-dambārīk, cross-cut chisel, 60
qalamdān-sāz, pen box maker, 238
qalam-e ᶜaksī, engraving chisel, engraved work, 37
qalam-e būm, flat embossing chisel, punch, 36
qalam-e dīzī, inside roughing chisel (Mašhad), 133
qalam-e gerd, hollow chisel†
qalam-e ḫūšeh, oval-faced chaser punch, 36
qalam-e kaf-taḫt, chisel for resetting background, 36
qalam-e kandan, cutting chisel*
qalam-e kaptarāšī, roughing chisel, 132
qalam-e labeh-ye gerd, half-round cold chisel†
qalam-e mofraz, smoothing chisel, 132
qalam-e monabbat, embossing chisel, 36, woodcarving chisel, 97
qalam-e monabbat-kārī, carving chisel, 97
qalam-e mū (hī), hair brush, 165, plasterer's brush, 135
qalam-e nāḫonī, chisel for cutting sheet metal, 36, 60, crescent-shaped chaser punch, 37
qalam-e naqqārī, carving chisel, 129
qalam-e nīmbor, cold chisel for parting metal, 36
qalam-e nīm-kāleh-pūš, intermediate size chisel, 132
qalam-e pardāz, chisel with short linear edge, 36
qalam-e qaičī-kār, boiler maker's cold chisel†
qalam-e qorṣum, roughing chisel, 36
qalam-e ṣalībī, cross-edged chisel†
qalam-e šāneh, toothed chisel, 128
qalam-e sāyeh, serrated chisel, 36
qalam-e šiyār, groove-cutting chisel†
qalam-e sūzanī, fine-pointed chisel, 129
qalam-e tah-sāvī, inside smoothing tool (Mašhad), 133
qalam-e taḫt, flat cold chisel†
qalam-e yak-tū, chisel marking small circles, 36
qalam-gīrī, tracing lines with a fine chisel, 36, outlines*
qalamī, grafting by drill, 271
qalam kandan, to engrave, 37
qalam-kār, printed textile, chintz, 225
qalamkār-sāz, textile printer, 225
qalam-nāḫonī, 60; see *qalam-e-nāḫonī*
qalam-pahn, broad cold chisel, 60
qalam-yatū, chisel marking small circles; cf. *qalam-e yak-tū*, 36
qalam zadan, to sculpture, to cut, 129, to scrape stone pot (Mašhad), 131
qalam-zan, engraver, chaser, embosser, 28, 35, fretworker*
qalam-zanī, chiseling, engraving, 37, embossing, 35, sculptured work, 129
qalāvīz, thread tap, 60
qalbīl, sieve, strainer, 115
qalbīleh, bolster on pivoted coach bogie, 90
qālčī, silver smelter, refiner, 33
qāleb, molding box, 116, 135, mold, 18, 238, 300, molding pattern*, profiled roller, 30, swage, 94, brick mold, 110, hoop mold, 154, peg inside weft ball, 211, rope guiding mold, 222, hatter's molding block, 224, printing block, 98, 225, shoemaker's last, 230
qāleb-e ābī, printing block for blue, 226
qāleb-e bālā, upper half of molding box, 18
qāleb-e felezzī, metal mold, 157
qāleb-e ḫūšeh, swage die, 26
qāleb-e kāšī, tile mold, 157

qāleb-e langar, core molding box, 18
qāleb-e meškī, printing block for black, 225
qāleb-e mīḫparč, rivet head punch, 26
qāleb-e pā'īn, lower half of molding box, 18
qāleb-e qermez, printing block for red, 225
qāleb-e rūš, corner decoration of trunk, 88
qāleb-e saffālīn, potter's saggar, 164
qāleb-e siyāh, printing block for black, 225
qāleb-e taneh, planishing iron, 26
qāleb-e tarāš, potter's chuck, 156
qāleb-e zabāneh, mold for pen box, 239
qāleb-e zard, printing block for yellow, 226
qāleb ḫālī kardan, to empty a mold, 157
qāleb kardan, to guide rope strands, 222
qāleb-tarāš, printing block cutter, 98
qāleb zadan, to mold, 300, to press clay into a mold, 157, to place hat on block, 223
*qal*ᶜ*-e laḥīm*, soldering tin, 61
*qal*ᶜ*gar*, tinner, 31
qālgar, silver smelter, refiner, 33
qālī, carpet, 199
qālī-bāf, carpet weaver*
qalī'eh, qaliyā, qaliyāb, wood ash, potash, 160, 179, 194, 300
qaliyāb-e qomī, potash from Qom, 160
qaliyāb kardan, to rinse in potash solution, 194
qaliyān, water-smoking pipe, 236
qāl kardan, to refine, to separate precious metal, 33
qallā', potash burner, 160
qaltabān, roof-rolling stone, 114
qaltāk, qaltak, guide pulley, 257
qālūb, qālub, oil-pressing tray (Iṣfahān), 297; cf. *qāleb*, hatter's molding block, 224, printing block (Yazd), 225
qalyān, see *qaliyān*, 236
qambileh, kamela, a red dye, 190
qamčī, beam on threshing wain (Šīrāz), 274
qāmeh, a certain stage in inlaid work, 96, carved wooden window, 98
qanāt, underground water channel, 154, 246, 249, 250, 251, 252, 253, 254, 255, 256, 258, 259, 282
qanāt naḥ, branch channel, 254
qand, candy, 300
qandān, sugar basin, 32
qand-e kalleh, loaf sugar, 300
qand-šekan, sugar loaf splitter, 56
qannād, confectioner, sugar boiler, 300
qannādī, sweetmaking, 300
qapān, steelyard, 62
qapān-dār, man who has steelyards for hire, 65
*qar*ᶜ, boiler flask of still, retort, crucible, 163
*qar*ᶜ*ambīq*, distilling apparatus, 163
qaraqač, cultivated elm tree (*ulmus densa*) (Āẕarbaijān), 77
qarār, setting tool, hammer and swage, 52, vat*
qarār-e rū, qarār-e rū'ī, set hammer, 52
qarār-e zīr, swage, 52
qarqareh, ratchet drill, 60, sheaf pulley, 297, 299
qarqarī, pulley, 221
*qaṣ*ᶜ*at* (pl. *qiṣā*ᶜ) dish, plate, 156
qāsem, qāsem-ābī, water bailiff, 255
qāšoq, see *qāšuq*, 29
qaṣṣāb-ḫāneh, slaughterhouse, 231
qaṣṣār, fuller, 222
qāšuq, spoon, 29, tool to empty rock holes, 130, water wheel bearing, 291
qāšuq-e šāhī, sherbet ladle (Ābādeh), 97
qāšuq-e šarbat, sherbet ladle, 97
qāšuq-tarāš, spoon carver (Ābādeh), 98
qātelī, multicolored decorative margin, 98
*qat*ᶜ *kardan*, to cut off, 52, to cross-cut timber†
*qaṭ*ᶜ*-kon*, cross-cut saw, 82
qatmeh, wool thread, 186
qāz, bearing for batten shaft, 204
qāzak, breast beam; cf. *kāğazak*, 204
qel-e jakt, plow stilt (Ḫorāsān), 263
qel-e jakt-e jelō, front plow stilt, 263
qelift, feather joint (Šīrāz), 85
qeltondegī, smoothing, polishing, 40
qermez, crimson, scarlet, cochineal, 190, insect producing cochineal*, red-colored, 225
qermez-dāneh, cochineal, 189
qermez-e parpar, purple-colored, 163
qesmat-e motaharrek, movable jaw of vice†
qesm-e ᶜ*ajamī*, a certain section in the turquoise mine, 38
qesm-e čoğāleh, a certain section in the turquoise mine, 38
qesmeh, sections in mine, 39
qesm-e šajarī, a certain section in the turquoise mine, 38
qesm-e ṭufūl, a certain section in the turquoise mine, 38
qezelgoz, beech tree (*Fagus silvatica, F. orientalis*) (Gīlān), 77
qīf, funnel, 30
qīl, pitch (Mašhad); cf. *qīr*, 132
qilī'eh, potash, 160
qīr, pitch, mixture of sand and pitch; cf. *qīl*, 35, 132
qofl, lock, 69, gun lock, 60
qofl-e āhan, padlock, 69
qofl-e aspī, spring lock shaped like a horse, 70
qofl-e fanar, padlock with screw key, 69
qofl-e fanarī, push-key spring lock, 70
qofl-e ḥurūfī, keyless letter combination lock, 72
qofl-e lūleh, tubular padlock, 71
qofl-e rūmī, door lock with cogged wooden bolt, 66

qoflgar, *qofl-sāz*, locksmith, 66
qolāb, hook, 63, 65, hooked scraper, 101, hooked knotting knife, 215, spinning hook, 221, iron fork, 275
qolāb-e kūreh, slag hook, 50
qolāb kardan, to round edges of timber, 101
qolāj, a certain flat bread (Gorgān), 291; see *ġolāj*
qolfak, table around potter's wheel, 155, upper bearing of potter's wheel, 155, end batten of weaver's reed, 195
qolfeh, bearing block in frit mill runner, 151
qolvar-būzā, anvil rammed into ground (Burūjerd, Ḫoramābād), 29
qolvar-vasaṭ, medium-sized anvil (Burūjerd), 29
qolveh, roughed stone block, 132
qomčeh-lājvard, lump of cobalt oxide, 163
qondāq-e qalbīleh, cross bar on coach bogie, 90
qoreh āqāj, elm tree (*Ulmus spp.*) (Āstārā), 77
qorṣ, pulley driving warp spool, 184
qorṣak, spindle nut, 39
qorṣ-e avval, driving pulley, 46
qorṣ-e band, large pulley, 46
qorṣ-e dōvom, intermediate pulley, 47
qorṣum, finishing chisel, 37, chisel for roughing surface, 37
qōṭī, case containing balance, 63, jewelry box*
qōṭī-sīgār, cigarette box, 32
qōṭī-tūtūn, snuff box, tobacco container, 32
qōṭī-ye čarḫ, bearing frame, 45
qoudeh, bow string (Koulī tribe), 91
qoud-kaš, bow string tightener, 91
qous, milling cutter, 87
qūl, horse's harness, 275, horizontal clamping bar, 297, 299, brushwood (Iṣfahān), 109
quṭn, cotton, 178
quṭnī, made of cotton, cotton garment*
quṭun, cotton, 178

radīf, weaving shed, 200, 204
radīf-e dōvom, counter shed, 200
rag, course of bricks, 111
rageh, metal lode, vein, 15
raḫ, plow (Ḫorāsān); cf. *raḫt*, 263
raḥā, millstone, grinding mill*
rāh-gā, runner of mold, 18
rāh-pūd, cross-cut wood, 98
rāh-qās, guide roller, 45
raḫt-e jīgō, plow (Zābol); cf. *raḫ*, 263
raḫt-e jūġ, plow (Ḫorāsān), 263
raᶜiyyatī, peasant, cultivator, 182
rāj, beech tree (*Fagus silvatica, F. orientalis*) (Manjīl); cf. *rāš*, 77
rajeh kardan, to prepare the warp, 205
randeh, scraper, turning tool, 26, carpenter's plane, 82, potter's turning tool, 156
randeh-abzār, molding plane, 84
randeh-baġal, sash plane, 84
randeh-boland, *randeh-dastgāh*, jointing plane, 84
randeh-darajehdār, adjustable plane, 83
randeh-dō-dast, double-handled jack plane, 82
randeh-dō-rāheh, rabbet plane†
randeh-dō-tīġ, smoothing plane, 83
randeh-farangī, European-type plane, 82
randeh-fārsī, double-handled plane, Persian-type plane, 82
randeh-fouġān, jointing plane (Mašhad), 84
randeh-goudrand, convex profiled plane†
randeh-ḫašḫāš, toothing plane (Tabrīz), 84
randeh-ḫašī (Tehrān), *randeh-ḫašū* (Šīrāz), toothing plane, 84
randeh-ḫaṭgīrī, toothing plane*, scraper, 27
randeh-kabūtarī, spoke shave†
randeh-kaf-e sīneh, convex compass plane, 84
randeh-kafrand, routing plane, 84
randeh-kaj, oblique-edged scraper, 30
randeh kardan, to plane, 99
randeh-kās, concave compass plane, 84
randeh kašīdan, to plane, 84
randeh-kās-ō-sīneh, shipwright's plane†
randeh-koneškāf, rabbet plane†
randeh-mīleh, a certain molding profile, 84
randeh-mošteh, *randeh moštī*, spoke shave*
randeh-motaḥarrek, adjustable plane, 83
randeh-nāḫonī, crescent-edged turning tool, 27
randeh-nīmbor, round-edged scraper, 30
randeh-paḫ, straight-edged turning tool, 27
randeh-pardāḫt, smoothing plane, 82
randeh-pasrand, spoke shave*
randeh-qāšī, jack plane, roughing plane, 82
randeh-ṣāf, square-edged scraper, 27
randeh-ṣāf-kon, smoothing plane, 98
randeh-šamšīrī, oblique-edged turning tool, 27
randeh-sarkaj, turning tool with up-turned edge, 27
randeh-sīneh, convex compass plane, 84
randeh-tah-rand, routing plane, end plane, 84
randeh-taḫt, square-faced scraper, 30
randeh-ṭarḥ-e farangī, dovetailing plane†
randeh-ṭūlānī, jointing plane, 84
randeh-yak-tīġ, jack plane, 82
randeh-ye koneškāf, rabbet plane, grooving plane, 84
randeš, copper shavings, 28, 162
randīdan, to plane, to polish, to smooth*
randīdan sar-čūb, to plane across the grain†
rāneh, frame of threshing wain, skid, 274
rang, colored glaze, 160, color, dyestuff, 194
rang afgandan, to tint, to color, to dye, 193
rang āmīzī kardan, to apply color pigments, 166
rang-bast, fixed dye, fast color, 190

rang-e avval, first color applied to textile printing, 225
rang-e čahārom, fourth color applied in textile printing, 226
rang-e dōvom, second color applied in textile printing, 225
rang-e fīrūzeh, turquoise color; cf. *fīrūzeh*, 162, 167
rang-e kermānī, indigo blue, royal blue, 192
rang-e pādšāh, red dye from *Onosma* spp., 191
rang-e rouġan, *rang-e rouġanī*, oil paint†
rang-e sābīdeh, ground leaves of indigo plant, 192
rang-e sevom, third color applied in textile printing, 226
rang-e šotorī, a brown color, 192
rang-e vasmeh, indigo blue, royal blue, 192
rang kardan, to emboss and paint trunk decoration, 88, to tint, to dye, to color, 193, 224
rang-lāk, a dyeing tincture, by-product of shellac, 191
rang-raz, dyer, 193
rang-razḫāneh, dye house, 226
rang rīḫtan, to dye, 232
rang-rīz, dyer, 193
rang-sāz, painter*
rang-varkānī, pouring of glaze, 164
rang zadan, to pour glaze, 164, to dye, 194, to tint, to color*
rāš, beech tree (*Fagus silvatica*, *F. orientalis*) (Manjīl); cf. *rāj*, 77
raṣāṣ, tin, lead, 162
rasīdan, to mature, 233
rāst-e dār, plow beam (Gīlān), 262
ravānkaš, bed of turner's lathe, 91
raz, vine, grapevine, vineyard, 244
razā, hook on plow beam, 262
razbān, vine dresser, 271
razdār, alder tree (*Alnus subcordata*) (Āstārā), 77
reġ, number of knots on one *gereh*, 213
reḫez, plow sole (Ḫorāsān), 263
reṣūṣ, foreign steel blades with fine grain, 55
rezīn, rubber tire (fr. Fr. *résine*), 90
rīg, grit, sand, 18, 113, polishing sand, gravel, 31, pebble, 161, pottery mass rich in quartz sand, 160, 165
rīgdān, molder's sandbox, 18, stand holding warp spools, 184
rīg-e čaḫmāq, flint, quartz, pebble, 160
rīḫtan, to pour, to cast, 20, to place, 108, to spin (Nā'īn), 185
rīḫtan bā čarḫ, to spin on the wheel (Nā'īn), 187
rīḫtan be qāleb, to cast into a mold, 23
rīḫtehgar, founder, foundryman, 18
rīḫtehgar-e mes, copper foundryman*
rīḫvai, friable soil in underground water channel (Kermān), 253
rījeh, ingot mold, 22
rījeh-barīk, ingot mold for bars*
rikāb-e gelgīr, foot board on coach, mudguard, 90
rikāb-e mālband, iron holding coach beam, 90
rīsandeh, spinner, 185
rīš-e bābā, a grape variety, 244
rīš-e bīnī, *rīš-bīnī*, plow wedge (Kalārdašt), 264
rīšeh, fringe of carpet, 215
rīšeh hava-ye čūbeh, Indian alkanet root, 191
rīsīdan, to spin, 185
rīsmān, thread, yarn, 186, sawyer's marking string, 80, 127, builder's string, 108, 110, silk thread, 183, transmission cord, 186, cotton thread, 46, warp thread, 221, thread for mat warp, 220, ropemaking cord, 221, sewing cotton, 186, stay string, 287
rīsmān-bāf, ropemaker, 221
rīsmān-e kār, builder's string, 108
rīsmān-pīč, reel with cotton thread*
rīstan, to spin, 185
rīšteh, warp (Māzandarān), 204
rīt, wooden block*
rīz, eye bolt, 267
rīzandeh, crushed, powdered*
rīzeh, eyelet at end of fiddle bow, 85
rīzeš kardan, to pour metal, 20
rīzīdan, to crush, to powder, to pulverize, 151
robb-e anār, pomegranate syrup, 300
roḫ, swage, 52, harness mail, 206
roḫbān, brick bond
ros, potter's clay, 151
rouġan-dān, oil pot, 84
rouġan-dūreh, oil storage jar, 157, 300
rouġan-e bazrak, linseed oil, 84, 239, 296
rouġan-e bazr-eʿalaf, linseed oil, 135
rouġan-e berenjīl, *rouġan-e bīdanjīr*, castor oil, 296
rouġan-e čerāġ, lamp oil, 233, 296, oil for honing stone, 84
rouġan-e gūsfand, melted sheep butter, ghee, 291, 295
rouġan-e ḫašḫāš, poppy seed oil, 28, 296
rouġan-e ḫwoš, sesame oil, 296
rouġan-e kakuj, rape oil, 296
rouġan-e kāpšeh, mustard seed oil, 296
rouġan-e karčak, castor oil, 84, 296
rouġan-e karreh, melted butter, ghee, 295
rouġan-e konjed, sesame oil, 296
rouġan-e mendāb, rape oil, 296
rouġan-e pambeh, *rouġan-e pambeh-dāneh*, cottonseed oil, 18, 296
rouġan-e sandalūs, *rouġan-e sandarūs*, lacquer used for inlaid work, 97, sandarac oil, 135
rouġan-e talḫ, common oil, a mixture of rape and mustard oil, 296

rouġangar, oil miller*
rouġanī, oil miller*
rouġan-kadeh, oil mill, 296
rouġan-kamān, lacquer, 239
rū, brass*, face of gem, 40, transmission cord, 186, outside of hide, 232
rūʾā, cloth shoe upper (Ābādeh), 228
rūbā, polishing powder, 40
rūbāleš, cushion cover (Rašt), 218
rū-band, tie bar, 287
rūbandeh, iron bar holding springs on axle, 90
rūbūn, mud roof (Šīrāz), 114
rūd, river, 246
rūdeh, gut, leather strip, 235
rūdeh-gūsfand, sheep's gut, 180
rūdī, sieve warp, 235
rū-dīvārī, wall hangings, 218
rūʾeh, cloth shoe upper, 228
rūʾeh čīdan, to make uppers, 228
rūham časbāndan, to glue together, 238
rūhan, finest Indian steel, 52
rūhbān, brick bond, 113
rūhīnā, finest Indian steel, 52
rūh-tūtiyā, zinc*
rūʾī, slip, engobe, 166, runner of frit mill, 151
rūʾīgar, brassworker, 28
rū-kaš, veneer, 80
rū kūpī pīčīdan, to wind onto spool (Kāšān), 196
rū leḥāf-dārāʾī, bed quilt cover, 218
rū māsūreh pīčīdan, to wind on to bobbin (Nāʾīn), 188
rū-mīz, tablecloth, 218
rūnās, *runiyās*, madder, a red dyeing root, 190, 226
rūneh, hoop to suspend coach boot, 90
rūš, front side of metal work, 36
rūš āj kardan, to rough surface, 73
rū-sāzī kardan, to treat surface, 36, 135
rūst, clay-type of soil in underground water channels requiring hoop lining, 253
rustār, peasant, cultivator, 261
rūtāh, mill runner, 288
rūtī, sieve warp made of guts or leather strips; cf. *rūdī*, 235
rūvā, cloth shoe upper (Ābādeh), 228
rūvar, upper of a cloth shoe, front part of upper, 228
rūvar čīdan, to knit cloth shoe upper, 228
rūveh, top of cloth shoe upper, 228
rūy, brass*
rūyeh, book cover, case, 238
rū-ye ḥarak, surface board of file-cutting bench, 58
rūyeh-ye čarmī, *rūyeh-ye mīšeh*, leather book cover, full-case cover, 238
rū-ye mīz, table top, 87
rūy-e ṣufr, a yellow alloy*
rūygar, brassworker, coppersmith, brazier; cf. *rūʾīgar*, 28
rūygarī, brazier's craft; cf. *rūʾīgar*, 28
rūyīn, brazen*
rū-zamīnī, horizontal loom, 214
rū-żarb, main cut of a file†

sabad-bāf, *sabadčī*, *sabadgar*, basket plaiter, 221
šabakeh, pierced metalwork, 37, pierced woodwork*
šabakeh-eslīmi, *šabakeh-ye eslīmī*, pierced steel work, 57, 72
šabakeh-kār, steel fretworker, 72
šabāneh-rūz, day and night, a period of time in water allocation, 254
sabbā, large vessel, 153
ṣabbāġ, textile dyer, 193
sabd, basket, 221
šabdar, clover, 244
sabedī, basketry lid, 194
šabeh-kaš, hemstitch, 219
sābīdan, to smooth forged file, 58, to smooth stone pot*, to grind ceramic materials, 122, 151, to grind on an edge mill, 296, to file, 58; see *sāvīdan*
sābīdan bā souhān, to finish fretwork by filing, 73
sabok-čarḫ, idling wheel on wire drawing bench, 44
šabr, scraper, 60 (Iṣfahān, Šīrāz, fr. Ger. *Schaber*); cf. *šāb zadan*
šabr-dam-pahn, flat scraper, 60
šabr-pahn, flat scraper, 60
šabr-qāšoqī, *šabr-qāšuqī*, bearing scraper, hollow scraper, 60
šabr-seh-gūš, three-cornered scraper, 60
šabr-taḫt, flat scraper†
sabū, time unit for water allocation (Yazd), 255
ṣabūḥ, large water container*
ṣābūn, soap, 35, 179, 238
ṣābūn-e Qomī, soap from Qom, 238
ṣābūn-e safīd, a leather dye, 232
ṣābūn kašīdan, to apply soap, 238
sābūrqānī, hardenable steel, 8
sabūs, bran, 196, 279
sabz, green pickling dye for inlaid work, 93, green-colored glaze, 162
šāb zadan, to scrape metal (Tehrān)†; cf. *šabr*
šāb-zan, metal scraper†
šāb-zan-e seh-pahlūʾī, three-cornered scraper†
šāb-zan-e taḫt, flat scraper†
sabz-e nabī, a green dye, 192
sačmeh, shot, 59
sadd, weir, dam, dyke, 246
ṣad-par, fly wheel of cotton gin, 180
ṣā-eškeneh, calc-spar, calcite*

ṣāf, floor board, 107, turning tool with mildly curved edge, 27
šaffāf, transparent, 162
ṣaffār, tinner, coppersmith, 31
ṣafḥeh, surface plate, 51, 61, flat sheet, 24
ṣafḥeh-gerd, cylindrical mantle, 24
ṣafḥeh gerd kardan, to bend a flat round, 24
ṣafḥeh-ye sāyeh-zanī, surface plate†
ṣafḥeh-ye sendān, anvil's flat surface, 51
ṣafḥeh-ye sūrāḫ, holing block, 52
ṣāfī, planishing hammer, 52, surface plate, 61
safīd, white, 39
safīdāb, whiting, 39, white lead, tin oxide, 162, or mixture of both, 162
safīdār, white poplar, aspen (*Populus alba*), 77
safīdgar, tinner, tinsmith, 31
safīd kardan, to tin a copper vessel*, to bleach*, to husk rice, 290
safīd-palot, white poplar, aspen (*Populus alba*) (Caspian provinces, Fārs), 77
safīd-ray, alloy of copper and tin, bronze, 13, 18
ṣafīd-rūḥ, mercury, bronze, zinc oxide*
ṣāf kardan, to stretch, to smooth metal, to make even, 22, 26, 37, to harrow, 267
šafreh, wood chisel (Šīrāz), 84, cloth shoe sole knife, 229
ṣāf šodan, to become smooth*
šaft-ālū, peach, 244
šafteh, rod to beat cotton before bowing, 180
sag-e dast, support for pivoted coach bogie, 90
šāgerd, craftsman's apprentice, 38, assistant, 31
šāgerdeh, large press block in oil mill, 299
šāḫ, horn or anvil's beak, 51, horn handle on carpenter's plane, 82, iron spindle arms, 185, iron skewing hook, 234
šāhan, *šāhand*, *šāhang*, beam of balance; cf. *šāhin*, 63
šaḫār, wood ash, sal ammoniac, vitriol*
šāh-ballūṭ, chestnut tree (*Castanea vesca*), 77
saḫdār, yew-tree (*Taxus baccata*) (Siyārat, Dāmiyān), 78
šāḫeh, branch hook, 208
šāh-fanar, main leaf in laminated spring, 90
šāh-gardeh, footrest on lathe to hold drilling tool, 92
ṣaḥḥāf, bookbinder, 237
ṣāḥibī, a grape variety, 244
šāhin, *šāhīn*, beam of balance; cf. *šāhan*, 63
sahm, share of irrigation water, 255, time unit for water allocation, 255
ṣaḥq, rubbing, bruising, pulverizing, 151
sāḫtan rū-ye čarḫ, to throw on wheel, 165
šāh-tūt, black mulberry tree (*Morus nigra*), 78
šāḫur, *šāḫureh*, kiln, furnace*
sāʾīdan, to grind; cf. *sāvīdan*, 151
sāʾīdan-e bulūr, to grind glaze frit*
ṣaifī, crop sown in summer, 271
ṣaifī-kārī, summer crops and vegetables, 257
saim, neck peg on yoke (Ḫorāsān); cf. *sīm*, 262
saimband, neck ropes on yoke (Ḫorāsān), 262
ṣaiqal, polishing steel, 40, burnisher, 35, 232
ṣaiqalgar, polisher, 35
ṣaiqal kardan, *ṣaiqal zadan*, to polish, to burnish, 128, 232
saīraqānī, the "male" iron for swordmaking, 55
šaiṭānak, tumbler pin securing lock, 66, 68, eccentric pin, 279
sāj, teakwood (*Tectona granda*), 78, 92, 93, bread-baking pan, 291, hatter's fulling dish, 224
šajareh, ornaments on mirror frame, 88
šajarī, turquoise mixed with matrix, 39
šakar, sugar, 291, 295, 300
šakar-sang, quartz, rock crystal, pebble, 151
sāket, Morse bush (fr. Eng. socket), 60
sakirlāt, scarlet, 190
šakl, a molding pattern, 18
šakl-e miṯālī, molding pattern, 18
šāl, cloth covering printing dye, 226
salam, acacia tree (*Acacia* spp.), 78, tanning bark from acacia tree*
ṣalāyat, mortar, rubbing stone, 151
šāldeh, foundation, foundation trench; cf. *šālūdeh*, 108
saljū, rafter, 107
šalleh-čūb, neck peg on yoke, 262
šaltūk, unhusked rice, paddy, 271, 290
šaltūk-kārī, rice growing, 271
šālūdeh, foundation, foundation trench; cf. *šāldeh*, 108
šām, dinner, 293
šamak, thrust bearing of potter's wheel, 155
samak-e ḫwāb, upper diversion pole, 209
samak-e pāʾīn, lower diversion pole, 209
samar, yoke peg (Hamadān), 262
saṃbūrak, grate of kiln, 116, 126
šamdūnī, bushes fixing spokes to rim (Šīrāz for *šamʿdānī*), 90
samovar, Russian type of tea urn, 28
šamšād, boxtree (*Buxus sempervirens*); cf. *šemšād*, 78
šamšeh, a certain brick profile, 123, jibbet lever, 204, rod heddle, 214
šamšeh-hašt, a certain brick profile, 123
šamšeh-šīš, a certain brick profile, 123
šamšīrak, jibbet lever, 132, 204, plow column (Varāmīn), 263
šamšīrgar, *šamšīr-sāz*, swordsmith, 56
šamšīrī, turning tool with oblique edge, 27
šan, sand, 113
šanāhak, lime-sand mortar, 113

šānak, plow column (Kalārdašt), 264
ṣandal, white sandalwood (*Santalum album*), 76, 78
ṣandal-e surḫ, red sandalwood (*Pterocarpus santalinus*), 78
ṣandalī, chair, driver's seat, 87
ṣandalī-dozd, emergency seat in coach, 90
sandalūs, sandarac resin, 239
ṣandūq, trunk, casket, chest, 88, 97
ṣandūq-e dardār, trunk with front door (Borūjerd), 88
ṣandūq-e maḫmal, velvet-covered trunk, 88
ṣandūqī, a hollow wall, 111
ṣandūq-sāz, chest maker, trunk maker, 88
šāneh, cartridge frame, 60, toothed tool to decorate pottery, 153, 155, comb, 99, weaver's reed, 195, 204, 205, 209, beater comb, 200, 216, mat weaver's comb, 220, carding comb, 222, winnowing fork, 276, plow stilt, 262, 264, bearing block on edge runner pole, 296, hatter's scraper, 224
šāneh-bāfandegī, weaver's reed, 195
šāneh-bandī, weaving reed maker, 195
šāneh kardan, to comb goat hair or wool, 177, 233, to scrape felt, 224, to comb fibers, to card, 222
šāneh-mīk, wool comb (Kalārdašt), 182
šāneh-mīk zadan, to comb wool, 182
šāneh-sāz, combmaker, 99, reed maker, 195
šāneh-ye šotor, thrust bearing of potter's wheel, 155
šāneh zadan, to comb dirt and burrs off a sheep, 179, to compact weft, 216, to card, 222
sang, matrix in turquoise gems, 39, stone weight, 45, stone, 108, 113, 127, a certain quantity of water, 255, stone acting as water wheel bearing, 283, edge runner stone, 296
sang-āb, measure for a certain quantity of water used in irrigation, 255
sangak, pebble, 294, bread baked on hot pebbles, 291
sangāneh, stone lining near mouth of underground water channel, 253
šangarf, cinnabar, vermilion*
šangarf-e zāvūlī, red lead, lead oxide, 161
sang-bar, leather tip of cloth shoe, 230
sang-čīn, stone lining near mouth of underground water channel, 253
sang-e āhak, limestone, 126
sang-e āteš, flint, 160
sang-e bālā, runner, upper millstone (Alburz), 278
sang-e bargān, a soft stone used by glassmaker, 170
sang-e bulūr, flint, quartz*
sang-e buneh, weight, 299
sang-e buzurg, bed stone, nether millstone, 278
sang-e čaḫmāḫ, *sang-e čaqmāq*, flint, quartz, 59, 151
sang-e gandomī, a fine green marble (Yazd), 129
sang-e iskāf, shoemaker's lap stone, 229
sang-e kārmāleh, counterweight, pressing weight, 297, 299
sang-e kūčak, runner, upper millstone, 278
sang-e lājvard, cobalt oxide, 163
sang-e maᶜdan, ore, minerals, 15
sang-e mādeh, bed stone, nether millstone (Šīrāz); cf. *sang-e nar*, 278
sang-e marmar, marble, 127, stone used for dough rolling, 293, bookbinder's cutting block, 238
sang-e meškī, rubbing stone, 163
sang-e mohreh, smoothing stone, polishing stone, burnisher, 153
sang-e nar, runner, upper millstone (Šīrāz); cf. *sang-e mādeh*, 278
sang-e narm, edge runner, 189, 296, 297
sang-e ᶜorām, honing stone, 231
sang-e pā, pumice stone, rubbing stone, 224, 232
sang-e pāʾīn, bed stone, nether millstone (Alburz), 278
sang-e penz, pumice stone (Šīrāz), 34, 88
sang-e qabr, tombstone, 132
sang-e qapān, moving weight of steelyard, 65
sang-e qibṭī, fuller's earth, 224
sang-e rū, runner, upper millstone, 277, 278
sang-e rūmī, a special fine honing stone, 27, 57, 84
sang-e safīdāb, whiting, 39, 300
sang-e sāʾī, *sang-e sāyī*, grinding stone, 57, grinding wheel, 37
sang-e sehlāyeh, rubbing stone, 163
sang-e siyāh, soft stone for making pots (Mašhad)*, gray marble (Šīrāz), 129
sang-e sō, honing stone (Mašhad), 58, 84, 92
sang-e sombādeh, carborundum stone, 122, emery stone, 57, 128
sang-e somāq, fine marble, porphyry, 129
sang-e sou, see *sang-e sō*
sang-e tah-gāh, bed stone of edge mill, 296
sang-e tarāšīdeh, a hewn stone, 128
sang-e vardeh, edge runner, 302
sang-e vazn, weight for balance and scales, 63
sang-e zīr, bed stone, nether millstone, 277, 278
sangīneh-sāz, stone paste potter, 151, 165
sangīneh-sāzī, making of stone paste ware, 151
sang kašīdan, to burnish gold inlaid work, 73
sang-kūb, shovel to straighten pebbles in baker's oven, 294
sang-kūh, pebble heap in baker's oven, 294
sang-šekan, quarryman, 126, 127

sang-šū'ī, ore-washing section, 16
sang-taraš, stonecutter, stone pot maker, 130, stonemason, 128
sang zadan, to grind on a grinding stone†
sanjāq, ornamental pin, 32
sanj-e bārūt, powder measure*
ṣannāᶜ, artisan, craftsman*
sapīdāb, white lead, tin oxide, 162, or mixture of both, 162; cf. *safīdāb*
sapīdeh-zanān, white lead, 161
sapūs, bran, 279
sāqeh-ye tarāzū, beam of balance, 63
sāqiyeh, water-lifting wheel, 259
saqiz-e safīd, *saqiz-safīd*, pistachio tree (*Pistacia terebinthus*), 78, 189
ṣaqlgar, polisher, 35
saqqā, water carrier*
saqqā-ḫāneh, storage container for drinking water, 30
šāqūl, plumb line, pendulum, 111
sar, ash tree (*Fraxinus excelsior*) (Katūl), 78
šār, boxtree (*Buxus sempervirens*) (Šīrgāh), 78
sarām, top beam of windmill (Ḫorāsān), 287
sarand, medium-mesh sieve*
sar-andāz, reinforcing beam, 297, 299
sarang kardan, to sift, 277
šaᶜrbāf, brocade weaver*
sar-band, overlap of rushes in mat weaving, 220
sarbandān, stone supporting mill bearing, 283
sar band kardan, to join the ends, 154
sarbīn, cypress tree (*Cupressus sempervirens*) (Caspian provinces), 78
sarčang, top of carding bow, 180
sar-čūbī, wooden stick, 39
sardar, ceiling joist, 114
sardsīr, temperate region, 241
sar-e āhan, plowshare (Ḫorāsān), 263
sar-e āvīzān, shackle on steelyard to suspend load, 65
sar-e čāh, mouth of channel shaft, 252
sar-e čarḫ, working top of potter's wheel, 155
sar-e dam, tuyères, windpipe, 29
sar-e dār, end beam of weaver's loom, 220
sar-e darajeh, runner of a casting, 18
sar-e dīg, kettle lid, 28
sar-e dūlčeh, wooden stopper of drinking water container, 234
sāreh, rice-husking pestle, 290
sar-e kamān, top of carding bow, 180
sar-e kār, working top of potter's wheel, 155, warp beam, 220
sar-e kūreh, charging hole of furnace, 19, flue of kiln, chimney*, drying chamber above furnace, 159
sar-e kūzeh, spout of jar, 155
sar-e mīl, journal of axle, 90, 282
sar-e nō, grain hopper (Alburz), 278
sar-e qaliyān, pipe cob, 133, 155
sar-e qočāq, iron ferrule at end of beam, 90
sar-e qolāb, hook on carpet-knotting knife, 215
sar-e sabok, shackle to suspend steelyard for light loads, 65
sar-e sangīn, shackle to suspend steelyard for heavy loads, 65
sar-e seh-panjeh, working table of potter's wheel, 155
sar-e tah-tīr, bearing end of thrust pin, 286
sar-e tīšeh, blade of hoe, 261
sar-gāh, upper warp beam (Māzandarān), 204
sar-gāzak, beam carrying top bearing, 287
sarḥadd, alpine pasture region, 241
sarḫak, top roller on well*
sarījeh, time-measuring bowl*
sarīs, wheel of windmill*
sarkaj, turning tool with upturned edge, 27
sar-kaš, bar to guide camel's head, 297
sar kašīdan, to draw out boiled sugar, 301
sar-kūpī, thread wound onto spool (Kāšān), 196
sar-māleh, top tray, mat, 298
sar-mīḫ, lathe center, 91
sar-mīl, polished end of pile wire for velvet weaving, 209
sar-mīrāb, chief water bailiff, 256
sar-mošteh, *sar-moštī*, winch-locking peg, 297, 298
sarnak, plowshare (Ḫorāsān), 263
sarnāl, beam over verandah, 114
sarōbī, yoke band (Zābol), 262
sarrāj, saddler, 234
sar-randīdan, to plane wood across the grain†
sar-qāmeh, eyelet at ends of spring, 90
saršāneh, camel's draw harness, 296
sar-sū, top of aquifer, 252
sar-tāq, person in charge of water allocation (Nairīz), 256
sārū, *sārūj*, mortar made of sand, lime, and wood ashes, 113, sand-lime mortar for bath and cistern construction, 258
sarv, cypress tree (*Cupressus sempervirens*), 78
sarv-e āzād, cypress tree (*Cupressus sempervirens, C. horizontalis, C. fastigata*), 78
sarv-e kūhī, cypress tree (*Cupressus horizontalis*), 78
sās, bran, 279
šast-ᶜarūs, a grape variety, 244
šateqī, type of windmill south of Mašhad, 284
šāṭir, man who places dough in baker's oven, 293
šatīrak, heddle-balancing lever, 204
saṭl, bucket, brass kettle, 30
šatvī, crop sown in winter, 271
savād-e sorb, niello work, 33

sāvīdan, to smooth, to make even, 158, to grind, to polish, 122, to sand, 96; see *sābīdan*
savī kardan, to smooth, to make even, 38
sayyāf, swordmaker, 56
sāzū, windlass rope (Šīrāz), 258, reed rope, 135
sāzūbāz kardan, to attach straw ropes, 135
sed, ladder (Šīrāz), 111
sefāl, roof tile, 113, 156, earthenware, 151, sherd*
sefālgar, potter, 113
sefālīn, earthenware pipe, 15
šefreh, inside chisel; cf. *šifr*, 133
sefteh, *šefteh*, foundation paste, 108
šefteh, bookbinder's knife, 238
seft-kārī, brick-laying, building, 112
seft šodan, the thickening of syrup, 302
seh gorgeh, sand-lime-cement mortar (Šīrāz), 113
seh-gūš, triangular bead, 94
seh-kerān, a certain brick profile, 123
seh-lāʾī, plywood, three-ply, 80
seh-paḫ, three-cornered, 94
seh-panjeh, three-pronged axle end, 155
seh-pāyeh, tripod, 65, loom tripod, 200, grill of baking oven, 294
seh-qaddī, small brick, part of a brick, 112
seh-šāḫ, three-armed wheel top, 155
seh-šāḫeh, branch wood, 85
šehteh, a lime-mud mixture for foundations (Šīrāz)*
seḫtiyān, goat leather, 231
šekāf-e darajeh, backsight of gun, 60
šekāf-e randeh, slot in carpenter's plane†
šekāftan, to cut, 219
šekāfteh, slot in plowshare (Ḫorāsān), 263
šekanjeh, sash clamp (Mašhad), 86
šekastan, to break, to crush, 151
šelāl zadan, to turn weft at selvage*
šelīl, smooth almond tree (*Persica loevis*), 78
šelīt, cross harness; cf. *čelīt*, 206, 210
šelīt-e naqšeh, draw harness, 206, 211
šelleh siyāh, low-grade silk cocoon (Gīlān), 183
selmanīyeh, steel from Ḫorāsān, 55
šemš, ingot, 16, 22, 31, block of molten potash; cf. *šumš*, *šemšeh*, 161
šemšād, boxtree (*Buxus sempervirens*); cf. *šamšād*, 78
šemšeh, ingot stick, 31, straight-edge, 108, 116, batten, layer of plaster*, heddle rod, 214, heddle rod of *zīlū* loom, 210
šemšeh-gel, clay heap, 109
šemšeh-kāhgel, layer of rendering with mud-straw mortar*
šemšeh-melāṭ, jointing wood, plasterer's straight-edge, 123
šen, molding sand (Iṣfahān), 18, building sand, 113, river sand, 31, sand, 33; cf. *šan*
šen-āhak, mortar, 113
sendān, anvil, 24, 30, 44, 51
sendān-e dōkoreh, double-beaked anvil†
sendān-e ḫeštī, pointed end of anvil set in the ground, 51
sendān-e kāseh-mīḫ, small round anvil, 25
sendān-e kūčak, table anvil, inset anvil†
sendān-e lab gardān, edge-doubling anvil, 25
sendān-e mīḫ-sāzī, nail-forming anvil, 53
sendan-e motavasseṭ, medium-sized anvil, 25
sendān-e pūkeh, anvil in bottom of cartridge case, 60
sendān-e sūrāḫ, swage block, 52
sendān-e taḫt, large flat anvil, 25
senjed, jujube tree (*Zizyphus vulgaris*), 75, 78, or sorb wood (*Eleagnus angustifolia*), 78
sepāreh, bolt in hood lever, 90
sepestān, sebestens tree (*Cordia myxa*) (Bandar ᶜAbbās), 75, 78
serendīb, steel from Ceylon, 55
sereš, *serešk*, *serešt*, vegetable glue (Šīrāz); cf. *serīš*, 36, 125, 195, 238
serešt-e māhī, fish glue, 180
serīš, glue, paste; cf. *sereš*, 195, 238
serīš-e māhī, fish glue, 180, 238
serīš-e safīd, paste for lining cupboards, 86
serīš kardan, to paste on, to glue, 238
serīšom, glue, 238
serkeh, vinegar, 94, 164
setāreh, star-shaped ornament, 95, 219
siānfūr, *siānūr*, cyanide for hardening (fr. *Fr. cyanure*), 52
ṣibāġ, dye, tincture, 194
sībak, plow stay (Kalārdašt), 264
šifr, wood chisel (Mašhad); cf. *šefreh*, 84
sīḫ, stirring iron, 20, forge poker, 161, peg for warp plug, 185, shed rod, 235, saddler's awl, 234, baker's skewer, 294
sīḫčeh-ye yāʾī, hoop on tightening lever, 90
sīḫ-e āhan-sarkaj, scraper to remove oxide from molten metal, 162
sīḫ-e andāzeh, depth gauge, 133
sīḫ-e bošak, wood for lifting rod heddle, 235
sīḫ-e dast, spit carrying weft material, 235
sīḫ-e gerd, long round awl, 229
sīḫ-e kūreh, poker, 50
sīḫ-e neṣfeʾī, beaked anvil, 34
sīḫ-e sarkaj, tinsmith's beaked iron*
siḫtiyān, *saḫtiyān*, goat leather, morocco*
sikātūr, cocoon drier (fr. Fr. *siccateur*), 183
ṣilāyeh, grind stone, mortar, 151
šīldār, elm tree (*Ulmus* spp.) (Ḫajjīlār, Turcoman-Steppe), 78
sīleh, tanning pit, 231
silf, oil cake, 299
šilīt, see *šelīt*, 206

sīm, wire, 94, clay-cutting wire, 116, 155, blade in weaver's reed, 195, sieve wire, 236
sīmak, neck band on yoke (Zābol), 262
simān, portland cement (fr. Fr. *ciment*)†
sīm-e čūq, yoke peg (Varāmīn), 262
sīm-e berenj, brass wire*
sīm-e ṭelā, gold wire, 73
sīm-kāš, silver wire drawer, wire drawer, 42
sīm kašīdan, to cut clay with a wire, 157, fine drawing of wire, 43
sīm-sāvī, block for shaping wire, 94
sīneh, round back of scissors blade, 56
sīneh-dār, round-faced hammer, 29
sīneh-dār-čarsū, square-faced hammer, 29
sīneh-dār-sar-dokmeh, button-faced hammer, 29
sīneh-rand, convex compass plane (Tehrān), 84
sīneh-ye dandeh, cutting breast of saw-tooth†
sīnī, tray, bowl, 28, 32
sīnī-ye čūbī, shelf for silkworm breeding, 182
šīpā, board to support woven mat (Šīrāz), 220
sīr, a measure of weight, 62, garlic*
šīr, tap, cock, 18, 29, milk, 295
šīrāzeh, selvage, 220, crocheted rim on cloth shoe, 230, book trimming band, headband, 238
šīrāzī, a grape variety, 244
šīrdān, milk jar, 29, milk bottle, 170
šīrdār, maple tree (*Acer laetum* in Manzandarān), yew tree (*Taxus baccata* in Gīlān), 78
šīr-e angūr, *šīreh-angūr*, grape syrup, 145, 164, 300
šīreh, syrup, 291
šīreh-kašmeš, raisin syrup, 301
šīrḫešk, Cotoneaster (*Cotoneaster nummularia*), 78, 302
šīrīn, sweet, 291
šīrīnī, sweets, 302
sirinj, red lead, 161
sirišk = *serešk*, glue, 36, 125, 195, 238
sirištan, to mix, to knead, 152
sirīšum = *serīšom*, glue, 86
sirīšum-e māhī, fish glue, 86
sirīšum-ṭās, gluepot, 94
šīr-kanaf, linen, flax (*Linum utatissimum*) (Gīlān), 178
sirkeh, vinegar; cf. *serkeh*, 94, 164
šīrmāl, fine biscuit-like bread, 295
šīrvāneh, ironclad roof, 30, 114, gabled roof*
šīš, bead skewer, hexagonal compound bead, 93, 94, 95, hexagonal brick, 123
šīšeh, windowpane, glass, 86, 170, receiver of still, 163, glass, bottle, 170, frit, 160
šīšehgar, glassmaker, 169
šīšehgar-ḫāneh, glassworks, 169
šīšeh-sāz, glassmaker, 169
šīšeh-ye qoveh, glasses for wet batteries, 170
šīš-e tūlānī, *šīš-e tūlūnī*, a certain brick profile, 123
šīšpanj, a certain brick profile, 123
šīš pīčīdan, to join inlay beads into hexagonal compound beads, 94
šīš-sāvī, filing block for hexagonal beads, 94, 95
sitām, bar, 151
šīveh, sole of cloth shoe, 228
siyāh, black, printing block for black, 225
siyāh-dāneh, coriander seed, 295
siyāh-qalam, manganese oxide used for line tracing, 163, 166, outlines of tracing, 88
siyāh-sang, basalt block used for crushing of minerals, 151
šiyār, drill flute, 60
šiyār-e borīdeh-šekan, chip breaker groove in file cut†
ṣobḥāneh, breakfast, 293
sofāl, roof, tile, roof tile, 113, 156, earthenware, 151
sofāl-e mes, copper shavings, copper oxide*
soft-e bālā, socket in head member of door frame, 86
softeh, iron hinge, plaque, 86
soft-e pāʾīn, socket in doorsill, 86
soġārī, leather strip on carder's bow, 180
šoḫm, tilling, plowing, 266
šoḫm-e dō-dastī, Western-type plow, 266
šoḫm-kār, plow man, 266
šoḫm zadan, to plow, 266
sok, warp peg, 204, shutter to control flow of grain in mill, 279
sokmeh-duḫtan, to stitch, 217
sokmeh-dūz, embroiderer, 217
sokmeh-dūzī, embroidery, 217
šol-čūb, neck peg, 262
šol kardan, to loosen warp, 216
šoʿleh, the flame of a blowtorch†
som, hoof, 54
šomāreh, number punches, 60
soṃbādeh, emery, 38, 39, 133
soṃbādeh kardan, to sand a surface, to grind, 87
soṃbeh, punch, 60, auger, pointed chisel, 26, 36, 37, punching set hammer, 52, saw-setting punch, 82, wedge to retain press beam, 297, 299
soṃbeh kardan, to pierce line of holes, 36, to punch*, to drill*
soṃbeh-manganeh, wad punch, hollow punch, 60
soṃbeh-nešān, center punch, 60
soṃbīdan, to punch, to drill*
soṃbol-e hindī, grated roots of nard plant, 295
som-sāb, hoof rasp, 54, horn rasp, 52
som-tarāš, hoof-trimming knife, 54
som tarāšīdan, to trim a hoof, 54

soqāf-pūš, ceiling board, 114
šōqeh, spindle, 39
sorb, lead, 161, lead base for file cutting, 58, lead compounds in glaze making, 161
šorb, pivot on coach bogie, 90
sorb-e bāterī, *sorb-e mašīnī*, lead obtained from car battery, 161
šostan, to wash, 179, 302, to rinse, 194
šostan dar āb, to rinse in water, 226
šostan dar taġār, to wash minerals in a vat, 300
šotor, camel, 296
šotor-galū, *šotor-gelū*, craned snarling iron, 29, ratchet brace, 85, cranked chisel, 98
šotorī, camel-colored, 214
šotor-mohreh, iron bar to support coach footboard, 90
sotūn, bearing pillar, 46, 47, column, 107, 114, well pillar, 256
sotūnak, book cover cloth, 238
souhān, file, 60, 101
souhān-dastūr-dādeh, see *souhān-e dastur-dādeh*, 130
souhān-e arreh, saw-sharpening file, cant file, 58
souhān-e bārīk, narrow flat file, 130
souhān-e čahārgūš, square file, 58
souhān-e čahār pahlū, square file†
souhān-e čāqū'ī, knife-edged file, 58
souhān-e čūb, wood rasp, 84
souhān-e čūb-sāb, wood rasp, 84
souhān-e dastūr-dādeh, bent profile file, 130
souhān-e dōdam, saw-sharpening file, cant file, 82
souhān-e dom-mūš, *souhān-e dom-mūšī*, small round file, 58, 130
souhān-e dorošt, a coarse file, 58
souhān-e dō-sar, double-headed file, 130
souhān-e ferez šodeh, milled file† (*ferez*, fr. Ger. *fräsen*)
souhān-e gardandeh, rotary disk file†
souhān-e gāv-dombal, tapered file, 58
souhān-e gerd, round file, 58
souhān-e gord-e māhī, half-round file, 82
souhān-e ḫanjarī, cant file†
souhān-e ḫilālī, file with pointed cuts (instead of linear cuts)†
souhān-e ḫoš, coarse file†
souhān-e kārdī, knife-edged file, 58
souhān-e koloft, heavy file, 130
souhān-e māšīnī, machine file†
souhān-e motavasseṭ, medium or bastard file, 58
souhān-e narm, file with medium cut, 58, file for stone pot finishing, 131
souhān-e nīm-gerd, half-round file, 58
souhān-e pardāḫt, file with a fine cut, smoothing file, 58
souhān-e ṣafḥe'ī, rotary disk file†
souhān-e ṣaiqal, polishing file, 58
souhān-e ṣalībī, cross-cut file†
souhān-e seh-gūš, *souhān-e seh-pahlū*, three-square file, triangular file, 58
souhān-e sūzanī, needle file†
souhān-e taḫt, flat file, 58
souhān-e taḫt-e nōk-tīz, tapered flat file†
souhān-e taḫt-e sar-rīz, tapered file†
souhān-e taḫt-e sar-ṣāf, flat file†
souhān-e tak-żarb, single-cut file†
souhān-e tasmeh'ī, flat file (Šīrāz), 58
souhān-e yak-āj, single cut file†
souhān-e zabāneh'ī, tongue-shaped file†
souhān-e zabr, coarse file, 58
souhān-e ẓarīf, fine-cut file, smooth file†
souhān-e zūzaneqeh, trapezoid-shaped file†
souhān-kār, brass finisher, 29
souhān-kārī, filing away joints, air vents, and burrs, 20, smoothing by filing, 36
souhān kardan, to file, 29, 73
souhān-pāk-kon, file cleaner†
souhān-sāz, file cutter, 57
souveh, spindle bearing on spinning wheel (Ardistān), 186
sū'āleh, filings, 34
sū'āleh-ye mes, copper filing dust, copper scrapings, 94
sūhān (Šīrāz) = *souhān*
sūḫtāl, yew tree (*Taxus baccata*) (Kātūl), 78
sūḫtan, to fire a kiln, 116
sujjāj, glazemaker, 160
sūkut, musk willow (*Salix aegyptiaca*) (Gorgān), 78
sūlāḫ = *sūrāḫ*
sūlāḫ-e ᶜaiyār, metal tapping hole, 17
sūlāḫ-e dāš, slag-tapping hole, 17
sūlāḫ-e dastgāh, work opening in glass kiln, 170
sūlāḫ-e zambūrak, air vent in baking oven, 294
sūlāḫ kardan, to forge a hole, 52, to pierce, 73, to drill a hole, 73, 167
šumāl, size for dressing warp, 185
šumāl-ḫāneh, warp-dressing room, 185, warping place, 185
sumāq, sumach tree (*Rhus coriaria*), 78, 191
šumš = *šemš*, 22
šūn, elder tree (*Sambucus ebulus*), 78
šūnak, plow column (Alburz), 263, wedge on plow (Surmaq, Varāmīn); cf. *šānak*, *šāneh*, 263
sūrāḫ, hole in time-measuring bowl, 255, hole in end of plow beam, 262, hole for setting yoke beam, 262; cf. *sūlāḫ*
sūrāḫ-e darajeh, setting holes on frame of polishing lathe, 26
sūrāḫ-e parvā'ī, hole in plow beam (Ḫorāsān), 262
sūrāḫ-e pūkeh, touch hole in cartridge, 60

sūrāḫ-e sūz, touch hole of gun, 60
sūrāḫ-e zambūrak, air vent in baking oven, 294
šūrak, wedge, 263
šūrat, friable soil, loose soil, 253
ṣūrat, shining surface, 33
ṣūrat-e loᶜāb, clay slip, 158
šūreh, saltpeter, salt deposits, 163
surḫ, red*
surḫehdār, yew tree (*Taxus baccata* in Siyārat, Dāmiyān) or alder tree (*Alnus gentinosa* in Tehrān, Iṣfahān), 78
surmeh, auripigment, antimony, 163
surmehdān, a certain brick profile, 123
surmehʾī, deep blue hue of indigo, 192
surūb, lead (Kāšān); cf. *sorb*, 161
sūs, bran (Alburz); cf. *sabūs*, 196, 279
sūs-e jou, barley bran (Alburz)*
šustan = *šostan*, to wash, to rinse, 179
sūvāleh, filings, scrapings, 60
sūvāl-e mes, copper filings (Šīrāz); cf. *tūfāl*, 162
sūzan, firing needle of gun, 59, short wire peg to cut pots off the wheel, 155, needle, 228, 230, crochet hook, 218
sūzan-e gīveh-bāfī, shoemaker's needle, 228
sūzan-e ḫaṭṭkaš, *sūzan-e ḫaṭṭkašī*, scriber, 60
sūzan forū kardan, to pierce needle into cloth, 218
sūzan-sāz, needlemaker, 57

ṭā, rope for water drawing, 256
tāb, heat applied to metal, annealing, 23, warping in timber, 80, string tightener, 181, twist of yarn, rope, 222
ṭabāḫī, carcass wool, 177
tābāndan, to heat, to anneal*
ṭabaq, *tābaq*, trough containing tin granulate*, solder dish, 31, dish to collect precious metal filings; cf. *tāveh*, *tāvaq*, 34
ṭabaqeh, shelf in potter's kiln, 160
tabar, *tabareh*, axe, hatchet, 82, axe-shaped link between millstone and shaft, rind, 278
tabarḫūn, *ṭabarḫūn*, red Hyrcanian willow (*Ziziphus jujuba vulgaris*), 78
tāb dādan, to anneal, 23
tābeh, stove, 28
tāb-e pīč, batten tightener, 204
ṭabḫ, the firing of earthenware, 159, 164
tābīdan, to anneal, 23, to twist threads, silk, 196, to twist a rope*
tābīdeh kardan, to heat, 161
ṭableh, *ṭableh-ye qalam-dān*, pen box cover, 239
tabrīzī, black poplar (*Populus nigra, P. pyramidalis*), 78
tābū-bačeh, *tābūn-bačeh*, walking aid for little children (Šāh-Reżā), 154
tābūn, bread-baking pan, 292
tadhīn, oiling, painting*
tāfteh šodan, to become soft by annealing, 36
taftūn, *tāftūn*, baker's oven (Iṣfahān), 292
tağār, common beech tree (*Carpinus betulus* in Gorgān), 78
tağar, oriental beech tree (*Carpinus orientalis* in Katūl), 78
tağār, *ṭağār*, kneading trough, 293, washing tub, vat, 300
tağār-e bār-sūrī, mineral washing vat, 300
tah-gāh, bottom of edge mill, 296
taḥlīl, dissolving, suspending of minerals, 151
taḫmāḫ, mallet; cf. *tāqmāq*, *toḫmāq*, 98
tah-mālband, eyelet at end of coach beam, 90
taḫmīn, tracing surface, 122
ṭaḥn, grinding in a mill*
ṭā-ḫongī, rope made of rushes, 256
taḫt, large flat anvil, 25, shelf in silk nursery, 183, cloth shoe sole, 229, seat on threshing wain, 274
tahtāh, bedstone, nether millstone, 287
taḫt-e gurt-bāfī, *taḫt-e gurt-čīnī*, heddle-making device, 198
taḫt-e gūšeh, wooden disk for pinion, 283
taḫteh, flat ingot*, flat board on balance, 63, board, 79, 96, 263, blank for comb cutting, 99, wooden roof shingle, 113, coil rolling board, 152, bearing block, 155, board on carder's bow, 182, frame of roper's spinning head, 221, printer's bench, 226, polishing board, 232, work-bench, 233, board between plow and sole, 263, thrust bearing block, 281, windmill wing, 287, shutter controlling flow of grain, 279
taḫteh-āb-band, shutter of water mill, 281
taḫteh-barsang, wooden hoop, 279
taḫteh-dastgāh, tail stock board, 91
taḫteh-halbūn, flour retaining board (Iṣfahān), 279
taḫteh-ḫarak, lower board of file cutter's bench, 58
taḫteh-ḫūneh, board supporting mill pinion, 283, oil pressing board, 297, 298
taḫteh-kamān, board of carder's bow, 180
taḫteh-kūngāh, sitting board behind potter's wheel, 155
taḫteh-mālā, harrowing board; cf. *māleh*, 266
taḫteh-mes, sheet of copper*
taḫteh-mouj-dahī, velvet pressing board, 209
taḫteh-nešastan, sitting board, seat (Māzandarān), 220
taḫteh-pā, foot-protecting board, 261, footrest on spade, 261
taḫteh-pāḫūneh, beam carrying pinion axle (Iṣfahān), 283
taḫteh-rand, woodworking block, 94

taḫteh-randeh, planing block, 99
taḫt-e ḫwāb, bedstead, 87
taḫteh-ye kamān, see *taḫteh-kamān*, 180
taḫteh-ye langar, board on weighting mechanism, 45
taḫteh-ye nard, draughtboard, 97
taḫteh-ye qīr, pitch board*
taḫteh-ye rand-e baġalšīš-sāvī, filing block for beads, 94, 95
taḫteh-ye rand-e kašōʾī, filing board for smoothing inlaid slices, 96
taḫteh-ye rand-e mosallas-sāvī, filing block for triangular profiles, 94
taḫteh-ye rand-e parreh-sāvī, filing block for corner beads, 95
taḫteh-ye rand-e qofl, filing block for larger compound rods, 96
taḫteh-ye rand-e sīm-sāvī, wire filing block, 94
taḫteh-ye rand-e šīš-sāvī, filing block for hexagonal profiles, 94
taḫteh-ye šaṭranj, chessboard, 97
taḫteh-ye sāz, harness-balancing pulley, 204
taḫteh-ye savārī, seat of threshing wain, 274
tah-tīr, thrust block, 286
taḫt-kaš, maker of cloth shoe soles, 229
ṭāḫūneh, ground in a mill*
tāk, grapevine, 244
tā kardan, to fold, 239
takayol, ornamentation of threshold (Qazvīn), 88
tal, maple tree (*Acer monspesassulanum*) (Pol-e Safīd), 78
talafāt, reject in ceramic work, kiln waster, 154
talak, farmhouse (Gīlān)*
tālār, upper living room, 107
taleh, trap, 52
tāleh kūbīdan, to thresh with a flail, 273
talk, *talkeh*, peg joining yoke and plow beam (Ḫorāsān), 262
tamām-fanar, a full elliptic spring, 90
taman, treadle disk of potter's wheel (Šīrāz), 154
tamand, raised border of irrigated field, 268
tamar-hindī, tamarind tree (*Tamarindus indica*), 78
tambūš, *tambūšeh*, drainpipe, 153
tamīz kardan, to clean, 31, to sort silk cocoons, 183
tamlīd, key, 66
tān, warp (Māzandarān); cf. *tūn*, 184, warp thread, 220
ṭanāb, rope, 45, 221, rope to operate loom harness*, neck rope, 256, 262, scoop-pulling rope, 268
ṭanab-bāf, ropemaker, 221
ṭanāb-band, heddle rope, 200
ṭanāb-e kārmāleh, rope used for first pressing in oil mill, 297
ṭanāb-sāz, *ṭanāb-tāb*, ropemaker, 221
ṭanāf = *ṭanāb*, 45
ṭanāf-e langar, rope for weighting mechanism, 45, 299
taneh, body of vessel, 155, marking gauge, 81, spindle of milling device, 87
taneh-kūr, borax, 24
taneh-šōqeh, spindle pulley, 39
tan-e kūzeh, body of jar, 155
tan-e mateh, spindle of fiddle drill, 85, drill brace, 60
tan-e qofl, lock body, 70
tanestik, warp-winding stick (Kāšān), 195
tang, carpenter's clamp, 86, gluing press, 96, tightener on spinning head, 221, narrow slot along press pit, 298, wooden links on water wheel, 283, warp-tightening wedge, 210, 215, stay on circumference of water wheel, 283, bookbinder's press, 237, grape press, 300
tangār, borax, 24; cf. *taneh-kūr*, *tankār*, 61
tang-e bālā, warp beam lever*
tang-e fārsī, mitering board, 86
tang-e pāʾīn, ware-beam lever*
tang-e zangīreh, press for inlaid work, 96
tang kardan, to press grapes, 300
tang-kaš, tightening string, 180
tankār, borax, 61; cf. *tangār*, 24
tankareh, *tankireh*, water boiler, cauldron*
tān-pīčīdan, to wind a warp, 195
tān-tāb, warp-winding stick (Kāšān), 195
tanūr, *tanūreh*, kiln, furnace, 158, baker's oven, 292, lining of baker's oven, 153, penstock of water mill, 280
tanūr-e nān-pazī, baker's oven, 153
tanūr-e sangakī, baking oven with pebble floor, 294
tanūr-ḫāneh, bakehouse, bakery, 293
tanūrī, flat bread baked in *tanūr*, 293
ṭā-parīčeh, rope made of date fibers, 256
tāq, *ṭāq*, vault, 110, vaulted roof over kiln, 159, vaulted roof of baker's oven, 294
tāqā, *ṭāqā*, bleaching vat*
ṭāq-band, vaulted, arched, 111, 126
tāqeh, iron tire, 283
tāq-e kūreh, vaulted floor of kiln, 116, cupola over kiln, 159
taqmāq, mallet (Šīrāz); cf. *taḫmāḫ*, *toḫmāq*, *toqmāq*, 98
taqsīm-e āb, water distribution, 255
taqsīm-e dandāneh, pitch of saw-teeth†
taqsīm-e dandeh, pitch of saw-teeth†
taqsīm kardan, to divide irrigation water, 255
tār, warp, 184, 203, 214, guitar-like instrument, 98

tarāḫ, plow wedge, 263
tarāhī kardan, to draw a design, to sketch, 135
tarak, crack or split in timber*
tarāšeh-kūzeh, turning of pots, 156
tarāšīdan, to cut bricks or tiles, 122, to shave, to scrape, to turn, 233, to turn a pot, 155, 156, to grind, 57
tarāš kardan, to smooth a skin*
tarāz, level used by well-sinker, 252
tarāzū, pair of scales, 62, spirit level, 108
tarāzū-sāz, balance maker, 62
tarāzū-ye mesqālī, goldsmith's scales, 62
tār-bandeh, specialist warp winder, 215
tār bastan, to wind a warp, 214
tarḫā, *tarḫān*, wormwood (*Artimisia herba alba*) used as kiln fuel, 116
tarḫ-e farang, arris groove joint†
tarīb kardan, to rough gem stone, 39
tariyākī, pale green, yellow, 162
tark, flat metal strip, 88
tar kardan, to wet, 233
tarkīb, rough grinding, 39, mixture, compound, 151
tarm, hand pad, 226
tarmeh, goat-hair cloth, fine woolen cloth, 177
ṭarrāʾī, heddle maker, 198
ṭarrāz, embroiderer*
tār-sāz, guitar maker, musical instrument maker, 98
tāseh-kan, chisel for removing of background, 99
ṭās-e rouġan, oil pot, 84
tasmeh, belt, 35, 47, 57, 101
ṭašk, bowl, basin*
tašt, large bowl for time measuring, 255
taštak, time measuring bowl, 255, a time unit, 255, baking trough, 293
tašteqeh, time unit measured with bowl, 255
tašt šodan, to turn into a vessel, 26
taṭyīn, to paint, to whitewash, 164
tāvaq, dish to collect precious metal filings, 34; cf. *ṭābaq*, *tāveh*
tavar, millstone driver, rind (Iṣfahān), 52, 278
tāveh, stove, 28, pan, dish, 222, disk of threshing wain, 274; cf. *touveh*, 274
ṭāvīleh, stable *
teġeleh, camel's draw harness (Kāšān), 296
tejīr, mat curtain, blind, 221
ṭelā, gold, 163
ṭelā-bāf, brocade weaver, gold embroiderer*
ṭelā-kūb, goldbeater, 40, gold damascener, 41, gold-inlayer, 41
ṭelā-kūbī, gold-leaf tooling, 238
ṭelā kūbīdan šabakeh, to gild fretwork, 73
telembār, barn, rice store, 107, silkworm nursery (Māzandarān), 107, 182
termeh, brocade made of silk and wool, cashmere; cf. *tarmeh*, 177
termeh-bāfī, weaving of cashmere, brocade*
tifāl, wall (Iṣfahān), 110
tiflīsī, building with stones and bricks combined*
tīġ, cut of a file*, sword, knife, 155, cutting edge, 60, plane iron, 82, saw blade, 79, plowshare, 266, leather-cutting knife, 235, pile-cutting knife, 209, carpet-knotting knife, 215, hatter's trimming knife, 224
tīġ-e āhan, iron mill axle, 283
tīġ-e arreh, saw blade, 80
tīġeh, hollow ground cutting edges of tin snips, 26
tīġeh, single-brick wall, wall with bricks on-edge; cf. *tīġī*, 111
tīġeh-borandeh, cutting edge of auger drill†
tīġeh-pīšbor, precutting edge of auger drill†
tīġ-e mateh, drill bit, 85
tīġ-e miqrāż, scissor blades, 56
tīġ-e monabbat-kārī, carving chisel, 97
tīġ-e qāčī, *tīġ-e qāšī*, iron of roughing plane†
tīġ-e randeh, plane iron†
tīġ-e randeh dō-tīġ, double-plane iron†
tīġ-e randeh-ḫašī, toothed plane iron†
tīġ-e randeh-sād, single-plane iron†
tīġ-gerd, short round awl, 230
tīġī, single-brick wall, wall with bricks on-edge; cf. *tīġeh*, 111
tīġ-sāz, razor maker, 55
tīġ tarāšīdan, to scrape, 224
tilak, ash tree (*Fraxinus excelsior*) (Lāhījān), 78
tilimbār = *telembār*, 107
tilouʾeh, *tilūʾī*, vertical oil press pit, 297
tīn, fig tree (*Ficus carica*)*
tinkār = *tankār*, 147
tīr, ceiling joist, rafter, 114, axle of spinning wheel, 186, reed frame rod, 195, depilation beam, 231, wooden beam, 79, 300, plow beam, 263, 264, mill shaft, 286, 288, 290
tīrak, bar of marking gauge, 81, plow beam, 264, pole carrying edge roller, 296
tirāz, *ṭirāz*, embroidery, satin stitch, 217
tīrčūm, pole of threshing wain (Iṣfahān), 275
tīr-e bālā, upper beam*
tīr-e bardī, stick to attach warp to breastbeam, 204
tīr-e buzurg, main press-beam in oil press, 297, 298
tīr-e čarḫ, shaft of potter's wheel, 155, main shaft of cotton gin, 180
tīreh, windmill axle, 286
tīr-e ḫēš, plow beam (Iṣfahān), 263

tīr-e kūčak, prepressing beam in oil press, 297, 298
tīr-e pā, lathe bed, 91
tīr-e pā'īn, lower beam*
tīr-e sang-e narm, axle beam of edge runner, 296
tīr-e vaṣūl, crank of spinning wheel (Ardistān), 186
tīr-e zīrak, center post of edge runner, 296
tīrgar, arrow maker*
tīrkār, division of village land*
tīr-pā, lathe bed beam, 91
tīšeh, adze, 79, 82, brick cutter's hoe, 122, cultivator's hoe, 261
tīšeh-basteh kardan, to smooth stone surface with kernel hammer, 128
tīšeh-čaġī kardan, to smooth surface with kernel hammer, 128
tīšeh-dam-e qalam(ī), narrow-edged hoe, 123
tīšeh-dorošt, toothed stone pick, coarse kernel hammer, 131
tīšeh-narm, fine kernel hammer, 131
tīšeh-tāh, medium-toothed kernel hammer, 131
tīšeh-ye šāneh, toothed hammer, kernel hammer, 128
tīz, sharp, knife-edge bearing on balance, 63
tīzāb, nitric acid, any strong acid, 33, 163
tīzāb zadan, to put acid on touchstone*
tīzbor, chisel (Šīrāz), 60, hot chisel, 52
tīzbor-e pahn, broad cold chisel, 60
tīzbor-e sar nīzeh'ī, sheet metal chisel, 60
tīzbor-e zīr, anvil chisel, 52
tīz kardan, to sharpen, to grind, 57, to trim millstone, 288
tīzkon, cutlery grinder, 57
tōbreh, miner's leather bucket (Anārak), 15
tofāl, *tōfāl*, ceiling batten; cf. *tūfāl*, *tūbāl*, 87, 114
tōfāl-kūb, ceiling batten fixer, 87
tofang, gun, 59
tofang-e čaḫmāḫ, *tofang-e čaqmāq*, flintlock gun, 60
tofang-e dō-lūleh, double-barreled gun, 60
tofang-e dō-tīr, double barreled gun, 60
tofang-e gulūleh-zan, rifle, 59
tofang-e sāčmeh-zan, shotgun, 59
tofang-e sar-por, muzzle-loader gun, 59
tofang-e sūzanī, needle gun, 59
tofang-e tahī, breech-loading gun, 59
tofang-e tah-por, breech-loading gun, 59
tofang-e yak lūleh, single-barreled gun, 60
tofang-sāz, gunsmith, 59
toġār, dyer's earthenware vat, 193
toḫmāq, mallet (Iṣfahān); cf. *taḫmāḫ*, *taqmāq*, 85
toḫm-e abrīšam, silkworm eggs (Gīlān), 182
toḫm-e hendevāneh, melon seed acting as spindle bearing, 186
toḫm-e kerm, *toḫm-e kerm-e abrīšam*, silkworm eggs, 182
toḫm-e morġ, hen egg, 295
toḫm-e nōġān, silkworm eggs, 182
toḫm-e pambeh, cottonseed, 180
tokeh, a brick profile, 123
tombeh-jā, seed bed for rice, 271
tōn, tent fabric (Sīstān), 201
tōn-bāfī, weaving of tent fabric (Sīstān), 201
tond, design, 122
tong, water decanter, narrow-necked vessel, 28, 29
tongī, small bottle, 170
tonokeh, door panel, 86
ṭōqeh, iron band around pinion disk, 283; cf. *ṭouqeh*
toqmāq, mallet (Šīrāz); cf. *toḫmāq*, 84
toranj, a certain small brick profile, 123
ṭōreh, ridge tile or ridge sheet on roof, 30
totāḫ, plow handle, 263
touġal, baking trough, 293
tou-pīč = *tāb-pīč*, batten tightener, 204
ṭouq, cart wheel tire, 90, pointed end of weaver's shuttle, 204, bandage on threshing roller, 274, iron band around millstone, 279
ṭouqeh, iron band around pinion disk; cf. *ṭōqeh*, 283
ṭoureh, pack of inlay slices with backing boards, 96
touveh, fulling dish (Šīrāz); cf. *tāveh*, 222
tōveh-čūm, *tōveh-ye čūm*, threshing disk (Iṣfahān); cf. *touveh*, *tāveh*, 52, 274
tūbāl, bits, filings, hammer scale; cf. *tūfāl*, 162
tūbāl-e ḥadīdeh, iron hammer scale, 162
tūbāl-e mes, copper, shavings, 162, blue vitriol*
tūbāl-ḥadīd-e moḥarraq, hammerscale, 162
tufāl, *tūfāl*, copper oxide, 162, shavings, 162, ceiling batten, 87, burnt roof tile, 113
tūfāl-e mes, copper oxide, burnt copper, 162
ṭufūl, turquoise with matrix bands, 39
tūġdān, nettle tree (*Celtis caucasia*), 78
tugulū, rod of triangular shape for *ḫātam* work, 96
tūl, unglazed jar, 157
tūlakī, transplantation of rice (Dārāb)*
tūlkā, storage jar, 157
tūn, warp (Iṣfahān); cf. *tān*, 184, 203
tūneh, warp ball, 185, warp of *zīlū* loom (Iṣfahān, Kāšān), 210
tūn-e ḥammām, bath boiler, 28
tū-pāšneh, heel leather inside shoe, 230
tūp-e gū, wheel hub, 90
tūpī, profiled roller of bead rollers, 30
tūqmāq, mallet, 84
tūqūlū, large triangular beads, 96, see *tugulū*
tūr, *tūrī*, net for transporting chaff, 276, embroidery net, 219
tūreh, *ṭūreh*, window sill, 113

turk-bāf, Ghiördes or Turkish knot, 215
tūseh, alder tree (*Alnus subcordata* in Caspian provinces but *Planera crenata* in Šīrāz), 78
tūskāh, alder tree (*Alnus subcordata*, *A. glutinosa*) (Gīlān, Māzandarān, Gorgān), 78
tūt, *tūt-e safīd*, white mulberry tree (*Morus alba*), 78, 183
tūtiyā, impure zinc oxide, calamine, 12, 13

ūjā, elm tree (*Ulmus* spp.) (Caspian provinces), 78
ūjambar, yoke sling (Hamadān), 262
ūlās, common beech tree (*Carpinus betulus*) (Caspian provinces), 78
ulūkeh, hole at end of plow beam (Varāmīn), 262
uskineh, heavy chisel, 84; cf. *eškīneh*
usmud, antimony ore, 163
ᶜušr, fee for mining license, 18
usrub, lead (pl. of *sorb*), 161
ustād, master craftsman, 38

vāčīdan, to stretch, 22, to bow, to tease fibers, 180
vā gereftan, to take away, to remove from, to form, 170
vāgīreh, glassworker's form iron, 170, sample carpet, 216
vākār, soil preparation prior to sowing (Gīlān)*
vākū kardan, to clean, to trim, 116
vāl, threshing board (Āzarbaijān), 274
vān or *bān*, known in Kāšān as "spade handle wood," *čūb-e bīl-dastī*, seems to be myrobalan tree (*Prunus cerasifera*) grown in Kohrūd mountains, 78
vaqqeh, a measure of weight, 62
vār, branch point in irrigation channel (Natanz)*
varaq, *varaqeh-ye qalᶜ*, tin sheet, 31
varaq-e qalᶜ, sheet of tin foil, 31
varaq-e ṭelāʾī, gold leaf, 238
varbandak, millstone-lifting block, fulcrum block (Sīstān), 288
vard, weaver's heddle, 204, 205, 209, heddle mail, 198, 206, mail loop on cross harness, 207
vardāneh, bread-rolling pin, 293
vardāneh kardan, to flatten dough by rolling, 293
vardas, oven man in bakery (Qazvīn), 294
varšou, nickel-silver, 18
varšou-sāz, samovar maker, brazier, 28
vartāb, silk-ply winder, warp winder (Kāšān), 196
vartābī, twisting several threads of silk (Kāšān), 196
varzā-āhan, plowshare (Kalārdašt), 264
varzā-gāv, plowing oxen (Kalārdašt), 262
varz dādan bā dast, to wedge clay by hand, 152
varzīdan, to knead, 293
varzū, plowing oxen (Alburz); cf. *varzā*, 262
varzū-sarīn, plow reins*
vaš, cotton boll (Kāšān), 179
vāsāʾil-e kešācarzī, agricultural implements*
vaš kašīdan, to gin cotton, to separate cotton from seed (Kāšān), 180
vaṣleh, horizontal bar of spinning wheel (Māzandarān), 186
vaṣl-e parreh, tie string, 186
vašm, a hard wood used for tool handles, probably cornel cherry wood (*Cornus mascula*), 78, 84
vasmeh, leaf of the indigo plant*
vāvar, man in bakery who stretches dough (Qazvīn), 293
vāz, harrow (Iṣfahān), 266
vazīr-e fanar, leaf below main leaf in laminated spring, 90
vāz kardan, to take a portion from the bowed fleece, to spread, 222
vezg, *vezk*, wild elm tree (*Ulmus campestris*), 78
vors, cypress tree (*Cupressus horizontalis*) (Lūristān), 78

yaḫ-čāl, ice pond, 108
yaḫeh, slot in mill shaft (Šīrāz), 281
yāʾī, lever to lift hood of coach, 90
yailāq, summer quarters, 241
yak-ājurī, single brick wall, 111
yak-āteš, ceramic of one firing, biscuit ware, 163
yak-boroš, cut to slit inlaid pack open, 96
yak-faṣlī, made in one piece, 165
yak-gereh, Sehna carpet knot, 215
yak-lengeh, single sheet of inlaid work, 96
yak-tū, chisel marking single circle, 37
yamānī, Yemen steel, 55
yān, thresher skid (Hamadān); cf. *yōn*, 274
yāqūtī, a grape variety resembling ruby in color, 244
yāqūtiyeh, purple colored, 163
yarāq, large wooden mallet*
yarāq-e buzurg, main oil press block (Iṣfahān), 297, 298
yarāq-e dar, pierced steel door ornaments*, door knocker, 52
yarāq-e kūčak, wooden oil press block (Iṣfahān), 297, 298
yarkīd, weaver's beater comb, 216
yaš, marble from Yazd, 127, 129
yō, yoke (Iṣfahān), 262
yōn, skid of threshing wain, 274
yōnjeh, lucerne, alfalfa, 243
yūġān, neck peg of plow yoke (Ḫorāsān), 262

zabān-e gonješk, zabān-gonješk, ash tree (*Fraxinus excelsior, F. oxyphylla*), 75, 78
zabān-e gūniyā, flat leg of marking square†
zabāneh, locking piece in spring lock, 69, 70
zabāneh-qalamdān, container of pen box, 238
zabāneh-ye afzār, flat end of mill shaft (Šīrāz), 281
zabān-e kelīd, key bit, 66
zabbebeh, kind of violin, 35
zabr kardan, to serrate in crosswise direction, 41
zadan, to beat, to throw, 108
zaᶜfrān, saffron, 190, 277
zāġ, mordant, alum, vitriol; cf. *zāq*, *zāj*, 34, 163
zāġāb, container for pickling acid; cf. *zāqāb**
zāġ-e safīd, alum mordant, 226
zāġ-e siyāh, vitriol mordant, 225
zai, wooden beam in house foundation, 106
zaitūn, olive, olive tree (*Olea europea*), 78
zaitūn-e talḫ, margosa tree (*Melia azadirachta*), 78
zāj, vitriol, pyrite, iron sulphate, 163, copper sulphate*, alum, 189
zāj-e qalīᵓeh, potassium alum, 189
zāj-e safīd, aluminum sulphate, 189
zāj-e zard, yellow vitriol, 192, pyrite, 163, iron alum, 190
zajjāj, glassmaker; cf. *zujjāj*, 170
zālā, neck peg of plow yoke (Razan), 262
zalīl, yellow dye from Delphinium zalil, 191
zaṃbīl, basket, 221
zaṃbīl-bāf, zaṃbīl-sāz, basket plaiter, 221
zaṃbūr, zaṃbūrak, perforated kiln floor, grate, 159, 169
zamīn, background on metal work, 36
zamīn bastan, to prepare raised borders of an irrigated field, 268
zamīn kandan, to dig a field, 261
zān, beech tree (*Fagus* spp.), 78
zang-e šotor, camel bell, 18
zangūleh, donkey bell*
zanjelō, a certain rug design, 211
zanjīr, chain, 32, 43, 52, 63, 267, 268, 275
zanjīreh, stone vessel with thin wall, 131
zanjīrī kardan, to place mud bricks on edge for drying, 110
zānū-ye lūleh, stove pipe elbow, 30
zāq = *zāġ*, 34, 163
zāqāb = *zāġāb**
zar, gold, 163
ẓarᶜ, an old standard measure of length, 61
zarak, gold leaf*
zar andūdan, to gild*
ẓarat, silt in underground water channel, 254
żarb, striking, beating*, cut on a file†
zar-bāf, brocade weaver, 206
zar-bāfī, gold-woven, brocaded, embroidered*
zar-baft, brocade*
zar-bafteh, brocade*
zar be sang-e siyāh kašīdan, to essay gold on a touchstone*
żarbgāh-e čarḫ, coppersmith's polishing lathe, 26
zard, yellow, fawn-colored, 162, 225, 226
zardālū, see *čūb-e zardālū*, 78, apricot, 244
zard-čūb, zard-čūbeh, turmeric, curcuma, a yellow dye, 191, 277, 300
zardī, printing block for yellow, 226
zar-e aṣl, pure gold, 33
zar-e dastafšār, annealed gold*
zar-e ḫālis, pure gold*
zar-e ḫošk, pure gold*
zar-e rūkaš, gilded base metal*
zar-e sāv, pure gold*
ẓarf-e sefālīn, earthenware vat, 233
ẓarf-e sirīšum, glue pot†
zargar, zargār, goldsmith, 31
zarī, brocade*
zārīᶜ, peasant, cultivator, 261
zarī-bāf, brocade weaver, 206
zarī-bāfī, brocade weaving, 206
ẓarīf, fine cut of a file, 58
zarīn, cypress tree (*Cupressus sempervirens* var. *horizontalis*) (Caspian provinces), 78
zarkār, goldsmith*
zarkaš, gold wire drawer, 42
zar-kašīd, gold-thread embroidered*
zarkūb, goldbeater, 40, gold damascener*
zarnab, yew tree (*Taxus baccata*)*
zarnī, zarnīj, zarnīk, zarnīq, arsenic, 163
zarnīḫ-e zard, orpiment*
zar-nīšān, gold-inlaid steel*
zar-nīšangar, gold-inlay worker*
zar-pūš, gold embroidered*
zar-sāv, zar-sāveh, gold filings*
zarsāz, goldsmith*
zar-tār, zar-tārī, gold cloth, brocade, gold embroidered*
zar-varaq, blend of finely ground talcum powder and gypsum, 135
zavār-bandī, decorative margin in wood carving, 98
zāviyeh, protractor, 61, corner, edge, 239
zāviyeh-āzād, free angle of saw tooth or cutting tool†
zāviyeh-boreš, cutting edge on tool, 60, cutting angle on saw-tooth or cutting tool†
zāviyeh-kaš, protractor, 61
zāviyeh-ye borādeh, breast angle of saw-tooth or cutting tool†
zāviyeh-ye gōvieh, tool angle of saw-tooth or cutting tool†
zāzū, windlass rope, 109

zebreh, untrimmed brick, common brick, 122
zebr kardan, to make rough, 41, to dress a millstone (Šīrāz), 279
zeh, reinforced edge of molding box, 18, bow string, 26, 91, 132, cord to tighten bow saw, 82, cartridge edge, 60, string of carding bow, 180, gut string of cross harness of draw loom, 206, winding on circumference of spinning wheel (Nāʾīn), 186, hide strips on water draw pulley, 256
zeh-gīr, bow string maker*
zeh-kaš, bow string tightener (Iṣfahān), 91
zeh-mantaš, edge of wheel rim, 90
zeh-rūd, bow string, 39
zehvār, leg of marking gauge†
zeh-ye pūst-e āhū, gazelle hide lace, 276
zeh-ye varšou, half-round metal beading, 90
zelā, pigeon dung*
zelleh, common chain-stitch embroidery, 219
zī, string of cotton bow, 180, draw harness for animals, 257
zī-berāvān, yoke of water well (Behbehān), 257
ẕī lais-e maʿdanī, refined steel, 55
zīlū, a woven cotton rug, 199, 210, 211, 217
zīlū-bāf, cotton rug weaver, 210
zīnak, eccentric pin, 279, wood shaking feeder channel, 279
zīn-e kārmāleh, saddle-shaped depression in *press beam*, 297, 299
zīngar, saddler, furrier, 234
zinjār, rust, verdigris, 163
zīn-sāz, saddler, furrier, 234
zīrāb, stirring rod, 194
zīr-e boḫārī, oven base plate, 30
zīreh, bed stone, nether millstone, 151, bed stone of edge runner, 296, sole of cloth shoe*
zīr-e ḥarakī, adjusting block for cotton gin bearing (Kāšān), 180
zīr-e kār, core in veneer work, blind wood*
zīr-e korsī, feet of samovar base, 29
zīr-e kūreh, firing duct of kiln, 159
zīr-e pā, footboard of threshing wain (Šīrāz), 274
zīr-e sendān, anvil block, 51
zīr-e sīgār, ash tray, 29
zīr-e zamīn, living room in basement of house, 106
zīr-kār, wedge to hold comb*
zīr-mīḫ, thrust bearing, 155
zīr-sarī, block below heddle rod, 216
zīr-sū, bottom of aquifer, 252
zīr-żarb, secondary cut of a file†
ziyādeh, surplus, excess gut string of bow, 181
ẕōb kardan, to smelt, to melt; cf. *ẕoub*, 16, 19
zoġāl, coal, charcoal, 19
zoġāl-dān, coal bucket*
zoġāl-e čūb, charcoal, 79
zoġāl-e kōk, coke (fr. Eng. coke)*
zoġāl-e qīč, charcoal from a certain desert shrub*
zoġāl-e sang, mineral coal*
ẕorrat, millet, 242, 277
ẕoub kardan, to smelt, 16, to melt, 19
ẕoub-kārī, ingot foundry (Šīrāz), 23
zujāj, glass, 170
zujjāj, glassmaker, 170
zulfī, *zulfīn*, hitching hook (Ḫorāsān), 267, 268
zūr, force for driving tool, 98
zūrī, carving tool pushed by hand, 98

INDEX

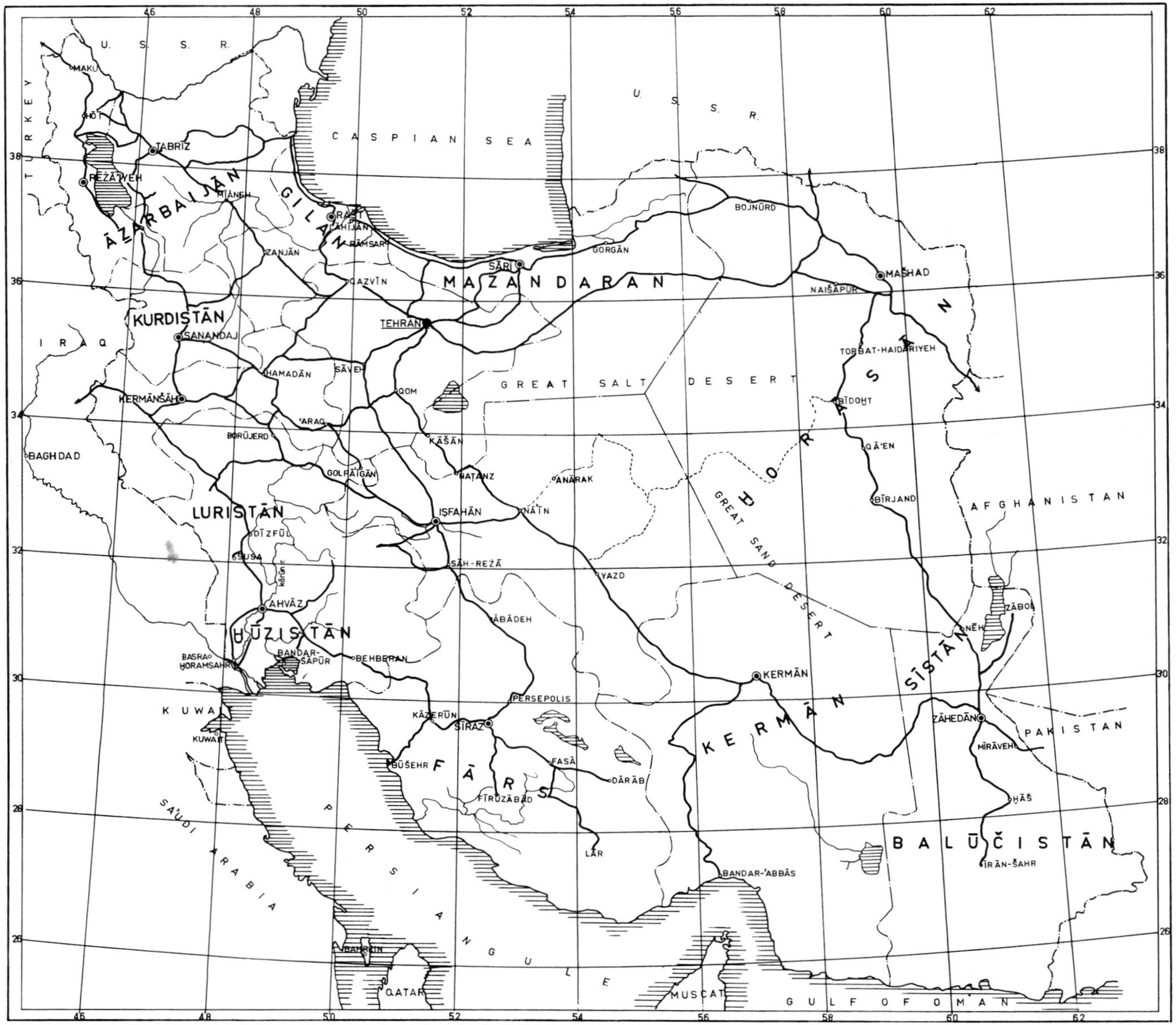
U. S. S. R.
TURKEY
CASPIAN SEA
ĀZARBAIJĀN
GILAN
MAZANDARAN
KURDISTĀN
LURISTĀN
HŪZISTĀN
FĀRS
KERMĀN
SĪSTĀN
HORASAN
BALŪČISTĀN
IRAQ
KUWAIT
SAUDI ARABIA
PERSIAN GULF
GULF OF OMAN
AFGHANISTAN
PAKISTAN
QATAR
BAHREIN
MUSCAT
GREAT SALT DESERT
GREAT SAND DESERT
MAKU
HŌI
TABRĪZ
REŽĀ'IYEH
MIĀNEH
ZANJĀN
RAŠT
LĀHIJĀN
RĀMSAR
QAZVĪN
SĀRĪ
GORGĀN
BOJNŪRD
MAŠHAD
NAIŠĀPŪR
TEHRĀN
SANANDAJ
HAMADĀN
SĀVEH
QOM
KERMĀNŠĀH
'ARAQ
BORŪJERD
BAGHDAD
KĀŠĀN
NAṬANZ
ANĀRAK
GOLPĀIGĀN
IṢFAHĀN
NĀ'ĪN
DĪZFŪL
ŠUSA
ŠĀH-REŽĀ
YAZD
AHVĀZ
ĀBĀDEH
BASRA
HORAMSAHR
BANDAR-ŠĀPŪR
BEHBEHAN
PERSEPOLIS
KĀZERŪN
ŠĪRĀZ
BŪŠEHR
FASĀ
DĀRĀB
FĪRŪZĀBĀD
LĀR
KERMĀN
BANDAR-'ABBĀS
TORBAT-HAIDARIYEH
BĪDOHT
QĀ'EN
BĪRJAND
NEH
ZĀBOL
ZĀHEDĀN
MĪRĀVEH
HĀŠ
ĪRĀN-ŠAHR
26
28
30
32
34
36
38
46
48
50
52
54
56
58
60
62